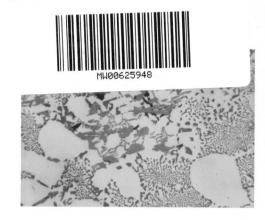

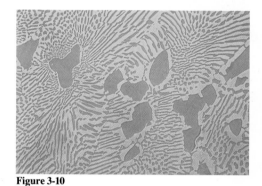

Figure 3-10

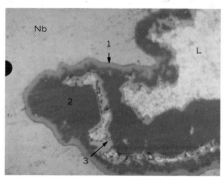

Figure 3-63

Figure 3-68

METALLOGRAPHY
Principles and Practice

McGraw-Hill Series in Materials Science and Engineering

METALLOGRAPHY
Principles and Practice

George F. Vander Voort

Supervisor
Applied Physics R & D
Carpenter Technology Corporation
Reading, Pennsylvania

McGraw-Hill Book Company

New York St. Louis San Francisco Auckland Bogotá Hamburg
Johannesburg London Madrid Mexico Montreal New Delhi
Panama Paris São Paulo Singapore Sydney Tokyo Toronto

This book was set in Times Roman by Jay's Publishers Services, Inc.
The editors were Anne Murphy and Susan Hazlett;
the production supervisor was Leroy A. Young.
The drawings were done by Wellington Studios Ltd.
R. R. Donnelley & Sons Company was printer and binder.

METALLOGRAPHY
Principles and Practice

34567890 DOCDOC 898765

ISBN 0-07-066970-8

Library of Congress Cataloging in Publication Data

Vander Voort, George F.
    Metallography, principles and practice.

    (McGraw-Hill series in materials science and
engineering)
    Includes bibliographical references and indexes.
    1. Metallography.   I. Title.   II. Series.
TN690.V36   1984   669'.95   83-22272
ISBN 0-07-066970-8

CONTENTS

Coatings / Graphite and Inclusion Retention

Aluminum / Antimony and Bismuth / Beryllium / Cadmium, Lead, Tin, and Zinc / Chromium, Molybdenum, and Tungsten / Cobalt, Manganese, Nickel, and Iron / Copper / Germanium and Silicon / Indium and Thallium / Magnesium / Niobium, Tantalum, and Vanadium / Precious Metals / Radioactive Metals / Rare Earth Metals / Selenium and Tellurium / Sodium / Titanium / Zirconium and Hafnium

Chapter 5   Hardness   334

Appendixes

Indexes

PREFACE

Metallography has proved to be an exceptionally useful metallurgical tool for both production and research work. Since the initial work of Sorby nearly 120 years ago, a multitude of techniques have been developed and applied to nearly every conceivable material. The vast scope of material available on this subject presents a formidable challenge to the student and to the practicing metallographer or metallurgist. This book brings together much of the existing knowledge pertaining to metallographic techniques and their application to the study of metals, ceramics, minerals, and polymers, although primary attention is given to metals.

This book concentrates on techniques relevant to visual and light microscopy—techniques fundamental to the study of macrostructure and microstructure. A similar treatment of techniques relevant to electron metallography is beyond the scope of this book, although some of the information presented is directly applicable. The historical development of metallographic techniques and the underlying scientific principles are discussed. Emphasis, however, has been placed on the practical problems associated with the use of these methods in order to facilitate their implementation. Metallography is both an art and a science, and both of these areas have been covered in detail. A complete list of recipes for polishing and etching solutions has been included plus comments regarding their safe and successful application. There are also extensive reference lists of key work at the end of each chapter to permit the reader to obtain additional information when needed. An extensive collection of macrographs and micrographs has also been included to illustrate the various methods discussed and to provide examples of their application to various materials.

This book should be useful to both undergraduate and graduate students in courses devoted to microscopy and physical metallurgy but should also prove useful to those studying ceramics, minerals, polymers, and carbonaceous materials. Engineers and technicians should find the book to be a valuable source of reference for use on the job. Although metallography is a relatively mature field, there has been substantial progress made in recent years in automation of sample preparation and in quantification of microstructural measurements, subjects that are thoroughly covered in this book.

The author wishes to acknowledge the contributions made by his colleagues during the preparation of this manuscript over the past 10 years. Specifically, he appreciates the advice and encouragement from the reviewers and the photographs of equipment supplied by their manufacturers. The advice and help provided by metallographers at Bethlehem Steel's Homer Research Laboratories—A. O. Benscoter, A. V. Brandemarte, J. W. Guidon, J. R. Gruver, L. L. Hahn, J. R. Kilpatrick, M. L. Longenbach, V. E. McGraw, E. C. Poetl, M. A. Rodriguez, and L. R. Salvage—and by his former coworkers—H. A. Abrams, R. L. Bodnar, B. L. Bramfitt, J. C. Chilton, R. J. Henry, R. W. Hinton, M. L. Lasonde, A. R. Marder, M. Schmidt, M. J. Roberts, J. P. Snyder, E. T. Stephenson, and L. R. Woodyatt—were invaluable. The author gratefully acknowledges the following people who offered advice or provided samples or photomicrographs: A. Boe (Struers, Inc.), G. W. Blann (Buehler Ltd.), R. D. Buchheit (Battelle-Columbus Labs), A. E. Calabra (Rockwell International), R. S. Crouse (Oak Ridge National Lab.), R. T. DeHoff (University of Florida), E. W. Filer (Cabot Corp.), N. J. Gendron (retired, General Electric Corp.), J. F. Golden (E. Leitz, Inc.), R. J. Gray (Oak Ridge National Lab.), N. D. Greene (University of Connecticut), J. A. Hendrickson (Wyman-Gordon Co.), J. N. Hoke (Pennsylvania State University), W. Hunn (E. Leitz, Inc.), H. M. James (Carpenter Technology Corp.), R. R. Jones (Lafayette College), G. Krauss (Colorado School of Mines), J. A. Nelson (Buehler Ltd.), E. C. Pearson (Aluminum Co. of Canada), A. W. Pense (Lehigh University), G. Petzow (Max-Planck Institute), T. Piotrowski (Engelhard Minerals & Chemicals), J. H. Richardson (The Aerospace Corp.), R. M. Slepian (retired, Westinghouse Electric Corp.), R. H. Stevens (Aluminum Co. of America), D. A. Thomas (Lehigh University), F. J. Warmuth (Special Metals Corp.), E. Weidmann (Struers, Inc.), W. E. White (Petro Canada Ltd.), D. B. Williams (Lehigh University), E. E. Underwood (Georgia Institute of Technology), and W. Yankauskas (retired, TRW).

George F. Vander Voort

METALLOGRAPHY
Principles and Practice

ONE

MACROSTRUCTURE

1-1 INTRODUCTION

Macroscopic examination techniques are frequently employed in routine quality control, in failure analysis, and in research studies. These techniques are generally a prelude to microscopic examination; however, in quality control, they are often used alone as a criterion for acceptance or rejection. A great variety of destructive and nondestructive procedures are available. The most basic procedure involves simple visual examination for surface features such as seams, laps, or scale.

This chapter describes only destructive test procedures; nondestructive methods are not covered. These destructive methods include the following procedures:

- Macroetching
- Contact printing
- Fracturing
- Lead exudation

Proper implementation of these methods is fundamental to the manufacture of materials. In quality control, the manufacturing routine is usually established according to set practices, and the macroscopic methods are used to detect deviations from the norm. In failure studies, one often does not know specific details of the manufacturing process and practices, and the engineer uses these tests to judge quality, to locate problem areas for further study, and, in some cases, to determine how the component was produced. In research studies, the processing steps are often varied, and the macroexamination is designed to show differences due to changes in manufacturing practices. Thus for each type of study, the specific details of the macroscopic examination will vary somewhat, and

1

the practitioner must have a thorough understanding of the test method, its application, and the interpretation of test data.

Interpretation of the data from these tests requires an understanding of the manufacturing process, since the macrostructure is dependent on the solidification and hot- or cold-working procedures used. There can be pronounced differences in macrostructure because factors such as casting method, ingot size and shape, and chemical analysis will significantly alter the solidification pattern. In addition, the use of manufacturing techniques other than traditional ingot casting, such as continuous casting, centrifugal casting, electroslag remelting, or hot-isostatic pressing, produce noticeably different as-cast patterns. Also, there is a wide variety of metalworking processes that can be applied to material made by any of the above processes, and each exerts a different effect upon the material. All these factors influence the interpretation of the test results.

No material can be said to be entirely homogeneous either macroscopically or microscopically. The degree of heterogeneity can vary widely depending on the nature of the material, the method of manufacture, and the cost required to produce the material. Fortunately, the usual degree of heterogeneity is not a serious problem in the use of commercial materials as long as these variances are held within certain prescribed limits. Certain problems, such as pipe and hydrogen flakes, are in general, quite harmful. The effect of other features, such as porosity, segregation, and inclusions, can be quite difficult to evaluate, and one must consider the extent of these features, the amount of subsequent metalworking, and the nature of the application of the material.

Of the metallographic procedures listed, the macroetch test is probably the most informative, and it is widely used for quality control, failure analysis, and research studies. Classification of the features observed with the macroetch test is often confusing because of the use of "jargon" created since the introduction of this test procedure. The macroetch test is covered in considerable detail in this chapter, and numerous examples of its application to a variety of materials are presented.

1-2 VISUALIZATION AND EVALUATION OF MACROSTRUCURE BY ETCHING

All quality evaluations should begin on the macroscale using tests designed to survey the overall field in a simple and reliable manner. After the macrostructure of a material has been evaluated, specific features can then be examined microscopically. Abnormalities observed on the etch disc can be studied by fracturing the disc or by preparing metallographic polished samples. Macroetching of transverse or longitudinally oriented samples, i.e., oriented with respect to the hot-working axis, enables the mill metallurgist to evaluate the quality of a relatively large area quickly and efficiently. Thus, macroetching is an extremely powerful tool and is a cornerstore of the overall quality program.

The earliest macroetchants were rather weak solutions used at room temperature. Reaumur (1683–1757) used macroetchants to distinguish between different types of steel and sketched the appearance of macroetched pieces of steel in his work. Rinmann promoted this technique in his book *On the Etching of Iron and Steel,* written in the late 1700s. Sorby, in his classic work published in 1887 "On the Microscopical Structure of Iron and Steel," showed "nature prints," which were inked contact prints of steel etched in moderately strong aqueous nitric acid solutions [1]. The early etching solutions have been reviewed in the classic text by Berglund [2].

1-2.1 Macroetching with Acid Solutions

The first "deep"-etching procedure for steel was developed by Waring and Hofamman using nine parts hydrochloric acid, three parts sulfuric acid, and one part water. Considerable adverse comment about the use of strong acids to evaluate highly stressed components was generated by this paper. Overall, the initial response to deep-acid etching was negative; however, numerous subsequent studies revealed the great value of such etchants.

After the initial work by Waring and Hofamman, considerable attention was devoted to the study of strong acids for deep etching steels. The most widely used deep etch consists of a 1:1 solution of reagent-grade† hydrochloric acid and water heated to 160 to 180°F for 15 to 45 min. Etching can be conducted on a saw-cut face, but better resolution is obtained with ground faces. Gill and Johnstin found that this etch was more selective in its attack than similar solutions involving nitric acid and water or sulfuric acid and water [3]. An important feature of this etchant is that evaporation does not significantly vary its composition during use.

The following items should be considered in the development of a macroetchant:

- The etchant should produce good all-around results, should be applicable to the majority of materials, and should reveal a great variety of structural characteristics and irregularities.
- The etchant should be simple in composition, inexpensive, and easy to prepare.
- The etchant should be stable during use or storage.
- The etchant must be safe to use and should not produce noxious odors.

The widespread popularity of the 1:1 hydrochloric acid and water etch is due to the fact that it satisfies these requirements better than other etchants. Appendix A lists macroetchants for iron and steel as well as for other metals.

The 1:1 hydrochloric acid and water etch attacks manganese sulfides readily but does not attack aluminum oxides. Steels high in aluminum content, such as the nitriding alloys, are etched best with an aqueous solution containing 10% hydro-

---

†The reagent grade contains 36.5 to 38% HCl, whereas the technical grade contains 28% HCl.

chloric acid and 2% nitric acid, developed by V. T. Malcolm. Etching is conducted at 180°F for 15 to 60 min.

As the alloy content increases, so does the degree of segregation and its associated problems. Etching is pronounced at the segregate-matrix interface, and segregate or matrix areas may etch out, leaving pits. Sulfides or carbides may also etch out, leaving pits. Before the investigator can distinguish between pits due to nonmetallic inclusions or segregates and carbides, the disc must be hardened and reetched. If the pits were due to nonmetallics, they will be present to the same degree in both the annealed and the hardened discs.

Watertown Arsenal [4] developed a variant of the standard etch that consists of 38 parts of hydrochloric acid, 12 parts sulfuric acid, and 50 parts water.† This reagent often produces a sharper definition of features than the standard etch, and like the standard etch, its acid concentration does not change markedly during use.

Macroetching provides an overall view of the degree of uniformity of metals and alloys by revealing:

- Structural detail resulting from solidification or working
- Chemical uniformity in qualitative terms
- Physical discontinuities due to solidification, working, etc.
- Weldment structure or heat-affected zones from burning operations
- Hardness patterns in non-through-hardened steels or patterns due to quenching irregularities
- Grinding damage
- Thermal effects due to service abuse

The first three features are best revealed by hot-acid etching, and the remaining four are best revealed by room temperature etchants. Macroetching is usually performed on ground surfaces, although in some cases, especially with cold etchants, better results are obtained when the surface is polished. Chemical segregation can be shown by certain cold etchants. The information obtained can be recorded by photographing the samples or, where possible, by contact printing.

In order to observe these features, one must sample the material properly and use the macroetch test procedure correctly. Fortunately, these test procedures are straightforward and simple to use as long as a few precautions are followed. In practice, one must consider the following test variables:

- Selection of representation samples
- Choice of surface orientation
- Proper preparation of sample surface
- Selection of the best etch composition
- Control of etchant temperature and etch time
- Documentation of test results

---

†Add the sulfuric acid *slowly* to the water and allow it to cool; then add the hydrochloric acid.

For routine mill inspection, the metallurgist generally cuts a disc from the top and bottom (occasionally the middle) of billets rolled from the first, middle, and last ingots. For certain products, discs are prepared from all the ingots, after rolling to the required billet size. These discs should be cut so as not to include any of the shear drag which may be present after hot shearing the billets to length or removing the top and bottom discard material. In general, the thickness should be held to ½ to 1 in, since the weight of larger discs is prohibitive for handling. Both cuts should be relatively parallel. It is advisable to cut discs with large cross sections into two or more pieces; cutting directly through the center of the disc should be avoided. Transverse discs are used in most cases, although longitudinal discs can be useful in evaluating segregation and mechanical heterogeneity. For routine work with steels, the saw-cut face is generally satisfactory for etching. For detection of fine details, a smooth ground surface is preferred. Some etchants require a smooth ground or a polished surface for proper delineation of macroetch features.

It is not necessary to remove the as-rolled scale from the disc, but any grease, dirt, or debris on the cut face should be removed. It is not advisable to hot-acid etch hardened steel discs, since they can crack or fracture during etching. Similarly, billets should be soft prior to cutting to prevent surface damage during cutting which will obscure the true etch pattern. Proper cutting and grinding techniques must be employed to avoid any damage from these sources.

1-2.2 Copper-Containing Macroetchants for Primary Structure

Macroetching steels with etchants containing copper ions predates the development of hot-acid etching. These copper-containing reagents are listed in App. B. Heyn's reagent was the first to be developed; some of the others stemmed from efforts to produce better results. The reagents are used principally to reveal phosphorus or carbon segregation and dendritic structure. At the time these reagents were first introduced, phosphorus segregation was an important problem in Bessemer steels. Today, however, little Bessemer steel is produced and phosphorus segregation is not a major problem. However, carbon segregation is still widely evaluated, especially in high-carbon steels. These etchants are employed primarily now in research studies and occasionally in quality control. One of the uses of these etchants has been to reveal the primary structure of materials, that is the gross structure resulting from solidification rather than the secondary or tertiary microstructure. More recently developed copper-containing macroetchants have been used to study strain patterns in stressed metals.

Stead's no. 1 reagent is one reagent that has been widely used. Stead recommended that the etch be used in the following way: A small amount of the etching solution is poured on the surface, and etching is allowed to proceed for about 1 min. The solution is drained off, and fresh solution is added. This process is repeated until the desired etch pattern is obtained. Magnusson [5] states that this procedure produces uneven etching across the sample and results are better if the specimen is etched by immersion, which is contrary to Stead's comment that immersion should never be used.

Magnusson has performed an exhaustive study of the use of Stead's reagent for revealing the primary structure of welds [5]. Magnusson states that the influence of the secondary and tertiary structure must be reduced so that the primary structure can be clearly observed. This can be accomplished by heat treating the specimen prior to etching. While normalizing produces improved results, best results are obtained by quenching and tempering. He recommends austenitizing at about 125°F (52°C) above the upper critical temperature. After a short (5 min) hold, the sample is quenched fast enough to form martensite and is tempered between about 1025 and 1250°F (552 and 677°C) for 1 h. Tempering above 1250°F produces indistinct contrast.

Stead's reagent is used with polished surfaces. According to Magnusson, after heat treatment the sample should be polished using nital etching between the final polishing steps. After the final polishing stage, the sample should be etched about 5 s in 0.5% nital. The sample is rinsed and dried and then etched by immersion. Etching is started with a solution of one part Stead's reagent plus three parts alcohol and one-quarter part water for 45 s. The sample is rinsed, and 5 to 10 drops of a 50-mL solution of 10% ammonia plus 10 drops of H_2O_2 is poured on the surface. The copper precipitate is removed by wiping with cotton. The sample is then etched twice for 30 s (rinse and dry between etches) in one part Stead's reagent and two parts alcohol and then in dilute Stead's reagent (dilution not specified, probably one part alcohol) for 15 s. Preetching with picral produces softer contrast. Magnusson also recommends preetching with a solution of 10 mL of 0.5% HNO_3 plus three drops of 4% picral for improved contrast.

Oberhoffer's reagent has also been widely used because of the good, uniform results obtained. However, well-polished surfaces must be used and best results are obtained if the polished surface is left to sit in air for about 1 h before etching, as pointed out by Magnusson. Pokorny has made a detailed study of the influence of the surface condition, using copper-containing reagents as the macroetchant [6]. Polishing produces two surface effects, a mechanically deformed layer and a chemically absorbed layer. Pokorny claims that primary etching works best in the presence of these two layers. Most other studies claim that the mechanically deformed layer must be removed. The chemically absorbed layer was studied after diamond and alumina polishing using AES (auger electron spectroscopy) and SIMS (secondary ion mass spectrometry) techniques, which showed that this layer consisted of oxygen-metal compounds plus sulfur or ammonium compounds, depending on whether polishing was conducted in an urban or a rural atmosphere. The chemical layer can be removed by ion bombardment. A clean metallic surface is obtained after removal of about 4 nm.

Pokorny showed that etching of freshly polished surfaces produced average results, while samples etched after standing in air or in a vacuum for 20 h produced very good results. He recommends that diamond polishing be conducted only long enough to remove the scratches from grinding and then the samples be aged in air before etching.

Buhr and Weinberg compared the results obtained with the standard 1:1 HCl and H_2O hot etch and with Oberhoffer's reagent to autoradiographs of directionally solidified AISI (American Iron and Steel Institute) 4340 doped with radioactive phosphorus [7]. This work stemmed from the statement of Kirkaldy et al. that Oberhoffer's reagent was unsuitable as a detector of phosphorus segregation. Both studies agreed that Oberhoffer's reagent would not produce a useful correlation between the rate of copper deposition and the alloy content. They observed that the hot-HCl etch brought out the outline of the dendrites but little else, did not reveal secondary branches, and attacked the phosphorus-rich regions. Oberhoffer's etch deposited copper preferentially on the phosphorus-depleted regions and delineated the phosphorus segregation fairly well. The phosphorus-depleted secondary branches were barely revealed, and the widths of these branches were similar to those revealed by the autoradiograph.

Buhr and Weinberg observed that copper was initially deposited preferentially on the phosphorus-depleted regions [7]. Then, a secondary etching attack occurred in these regions that was apparently associated with the structure, producing deeply etched acicular dark areas. This attack produced the dark appearance of the dendrite branches.

These authors studied the influence of carbon content on the action of Oberhoffer's reagent using the following steels:

Code	Weight %				
	C	P	Mn	Si	S
A	0.01	0.001	0.39	0.33	0.004
B	0.01	0.061	0.37	0.33	0.004
C	0.46	0.001	0.52	0.31	0.007
D	0.45	0.053	0.10	0.28	0.007

Steels A and C with low phosphorus content did not exhibit a dendritic pattern when etched with Oberhoffer's reagent. Steel B showed a slight indication, while Steel D exhibited a well-delineated dendritic pattern. These results clearly showed that carbon must be present along with sufficient phosphorus for the dendritic structure to be revealed. The influence of phosphorus level was also examined using AISI 4340 castings with 0.006, 0.020, 0.043, and 0.090% phosphorus. All four samples exhibited dendrite patterns after etching, with the pattern being more pronounced as the phosphorus level increased. According to Karl, the lower limit of phosphorus detection using Oberhoffer's reagent is 0.003% [8].

1-2.3 Macroetchants for Revealing Strain Patterns

In 1921, Fry published a method for revealing strain lines in iron and steel using both microscopic and macroscopic etching reagents. The macroetchant, Fry's no. 4 (see App. B), has been widely used. This solution contains considerable hydrochloric acid, which keeps the free copper from depositing on the sample during etching. A polished specimen is immersed in the solution for 1 to 3 min. It is then removed from the solution, and etching is continued by rubbing with a cloth moistened in the solution and covered with $CuCl_2$.† This is continuted for 2 to 20 min. The surface should be washed in alcohol (water should not be used for washing) and dried periodically for inspection. If the surface is not bright, rubbing is continued. Etching produces a pattern of light and dark bands corresponding to the location of the maximum shear stresses.

It is recommended that the samples be aged between 400 and 500°F for about 30 min prior to etching. If the etched surface appears dirty, it should be wiped with a cloth saturated with the etching solution. After etching, it is helpful to rinse the specimen in a fairly concentrated solution of hydrochloric acid. The sample can then be safely washed with water and dried. In addition to strain lines, the etch may produce grain contrast.

The studies of Koster [9] and MacGregor and Hensel [10] were instrumental in showing why some steels respond to Fry's reagent while others do not. Koster claimed that the variability in etch response was due to the effect of the aging treatment. Koster believed that Fry's reagent worked only after iron nitride was precipitated during aging. The nitrogen content and the form in which nitrogen is found is critical. Steels high in nitrogen content, such as Bessemer steels, etch readily in a few minutes, while open-hearth steels with lower nitrogen content require several hours or more to reveal the strain pattern. Steels with still lower nitrogen levels cannot be successfully etched. MacGregor and Hensel state that mild steels with 0.01 to 0.05% nitrogen are readily etched with Fry's reagent. They showed that a steel with low nitrogen content that would not respond to Fry's reagent could be successfully etched after light nitriding of the polished surface.

Bish has developed a method to reveal strain patterns in mild steel with low nitrogen content using a modification of Fry's reagent on mild steel plates deformed by punching [11, 12]. The surface is ground to remove about 1 mm of metal and then ground on coarse emery cloth with paraffin lubrication and then with 150-, 220-, 400-, and 600-grit SiC paper with water for the lubricant. The surface is next chemically polished in a solution consisting of 60 mL of H_2O_2, 140 mL of water, and 10 mL of HF. The sample is first degreased and then swabbed in the chemical polish for 10 s. It is then rinsed in water and dipped in a 20 to 50% solution of HCl in water, rinsed and dried. The specimen is then etched in the modified Fry's reagent by swabbing and immersion using a solution consisting of 36 g of $CuCl_2$, 144 mL of HCl, and 80 mL of water. A black deposit forms on the specimen and is removed by immersing the sample in the chemical polishing solution. This procedure also increases the contrast between the deformed and undeformed regions. The sample is next rinsed in water and dipped again in the dilute HCl solution, then rinsed and dried. Only analytical-grade HCl should be used for making up the solutions described by Bish. Bish claims that successful

† Use plastic gloves when performing this step of the process.

etching requires the removal of any surface damage produced during sectioning and grinding and the use of the chemical polish to remove damage from fine grinding. The chemical polish also appears to produce an active surface. Bish states that this procedure produces etching of the undeformed regions rather than the deformed regions, as is normally observed.

Macroetching procedures have also been developed to reveal strain patterns in nonferrous metals. Procedures for aluminum and nickel-base superalloys are given in App. C.

The strain pattern in most metals can be revealed by annealing the specimen after deformation so as to obtain recrystallization [13]. In the region that receives a critical amount of strain, generally 5 to 8 percent, grain growth is more rapid. This area shows up quite clearly upon macroetching.

1-2.4 Macroetch Specifications

The classification of macrostructures as a basis for acceptance or rejection of materials has been worked out and is now fairly straightforward. Serious defects and very good macrostructures are easily interpreted. In the case of the questionable macrostructure, however, the investigator must have experience and knowledge of the manufacturing procedures and the intended application before the macrostructure can be correctly classified. If the tested section is to be hot-worked to a smaller cross section, the mill metallurgist must know whether the additional hot work will improve the macrostructure sufficiently. Alternatively, rolling the bloom to a smaller size than originally desired in order to obtain a salable product must occasionally be recommended.

The American Society for the Testing of Materials (ASTM) has had a long involvement with macroetching techniques. The macroetching solutions for both ferrous and nonferrous metals were recently incorporated in a single specification, ASTM E340. ASTM has also developed specifications for evaluating the macrostructure of steels. In 1948, ASTM Specification A317, "Standard Method of Macroetch Testing and Inspection of Steel Forgings," was proposed. This specification showed macrographs that illustrated common features revealed by macroetching.

The first rating chart for macrostructure was published in 1957 as MIL-STD-430, "Macrograph Standards for Steel Bars, Billets and Blooms." This rating chart consisted of four series with eight macroetch pictures arranged in increasing order of severity:

Code	Type indication
A	Center defects
B	Subsurface defects
C	Ring defects
D	Miscellaneous defects (inclusions, flakes, and bursts)

The D category contained independent examples of particular types of imperfections. This chart is used in MIL-STD-1459A (MU), "Military Standard—Macrograph Standards for Steel Bars, Billets and Blooms for Ammunition Components."

MIL-STD-430 was revised, and the rating chart was changed in MIL-STD-430A. Two charts are used; the first chart shows three series of macroetch pictures with five picture per series:

Code	Type indication
S	Subsurface conditions
R	Random conditions
C	Center segregation

The second chart shows an example of a ring pattern which is judged acceptable in any degree and five examples of defects which are unacceptable in any degree (flute cracks, gas, butt tears, splash, and flakes). Both of these charts were adopted in 1968 in ASTM E381, "Standard Method for Rating Macroetched Steel."

In 1971, ASTM approved Specification A561, "Standard Recommended Practice for Macroetch Testing of Tool Steel Bars." This specification has a rating chart with two categories—ring pattern and center porosity—with six pictures per category. Another recently developed macroetch standard is ASTM A604, "Standard Method for Macroetch Testing of Consumable Electrode Remelted Steel Bars and Billets," adopted in 1970. This chart was developed to categorize and rate macroetch imperfections that are unique to these materials. Five examples of each class of macroetch imperfection are provided, with the severity increasing from A to E.

Class	Type indication
1	Freckles
2	White spots
3	Radial segregation
4	Ring pattern

These macroetch rating methods can be applied in a variety of ways. Steels made according to specific ASTM standards can be tested according to ASTM-agreed limits, implied industry limits, or producer-purchaser limits. Some ASTM standards state the chart method that is used but do not list macroetch limits. Other ASTM material specifications require macroetch tests but do not recommend a specific chart method.

1-2.5 Classification of Macroetch Features

Macroetching reveals many types of detail pertinent to the manufacturing process. It is important to categorize these defects and imperfections using unambiguous, universally understood terminology. Unfortunately, mill metallurgists do not all use the same jargon when describing macroetching features, which produces some confusion. The following lists the defects and imperfections associated with specific types of products.

1. Macroscopic features in castings
   a. *Blowholes.* Round or elongated, smooth-walled cavities that are due to entrapped air or gas generation from molding or core sand and inadequate venting.
   b. *Cold shut (cold lap).* An interface caused by lack of fusion between two streams of metal during die casting due to inadequate fluidity.
   c. *Contraction crack (hot tear).* A crack formed during cooling. The crack location is fixed by the casting design and contraction resistance due to the mold or cores.
   d. *Gas holes (pinholes).* Small, uniformly distributed spherical cavities with bright walls, due to gas evolution.
   e. *Oxide and dross inclusions.* Macroscopic included matter entrapped in the castings that results from the entry of slag or dross into the casting during pouring.
   f. *Sand holes.* Irregularly shaped cavities containing entrapped sand from the mold.
   g. *Shrinkage cavity.* Irregularly shaped cavities within the casting that are due to inadequate feeding.
   h. *Shrinkage porosity.* Irregularly shaped pores usually observed at a change of section or at the center of heavy sections that are due to inadequate feeding.
2. Macroscopic features in wrought ingot products
   a. *Surface defects such as seams or laps.* Seams are perpendicular to the bar surface and follow the hot-working axis. Laps are developed during hot working by the folding over of surface metal.
   b. *Pipe.* A remnant of the ingot-solidification cavity usually associated with segregated impurities. In so-called primary pipe, the cavity is opened to the atmosphere and the cavity surfaces are oxidized. In "secondary" pipe there is no opening to the atmosphere and the cavity surfaces are not oxidized. Secondary pipe can be healed by further hot working, while primary pipe cannot.
   c. *Burst.* An internal void or crack, generally in the center of the bar, due to improper hot-working procedures.
   d. *Center porosity.* Possibly due to a discontinuity, such as pipe, or to gas evolution.
   e. *Nonmetallic inclusions.* Generally concentrated toward the center of the

ingot during solidification. Many inclusions will appear as pits after hot etching.

f. *Metallic segregates*. Also concentrated toward the center of the ingot during solidification.

g. *Internal cracks*. Flakes and cooling cracks due to excessive hydrogen content.

h. *Dendrites*. Results from the solidification process and are present in most cast metals.

i. *Pattern effect* ("*ingot pattern*"). A result of the solidification characteristics of the ingot and not a cause for concern, unless inclusions have segregated to the pattern interface.

j. *Decarburization*. Occurs at the surfaces of steel ingots and billets during processing and shows up as a light etching rim.

k. *Carburized surfaces*. Surfaces that etch darker than the interior of the disc due to enrichment of carbon content.

l. *Hardness patterns and soft spots*. Revealed by etch contrast.

m. *Flow lines*. Result from hot working and are revealed on longitudinal samples. The inclusions and segregates elongated by hot working are preferentially attacked by etching.

3. Macroscopic features in continuously cast metals

a. *Axial porosity*. Porosity exhibited by continuously cast metals (as-cast) along the centerline that is due to incomplete feeding during solidification.

b. *Large inclusions*. Oxidation of the pouring stream, generally between the tundish and the mold, that produces large oxide inclusions.

c. *Segregation streaks*. Stressing (mechanical or thermal) of the solidifying steel that produces internal cracks which are immediately filled by metal enriched with sulfur from the interdendritic regions.

d. *Segregation bands*. Light and dark etching bands that are sometimes observed on transverse sections. These bands are produced by excessive or uneven secondary water spray cooling. They are also referred to as halfway or midway cracks, radial streaks, or ghost lines.

e. *Triple-point cracks*. Cracks that occur in continuously cast slabs. When observed on a transverse section, they are perpendicular to the narrow side of the slab within the V-shaped region where the three solidification fronts meet. These cracks are caused by bulging of the wide slab face, which results from inadequate containment of the solid shell.

f. *Centerline cracks*. Cracks that form in the center area of the cast section near the end of solidification. The cracks are caused by bulging of the wide slab face or by a sudden drop in centerline temperature.

g. *Diagonal cracks*. Cracks that occur in billets as a result of distortion of the billet into a rhomboid section. The distortion may be cause by nonuniform cooling, such as when two adjacent faces cool more rapidly than the other faces.

h. *Straightening or bending cracks*. Cracks that occur during straightening or bending procedures if the center of the section is still liquid or above 1340°C.

    i. Pinch-roll cracks. Cracks that can be caused by excessive roll pressure applied when the center is still liquid or above 1340°C.

    j. Longitudinal midface cracks. Surface cracks observed on slabs.

    k. Longitudinal corner cracks. Cracks at the corners of billets and blooms that are due to compositional and operating factors.

    l. Transverse, midface, and corner cracks. Surface cracks that occur at the base of oscillation marks. Steel composition is a critical factor in their formation.

    m. Star cracks. Surface cracks that occur in clusters, each having a starlike appearance. They are generally fairly shallow and are usually caused by copper from the mold walls.

4. Macroetch features of consumable electrode remelted steels

    a. Freckles. Circular or nearly circular dark etching spots due to concentration or carbides or carbide-forming elements.

    b. Radial segregation. Radially or spirally oriented dark etching elongated spots generally located at midradius. These areas are usually enriched with carbides.

    c. Ring pattern. Concentric rings (one or more) which etch differently than the bulk of the disc as a result of minor variations in composition.

    d. White spots. Globular light-etching spots due to a lack of carbide or carbide-forming elements.

1-3 APPLICATIONS OF MACROETCHING

The various imperfections or defects just described can be detected by hot-acid etching. Since the cross section usually provides more information than the longitudinal section, the general practice is to cut discs transversely, i.e., perpendicular to the hot-working axis. To facilitate handling, disc thickness should generally be 1 in or less. Longitudinal sectioning is used to study fiber, segregation, and inclusions.

1-3.1 Solidification Structures

The structure resulting from solidification can be clearly revealed by macroetching. Figure 1-1 shows the macrostructure of a transverse disc cut from a small laboratory-size steel ingot that was etched with 10% HNO_3 in water. At the mold surface, there is a small layer of very fine equiaxed grains. From this outer shell, large columnar grains grow inward toward the central, equiaxed region.

    Figure 1-2 shows the macrostructure of a 99.8% aluminum centrifugally cast ingot after a minor degree of reduction. There is a thin band of fine grains around the edge, which is considerably thicker in the area near the left side of the photograph. Rather coarse columnar grains are observed growing from the outer surface, merging at a spot which is off center.

Figure 1-1 Cold etch of disc cut from small ingot (10% aqueous HNO_3).

Figure 1-2 Macrostructure of centrifugally cast 99.8% aluminum after a minor amount of reduction ($3\frac{1}{4}\times$; etchant, solution of 5 mL HNO_3, 5 mL HCl, 5 mL HF, and 95 mL H_2O). *(Courtesy of R. D. Buchheit, Battelle-Columbus Laboratories.)*

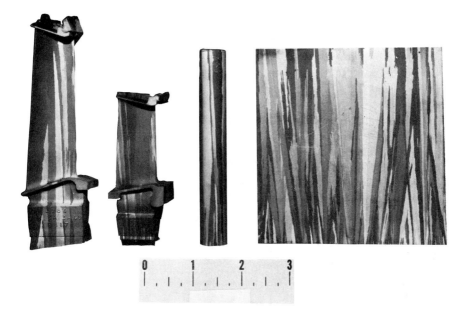

Figure 1-3 Macrostructure of directionally solidified nickel-base eutectic alloy (etchant, solution of 1 mL H₂O₂ and 99 mL HCl). *(Courtesy of W. Yankausas, TRW, Inc.)*

The presence of a coarse columnar grain structure can impart useful properties to a material that is to be used at high temperature. Considerable effort has been made to preferentially grow such grains in high-temperature alloys used in turbines. Figure 1-3 shows the macrostructure of a directionally solidified nickel-base eutectic alloy in several product forms.

1-3.2 Billet and Bloom Macrostructures

In general, the steelmaker uses the hot-acid etch on discs cut, with respect to the ingot location, from the top and bottom or the top, middle, and bottom of billets or blooms† rolled from the first, middle, and last ingots teemed from the heat. If a disc reveals a rejectable condition, billet material is rejected until the condition is removed.

Figure 1-4 shows "dirty" corners, a lap, several small seams, and freckle-type segregation in a hot-acid etched disc of bearing steel. The inclusion present in the dirty corner (lower right) is a Mn-Fe-Al silicate. Figure 1-5 shows ingot pattern and pits from inclusions in alloy steel. In Figure 1-6 the standard hot etching has revealed entrapped gas, heavy segregation, voids, and ingot pattern in a disc of AISI 4140 alloy steel. Figure 1-7 shows the microstructure near the center of this disc (longitudinal plane through the disc). The center of the disc is coarse and exhibits an open pipe condition and associated segregation.

---

†Blooms are rolled sections larger than 6 by 6 in, while billets are smaller than this.

Figure 1-4 Hot-acid etching of this disc from a bearing steel billet revealed broken corners, a lap (upper left), several small seams, and freckle-type segregation.

Figure 1-5 Hot-acid etching of this 9-in square disc of AISI 4142 alloy steel revealed ingot pattern and inclusion pits.

Figure 1-6 Hot-acid etching of this disc from an AISI 4140 alloy steel billet revealed entrapped gas, heavy segregation, voids, and ingot pattern.

Figure 1-7 Microstructure in central region of etch disc shown in Fig. 1-6 revealing an open pipe condition and segregation (unetched, $25\times$; etched with 2% nital, $50\times$).

Figure 1-8 Hot-acid etching of this disc from an AISI 1050 billet revealed a "cokey" center, inclusion pits, and a dendritic pattern.

Figure 1-9 Microstructure in "cokey" like center of etch disc shown in Fig. 1-8 revealing the depth of the etch attack (2% nital, $75\times$).

Figure 1-10 Hot-acid etching of this disc from an AISI 4145 modified alloy steel billet revealed hydrogen flakes.

Figure 1-8 shows a "cokey" center, pits, and a well-defined dendritic pattern in a disc of carbon steel. Figure 1-9 shows the microstructure (longitudinal plane through etched disc) in the "cokey" region. Note the coarse grains outlined by ferrite. Sulfide inclusions that are oriented in the hot-working direction were frequently observed in the ferrite phase. Note that the etch has severely attacked the sulfide stringers, which are more numerous in the "cokey" region.

In Figure 1-10, hydrogen flaking is sharply delineated by standard etching of a disc of alloy steel. Figure 1-11 shows a macroetched disc cut from a Ti-6Al-4V forging. Note the pronounced flow-line pattern around the forging lap.

1-3.3 Continuously Cast Steel Macrostructures

In recent years, continuous casting has become an important process for producing metals. Macroetching has been widely employed in the development of this technique, to evaluate the influence of casting parameters on billet and slab quality and on the quality of the wrought product. Some examples of the unique macroetch features that can be observed in such steels are given in the following examples.

Figure 1-11 Macroetching of a Ti-6Al-4V forging revealed grain flow and a forging lap (1¼×; etchant, solution of 10 mL HF, 15 mL HNO₃, and 75 mL H₂O for 2 min at room temperature). *(Courtesy of J. A. Hendrickson, Wyman-Gordon Co.)*

Figure 1-12 shows the macrostructure of continuously cast carbon steel. Hot-acid etching revealed an unconsolidated center and halfway cracks in the transverse (Fig. 1-12*a*) and longitudinal (Fig. 1-12*b*) discs. Figure 1-13 shows the macrostructure of carbon steel that contained a star-type crack pattern. This crack was not completely healed during rolling. Figure 1-14 shows an etched disc from the transverse section of continuously cast AISI 4140 that revealed a dendritic structure, center porosity, and a light etching band from induction stirring.

1-3.4 Consumable Electrode Remelted Steel Macrostructures

Electroslag-remelted and vacuum-arc-remelted steels can exhibit unique macroetch features. Steels produced using these refining practices have a grain structure with an oriented growth pattern which is essentially vertical but inclined toward the center which eliminates the central equiaxed portion of the ingot with its high inherent segregation and reduces both macrosegregation and micro-segregation.

Figures 1-15 and 1-16 show the macrostructures of billets rolled from electro-slag-remelted ingots and illustrate some of the unique features that can be encountered. Figure 1-15 shows an etched disc exhibiting a light freckle condition. Figure 1-16 shows a ring pattern and a few randomly dispersed pits.

1-3.5 Dendrite Arm Spacing

For many years, efforts to improve the properties of castings were directed primarily at refining the grain size. While these efforts definitely produced improvements in mechanical properties, it has since been recognized that other factors must also be controlled. Optimum properties can be achieved through control of the as-cast dendritic structure.

Figure 1-12a Hot-acid etching of a transverse disc from continuously cast AISI 1045 carbon steel revealed coarser dendrites at top compared to bottom, light center segregation, and halfway cracks. *(Courtesy of M. Schmidt, Bethlehem Steel Corp.)*

Figure 1-12*b* Hot-acid etching of a longitudinal disc from the center of the disc shown in Fig. 1-12*a* revealed the extent of the open center condition. *(Courtesy of M. Schmidt, Bethlehem Steel Corp.)*

Figure 1-13 *(Top of opposite page)*   Hot-acid etching of a transverse disc from continuously cast AISI 1008 carbon steel revealed a star-pattern open condition. *(Courtesy of M. Schmidt, Bethlehem Steel Corp.)*

Figure 1-14 *(Bottom of opposite page)* Hot-acid etching of this transverse section of continuously cast AISI 4140 revealed a dendritic structure, center porosity, and a band (arrow) from induction stirring. *(Courtesy of B. L. Bramfitt, Bethlehem Steel Corp.)*

Figure 1-15 Hot-acid etching of this disc from an electroslag-remelted tool steel billet revealed light freckle segregation and a faint, discontinuous ring pattern. *(Courtesy of M. H. Lasonde, Bethlehem Steel Corp.)*

Dendrites grow initially in the form of rods. However, growth perturbations or minor changes in the liquid around the growing dendrite occur. These temperature and compositional perturbations in the liquid cause bumps to form on the side of the rods, which grow outward into the liquid forming the secondary arms. In a like manner, tertiary arms can form on the secondary arms and so forth. Later, the liquid between the primary, secondary, and tertiary arms freezes. The planes containing the primary stalk and a secondary arm are called primary sheets. These planes are parallel to the direction of heat flow. Planes perpendicular to the primary sheets containing secondary and tertiary arms are called secondary planes. In the examination of dendrite structures, low magnifications (10X for example) are much more useful than high magnifications (100X and

Figure 1-16 Hot-acid etching of this disc from an electroslag-remelted tool steel billet revealed a well-developed ring pattern and a few randomly dispersed pits. (*Courtesy of M. H. Lasonde, Bethlehem Steel Corp.*)

higher). Figure 1-17 shows dendrites observed on a broken tensile bar from a casting. The primary and secondary arms are readily visible, and tertiary arms can be detected occasionally.

The primary and secondary arm spacings have been measured in solidification studies. The secondary arm spacing has been shown to be a sensitive measure of solidification phenomena. While most studies have measured the secondary arm spacing, Weinberg and Buhr measured the primary dendrite spacing because it changes more rapidly with freezing distance than the secondary arm spacing [14].

The basic difference between the primary and secondary arm spacings can be viewed in terms of nucleation and growth mechanisms. The primary dendrite stalks develop from grains that nucleate at the chill surface. Only those grains with

9X

Figure 1-17 Dendrites observed on a broken section of cast iron.

the proper crystallographic orientation will grow an appreciable distance into the liquid. In body-centered cubic metals, such as iron, the direction of dendrite growth is always the cube axis, i.e., <100>. The primary dendrite spacing depends upon the initial freezing conditions in the chill zone and thus is controlled by the nucleation rate. However, the secondary arm spacing is not a function of the nucleation rate at the chill surface but is controlled by the growth rate away from the surface. Thus, the critical factor for the secondary arm spacing is the rate of heat removal from the casting. The degree of heat removal changes constantly during most casting processes, and therefore measurement of the secondary arm spacing is of considerable value in the study of solidification. Although some qualitative information regarding dendritic spacing was known, Alexander and Rhines performed the first quantitative study of the solidification process [15]. In this report Alexander and Rhines discussed the problem of making measurements of dendrite spacing. In order to eliminate the need for corrections for orientation effect, they first made spacing measurements only in grains where the major dendrite axis was nearly in the plane of polish. Since this is a matter of judgment, some error can be introduced. They observed that not all of the secondary arms were well developed, and chose to measure only spacings between fully developed secondary arms. Since this is also a matter of judgment, error can result and the degree of repeatability of measurements suffers. They also observed that two characteristic spacings were present in the center of some of their ingots; they chose to record the larger spacing rather than the smaller or an average of the two.

In some metals, such as aluminum castings, it is difficult to measure dendrite arm spacings. In these metals, one can measure the dendrite cell size, which is the width of the individual cells, or the dendrite cell interval, which is the center-to-center distance between adjacent cells. In alloys with a small amount of interdendritic material, the cell size and cell interval are equal. However, as the amount of interdendritic matter increases, the cell interval becomes greater than the cell size, and the dendritic cell size is usually the preferred measurement. If the amount of interdendritic material is small, the line intercept method can be used to compute the number of cells per unit length and the average cell size.

1-3.6 Forging Flow Lines

Macroetching is widely used to study metal flow patterns due to hot or cold working. Figure 1-18a shows a disc cut from a close-die-forged steering knuckle made from AISI 4140 steel. The disc was deep-etched in the standard hot etch of hydrochloric acid and water. The flow lines can be observed, but they are much

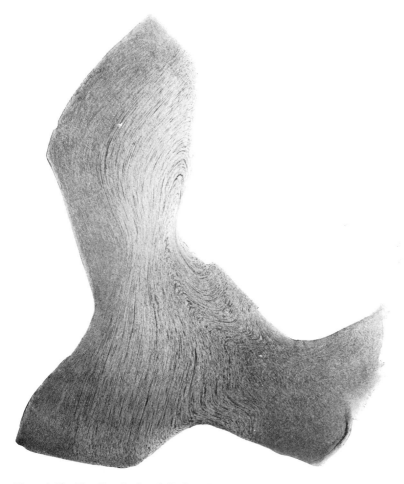

Figure 1-18a Flow lines in closed-die-forged AISI 4140 steering knuckle revealed by cold etching with 10% aqueous HNO_3 ($\frac{1}{2}\times$).

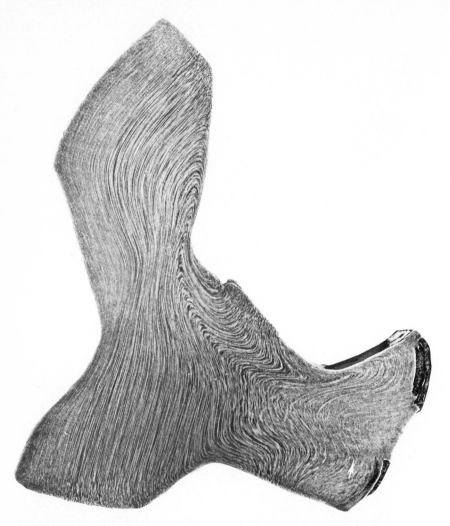

Figure 1-18b Flow lines in sample shown in Fig. 1-18a that were revealed by deep-acid etching and inking.

more plainly visible after inking, as shown in Figure 1–18b. India ink was rubbed over the surface of the component and seeped into the etched-out flow lines; the excess ink was wiped off the top surface.

Figure 1-19a shows a disc from a macroetched forging of Ti-6Al-4V; flow lines and segregation can be observed. Figure 1-19b shows the microstructure at the four areas. Area A exhibits a uniform alpha-beta structure, while the other three areas exhibit coarse, stringy alpha phase and coarse beta phase.

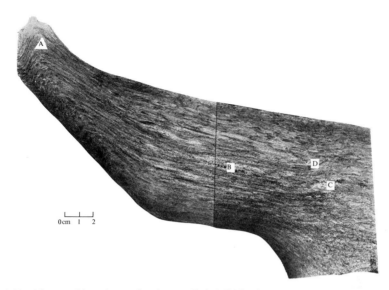

Figure 1-19a Macroetching of a section from a Ti-6Al-4V forging revealing metal flow pattern and segregation (etchant, solution of 10 mL HF, 15 mL HNO$_3$, and 75 mL H$_2$O, swabbed for 2 min at room temperature). *(Courtesy of J. A. Hendrickson, Wyman-Gordon Co.)*

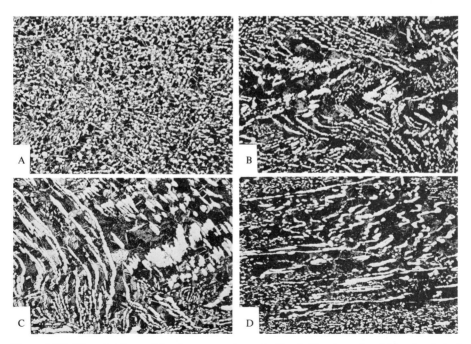

Figure 1-19b Microstructure of the four areas shown in Fig. 1-19a. Area A exhibits the desired uniform alpha-beta microstructure. Areas B, C, and D show regions of coarse, linear alpha (white) and course beta (dark) phase (60×; 10 seconds immersed with heavy agitation in 8 g NaOH in 60 mL water, heated to a boil after addition of 10 mL H$_2$O$_2$). *(Courtesy of J. A. Hendrickson, Wyman-Gordon Co.)*

1-3.7 Grain or Cell Size

As shown in some of the previous examples, macroetching usually reveals the as-cast grain structure, particularly when it is relatively coarse. Figure 1-20 shows a sample of AISI 1020 semikilled steel used as the handle of a basket in a continuous annealing furnace. The surface of the part was heavily decarburized during use, resulting in a coarse columnar grain structure in the decarburized layer. These grains are clearly revealed by etching. The interior, fine-grained structure exhibits a dull mat appearance.

In cast eutectic alloys, the eutectic cell size and the morphology of the eutectic are of the most interest. In hypoeutectic gray cast iron, solidification begins with the formation of austenite dendrites that grow as the temperature falls to the eutectic temperature. At the eutectic temperature, the liquid solidifies as a result of freezing of the eutectic of austenite and graphite. Usually the pattern of eutectic growth roughly approximates a sphere. Growth of the eutectic nuclei continues until they impinge on one another, producing a characteristic cell size which depends on the nucleation rate. Many of the copper-containing reagents (see App. B) can be used to reveal the eutectic cell size and Stead's reagent has been widely used. Eutectic cell size can also be measured by the intercept method. Studies have shown how processing influences cell size and how cell size influences properties.

The eutectic cell boundary exhibits a light etching appearance as a result of the entrapment of impurities, such as phosphorus and sulfur, at the interface. The eutectic cells are most easily viewed with the unaided eye or with low magnifications. In white cast iron, which freezes with an austenite-carbide eutectic, the eutectic cell boundaries can be faintly seen in columnar castings but not in equiaxed castings. In gray irons, there is no relationship between graphite flake size and the eutectic cell size. The eutectic cell size in nodular iron is much

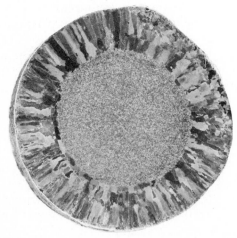

Nital　　　　　　　　　　　　　　　　　　　2X

Figure 1-20 Macroetching of a section cut from an AISI 1020 (semikilled) basket handle used in a continuous annealing furnace revealed coarse dendritic grain growth associated with decarburization.

finer than in gray iron; the finer cell size and the nodular graphite shape account for the remarkable properties of nodular iron.

Delineation of the eutectic cells in gray iron depends on either the segregation or the depletion of certain elements in the cell boundaries. A wide variety of techniques have been used to reveal the eutectic cells. Dawson and Oldfield [16] recommend the following:

1. 4% picral for 5 min—for ferritic type D gray iron
2. Stead's reagent for up to 1 h—good for low-phosphorus pearlitic irons
3. 10% aqueous ammonium persulfate for up to a few minutes—good for high-phosphorus (more than 0.2%) irons

Adams [17] recommends the following:

1. Heat tinting—especially useful for high-phosphorus irons
2. Deep etching in 25% alcoholic nitric acid—good for some high-phosphorus irons
3. Heating samples for 30 to 120 min at about 1300°F (704°C), then polishing and etching them with nital or picral—widely applicable method

Merchant has reviewed many of the methods used to reveal eutectic cells [18].

Eutectic cells can be easily revealed in pearlitic gray iron by heating the specimen below the critical temperature, for example, at about 1300°F (704°C), for 30 min to 2 h [17]. This procedure decomposes the pearlite in the center of the cells, while the pearlite at the cell boundaries is relatively unaffected because the phosphorus at the cell boundaries retards graphitization. With ferritic gray irons or gray irons that are almost or completely ferrite, the sample can be heated [19] to 1800°F (982°C), quenched into lead or salt at 1200°F (649°C), and held there for about 30 s before being quenched with water. This procedure produces a thin film of pearlite at the cell boundaries, while the cell interior is martensite plus some ferrite.

Merchant has studied the influence of composition on eutectic cell delineation [20]. He states that eutectic cell boundaries may be impossible to delineate if the sulfur level is below 0.01%. In the presence of appreciable manganese, addition of titanium improves eutectic cell delineation markedly. However, if the manganese content is low, addition of titanium desulfurizes the melt and reduces a procedure's ability to reveal the cell boundaries. The presence of phosphorus in cast iron does not ensure delineation of the eutectic cells. Carbide-stabilizing elements, such as Cr, Mo, or V, aid the delineation of eutectic cells. Elements such as Bi or Pb also help improve cell delineation.

Dawson and Oldfield [16] state that cell structures can be very difficult to reveal in certain samples, such as heavy sections of cast irons that contain medium to high phosphorus. Very large castings, such as ingot molds, are also difficult to etch for determining eutectic cell size.

While the grains in coarse-grained aluminum castings and wrought products can be revealed by many of the macroetchants listed in App. A, a number of investigators have employed color illumination to improve the grain contrast. Beck has used two etchants, listed in App. A, for revealing grains in aluminum [21, 22]. Illumination was provided by three universal microscope lamps angled to provide oblique light from three directions. Each lamp was fitted with a different color filter to increase the contrast of the reflections from adjacent grains. The sample could be rotated while it was examined at low (10 to 20X) magnification. The sample was kept rotating while the projected image was traced on a plastic sheet so that all the grain boundaries could be sketched.

Ryvola has also shown the value of color filters for improving grain contrast in macroetched aluminum samples [23]. Two illuminators, one with a red filter and the other with a green filter, were placed on opposite sides of the sample to cast oblique light. A blue filter was inserted between the sample and the objective of a stereomicroscope. Rotation of the sample was also used here to reveal all the grain boundaries. In most studies Ryvola employed Tucker's or Poulton's reagent (see App. A for composition) as the macroetch.

1-3.8 Alloy Segregation

Because most engineering alloys freeze over a range of temperatures and liquid compositions, the various elements in the alloy segregate during the solidification of ingots and castings. Segregation occurs over short distances, causing micro-segregation, and over long distances, producing macrosegregation. Microsegre-gation is a natural result of dendritic solidification because the dendrites are purer in composition than the interdendritic matter. Macrosegregation manifests itself in a variety of forms–centerline segregation, negative cone of segregation, A- and V-type segregates, and banding. These phenomena are the result of the flow of solute-enriched interdendritic liquid in the mushy zone during solidification; this flow is a result of solidification shrinkage and gravitational forces.

Macrosegregation can be detected by bulk chemical analysis. Tests on large ingots generally reveal low concentrations of carbon and alloying elements at the bottom and sides and enrichment at the top and along the centerline. Macrosegre-gation can be detected on fractures and on macroetched discs. In addition to the use of traditional macroetching and microetching, microsegregation has also been studied by autoradiography, microradiography, electron-probe microanalysis, and x-ray fluorescence. The study of segregation has become a relatively simple matter since the development of the electron microprobe. This instrument is capable of providing accurate, rapid determinations of compositional differences.

Figure 1-21 illustrates the use of macroetching to reveal segregation and shows a sample of carbon-manganese-chromium steel which cracked during extrusion (note the central burst). A transverse disc reveals a spot of segregation which is more readily observed on the longitudinal section. The streaks are martensitic with a hardness of 46 to 58 HRC (Rockwell hardness on the C scale), while the bulk hardness is below 20 HRC. The streak is enriched in C, Mn, and Cr.

Figure 1-21 Examples of segregation associated with central bursts in extruded AISI 1141 steel. The streaks, which consist of martensite, have a hardness of 46 to 58 HRC (Rockwell hardness on the C scale) while the matrix hardness is less than 20 HRC.

1-3.9 Carbide Segregation

Macroetching is also widely used with high-alloy steels to reveal carbide segregation. Figure 1-22 shows longitudinal sections of T1 high-speed steel that have been polished and etched, revealing carbide segregation.

1-3.10 Weldments

Welding has become one of the most important fabrication processes for a variety of reasons. In any study of welds, the initial step invariably centers on the development of the weld macrostructure. The weld macrostructure is established

$1\frac{3}{8}$

$1\frac{15}{16}$

$2\frac{1}{2}$

$3\frac{1}{4}$

Figure 1-22 Macroetching with 10% nital was used to reveal carbide segregation in polished sections from various sizes of rounds of T1 high-speed tool steel. (Diameters in inches below sections.)

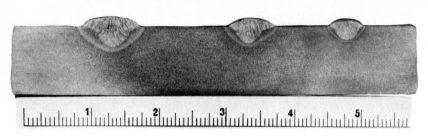

Figure 1-23 Macroetching used to reveal the influence of weld parameters on penetration depth and shape. Top example shows GMA (gas-metal arc) welds at a heat input of 45 kJ/in using atmospheres of 100% CO_2, argon plus 25% CO_2, and argon plus 2% O_2 (left to right). Bottom example shows submerged arc welds using heat inputs of 90, 60, and 30 kJ/in (left to right). (The etchant was 10% aqueous HNO_3.)

by the type of process employed, the operating parameters, and the materials used. Thus, metallography is a key tool in weld quality studies. Key terms in describing the macrostructure of fusion welds are the basic three components—the weld metal ("nugget"), the heat-affected zone (HAZ), and the base metal. Within the weld metal and the heat-affected zone, there are changes in composition, grain size and orientation, microstructure, and hardness. Thus one observes significant variations in microstructure as the weldment is scanned.

Macroetching is frequently employed to determine the influence of various changes in weld parameters on the size and shape of the weld metal, on depth of penetration, on weld structure, and on hardness. Figure 1-23 (top) shows the influence of the protective atmosphere on the shape and penetration of the weld metal. A carbon-manganese plate steel was welded using the gas-metal arc (GMA) procedure with a heat input of 45 kJ/in and 0.045-in diameter A675 filler metal wire. Three atmospheres were used: 100% CO_2 (left), argon plus 25% CO_2 (center), and argon plus 2% O_2 (right). Also shown in Fig. 1-23 (bottom) are three submerged arc weldments that were made using heat inputs of 90 (left), 60 (center), and 30 kJ/in (right). These examples clearly show how welding parameters can alter the size, shape, and penetration of the weldment.

Figure 1-24 illustrates the macrostructure of a weld in beryllium. This sample was polished and the macrostructure was revealed using crossed polarized light. Figure 1-25 shows the macrostructure of flash-welded titanium after etching.

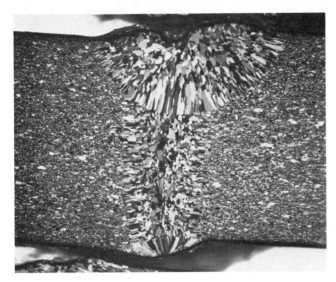

Figure 1-24 Crossed polarized light was used to reveal the macrostructure of this beryllium weldment. *(Courtesy of R. D. Buchheit, Battelle-Columbus Laboratories.)*

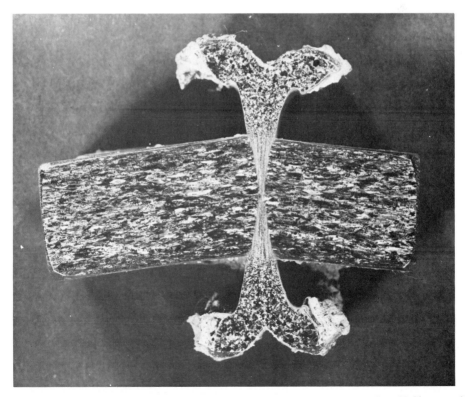

Figure 1-25 Macroetching (solution consisting of 1.5 mL HF, 15 mL HNO_3, and 80 mL H_2O) was used to reveal the macrostructure of this titanium flash weld. The extent of the metal extruded from the joint and the grain refinement in the junction is clearly revealed. *(Courtesy of R. D. Buchheit, Battelle-Columbus Laboratories.)*

(a)   (b)

Figure 1-26a Strain pattern revealed in a broken flat tensile bar of carbon steel using Bish's procedure (see Refs. 11 and 12).

Figure 1-26b Strain pattern in a cold-formed ASTM A325 high-strength bolt (before heat treatment) revealed by Bish's method (see Refs. 11 and 12). Note the thin strained surface layer beneath the cold-rolled threads.

1-3.11 Strain Patterns

As described previously, a number of etching procedures have been developed to reveal strain pattens in steel (App. B) and in aluminum and nickel-base alloys (App. C). Most of these procedures are qualitative in nature. However, Benson has calibrated etching response for residual stresses in AISI 4340, D6AC, and AISI 1045 steels [24]. Etching of the steel revealed regions of tensile elastic surface stresses, forming furrows aligned roughly perpendicular to the tensile stress direction. The furrow spacing was found to vary with the stress level.

The use of etching procedures to reveal strain patterns is illustrated in Figs. 1-26a and b. The left macrograph (Fig. 1-26a) shows the strain pattern observed in a flat tensile test specimen of a light-gauge plate steel, while the right macrograph (Fig 1-26b) shows the strain pattern in a cold-formed ASTM A325 bolt.

1-3.12 Failure Analysis

Macroetching can be a useful procedure for the failure analyst [25], as shown by the following examples. Cold etching reveals decarburized surfaces. Figure 1-27 shows a disc cut transversely from a heat-treated steel bar that was cold-etched with 10% nitric acid in water to reveal a light etching rim of decarburization.

Figure 1-27 Macroetching with 10% aqueous HNO₃ was used to reveal the decarburized surface on this bar (¾×).

Figure 1-28 shows a disc cold-etched with 10% aqueous nitric acid that had been cut from a cracked 3½-in diameter AISI H11 pump plunger. Cracking was detected during finish grinding. Since microscopic examinations showed that both the crack wall and OD (outside diameter) surface were nitrided, cracking occurred prior to nitriding.

Figure 1-29 shows a section that was cut from a carburized AISI P2 die. The etch pattern is characteristic of a carburized steel sample where the case is hard [65 HRC (Rockwell hardness on the C scale)] and the core is unhardened [85 to 86

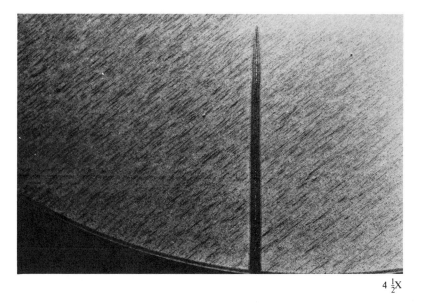

$4\frac{1}{2}$X

Figure 1-28 Macroetching of a disc cut from a cracked AISI H11 pump plunger revealed a dark rim around both the surface and the crack. This rim indicates the depth of the nitrided surface layer and showed that the crack was present before nitriding.

Figure 1-29 Macroetching (10% aqueous HNO_3) of a disc cut from this carburized AISI P2 part revealed a heavy case at both the ID and OD. The surface was 65.5 HRC (Rockwell hardness on the C scale) while the center was at 85 to 86 HRB (Rockwell hardness on the B scale).

HRB (Rockwell hardness on the B scale)]. Note that the high-carbon hardened case etches with a dark coloration, while the unhardened core appears light.

Parts subjected to abusive grinding have a characteristic scorch pattern when cold-etched. Figure 1-30 shows an AISI D2 die that cracked because of thermal stresses from grinding in the as-quenched (untempered) condition.

Figure 1-30 Macroetching (10% aqueous HNO_3) was used to reveal grinding scorch on the surface of this AISI D2 die. Grinding damage resulted because the die had not been tempered.

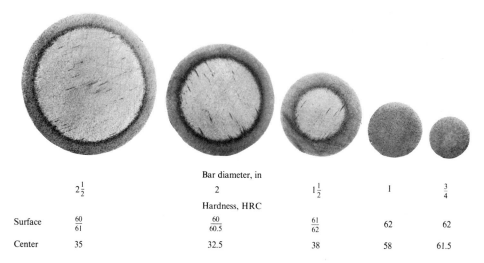

	Bar diameter, in			
$2\frac{1}{2}$	2	$1\frac{1}{2}$	1	$\frac{3}{4}$
	Hardness, HRC			
Surface $\frac{60}{61}$	$\frac{60}{60.5}$	$\frac{61}{62}$	62	62
Center 35	32.5	38	58	61.5

Figure 1-31 Macroetching (10% aqueous HNO_3) was used to reveal the extent of hardening in these AISI 1060 carbon steel round bars.

1-3.13 Response to Heat Treatment

Macroetching can also be used to determine the hardenability of various steel bars subjected to known heat treatment conditions. This procedure, coupled with hardness testing, was widely used prior to the adoption of hardenability analysis. As an illustration, Fig. 1-31 shows discs cut from round bars of AISI 1060 carbon steel ranging in size from a diameter of ¾ to 2½ in. The two smallest sizes were through-hardened, that is, the center region contains more than 50% martensite, and the etch pattern was uniform. The other three sizes exhibit a case and core pattern, since the central region was unhardened. For this test, all bars were austenitized at 1525°F (829°C), brine quenched, and then tempered at 300°F (149°C). The bar length was twice the diameter, and the etched section was taken from the center.

Cold etching is also useful in studying the results of surface-hardening treatments. Figure 1-32 shows the results of induction hardening of gear teeth made from AISI 1055 carbon steel. The areas hardened and the depth of the hardened zone are quite apparent.

1-3.14 Flame Cutting

Figure 1-33 illustrates the use of the cold etch to reveal the extent of the heat-affected zone developed during flame cutting of two AISI S5 gripping cams. The etched discs clearly show the effect of different heat inputs on the depth of the heat-affected zone.

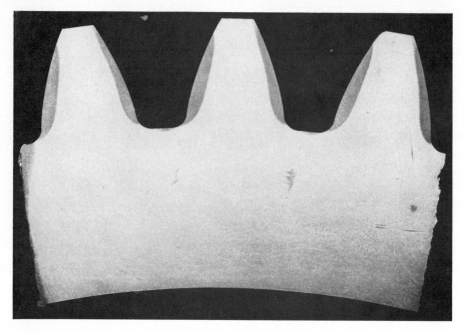

Figure 1-32 The depth and extent of hardening in these induction-hardened gear teeth made of AISI 1055 carbon steel was determined by macroetching with 10% aqueous HNO_3. Surface hardness was 53 to 54 HRC (Rockwell hardness on the C scale), while the unhardened area was about 23 HRC.

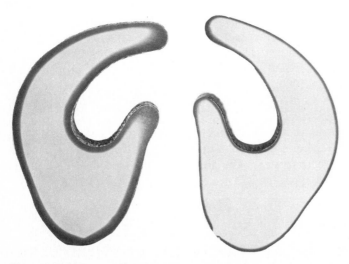

Figure 1-33 Macroetching (10% HNO_3 in water) was used to reveal the extent of the heat-affected zone produced during flame cutting of these AISI S5 tool-steel gripping cams.

1-4 MACROSTRUCTURE REVEALED BY MACHINING

The macrostructure of certain metals and alloys can be revealed by machining. This was first shown by Dewrance in 1927, but no details were provided. Subsequently, Ljunggren showed that the grain structure of soft iron was revealed when the surface was scribed with closely spaced ruled lines just as if it had been etched [26]. Ljunggren also showed that the macrostructure of relatively pure lead was revealed by planing with a microtome. Best results were obtained with the knife blade inclined at an angle of about 4.5° (see Fig. 109, Ref. 26).

Clarebrough and Ogilvie used machining to study the macrostructure of pure lead [27]. The samples were annealed to produce an average grain size of about 5 mm. Orthogonal cuts were made with a high-speed steel microtome with a depth of cut of 0.001 in. Examination of the cut surfaces revealed transverse marks extending across some grains in a direction perpendicular to that of the cut. Grain boundaries were revealed by a change in pitch of these marks. Maximum contrast was obtained when a grain with strong markings was adjacent to a grain without marks. Etch pit techniques, which were used to determine the orientations of grains with strong markings and those without marks, showed that grains with a [100] direction close to the direction of machining formed strong surface marks while grains with a [111] direction close to the direction of machining did not produce marks.

Hanson and Pell-Walpole state that the machining method is the best method for revealing the macrostructure of cast bronzes [28]. They recommend using a sharp, square tool 0.01 in across at the tip, with a depth of cut of 0.01 in and a feed of 0.01 inch.

1-5 THE FRACTURE TEST

Examination of test sample fractures is a well recognized, simple test for evaluating the quality of metals. Indeed, such tests have been conducted since the production of metals first began. In this section, the use of macroscopic examination of sample fractures to evaluate the macrostructure and microstructure of quality control specimens is reviewed.

The breaking of test pieces for examination can be a very crude operation, or it can be carefully controlled in test machines. The simplest procedure is to support the sample on its ends and strike the center with a sledgehammer. In the fracturing of hardened steel discs, a mold can be designed to support the specimen edges, while a top cover is used to locate a chisel over the center of the specimen. The chisel is struck with a sledgehammer to make the break. The mold prevents the broken pieces from striking personnel in the area. If the fracture is desired at a particular spot, it is useful to nick the specimen at the desired spot, and a fracture press is a very useful tool for such work. One end of a specimen can also be placed in a sturdy vise and the specimen struck on the other end. Body-centered cubic metals are occasionally refrigerated in dry ice or liquid nitrogen to facilitate breaking. Face-centered cubic metals can be difficult to fracture by these methods, especially if the section thickness is appreciable.

Some of the uses of fracture examination include:

- Identification of specimen composition
- Detection of inclusion stringers
- Detection of degree of graphitization
- Assessment of grain size
- Assessment of depth of hardening
- Detection of overheating
- Evaluation of quality

These items are discussed in the sections that follow. A general review of some of these topics is provided in the book by Enos [29].

1-5.1 Composition

In the identification of unknown metals in the field [30], fracture examination can provide a clue to the identity of the material. Along with other visual features, such as color and apparent density, the fracture appearance can be used to provide a rough separation of metals. Ostrofsky provides the following guidelines for use with iron-base alloys [30]:

Metal	Fracture appearance
Gray cast iron	Coarse grain, gray
Malleable iron	Fine grain, black
Wrought iron	Fibrous, light gray
Low-carbon steel	Fine grain, light gray
Tool steel	Very fine grain (silky), light gray

Prior to the development of rapid chemical analysis procedures, the steel melter followed the progress of the refining process by fracture examination. A small sample was poured and cooled rapidly. The sample was broken, and the fracture "read." Obviously, some experience was required. The approximate carbon content was assessed by the degree of brittleness or toughness of the fracture. High oxygen content could be detected by observation of blowholes in the specimen.

1-5.2 Inclusion Stringers

Inclusion stringers of macroscopic size can be readily detected on a fractured specimen after heat tinting in the blue heat range. This procedure is described in

Figure 1-34 Macrograph of a hardened, fractured, and blued macroetched disc revealing inclusion stringers (white streaks).

ASTM Specification E45. There are ASTM specifications that provide fracture test limitations for acceptance for a number of specific materials. Figure 1-34 shows an example of inclusion stringers revealed by use of this procedure.

In most cases where the test is applied, the macroetch discs from the ingots tested are hardened, fractured, and blued on a hot plate or in a laboratory furnace. In general, heating to 500 to 700°F (260 to 371°C) is adequate, although slightly higher temperatures may be required for high-chromium grades. The fracture is always broken so that the fracture plane is longitudinal. The ASTM specifications describe both qualitative and quantitative methods for assessment of inclusion severity. The qualitative assessment can be conducted by comparing the samples to the ten standards in ISO Specification 3763 and noting the distribution of the stringers (core, surface, or uniform). Quantitative assessment requires measuring the length and/or thickness and counting the number in each size range.

1-5.3 Degree of Graphitization

Chill and wedge tests have both been widely employed in the manufacture of gray and white irons to reveal the carbide stability, or the tendency of an iron to solidify as white iron rather than gray iron. These tests show the combined effect of melting practice and composition on carbide stability but are not a substitute for chemical analyses.

Figure 1-35 Fractograph of wedge test specimen of cast iron. The white areas indicate the presence of iron carbide, while the dark areas indicate that flake graphite is present.

Each test uses a different procedure to cast the sample. The chill test uses a small rectangular casting where one face is a chill plate, while the wedge test employs a wedge-shaped casting. In the wedge test, the cooling rate varies with the wedge thickness, and chill plates are not used in the wedge test mold.

After casting a specimen with either method, the sample is broken and the fracture is examined (see Fig. 1-35). In the chill test, the depth of the chill (white iron) is measured. The appearance of the zone between the fully white and fully gray fractures plus the chill depth is an indicator of melting conditions. In the wedge test, the distance from the wedge tip to the end of the white fracture is measured, usually to the nearest $\frac{1}{32}$ of an inch.

In the production of tool steels, the fracture test may be used to detect graphite in tool steels that intentionally incorporate graphite or in high-carbon tool steels that should be free of graphite. Figure 1-36 shows four fractured test discs of a high-carbon steel that contains considerable undesired graphite as a result of the accidental addition of aluminum.

1-5.4 Grain Size

The prior-austenite grain size of high-carbon martensite steels, such as tool steels, can be assessed by comparing a fractured sample to a series of graded fractured specimens. The method is simple, accurate, and reproducible, and it is discussed in detail in Chap. 6.

1-5.5 Depth of Hardening

The depth of hardening in case-hardened steels, such as carbon tool steels, can be assessed through the use of fractured samples. The P-F (penetration-fracture) test developed by Shepherd is commonly used for evaluating carbon steel heats [31].

Figure 1-36 Fractograph of fractured hardened macroetched discs of AISI W1 (1.3% carbon) tool steel that were excessively graphitized as the result of a high, undesired aluminum content.

In this test, a ¾-in diameter, 4-in long sample is austenitized at the recommended temperature, quenched in brine, and fractured. The case depth is measured based on the change in fracture appearance. After fracturing, the surface is usually ground, etched, and its hardness tested to define the depth to a specific hardness.

1-5.6 Detection of Overheating

Fracture tests have also been used to detect overheating during soaking prior to hot working. In this test, a rectangular section, roughly 1-in square by 3 to 4 in long, is cut from the suspect material. It is normalized, quenched and tempered to 321 to 341 HB (Brinell hardness number), and fractured at room temperature. The appearance of coarse-grained facets on the fracture indicates overheating [32].

1-5.7 Evaluation of Quality

Fractures of longitudinal or transverse sections cut from wrought products or castings have been used for many years to evaluate metal quality. The fracture can reveal texture, flaking, graphitization, slag, blowholes, pipe, inclusions, and segregation. The general fracture appearance can be classified as coarse or fine, woody, fibrous, ductile, or brittle. Fibrous fractures result from microstructural anisotropy produced by alloy segregation or inclusions. Longitudinal fractures in wrought iron exhibit a classic fibrous appearance. Woody fractures generally result from gross alloy or nonmetallic segregations.

Fractures that occur during service or processing sometimes reveal features that indicate quality problems. Figure 1-37 shows a fractured case-hardened carbon steel bar that broke during heat treatment. The fine outer rim of the fracture reveals the depth of hardening. The central coarse-grained area indicates an unsound condition. Hot-acid etching of a disc cut from behind the fracture reveals a loose center and a segregated condition.

The fracture appearance of tensile test specimens has long been regarded as an index of quality. If the tensile test fracture does not have gross defects, its appearance is classified as irregular, angular, flat, partially cupped, or full cup-and-cone fracture. A full cup-and-cone fracture is generally regarded as the optimum fracture in the tensile test. Johnson and Fisher have conducted an extensive study of the fracture appearance of tensile bars and the relationship of the fracture to the test results [33]. For a given type of steel, such as normalized carbon steels or quenched and tempered alloy steels, there is an approximately linear relationship between tensile strength and tensile ductility.

The fracture test has been widely applied in the production of copper castings [34, 35]. The fracture test is often coupled with the removal of the gating or feeding portions of the casting. In copper-based castings, the color of the fracture provides considerable information [28]. The fracture color is influenced by alloy composition and the presence of various phases or constituents. A fracture of the alpha solid-solution phase of tin bronze appears red-brown, while a fracture of the tin-rich delta phase appears blue-white. Copper phosphide appears pale blue-gray, while lead appears dark blue-gray. Bronzes with low tin and phosphorus content are reddish brown. As the tin or phosphorus content is increased, the fracture appearance changes to gray-brown and then to gray. The addition of zinc in copper castings imparts a brassy yellow color to the fracture. Localized color variations in fractured copper-based castings indicate the presence of defects.

Figure 1-37 The fracture of this eutectoid carbon bar that broke during heat treatment reveals the depth of hardening and an unsound center condition. Hot-acid etching of a disc from behind the fracture reveals the unsound center and extensive segregation.

The texture of bronze fractures varies with compositions and grain size [28]. Increases in tin or phosphorus usually produce finer, silkier fractures, while lead additions produce a granular appearance. Bronzes with low tin contents often have a fibrous texture. Coarse-grained castings often exhibit coarse intergranular facets on the fracture, while chill-cast specimens usually exhibit fine fractures.

Considerable effort has been devoted to the study of fractures of red brass (ASTM B208). This work [34, 35] has shown that high-quality melts exhibit chill block fractures with at least 2 in of fine blue-gray structure and a columnar structure up to ¾ in from the chill face. Fractures of melts of intermediate quality have a coarser lighter blue-gray structure and less columnar depth and appear reddish rather than deep-blue. Fractures of low-quality melts have little clear blue-gray and columnar structure. These fractures may appear mottled because of a high gas content.

1-6 SPECIAL PRINT METHODS

A wide variety of special print methods have been developed to record deep-etched macrostructures, the distribution of oxide or sulfide inclusions, or the distribution of phosphorus or lead. Chemical spot tests have also been developed to identify the presence and location of a variety of chemical elements. Of these methods, only the sulfur print is used widely today.

1-6.1 Contact Printing

In a monumental work on the microscopic structure of iron and steel, Sorby described his method of "nature-printing" of deep-etched samples [1]. Sorby prepared blocks of metal which were "sufficiently well'bitten' with moderately strong acid to enable me to print with ink as from a wood block."

A contact print is made by rolling india ink on the surface of a deeply etched sample and pressing a piece of paper on this surface, being careful not to move the paper. Pressure is applied by a printing press or with a roller, and the paper is then peeled off. The method has been employed chiefly when photographic equipment is unavailable.

1-6.2 Sulfur Printing

The sulfur print technique is an exceptionally useful procedure for studying the heterogeneity of steels. During solidification; most of the impurities, such as sulfur and phosphorus, are rejected into the interdendritic liquid. Thus, the last areas to solidify become highly enriched in impurities. This phenomenon is used to advantage in macroetching, where the corrosion rate difference between the dendritic and interdendritic regions, segregate and matrix, and so forth allow the macrostructure to be observed.

Because the solubility of solid sulfur in iron is very low, nearly all the sulfur is precipitated as sulfide inclusions. Sulfide distribution is influenced by the steelmaking process, with the degree of deoxidation being a primary factor. In steels with a very high oxygen content (low carbon content, no strong deoxidizers), most of the sulfides are found in the central portion of the ingot. In steels with low oxygen contents (medium or high carbon content, additions of silicon, aluminum, etc.), the sulfides are more uniformly distributed.

The early history of the sulfur print method has been reviewed by Berglund [2]. The method used today was developed by Baumann in 1906, but a similar technique was developed by Heyn earlier in 1906. In Heyn's method, a piece of silk is placed on the ground steel surface and is moistened with a solution containing 10 g mercuric chloride, 20 mL hydrochloric acid, and 100 mL water. The solution attacks the sulfide inclusions, producing hydrogen sulfide gas, which reacts with the mercuric chloride, precipitating black mercuric sulfide on the silk. This results in a mirror image of the sulfide distribution on one face of the ground sample. It is claimed that the method also shows the distribution of phosphorus, but this claim has never been proven conclusively.

Baumann's method, which is being used today in preference to Heyn's method, employs ordinary photographic paper soaked in dilute sulfuric acid. The photographic paper should be thin so that good contact is achieved with the surface. While glossy papers produce sharper prints, they are slippery, and it is difficult to prevent blurring of the image. Consequently, matte finishes are preferred. Bromide-type papers are preferred to chloride-type papers.

To obtain good prints, a ground surface is required. Polished surfaces can be used but do not produce improved results. Indeed, paper slippage resulting in blurred images is more common with polished surfaces. The surface to be printed must be carefully cleaned; otherwise, dark spots will result. Many solvents commonly employed in the metallography laboratory are suitable for cleaning. It is not uncommon to read recommendations in the literature suggesting cleaning with gasoline, petroleum ether, or carbon tetrachloride. However, in the interest of safety in the laboratory, use of solutions of this type should be avoided. Instead cleaning with acetone, alcohol, or 1,1,1-trichloroethane is recommended.

Preetching the surface of steel samples with 10% nitric acid in water often helps to obtain quality sulfur prints. The preetch improves the image intensity and promotes contact adhesion. Steels with less than 0.010% sulfur give faint prints, and preetching produces a more distinct print. Preetched surfaces can be printed several times, whereas only one print can be obtained from ground surfaces of steels with normal sulfur levels. However, with resulfurized steels, the first print is usually so dark that all details are obscured, and a second print from the ground surface (no preetch) produces a better rendition of the sulfur distribution.

The photographic paper is soaked in a solution containing 1 to 5% sulfuric acid in water; a 2% solution is used most often. A more dilute solution can be used for resulfurized steels or for printing very large surfaces where some time is required to cover the sample with the paper.

In general, the paper is soaked for 1 to 5 min in the solution of dilute acid; a 3-

min soak is widely employed. Longer soaking times can cause swelling of the gelatin surface of the film, which produces poor results. After the soaking period, the excess solution is allowed to drip off the paper. Some metallographers lay the photographic paper on blotter paper to remove the excess solution. The surface of the photographic paper should be relatively dry before laying it on the steel surface in order to prevent image blurring.

The emulsion side of the paper is placed on the surface of the steel sample and left in contact for 2 to 10 min, depending on the sulfur content of the steel. The sulfuric acid reacts with the sulfide inclusions, producing hydrogen sulfide. Any bubbles under the paper from entrapped air or from hydrogen sulfide must be carefully moved off the edge of the sample using a roller, squeegee, or sponge. Care must be exercised so that the paper does not slide.

Several procedures have been used in placing the paper on the sample. Most commonly, the sample is placed on the workbench or in a vise, if the sample is small, with the ground surface upward. This technique has the advantage that air bubbles can be observed and removed. If air bubbles are not removed, white spots will be present on the print. Some prefer to lay the photographic paper with the emulsion side up on a glass plate and then press the ground surface onto the paper. Others prefer to use blotter paper rather than glass. With either of these procedures, the air bubbles cannot be observed and removed.

In general, the same contact time should be used for the majority of steel samples so that print intensities can be compared; 5 min is usually preferred. With resulfurized steels, a 2-min contact time is often preferred; for very low sulfur steels, a 10-min contact time is often used along with preetching. The entire process can be conducted under room illumination without damage to the paper. Strong sunlight, however, should be avoided.

After the contact time has elapsed, the print is peeled off carefully and examined. It is best not to handle the prints excessively before washing, fixing, washing, and drying. Washing is conducted in clear running water for about 15 min. The print is next fixed permanently in the usual photographic fixing solution for 15 to 20 min. This is followed by a second water wash for about 30 min. Finally, the prints are dried.

Such a print will clearly show the distribution of sulfur by the presence of darkly colored areas of silver sulfide. The print, of course, is a mirror image of the sulfur distribution in the sample. The chemical reactions occurring during sulfur printing are probably the following [36]:

$$(Fe,Mn)S_{(inclusion)} + H_2SO_4 \rightleftharpoons H_2S \uparrow + FeSO_4 + MnSO_4 \qquad (1\text{-}1)$$

$$H_2S + 2AgBr_{(emulsion)} \rightleftharpoons Ag_2S \downarrow + 2HBr \qquad (1\text{-}2)$$

The liberated hydrogen sulfide gas can become entrapped in voids or holes on the steel surface. Thus, when the paper covers these open areas, trapped hydrogen sulfide gas will often leave a brown color on the paper, indicating the presence of a gross sulfide segregate. In interpreting the sulfur print, one must recognize these areas as cracks or holes rather than sulfur segregation.

Sulfur print methods for fractured surfaces were developed by Rogers in 1912 and by Portevin in 1919, but the complexity of these methods has in general inhibited their use. There is need for a modern, simplified method for use in failure analysis.

Several investigators have used transparent films for sulfur printing. If transparent film is used, the print can be used to reproduce a reverse image of the sulfur print, and thus it is not necessary to photograph the sulfur print to make duplicates. O'Neill used a photomicrometer to examine his transparent sulfur prints and obtained quantitative measurements of sulfur content as a function of print density [37].

Farmer has developed a sulfur print method applicable to resulfurized copper alloys [38]. The standard method does not produce an image on resulfurized copper, even if a 10% sulfuric acid solution is used. The technique developed for free machining copper is similar to the standard method but incorporates an applied potential. The copper sample is ground and cleaned. The usual photographic bromide paper is soaked for 3 to 4 min in 2% aqueous sulfuric acid, and the excess acid is drained off. The emulsion side of the paper is placed on the

Figure 1-38 Mirror-image sulfur print of the macroetched disc shown in Fig. 1-6.

ground surface, and any air bubbles are removed. The specimen with the paper underneath is placed on an aluminum plate. The aluminum plate contacting the paper is connected to the positive terminal of a dc power supply, and the specimen is connected to the negative terminal. A potential of 3 V is applied for 10 s, producing an image of the sulfur distribution. The print is then removed and processed in the usual manner.

Figure 1-38 illustrates the use of sulfur prints in the study of macrostructures and shows a sulfur print of the macroetched disc presented in Fig. 1-6. Note that the sulfur print exhibits the same features as revealed by macroetching.

The intensity of sulfur prints can be influenced by chromium in the sulfides, a problem that was recognized in work with stainless steels. Monypenny, in his classic book on stainless steels, states that sulfur prints in stainless steels frequently do not show images [39]. In some of these stainless steel alloys that print poorly, the manganese content is about 0.20%, while chromium is 18% or greater. However if the manganese content in the stainless is 0.60% or greater, a print can be obtained. Garvin and Larrimore examined sulfur print response in AISI 430 stainless steel [40]. These authors made four ingots with 0.08, 0.42, 0.77, and 1.56% manganese. Low-manganese heats contained chromium sulfides and did not produce an image on the sulfur print. As the manganese content increased, print intensity increased. Figure 1-39 shows sulfur prints of discs cut from steels with two slightly different compositions but with the same sulfur content. On the right is a print of normal intensity in which little chromium is present in the sulfides, while on the left is a sulfur print which is considerably lighter because considerable chromium is present in the sulfides.

Figure 1-39 Sulfur print intensity is influenced by the composition of the sulfide inclusions. Both of the sulfur-printed discs shown contain 0.06% sulfur, but the print on the left is very light because most of the sulfides contain considerable chromium and are low in manganese content. The sulfides in the disc at the right contain very little chromium.

1-6.3 Oxide Printing

A technique for showing the distribution of oxide inclusions containing iron was developed by Niessner [41]. In this report it is claimed that a certain minimum amount of iron must be present in the oxides to obtain results, but the amount required was not determined. The original method is as follows: Gelatin paper is moistened in an aqueous solution containing 5% hydrochloric acid for about 5 min. The gelatinized side of the paper is blotted dry and pressed onto the polished surface of the steel sample for about 5 s. The paper is then removed and placed in an aqueous solution containing potassium ferrocyanide (20 g $K_4Fe(CN)_6$ to 1000 mL water). This solution develops the image. Potassium ferricyanide may also be used but at a lower concentration. The print exhibits a light-blue color over the contact area. Dark-blue spots are present at places where iron-containing inclusions were present.

Dienbauer modified the method by adding 15 g of sodium chloride to the dilute hydrochloric acid solution and by using photographic paper in place of gelatin paper [42]. These changes generally produced sharper images. It is claimed that both the sulfides and the iron-containing oxides are revealed on the same print with this procedure.

Grubitsch modified the oxide print method of Niessner by using cellophane film in place of gelatin paper [43]. This reportedly eliminated the air bubble problem, improved image sharpness, and permitted detection of small inclusions. Cellophane 0.025 mm thick is soaked for a few minutes in water. After the cellophane dries, a few drops of a 20% aqueous solution of quinoline-Etl are distributed over the surface of the film. After about a minute, the solution is wiped off. The film is placed on a polished sample, and an etching solution consisting of equal parts of a 1.2% ferrocyanide solution and a 0.25% hydrochloric acid solution is applied. After 2 to 2½ min, the etching solution is washed off and the film is removed and developed in a 2.5% solution of potassium ferrocyanide in water and then rinsed. The film image is next oxidized in a solution of 1 mL of 3% H_2O_2 in 100 mL water.

1-6.4 Phosphorus Printing

In addition to the chemical etchants that are claimed to reveal phosphorus segregation, a number of phosphorus printing methods have been developed. Canfield developed the first method for printing phosphorus segregation [44]. A sample with a ground surface is immersed in a solution consisting of 5 g $Ni(NO_3)_2$ plus 1.5 g $CuCl_2$ dissolved in 12 mL hot H_2O, 6 g $FeCl_3$, and 150 mL methanol (a few milliliters of HNO_3 may also be added). After 1½ to 3 min, a colored surface layer begins to form. This layer can exhibit a wide range of colors from pale brown to purplish red. Segregation shows up as white streaks or spots. This pattern can reportedly be transferred to photographic paper. A sheet of photographic paper is soaked for several minutes in a 5% solution of potassium ferricyanide in water. The paper is placed face up on blotting paper, and the coated steel surface is placed against the paper for about a minute. The paper is rinsed and fixed. The segregated areas should show up as a blue color. Canfield states that the segregation is probably phosphorus, although this was not proved.

Another phosphorus print method was developed by Niessner [45] and is described by Feigl [46], Enos [47], and Kehl [48]. Two solutions, a soaking and a developing solution, are used. Niessner and Feigl state that filter paper is soaked in an ammonium molybdate–nitric acid solution (concentration not given). Enos, referencing the work of Niessner and Feigl, states that this solution should contain 5 g ammonium molybdate dissolved in 100 mL cold water, which is then added to 35 mL nitric acid. The excess solution is drained off, and the paper is placed on the surface of the sample. Niessner states that polished samples were used in his study. After a contact time of 3 to 5 min, depending on the phosphorus level, the paper is removed and placed in a developing solution. According to Niessner and Feigl, this solution consists of 50 mL $SnCl_2$, 50 mL HCl, and 100 mL H_2O. Since $SnCl_2$ is a powder rather than a liquid, we might assume that this is 50 mL of water saturated with $SnCl_2$. Enos and Kehl state that the developing solution is made by adding 5 mL of a saturated $SnCl_2$ solution to a mixture of 50 mL HCl and 100 mL H_2O. The paper is immersed in this solution for 3 to 4 min, and any iron salts and lower oxides of molybdenum that were absorbed by the paper dissolve. Initially, the print should appear yellow, but after about 45 s, a blue color is observed wherever phosphorus was present. Because the filter paper is attacked by the solution of $SnCl_2$ and HCl, a pinch of alum is added to the developer to harden the paper. After development, excess acid is washed off in flowing water and the paper is dried.

This author has tried this procedure using all possible mixtures but has been unable to obtain a useful print. With the procedure described by Enos and Kehl, a yellow color was obtained but not blue. Increasing the $SnCl_2$ content gave a strong blue color, but the resultant print was blotchy and devoid of any useful information. Canfield's method has also been tried, again, without useful results.

Phosphorus printing is rarely, if ever, performed today. Indeed, there is some question as to whether phosphorus distribution can be revealed by print methods. Since in general sulfur and phosphorus segregate in the same manner, segregation can be clearly revealed by the simple, proven sulfur print method. In steels with a very low sulfur content, a phosphorus print would be useful.

1-6.5 Lead Printing and Exudation Test

Lead, which is added to steels to improve machinability, requires special attention by the steelmaker in order to obtain a uniform distribution of the lead. Because of the potential variability in the distribution of lead, macroscopic testing is a key tool in quality control. Three techniques are available for revealing the lead distribution—macroetching, lead printing, and lead exudation. The latter technique, frequently referred to as the lead "sweat" test, is the most frequently used because of its simplicity.

Bardgett and Lismer developed an electrolytic etching technique that reveals lead segregation [49]. The disc is cleaned and electrolytically etched in a solution of ammonium acetate, which can be prepared using either of the following procedures:

Method A: 50 g ammonium acetate
              1000 mL water

Method B: 75 mL glacial acetic acid
              900 mL water
              Addition of ammonium hydroxide until the solution is just alkaline

The solution is placed in a stainless steel container which is attached to the positive terminal of a 6-V battery. The billet disc is placed on the bottom of the vessel, surface upward. A platinum wire loop extending across the surface is attached to the negative terminal of the battery and is suspended about ¼ in above the sample surface in the solution. The loop is moved around above the surface for 30 to 60 s. The location of lead segregates are shown by the formation of a sharp brown stain.

Lead print methods can also be used to reveal the lead distribution. Volk used gelatin paper soaked in concentrated acetic acid [50]. The paper is placed on the surface of the disc for about 1 min. It is then removed and placed in water saturated with hydrogen sulfide for about 2 to 3 min. The location of the lead is indicated by brown spots of lead sulfide on the gelatin paper.

Northcott and McLean used a lead print method developed by Ledloy, Ltd. [51]. Three solutions are required:

Solution	Components
Printing solution	25 g tartaric acid 100 g ammonium acetate 250 mL water
	Saturation of resulting solution with H_2S
Developing solution	Water saturated with H_2S
Clearing solution	10% aqueous ammonium persulfate or tartaric acid solution saturated with H_2S.

The ground billet disc is first etched with an aqueous solution of 50% HNO_3, washed, and dried. Gelatin paper is soaked in the printing solution and then placed on the surface of the disc. The back of the paper is kept moist with the printing solution. After 2 to 3 min, the paper is removed and placed in the developing solution. Intense black staining due to dissolved iron is observed. Some of this black stain is removed in the developing solution and the balance in the clearing solution. After clearing, the print is washed in clean developing solution to counter fading. The print is then washed in water, rinsed with alcohol, and dried.

Bardgett and Lismer developed an electrographic method of lead printing using caustic soda as the printing solution and sodium sulfide as the developing solution. However, they later found that a method suggested to them by Wragge, which uses gelatin paper soaked in an 10% ammonium acetate solution, was better [49]. The excess solution is drained off, and the paper is placed, gelatin side upward, on a double layer of blotter paper. The blotter paper has been previously soaked in the same solution and rests on a flat aluminum plate that is attached to the negative terminal of a battery or power supply. The surface of the sample is pressed into the gelatin surface. A smooth ground surface can be employed, but results are best using a polished specimen. A small brass plate, which is connected to the positive terminal of the power source, is placed on the back of the disc. A voltage of about 2 V/in^2 of surface is applied for about 2 min. The power is then turned off, and the gelatin paper is placed in an aqueous 5% ammonium acetate solution for 30 s. A small quantity of water saturated with tartaric acid should be added to the ammonium acetate solution. Next, the paper is washed and soaked in a weak aqueous hydrogen sulfide solution until the print details are revealed adequately. The hydrogen sulfide solution should not be near enough to the ammonium acetate solution for contamination to occur.

The iron-staining problem encountered with the use of ammonium acetate solutions can be eliminated by the use of dilute caustic acid solutions, as developed by Wragge [52]. In this method a desilvered matte-type printing paper, a toughened fine-grained filter paper, or a smooth-surfaced gelatinized white blotter paper can be used. Both ferrous and nonferrous leaded metals can be printed using Wragge's procedure. For either metal, the surface should be ground and macroetched. The printing paper is immersed in a 5% aqueous NaOH solution for about 2 min, lightly dried between blotter papers, and placed on the metal surface. Air bubbles should be removed. A contact time of 2 min is adequate for both steel and brass specimens. The paper is removed and developed for a few seconds in a freshly prepared 5% aqueous sodium sulfide solution. Prints made on steel specimens should be washed for 10 to 15 min before drying. For copper alloys, a slight brown stain on the print can be removed after development by soaking the print about 15 s in an aqueous 10% potassium cyanide solution. The print can then be washed and dried. Figure 1-40 shows an example of lead distribution in a leaded free-machining steel, revealed using either Wragge's printing method or the sweat test.

The lead exudation test is the most commonly employed technique for detecting lead segregation [49]. The billet disc is coated with a thin layer of light oil and heated in a small furnace to 1290°F (699°C). The disc is held at temperature for 10 min for each inch of thickness. A minimum thickness of 2 in is usually recommended. Globules or beads of lead will exude from the steel wherever lead is segregated.

To evaluate the degree of lead segregation, the disc is compared to a set of standards, such as shown in ASTM Specification A582. The applicable ASTM standard or a customer-manufacturer agreed-on limit is used as the acceptance or rejection criterion. If the billet disc exhibits a rejectable condition, a portion

$\sim \frac{3}{8}X$ $\sim \frac{3}{8}X$ $\sim 2\frac{1}{4}X$

Figure 1-40 Wragge's lead print method (left) and the lead sweat test (center) were used to reveal the lead distribution in this free-machining steel billet disc. A few small spots of lead segregation were detected (right), otherwise the lead distribution was quite uniform.

adjacent to the disc is scrapped and another disc is tested. This process is repeated, as required, until the segregation is removed. Lead segregation is most commonly encountered at the bottom end of the ingot.

Bardgett and Lismer studied lead exudation using hot-stage microscopy [49]. A sample from a region containing lead segregation was photographed with a cine camera during heating and the resulting photographs reveal that a small amount of lead exudation occurred at temperatures as low as 86°F (30°C). When the samples reached 455 to 464°F (235 to 240°C), lead beads suddenly spurted out onto the sample surface. At 662 to 752°F (350 to 400°C) the beads spread out over the surface and coalesced. Chemical analysis of the beads showed that they were 98 to 99% lead (Pb). Heating above 464°F (240°C) caused the bright metallic beads to oxidize, with the color changing from bright red to yellow and finally to gray. These results showed that exudation occurs at temperatures well below the melting point of lead, which is about 621°F (327°C).

The exudation test has also been used to evaluate steels treated with bismuth, another low-melting-point metallic additive used to improve machinability. Bismuth melts at about 520°F (271°C), which is about 100°F lower than the melting point of lead. Exudation tests on bismuth-treated steels are performed at about 1200°F (649°C).

1-6.6 Miscellaneous Print Methods

Singleton has described a simple test for evaluation of mill scale removal after shot blasting [53]. The test is performed immediately after shot blasting, and the surface should be free of loose rust, dust, oil, grease, etc. A solution of copper sulfate is applied to the surface, causing copper to deposit on areas free of mill scale. Any remaining patches of mill scale appear as dark areas against the copper background. These areas are compared to a standard set of illustrations to assess the amount of mill scale remaining on the surface. The test solution consists of a mixture of aqueous 4% anhydrous copper sulfate in 1% sulfuric acid. A small addition of a wetting agent, such as Teepol, is recommended. Since the solution is poisonous and contains a strong corrosive acid, it should be handled carefully.

Picard and Greene have described printing methods to detect contamination of metallic surfaces by foreign metals that results from machining, brushing, and/or accidental contact [54]. Using this method, these authors have detected iron contamination on the surfaces of nickel, titanium, and zirconium and copper contamination on stainless steel. For printing, they use either desilvered unexposed or exposed single-weight Polycontrast photographic paper. The choice of exposed or unexposed paper depends on the color of the precipitate formed. If a light precipitate is formed, black exposed paper provides the best contrast. Exposed paper was used to reveal porosity in a number of metallic coatings. The test is performed as follows: The paper is saturated in the appropriate electrolyte solution and placed on the test surface. After an appropriate time, it is placed in a developing solution, rinsed in distilled water, and dried. For steels, including stainless steel, they employed a 5 wt % Na_2SO_4 solution as the electrolyte, and for copper-clad aluminum, they used a 3 wt % NaCl solution as the electrolyte.

Hunter et al. have described electrographic print tests that employ procedures used in colorimetric spot testing for the detection of a variety of metals [55]. In this method, gelatinized paper (e.g. desilvered photographic paper) is soaked in an appropriate electrolyte and placed on an aluminum block. The specimen is placed on the paper, and pressure is applied. Current from a 6-V battery is applied, with the aluminum block as the cathode and the sample as the anode. An ammeter is used to measure the current flow to ensure rapid dissolution. The current required depends on the size of the sample, the element to be detected, and the electrolyte chosen. In general, application of the current for 30 s was adequate. These authors have used this procedure for detecting a wide variety of inclusion types in many different metals, for alloy identification, and for detecting porosity in metallic coatings.

1-7 SUMMARY

This chapter has presented information pertaining to the visualization and interpretation of the macrostructure of metals. These techniques permit examination of a large number of materials using either nondestructive or destructive methods. When areas of questionable quality are detected, microscopic analysis may be desired to more clearly identify the nature of the problem. Thus, macrostructural examination is often the prelude to microscopic examination. Macroscopic examination is clearly a fundamental step in both quality control and failure analysis.

REFERENCES

1. Sorby, H. C.: "On the Microscopical Structure of Iron and Steel," *J. Iron Steel Inst.,* pt. 1: 1887, pp. 255–288.
2. Berglund, T.: *Metallographers' Handbook of Etching,* Sir Isaac Pitman & Sons, Ltd., London, 1931.

3. Gill, J. P., and H. G. Johnstin: "Deep Acid Etch Test. An Interpretation for Tool Steels," *Met. Prog.*, vol. 22, September 1932, pp. 37–42.
4. Yatsevitch, M. G.: "Essential Factors in Conducting the Macroetching Test under Usual Practical Conditions of Production Work," *Trans. Am. Soc. Steel Treat.*, vol. 21, 1933, pp. 310–342.
5. Magnusson, E.: "Primary Etching of Welds," *Jernkontorets Ann.*, vol. 131, no. 6, 1947, pp. 212–224.
6. Pokorny, A.: "The Influence of the State of the Surface on the Etching Effect," *Prakt. Metallogr.*, vol. 17, 1980, pp. 23–28.
7. Buhr, R. K., and F. Weinberg: "Etching Steel to Determine Phosphorus Segregation," *J. Iron Steel Inst.*, vol. 205, 1967, pp. 1161–1164.
8. Karl, A.: "Investigations into the Suitability of the Oberhoffer Etch for Identifying Surface Defects," *Prakt. Metallogr.* vol. 15, 1978, pp. 469–485.
9. Koster, W.: "Effects of Nitrogen in Technical Iron," *Arch. Eisenhuettenwes*, vol. 3, 1930, pp. 637–658.
10. MacGregor, C. W., and F. R. Hensel: "The Influence of Nitrogen in Mild Steel on the Ability of Developing Flow Layers," *J. Rheology*, vol. 3, 1932, pp. 37–52 (see abstract in *Metals and Alloys*, vol. 3, May 1932, pp. 127–128).
11. Bish, R. L.: "A Method of Revealing Deformation in Mild Steel," *Metallography*, vol. 11, 1978, pp. 215–218.
12. Bish, R. L.: "The Action of Fry's Reagent on Steel," *Metallography*, vol. 12, 1979, pp. 147–151.
13. Giedenbacher, G., and F. Sturm: "Deformation Zones in Notched Flat Tensile Specimens," *Prakt. Metallogr.*, vol. 15, 1978, pp. 3–10.
14. Weinberg, F., and R. K. Buhr: "Solidification Studies of Steel Castings," *Iron Steel Inst., London, Spec. Rep. 110*, 1968, pp. 295–304.
15. Alexander, B. H., and F. N. Rhines: "Dendritic Crystallization of Alloys," *Trans. Am. Inst. Min. Metall. Eng.*, vol. 188, 1950, pp. 1267–1273.
16. Dawson, J. V., and W. Oldfield: "Euctectic Cell Count - An Index of Metal Quality," *BCIRA J.*, vol. 8, no. 2, 1960, pp. 221–231.
17. Adams, R. R.: "Cast Iron Strength vs. Structure," *Trans. Am. Foundrymen's Soc.*, vol. 50, 1942, pp. 1063–1103.
18. Merchant, H.D.: "Metallography of Eutectic Cells in Cast Iron," *Foundry*, vol. 91, 163, pp. 59–65.
19. Boyles, A.: *The Structure of Cast Iron*, American Society for Metals, Cleveland, 1947.
20. Merchant, H. D.: "Eutectic Cells in Cast Iron. Structure and Delineation," *Trans. Am. Foundrymen's Soc.*, vol. 70, 1962, pp. 973–992.
21. Beck, P. A., et al.: "Grain Growth in High-Purity Aluminum and in an Aluminum-Magnesium Alloy," *Trans. Am. Inst. Min. Metall. Eng.*, vol. 175, 1948, pp. 372–400.
22. Beck, P. A., M. L. Holzworth, and P. R. Sperry: "Effect of a Dispersed Phase on Grain Growth in Al-Mn Alloys," *Trans. Am. Inst. Min. Metall. Eng.*, vol. 180, 1949, pp. 163–192.
23. Ryvola, M: "Rapid Way to Determine Aluminum Grain Size," *Met. Prog.*, vol. 105, June 1974, pp. 80–81.
24. Benson, D. K.: "Residual Stress Measurement in Steels Using a Chemical Etchant," *Metall. Trans.*, vol. 3, 1972, pp. 2547–2550.
25. Vander Voort, G. F.: "Macroscopic Examination Procedures for Failure Analysis," *Metallography and Failure Analysis*, Plenum Press, New York, 1978, pp. 33–63.
26. Ljunggren, B. O. W. L.: "Method of Sclero-Grating Employed for the Study of Grain Boundaries and of Nitrided Cases; Grain Structures Revealed by Cutting," *J. Iron Steel Inst.*, vol. 141, 1940, pp. 341p–404p.
27. Clarebrough, L. M., and G. J. Ogilvie: "Development of the Macrostructure of Metals by Machining," *Machining-Theory and Practice*, American Society for Metals, Cleveland, 1950, pp. 110–122.
28. Hanson, D., and W. T. Pell-Walpole: "Methods of Assessing the Quality of Cast Bronzes," *Chill-Cast Tin Bronzes*, Edward Arnold, London, 1957, pp. 22–55.

29. Enos, G. M.: "Fractures," *Visual Examination of Steel,* American Society for Metals, Cleveland, 1940, pp. 37–54.
30. Ostrofsky, B.: "Materials Identification in the Field," *Mater. Eval.,* vol. 36, August 1978, pp. 33–39, 45.
31. Shepherd, B. F.: "The P-F Characteristic of Steel," *Trans. Am. Soc. Met.,* vol. 22, 1934, p. 979–1016.
32. Strohm, J. R., and W. E. Jominy: "High Forging Temperatures Revealed by Facets in Fracture Tests," *Trans. Am. Soc. Met.,* vol. 36, 1946, pp. 543–571.
33. Johnson, H. H., and G. A. Fisher: "Steel Quality as Related to Test Bar Fractures," *Trans. Am. Foundrymen's Soc.,* vol. 58, 1950, pp. 537–549.
34. Baker, F. M., C. Upthegrove, and F. B. Rote: "Melt Quality and Fracture Characteristics of 85-5-5-5 Red Brass," *Trans. Am. Foundrymen's Soc.,* vol. 58, 1950, pp. 122–132.
35. French, A. R.: "Melt-Quality Test for Copper-Base Alloys," *Foundry Trade J.,* vol. 98, 1955, pp. 253–257, 281–293.
36. Poole, S. W., and J. A. Rosa: "Segregation in a Large Alloy-Steel Ingot," *Trans. Am. Inst. Min. Metall. Eng.,* vol. 162, 1945, pp. 459–473.
37. O'Neill, H.: "Quantitative Printing Methods for the Study of Segregation in Steel," *Metallurgia,* vol. 45, 1952, pp. 215–216.
38. Farmer, J. S.: "Sulphur Printing of High-Sulphur Copper," *Met. Mater.,* June 1979, p. 35.
39. Monypenny, J. H. G.: *Stainless Iron and Steel,* vol. 2, 3d ed., revised, Chapman and Hall, Ltd., London, 1954, p. 96.
40. Garvin, H. W., and R. M. Larrimore: "Metallurgical Factors Affecting the Machining of a Free Machining Stainless Steel," *Mech. Working of Steel,* 11, Met. Soc. Conf., vol. 26, American Institute of Mining, Metallurgical and Petroleum Engineers, 1965, pp. 133–150.
41. Mitsche, R.: "The Detection of Oxide Inclusions in Steels by Imprints," *Berg Huettenmaenn Jahr.,* vol. 83, 1935, pp. 127–133.
42. Dienbauer, H., and R. Mitsche: "Metallographic Printing Methods," *Berg Huettenmaenn Jahr.,* vol. 86, 1938, pp. 33–35.
43. Grubitsch, H.: "The Use of Cellophane in the Oxide Print Method of Niessner," *Arch. Eisenhuttenwesen,* vol. 16, August 1942, pp. 79–80.
44. Canfield, R. H.: "Phosphor Prints. A New Method of Detecting Phosphorus Segregations in Steel," *Chem. Metall. Eng.,* vol. 30, no. 12, 1924, p. 470.
45. Niessner, M.: "New Methods for Chemical Identification of Alloying Additions and Nonhomogenieties in Metallic Materials," *Mikrochemie,* vol. 12, 1932, pp. 1–24.
46. Feigl, F.: *Spot Tests,* vol. 1, 4th ed., Elsevier Publishing Company, New York, 1954, pp. 426–427.
47. Enos, G. M.: *Visual Examination of Steel,* American Society for Metals, Cleveland, 1940.
48. Kehl, G. L.: *The Principles of Metallographic Laboratory Practice,* 3d ed., McGraw-Hill Book Company, New York, 1949.
49. Bardgett, W. E., and R. E. Lismer: "Mode of Occurrence of Lead in Lead-Bearing Steels and the Mechanism of the Exudation Test," *J. Iron Steel Inst.,* vol. 151, pt. 1, 1945, pp. 281p–301p.
50. Volk, K. E.: "The Metallographic Proof of Pb in Steel," *Arch. Eisenhuettenwesen,* vol. 16, 1942, pp. 81–84.
51. Northcott, L., and D. McLean: "The Structure and Segregation of Two Ingots of Ingot Iron, One Containing Lead," *J. Iron Steel Inst.,* vol. 148, 1943, pp. 429p–439p.
52. Wragge, W. B.: "'Lead Printing' Ferrous and Non-Ferrous Metals," *Metallurgia,* vol. 32, May 1945, pp. 3–6.
53. Singleton, D. W.: "A Simple Test for the Detection of Residual Millscale on Shotblasted Steel Surfaces," *Iron Steel,* vol. 41, January 1968, pp. 17–19.
54. Picard, R. J., and N. D. Greene: "Detection of Surface Contamination by Corrosion Printing," *Corrosion,* vol. 29, 1973, pp. 282–284.
55. Hunter, M. S., J. R. Churchill, and R. B. Mears: "Electrographic Methods of Surface Analysis," *Met. Prog.,* vol. 42, 1942, pp. 1070–1076.

TWO

SPECIMEN PREPARATION FOR LIGHT MICROSCOPY

2-1 INTRODUCTION

The preparation steps for light microscopy, often viewed as a tedious, frustrating process, are of great importance, since the true microstructure may be partially or fully obscured by poor technique or execution. Improperly prepared samples can lead to erroneous interpretations, which can produce disastrous, expensive consequences. While every sample need not be perfectly prepared to publication quality, any minor deficiencies, such as very fine polishing scratches, must not alter the structure to the point that correct interpretation becomes difficult. Many problems can be encountered, some of which are merely annoying, while others, if not recognized, are quite damaging. In situations where one is merely interested in observing the structure without recording it on film, sample preparation can be simplified without altering the results if one has a thorough understanding of the potential problem areas.

In this chapter, the techniques used to prepare metallographic samples for light microscopy are reviewed in detail. Attention is given to the problems that may be encountered and methods for their control and elimination. Specific comments are provided regarding preparation procedures for different materials. Techniques suitable for one type of material can be totally unsuitable for other materials. References 1 to 4 are general references describing specimen preparation.

2-2 SAMPLE SELECTION

Because sample preparation is time-consuming and involves some expense, adequate attention and thought must be given to the selection of samples with respect to the number, location, and orientation within the test piece or component. Commercial materials are not homogeneous; thus, a single randomly chosen sample from a large volume of metal may not be representative of the range of conditions that are present. Sample selection can be designed to produce a sample with average or "typical" conditions, or samples can be deliberately chosen to reveal the worst condition. Each selection method has its merits. In addition, sampling schemes are often fixed by material specification requirements.

The number of samples required to characterize a component depends on the size and complexity of the part and the nature of the service conditions. Testing will be much more extensive for materials going into a jet engine than for materials going into a lawn mower. Basically, sampling must be just adequate to provide a statistically reliable description of material quality but not so extensive that test costs are excessive.

The location from which the test sample is taken is often chosen on the basis of convenience in sectioning. While random sampling is usually desirable from a statistical viewpoint, it is usually impractical, because the cutting operation would render the balance of the product unsalable. Even in cases where an occasional part must be destructively tested (per specification requirements), random sectioning is usually not performed. In general, critical locations are tested, and in most testing systematic sampling is the preferred sampling method. Standard test locations used in systematic sampling are defined and include, for example, the opposite ends of a bar, billet, or bloom. Because solidification produces compositional gradients, the center, midthickness, and subsurface locations of thick materials are often examined. If typical conditions are desired, the midthickness location is tested.

The orientation of the test plane depends on the manufacturing process, product shape, and features to be studied. In a casting, all planes are essentially identical, but the radial orientation, i.e., parallel to the direction of solidification, is often preferred. Tests on castings are usually made on a convenient appendage to the casting that can be easily removed or on part of the feeding system. A less satisfactory procedure is to test a small cast (keel block) sample made at the same time as the casting. The ideal sample would be one cored from the casting in an area that is to be machined away during further processing. This procedure is, however, more expensive than the others, but the sample is more representative. As an alternative, nondestructive metallographic examination can be performed at a specific surface location using either mechanical or electropolishing methods.

In the testing of wrought materials, three basic test orientations are employed. Transverse planes are perpendicular to the hot-working axis, while longitudinal and planar surfaces are parallel to the direction of elongation. In a round bar, rod, or wire, all planes parallel to the hot-working axis are equivalent. In a square bar, the planes parallel to the hot-rolling direction are equivalent longitudinal planes. In a rectangular section or in a plate, the planar surface is parallel to the hot-working axis, has the largest surface area, and is the surface in most frequent contact with the mill rolls. The longitudinal plane is perpendicular to the planar surface and parallel to the hot-working axis. Metal flow patterns are different in rounds, squares, or plate shapes and influence the appearance of the microstructure viewed on these planes. This difference is accentuated by composition, inclusion content, number of phases, and processing variations. In the examination of wrought materials, the longitudinal plane provides information about segregation and inclusion deformability not obtainable on transverse sections. The microstructure often appears more uniform on transverse sections.

2-3 SECTIONING

Although there are some situations where a sample is the correct size for sample preparation, in most cases sectioning is required. A variety of machining procedures can be applied, but regardless of the method chosen, cutting must not significantly alter the bulk structure. Some damage will usually occur at the cut surface, but the extent of the damage can be minimized. The depth of the damage varies with the technique used and the material being cut.

To obtain samples from large failed components, it is common to burn out a section containing the area of interest. Because burning alters the microstructure for a substantial distance from the cut, one should burn well away from the area of interest and do subsequent sectioning with standard machining techniques.

Reasonably small-sized samples can be handled with equipment found in a typical metallographic laboratory, such as a shear, band saw, abrasive cutoff saw, and high- or low-speed diamond saws. A number of more specialized devices can also be used. These devices are described in the sections that follow.

2-3.1 Fracturing

Sectioning of as-quenched, high-hardness martensitic steels can be done with an abrasive cutoff saw, but it is difficult to completely prevent cutting-induced heat from altering the microstructure and hardness, regardless of the care taken during cutting. An alternate procedure, commonly used with tool steels, is to fracture the sample and then polish the fracture surface. Less-brittle steels can be refrigerated in liquid nitrogen prior to breaking to obtain a flatter surface. Fracturing has also been used on other brittle materials such as carbides or ceramics.

2-3.2 Shearing

Low-carbon sheet steel and other thin, reasonably soft materials can be cut to size by shearing. While little heat is generated, shearing does produce substantial deformation and is not recommended for those materials that are sensitive to mechanical twin formation. The area affected by shearing must be removed by grinding. Shearing is a fast, simple, effective sectioning technique. Figure 2-1 illustrates the deformation and damage produced by shearing. (See also Fig. 3-2 in Chap. 3.)

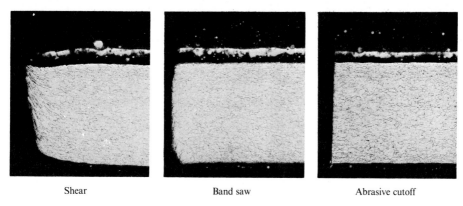

| Shear | Band saw | Abrasive cutoff |

Figure 2-1 Influence of cutting procedure on deformation and damage to porcelain-enameled steel, 45×, 2% nital, polarized light. *(Courtesy of A. O. Benscoter, Bethlehem Steel Corp.)*

2-3.3 Sawing

Materials softer than about 350 HB can be cut by sawing. A simple hacksaw can be used, but a band saw or power hacksaw is less tedious to use. Sawing does produce a rough surface, considerable heat, and deformation, as illustrated in Fig. 2-1. Samuels [3] has measured the scratch and deformation depths associated with hacksawing and other machining and grinding operations, as summarized in Table 2-1. Because the damage depth may be substantial, a significant amount of metal must be removed in grinding to produce a strain-free surface and the true microstructure.

2-3.4 Abrasive Cutting

Abrasive cutting is the most common metallographic sectioning method. Its popularity is due to the wide range of sample hardnesses that can be cut and the excellent quality of the surfaces produced, as shown in Fig. 2-1. Figure 2-2 shows a typical commercial laboratory abrasive cutoff machine† used for sectioning metallographic specimens. These machines use either consumable or nonconsumable cutting wheels.

In abrasive cutting, a thin rotating disc of a suitable abrasive in a supporting media is used. Because the abrasives are randomly oriented particles, they contact the work piece at various angles, many of which are unfavorable for cutting. However, those particles that are properly aligned produce effective cutting. The improperly aligned particles generate frictional heat and can scratch or gouge the

---

†Illustration of a particular manufacturer's product in this text should not be interpreted as endorsement of the product. Likewise, competitive products not shown should not be construed as a negative endorsement.

Table 2-1 Depth of plastically deformed layer produced on annealed polycrystalline 70:30 brass by machining, grinding, and abrasion processes

Process					Depth, μm		
	Abrasive						Total
Nature	Type	Grade	Conditions	Lubricant	Scratches	Grosser deformation†	deformed layer†
Abrasive cutoff wheel	Alumina	A 60 DE wheel		Proprietary oil-water emulsion	4	16	700
Hand hacksaw			18 t.p.i., roll-set blade	Nil	100	55	750
Surface grinding	Alumina	28A 46 KVBE wheel	0.001-in feed, machine surface grinding	Proprietary oil-water emulsion	6	50	350
			0.0001-in feed, machine surface grinding	Proprietary oil-water emulsion	4	30	150
	Alumina	38A 60 MVBE wheel	Hand grinding	Nil	15	40	170
Lathe turning			0.001-in feed	Proprietary oil-water emulsion	1	15	150

Process	Abrasive	Grade	Operation	Lubricant			
Belt surfacing	Alumina	100 mesh	Specimen hand-held	Nil	15	35 25	250
	Silicon carbide	80 grade	Specimen hand-held	Water	10	45	240
		120 grade			5.5	25	190
		240 grade			3.5	15	95
		400 grade			1.2	5	60
Filing			Bastard cut	Nil	70	55	450
			Second cut	Nil	30	50	370
Abrasion on abrasive papers	Emery	1/0 grade	Hand abrasion	Kerosene	1.8	7.5	45
		2/0 grade	Hand abrasion	Kerosene	1.0	7.0	38
		3/0 grade	Hand abrasion	Kerosene	0.4	4.0	30
		4/0 grade	Hand abrasion	Kerosene	0.3–1.0‡	3–10‡	20–50‡
	Silicon carbide	220 grade	Hand abrasion	Water	2.0	7.5	77
		400 grade	Hand abrasion	Water	1.5	6.5	43
		600 grade	Hand abrasion	Water	0.8	5.0	22
Abrasion on fixed-abrasive laps	Alumina	10–20 µm grade	Hand abrasion	Nil	0.3	3	16

†Depth beneath the root of the surface scratches or machining marks.
‡The higher values result from clogging of the paper, which occurs very readily.
Source: From Samuels, Ref. 3.

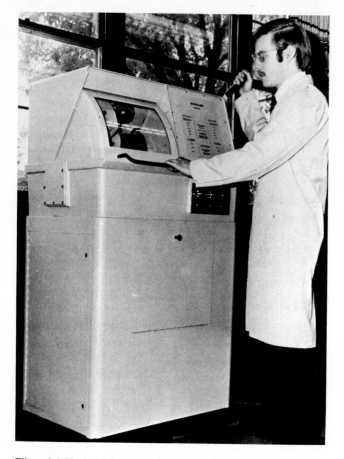

Figure 2-2 Typical laboratory abrasive cutoff saw. *(Courtesy of Buehler Ltd.)*

surface. While the frictional heat promotes cutting, it can damage the sample, and thus a coolant must be employed. In general, cutting with the sample submerged in the coolant is preferred. Dry cutting, frequently used in production, produces a burned surface with a characteristic scorch pattern.

Nonconsumable cutoff wheels use diamond particles bonded to a suitable disc material. Several types of blades are available that use either a resin or a metal bond to a metal core. Since these wheels become loaded with sample material, they must be dressed periodically during service to produce cutting. These wheels are used in either low- or high-speed saws. High-speed diamond saws are commonly used in cutting ceramics and minerals. The low-speed diamond saw is a more recent development, and because of its attractive characteristics, it is described in greater detail later in this section.

Consumable abrasive cutoff wheels use either silicon carbide for cutting nonferrous metals or aluminum oxide (alumina) for cutting ferrous metals. Some users also prefer alumina wheels for cutting aluminum, chromium, nickel, and tantalum. The abrasive grain size can be coarse or fine. Coarse abrasives are preferred for production work, since they produce fast, clean cuts. Wheels with fine abrasives produce smoother cuts and are preferred for delicate work.

Consumable wheels come in a variety of sizes and thicknesses. Wheels up to 12 in in diameter are used in laboratory cutoff machines. Thicker wheels produce more deformation than thinner wheels, as shown by the study of Szirmae and Fisher [5] on iron containing 3.25% silicon. Their work showed that the damage depth due to cutting with a thick wheel can be as great as 1 mm. The maximum damage depth with a thinner wheel was about 0.55 mm. With either wheel thickness, the average damage depth was about 0.20 mm. Wellner measured the depth of deformation in a variety of metals sectioned by the following methods: abrasive cutting, spark erosion, and low-speed diamond sawing [6]. Damage depth was greatest for surfaces cut with abrasive wheels and varied from 0.085 to 0.25 mm, depending on the metal cut. Wellner's results are shown in Fig. 2-3.

Abrasive wheels use either resin or rubber for bonding. Resin-bonded wheels are used for dry cutting, while rubber-bonded wheels are used for wet cutting and are, therefore, preferred for metallographic work. Unfortunately, rubber-bonded wheels can produce noxious odor of burning rubber as the wheel is consumed. Many laboratories place a ventilation hood over the cutoff machine to remove these odors. Coolant additions, consisting of a water-soluble oil and a rust inhibitor, are used to minimize corrosion of machine parts, and they often contain an additive to minimize or disguise the odor. Rubber-bonded wheels do have a definite shelf life, typically about 1 to 1½ years. The month and year of manufacture is generally printed on the wheels. To produce maximum life, the wheels

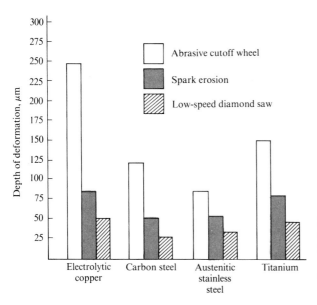

Figure 2-3 Depth of deformation in different metals due to cutting method. *(From Wellner, Ref. 6, courtesy of Dr. Riederer-Verlag, GmbH.)*

should be laid flat on a stiff shelf surface in a dry atmosphere. They should never be stacked on edge, since distortion can result.

Consumable abrasive cutoff wheels are available with different degrees of bonding; i.e., the amount of porosity is varied to control wheel hardness. A "soft" wheel has a relatively porous rubber bond which permits the wheel to be consumed at a fast rate. A soft wheel is desirable for cutting hard materials, since breakdown exposes cutting abrasive more readily. "Hard" wheels contain little porosity and break down at a slow rate and thus are preferred for cutting soft materials. Therefore, for optimum cutting action, the wheel wear rate must be matched to the hardness of the material being cut. A wheel that does not wear will not cut. If a wheel stops cutting, it probably has become glazed with specimen material. Rather than cut, it generates heat and damages the sample. This problem is usually encountered when a hard rubber-bonded alumina wheel is used to cut a hard material. The hardness code on the wheel should be checked before it is used for cutting to ensure that the proper wheel is being used.

During cutting, coolant should be directed at the cut and the wheel. Submerged cutting is usually preferred, especially for heat-sensitive materials. Coolant flow should be uniform, otherwise nonuniform wheel wear and poor cuts result. The flow pattern should be checked periodically, since hoses can become clogged with cutting debris.

Improper cutting technique can result in specimen damage and wheel breakage. Loose clamping of samples is a prime cause of wheel breakage. Excessive initial pressure, especially if the surface is not perpendicular to the wheel, is another common cause of wheel breakage. If the wheel does not break, a curved cut will be produced. A steady, firm pressure should be applied during cutting, but not enough pressure to stall the wheel, damage the sample, or break the wheel. If the cutting rate is quite low, the optimum wheel may not have been chosen. Application of cyclic pressure can help promote wheel breakdown and faster cutting. In most machines, the cover must be in place during cutting, which protects the operator from flying pieces of broken wheels.

The exceptional hardness of diamond makes it an ideal material for abrasive cutting; however, because of its high cost, diamond must be used in nonconsumable wheels. The diamond bort abrasive of the proper size is attached to a metal wheel using resin or metal bonding. Particles are dispersed intermittently or continuously around the wheel periphery.

Intermittent dispersion is used with metal-bonded "rim-lock" cutting wheels [7]. The metal disc has many small notches cut into the periphery to hold diamond particles. Rim-lock diamond wheels produce a relatively thick cut and are ideal for high-speed cutting of minerals or ceramics, using kerosene or other suitable lubricants. Constant cutting pressure is required to avoid damage to the wheel. Continuous-dispersion diamond wheels are also used to cut minerals, ceramics, or refractory materials.

For precision cutting of metallographic specimens or TEM (transmission electron microscopy) thin sections, very thin, small-diameter "wafering" blades are used. They are available in several diameters and a variety of abrasive types, both consumable and nonconsumable. Nonconsumable diamond wheels with a low diamond concentration are preferred for sectioning hard materials, while higher diamond concentrations are preferred for softer materials [7].

One use of these blades is in precision wafering machines such as the low-speed diamond saw, a machine mentioned earlier in this section, used for delicate sectioning work, since nearly any material can be cut. Wheel rotation is typically 200 r/min, about one-tenth that of ordinary diamond saws. The low cutting speed and the sharp, hard diamond abrasive produce surfaces with very little damage, as shown in Fig. 2-3. Blades with either low or high diamond concentrations are generally available in thicknesses between 0.006 and 0.015 in and diameters from 3 to 5 in. These blades are ideal for sectioning hard minerals, carbides, refractories, or ceramics and are widely used for sectioning delicate materials such as printed circuit boards. Softer metals can also be cut, but frequent wheel dressing is required to maintain cutting.

Nelson and Ahmed have shown that the choice of cutting lubricant can significantly alter the cutting rate [8]. Their tests on different materials using mineral spirits or a proprietary lubricant (Isocut Fluid) showed that improvements in cutting time from 16 to 75 percent could be obtained with the proprietary lubricant.

2-3.5 Microtomy

Preparation of samples with a microtome is a very common biologic technique but has rather limited applications for the metallurgist. In 1927, Lucas suggested microtomy as a preparation technique for soft metals, and it has been used frequently for preparing lead specimens and polymers. Reinacher used a microtome with a tool-steel knife to prepare annealed silver, copper, and silver-copper alloys and a tungsten carbide–tipped knife for palladium and platinum.

Stevens and Gillmeister have shown that ultramicrotomy can be applied to microstructural analysis [9]. Samples to be sliced are first embedded in epoxy for support. The thin section or the bulk surface can be examined using a wide variety of analytical techniques. Ultramicrotomy is also useful in serial-section analysis. The sectioning precision helps in locating specific features within a bulk sample.

2-3.6 Wire Saws

The need to produce damage-free, single-crystal surfaces has fostered development of wire saws. Although the technique of wire sawing has been known since antiquity, its use in metallography is comparatively recent. Basically, a fine wire is continuously drawn over the sample at a controlled pressure. Cutting can be performed with an abrasive slurry applied to the wire, by a chemical solution (generally acidic) dripped onto the wire, or by electrolytic action. Although cutting rates are very low, the deformation produced is negligible.

Wire saws employing abrasives are quite popular in the electronics industry. Nearly any abrasive can be employed, as long as it is significantly harder than the material being cut. Abrasives can be mixed with a lubricant in slurry form and applied to the wire, or the abrasive can be bonded to the wire. The latter method frequently uses diamond as the abrasive. A lubricant is employed to prevent the wire from being pinched in the cut and to minimize heat generation. Water is used with diamond-impregnated wires to remove debris from the cut. Light cutting pressures produce best results; no benefit is gained from higher pressures. Wire tension must be high in order to get good cuts; thus, very high tensile strength steel wire is commonly used. Diamond particles can be bonded to the wire by copper plating.

2-3.7 Electric Discharge Machining

Electrically conductive materials can be sectioned by electric discharge machining (EDM). Cutting is accomplished by an electric discharge between an electrode and the sample submerged in a dielectric fluid. Cutting rates are reasonably high regardless of the sample hardness. Tool-and-die makers use this technique extensively.

EDM does produce significant changes at the machined surface. The outer surface is molten and solidifies epitaxially and frequently is observed as a white-etching surface layer on steels. This zone exhibits high hardness, which is due to the presence of as-quenched martensite, and retained austenite. High residual tensile stresses are produced. Beneath the white-etching as-cast layer is a dark-etching heat-affected zone.

2-3.8 Micromilling

Micromilling devices, which use diamond or Borazon tools, have been developed and are used to prepare high-quality surfaces suitable for examination or electropolishing. Although micromilling is not a sectioning technique, it is a machining process that produces surfaces similar to those made by microtomy. Micromilling produces reflective surfaces with a scratch depth of about 0.1 μm. Results are best with soft metals, such as copper, zinc, aluminum, gold, and silver. Acceptable results have been produced on cast irons, but surfaces on steel samples are inadequate without subsequent preparation. The process is relatively fast, porosity and cavities are revealed without distortion, and edge retention is excellent.

2-3.9 Summary

Sectioning is required in most metallographic work to produce a sample convenient for further processing. Numerous devices are available and suitable. In general, abrasive cutoff machines, band saws, and low-speed diamond saws are the most commonly employed devices used by metallographers. Shearing is very common with thin materials such as sheet or foil. Each technique has advantages and disadvantages. Cutting imparts some damage to the sample, and this damage varies with the method used, the material cut, and the techniques employed. Important variables include the applied pressure and the use of coolants or lubricants. Careful attention must be given to the sectioning process in order to obtain high-quality polished surfaces.

2-4 MOUNTING

When working with bulk samples, mounting may not be required; however, if the sample is small or oddly shaped, mounting may be necessary. If sample edges are to be examined, mounting may be required along with other measures to be described in this chapter. A few automatic polishing devices can handle bulk unmounted samples and produce acceptable edge retention. Other automatic devices require that samples be a specific size, and samples used with these devices must be mounted. Many types of mounting materials can be employed to satisfy nearly any requirement. The wide variety of materials available does present a selection problem, and information about these materials is given in the discussion that follows.

Mount size and shape is sometimes influenced by the size and shape of the part to be mounted. In general, most mounts are round with diameters of 1, 1¼, or 1½ in. Mount height is usually ½ to ¾ in. These standard sizes are accommodated by automatic grinding and polishing machines and generally fit within the specimen chambers of the scanning electron microscope (SEM) or microprobe. Samples larger than this can be cut down and mounted or handled unmounted. As the sample area to be polished increases, it becomes more difficult to keep the surface flat and obtain a high-quality polish over the entire surface, especially if hand polishing is used. Mount thickness is important if samples are hand-polished, since mounts more than ¾ in high are difficult to hold flat.

Square or rectangular mounts are sometimes employed, especially in x-ray diffraction work where a relatively large surface, typically ¾ by 1½ in, is needed. Many mounting materials react with the x-ray beam, producing spurious x-ray peaks. Kold Mount, an acrylic, is ideal for such work. For pole-figure texture studies of sheet metal, the sheet sample can be glued to a sheet of Plexiglas so that the planar surface can be polished. With rectangular mounts, the length should be kept no more than twice the width for best polishing results.

In selecting a mounting material and technique, several factors other than physical dimensions must be evaluated. The material and technique employed must not damage the specimen. Heat generation in compression mounting can be substantial. The so-called cold-mounting resins can exhibit considerable differences in the amount of heat produced during polymerization. If minor amounts of heat will alter the microstructure, the lowest exotherm cold-mounting resins must be employed. Compression molding mounting will damage thin, fragile, or friable specimens. Shrinkage stresses can be high enough to pull a protective plating from the sample.

Another factor to consider is the inherent resistance of the mounting material to the solvents and etchants to be used, particularly if the etchant is to be heated. For edge examination, the degree of bonding and the grinding and polishing rates relative to the sample are important. Fissures between the sample and mount can create havoc with bleeding and staining. The ability to fill porosity or cracks varies considerably, and special techniques may be required for best results. In some instances, a transparent mount may be desired. For microprobe, SEM examination, or electropolishing, a conductive mount is desirable. With nonconductive plastic mounts, the degree of charging or generation of spurious x-ray signals varies with the mounting material. All the above factors must be considered prior to selecting the mounting material. A little planning at this stage can prevent frustration later on.

2-4.1 Cleaning

Prior to mounting, it is often necessary to clean samples. Cleaning may also be needed prior to plating for edge retention. With certain samples, for example, those in which surface oxide layers are to be examined, cleaning must be limited to very simple treatments or the detail to be examined may be lost.

A distinction can be made between physically and chemically clean surfaces. Physical cleanliness implies freedom from solid dirt, grease, or other debris, while chemical cleanliness implies freedom from any contaminant. In metallographic work, physical cleanliness is usually adequate and nearly always necessary. Surface cleanliness is important in SEM or microprobe work; surface films, even fingerprints, can produce spurious results.

In machining operations, cutting fluids, oils, or greases are left on the metal surfaces. Coolant debris from laboratory abrasive cutting is a common problem, especially if the surface is porous. Vapor degreasing is frequently employed to remove oil and grease. All laboratories should use ultrasonic cleaners before and during sample preparation. Any cleaning operation should always start with the simplest, gentlest solutions, e.g., soapy water, alcohol, or acetone. If these prove inadequate, various dilute aqueous acidic solutions or neutral or basic detergent solutions can be tried.

Ultrasonic cleaning is the most effective cleaning tool for routine use. Cleaning results from cavitation, a phenomenon that occurs in many liquids. Passage of an ultrasonic wave through a liquid produces fluctuations in hydrostatic pressure. An acoustic wave consists of an alternating pressure front that moves at a particular velocity in the liquid. In an ultrasonic cleaner, a standing wave is produced as a result of reflections, leading to a stationary wave front. However, the alternating pressure/rarefaction phase persists. Most liquids exhibit an amplitude threshold level above which cavitation occurs. The frequency and amplitude of the acoustic wave and the cleaning medium all influence cleaning action. Tank design is also important.

Some users fill the tank with a soapy water solution and immerse the sample directly in the solution. Effective cleaning is obtained, but the dirty solution must be changed frequently. To avoid this problem, others prefer to place about an inch of water in the tank and then place a beaker containing water or some other solvent and the sample inside the tank. Only the liquid in the beaker becomes contaminated, thus simplifying cleaning. This method produces greater flexibility of operation and is preferred. A cleaning time of 2 to 5 min is usually adequate. Very soft samples can be damaged by the cavitation; therefore, if ultrasonic cleaning is needed, times should be 30 s or less. For degreasing, trichloroethylene or acetone are frequently used, although lower cavitation energies result. For dust or dirt removal, water is adequate, but a mixture of about 10% alcohol in water may be more efficient.

2-4.2 Adhesive Mounting

Adhesive mounting is used in petrographic thin-section work, but the technique has limited metallographic application. It is usually employed when the planar surface of sheet samples is to be polished, as illustrated in Fig. 2-4. For example, to study spangle formation in galvanized steel, a section about ½ by 1 in is glued to a piece of Plexiglas of slightly larger size. Substrate thickness should be about ½ in for ease of holding. Two-sided adhesive tape, epoxy cement, Canada balsam, or Lakeside 70 cement can be used as glue. In the study of coatings, one can examine successively polished planar surfaces until the base metal is reached.

2-4.3 Clamps

A variety of mechanical clamping devices have been used by metallographers, most frequently for preparing transverse or longitudinal sheet surfaces. Clamps are a very fast mounting technique and can be highly effective, producing excellent edge retention. The use of clamps has frequently been criticized because of the possible entrapment of polishing abrasive and etchant seepage. These problems can be completely eliminated by good technique.

Clamps, are generally machined from plate stock about ¼ in thick that has been cut into blocks about ½ by 1½ in, as shown in Fig. 2-4. Holes are drilled into

Figure 2-4 Examples of adhesive mounting (left) for planar surface examination and mechanical clamps (right). The clamp has plastic spacers between the specimens.

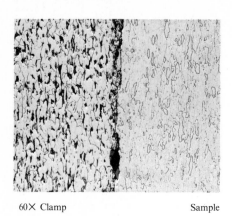

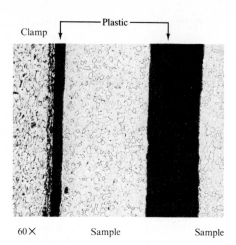

60× Clamp   Sample

Figure 2-5a Example of excellent edge
retention achievable with mechanical
clamps. No spacers between sheet metal
samples.

60×   Sample   Sample

Figure 2-5b Example of excellent edge
retention achievable with mechanical
clamps. Plastic spacers between sheet metal
samples.

each end of the clamp halves. One half is threaded to receive a bolt of suitable length. The mating holes in the other half are made just large enough to clear the threads. Bolts of different lengths and clamps of different lengths can be used to handle different size samples. Samples are cut or sheared to a length that will fit between the bolts. To mount samples, the clamp is elevated slightly at each end with spacers and the samples are placed inside the clamp, with the surface to be polished protruding slightly below the clamp. The spacers under the clamp ends permit a controlled amount of the sample to be ground off to remove any deformed metal at this edge. The bolts are then tightened. Notation is made of the sample identifications within the clamp, generally in reference to the side of the clamp with the bolt head. Next, the clamp is placed in a heavy vise, and the tightening is completed with a large, husky screwdriver. In this manner, a very tight mount is obtained, and seepage and abrasive entrapment is minimized. If the sample surfaces are somewhat rough, a thin piece of plastic, lead, or copper can be placed between the samples before tightening. Alternatively, the samples can be coated with an adhesive or epoxy cement before placing them inside the clamp. It is also possible to grind the samples through 600-grit paper and then apply epoxy resin to the surface, drawing the epoxy into any crevices by vacuum impregnation. Most of these techniques are not necessary if the samples are flat and uniform in thickness. Figures 2-5a and b illustrate the degree of edge retention that can be obtained with clamps.

The clamp material chosen is important. The material should be similar in composition to the material to be mounted to avoid galvanic effects that would inhibit etching. If the clamp material is more readily attacked by the etchant than the sample, the sample will not etch.

2-4.4 Plastic Mounting Materials

The introduction of phenolic compression molding mounting in the 1930s was viewed by metallographers as a wondrous achievement and became instantly popular. Since then, many other polymeric materials have been developed and quite a few have been found eminently suitable as mounting materials. These materials can be grouped into two categories: those that require heat and pressure for curing and those that cure at or near room temperature. The former group are usually obtained as powders, while the latter group can be obtained as two liquids or a liquid and a powder.

Compression mounting Plastics that require heat and pressure for curing are known as compression mounting materials. Two basic types are available. Thermosetting resins require heat and pressure during the molding cycle but can be ejected from the mold at the molding temperature. Examples include the very familiar phenolic plastic, Bakelite, diallyl phthalate, and the recently introduced epoxies such as Plastimet or Epomet. Bakelite normally contains wood flour to increase the hardness but can be obtained as 100% resin (Bakelite amber). Diallyl phthalate can contain mineral, glass fiber, or copper flake. Mixtures of melamine and phenolic have also been used. The properties of common thermosetting resins are given in Table 2-2.

Thermoplastic resins require heat and pressure during molding but must be cooled to ambient temperature under pressure. Examples include transparent methyl methacrylate (known as Lucite or Transoptic), polystyrene, polyvinyl chloride (PVC), and polyvinyl formal (Formvar). Properties of common thermoplastic mounting materials are given in Table 2-3. Hardness measurements for common mounting materials are listed in Table 2-4.

Mounting of these resins requires a heated press,which can be quite simple or highly automated, as illustrated in Fig. 2-6. Most resins require a temperature of about 300°F (149°C) and a pressure of 4200 lb/in^2. Pressure requirements vary with the mount diameter. A high-capacity heater is placed around the mold to provide rapid heating. For cooling, copper chill blocks or water-cooled jackets are placed around the mold after removing or turning off the heater. Automated presses, such as the Struers Prontopress, incorporate heating and cooling devices in the same enclosure around the mold. While cooling under pressure is required with thermoplastic materials, the same procedure can be used with thermosetting resins, thus producing a tighter bond and less shrinkage.

To mount samples, the specimen must be cut to a size that will fit inside the mold with adequate clearance. If the sample has sharp corners, they should be beveled, if possible, to minimize cracking potential. The larger the sample with respect to the mount size, the greater the tendency for mold cracking at sharp corners. These cracks produce bleeding problems. The surface to be polished is placed face down on the center of the ram surface. With a small sample, if one surface is of interest, this edge can be centered. Clearance between sample and mold wall should be at least ⅛ in. Some samples may need support so that they will

Table 2-2 Typical properties of thermosetting molding resins[†]

Resin	Molding conditions			Heat distortion temp., °C[‡]	Coeff. of thermal expansion, in/(in·°C)	Abrasion rate, μm/min[§]	Polishing rate, μm/min[¶]	Transparency	Chemical resistance
	Temp., °C	Pressure, lb/in^2	Time, min						
Bakelite (wood-filled)	135–170	2500–4200	5–12	140	$3.0–4.5 \times 10^{-5}$	100	2.9	Opaque	Attacked by strong acids and alkalies
Diallyl phthalate (asbestos-filled)	140–160	2500–3000	6–12	150	$3–5 \times 10^{-5}$	190	0.8	Opaque	Attacked by strong acids and alkalies

[†]Data compiled from the literature, see Ref. 10.
[‡]Determined by method ASTM D648-56.
[§]Specimen 1-cm^2 area abraded on slightly worn 600-grit SiC under load of 100 g at rubbing speed of 10^4 cm/min.
[¶]1-in diameter mount on a wheel rotating at 250 r/min covered with synthetic suede cloth and charged with 4–8-μm diamond.
Source: From Miley and Calabra, Ref. 10.

Table 2-3 Typical properties of thermoplastic molding resins†

Resin	Molding conditions						Heat distortion temp., °C‡	Coeff. of thermal expansion, in/(in·°C)	Abrasion rate, μm/min§	Polishing rate, μm/min¶	Transparency	Chemical resistance
	Heating			Cooling								
	Temp., °C	Pressure, lb/in²	Time, min	Temp., °C	Pressure, lb/in²	Time, min						
Methyl methacrylate	140–165	2500–4200	6	75–85	Max.	6–7	65	$5–9 \times 10^{-5}$		7.5	Water white to clear	Not resistant to strong acids and some solvents
Polystyrene	140–165	2500	5	85–100	Max.	6	65					
Polyvinyl formal	220	4000	—				75	$6–8 \times 10^{-5}$	20	1.1	Light brown, clear	Not resistant to strong acids
Polyvinyl chloride	120–160	100	Nil	60	4000		60	$5–18 \times 10^{-5}$	45	1.3	Opaque	Resistant to most acids and alkalies

†Data compiled from the literature, see Ref. 10.
‡Determined by method ASTM D648-56.
§Specimen 1-cm² area abraded on slightly worn 600-grit SiC under load of 100 g at rubbing speed of 10^4 cm/min.
¶1-in diameter mount on a wheel rotating at 250 r/min covered with synthetic suede cloth and charged with 4–8-μm diamond.
Source: From Miley and Calabra, Ref. 10.

Table 2-4 Hardness of common mounting materials

Material	Hardness, HRM ± 95% CL†
Thermosetting resins	
Phenolic (Bakelite)	
Red	113.3 ± 1.9
Black	110.3 ± 1.4
Green	113.3 ± 0.9
Brown	111.7 ± 0.8
Mottle (green/brown)	109.7 ± 0.7
Amber	118.2 ± 2.2
Melamine-phenolic (Mount All)	112.0 ± 0.7
Diallyl phthalate	
Blue, short glass fibers	99.5 ± 0.9
Green, short glass fibers	103.5 ± 1.2
Red, short glass fibers	106.1 ± 1.5
Epoxy	
Plastimet	109.7 ± 0.6
Epomet	100.9 ± 1.2
Struers no. 5	89.3 ± 0.7
Thermosplastic resins	
Methyl methacrylate (Lucite, Transoptic)	91.3 ± 2.2
Castable resins	
Acrylics	
Kold Mount	56.8 ± 7.7
Kold Weld	34.9 ± 7.4
Sampl Kwick	43.2 ± 1.7
Polyester	
Castoglas	89.0 ± 2.3
Castolite	60.0 ± 3.4
Epoxy	
Epo-Mix Epoxide	71.9 ± 3.1
Epoxide	72.8 ± 6.5
Epo Kwick	27.2 ± 7.8
Conductive mounts	
Copper diallyl phthalate	89.9 ± 3.4
Aluminum-filled phenolic	44.2 ± 2.3

†As a comparison, a brass sample with a hardness of 42.5 HRB (Rockwell hardness on the B scale) had a hardness of 103.7 HRM (Rockwell hardness on the M scale)—100 kg, ¼-in steel ball indenter. Values are given plus and minus the 95% confidence limit (CL).

stand perpendicular to the ram. With sheet samples, it may be possible to bend a small part of one or both ends at right angles to support the sample. Small spring clips, binder clamps, and springs can also be used to hold samples in the desired position. Very thin materials fold over when compression-mounted, and castable resins may be more suitable. To avoid the folding problem, application of pressure should be delayed for awhile so that the resin can become molten. Then the usual pressure can be applied. Samples with fragile coatings can also be

Figure 2-6 Example of an automatic press (Struers Prontopress). *(Courtesy of Struers, Inc.)*

damaged by compression molding. When in doubt, a castable resin should be used. It is not uncommon to observe protective platings pulled off the sample by the shrinkage stresses associated with compression mounting materials.

After the sample is oriented on the ram, the ram is lowered until it reaches the bottom of the mold. The desired mounting powder is poured into the mold. The amount of powder must be sufficient to make a mount with a height greater than the sample or at least ½ in high. The top of the die can be damaged if it presses against the top of the sample. The top of the die is fitted into the mold and fixed in placed to contain the pressure. Heat and pressure are applied according to the mounting material requirements. Temperature control is more critical than pressure control. The minimum required temperature must be reached but should not be exceeded, because charring will occur with thermosetting resins or bleed-out will result with thermoplastic resins. Some thermosetting resins, chiefly Bakelite, can be obtained as preformed, partially cured slugs. The preform can be used instead of powder with bulk samples, thus reducing the curing time. The preform is placed in the mold cavity above the sample and will be forced down and around the sample during curing.

Improper control of the mounting cycle can result in a number of mount defects. Figure 2-7 illustrates typically encountered compression molding defects and their causes and remedies. Thermal expansion characteristics of these materials (see Tables 2-2 and 2-3) can produce either beneficial or harmful effects, depending on sample shape. Because these plastics expand more than most metals [3], the greater shrinkage during cooling produces tight mechanical bonding. None of these resins will physically adhere to a sample. With a tubular shape, a

Bakelite and Diallyl Phthalate:

DEFECT	CAUSE	REMEDY
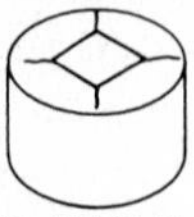 Radial Split	Too large a section in the given mold area. / Sharp cornered specimens.	Increase mold size. / Reduce specimen size
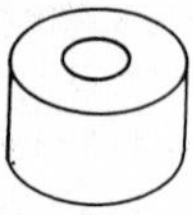 Edge Shrinkage	Excessive shrinkage of plastic away from sample.	Decrease molding temperature. / Cool mold slightly prior to ejection.
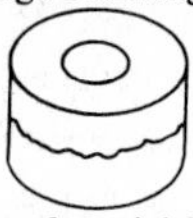 Circumferential Splits	Absorbed moisture. / Entrapped gasses during molding.	Preheat powder or premold. / Momentarily release pressure during fluid state.
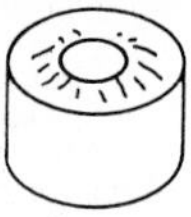 Burst	Too short a cure period. / Insufficient pressure.	Lengthen cure period. / Apply sufficient pressure during transition from fluid state to solid state.
 Unfused	Insufficient molding pressure. / Insufficient time at cure temperature. / Increased surface area of powdered materials.	Use proper molding pressure. / Increase cure time. / With powders — quickly seal mold closure and apply pressure to eliminate localized curing.

Transoptic:

DEFECT	CAUSE	REMEDY
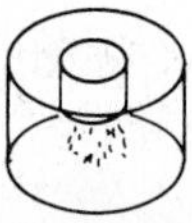 Cottonball	Powdered media did not reach maximum temperature. / Insufficient time at maximum temperature.	Increase holding time at maximum temperature.
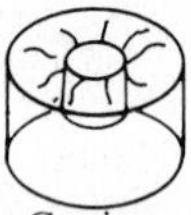 Crazing	Inherent stresses relieved upon or after ejection.	Allow cooling to a lower temperature prior to ejection. / Temper mounts in boiling water.

Figure 2-7 Typically encountered compression molding defects and their causes and remedies. *(Courtesy of Buehler Ltd.)*

tight bond will occur at the OD (outside diameter), but a gap will occur at the ID (inner diameter) [10].

Bakelite is the most commonly used compression molding material because of the simplicity of its use, the good results obtained with it, and its low cost. Edge retention with Bakelite is poorer than with many other resins but can be improved if the resin is cooled under pressure and if automatic polishing is employed (see Fig. 2-8). Shrinkage is lower with diallyl phthalate than with Bakelite (0.003 to 0.005 in/in versus 0.004 to 0.008 in/in) [11]. Diallyl phthalate exhibits better resistance to strong acids or heated etchants than Bakelite. Diallyl phthalate or compression mounting epoxy are more resistant to heated etchants, such as boiling alkaline sodium picrate, than Bakelite, which deteriorates substantially.

The recently developed compression mounting epoxies exhibit low shrinkage and produce excellent edge retention. The molding pressure used, 3000 lb/in^2, is lower than for Bakelite, and molding defects are much less common.

Thermoplastic mounting materials can be used with thin or fragile specimens because the required molding pressure can be applied after the resin is molten. The transparency of methyl methacrylate (Lucite) and polyvinyl formal (Formvar) can be useful when grinding must be controlled to locate a particular defect or area of interest. A disadvantage is that these materials soften if frictional heat is generated during grinding or polishing. Shrinkage is high, producing gaps and poor edge retention. Some problems with chemical resistance may be encountered, since the thermoplastics are attacked by strong acids and are partially soluble in organic solvents such as acetone. The abrasion and polishing rates of thermoplastics are lower than for thermosetting materials. In general, thermoplastic materials are used only when transparency is required.

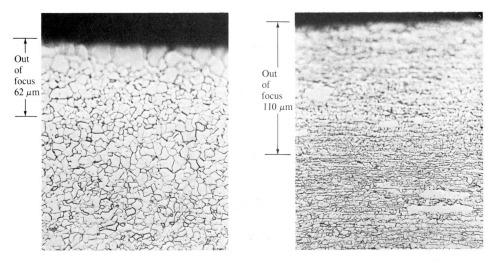

Figure 2-8 Example of limited edge retention of Bakelite mounts. Left, automatic polishing; right, hand polishing (320×, 2% nital etchant, low-carbon steel).

Castable mounts The castable resins, often referred to as "cold-mounting" plastics, have become quite popular since their introduction in the 1950s. Characteristics of these materials complement those of the compression mounting materials and offer many advantages to the metallographer. In general, these materials are two-component systems, most frequently two liquids, but can also be a liquid and a powder. One component is the resin and the other is a hardener. Several types are available, and they are usually classed as acrylics, polyesters, or epoxies. A wide variety of mold shapes are used, although the standard round mount sizes are most common.

Resin and hardener must be carefully measured (by weight or by volume, depending on the instructions provided) and thoroughly mixed before casting. If this is not done, the sample may not harden. Many materials have been used as molds including aluminum foil, aluminum or Bakelite rings, and Teflon or silicone rubber cups. If the mold is to be reclaimed and used over, a release agent such as vacuum grease must be used with some castable resins, particularly epoxy. Epoxy mounts can be removed from silicone rubber mounts without use of a release agent. Some metallographers do not like to handle epoxy samples and prefer to leave the mold attached to the sample permanently. A simple procedure to use is as follows: A flat plate is covered with a sheet of aluminum foil. Duco cement is applied liberally to one end of a phenolic ring form of the desired diameter, and this surface is pressed against the aluminum foil. The sample is placed inside the ring form with the side to be polished against the foil. The mixed epoxy, or other resin, is poured around the sample after the Duco cement hardens. After the epoxy is cured, the sample, permanently enclosed by the ring, can be pulled easily off the aluminum foil without damage to the foil.

Although some laboratories use epoxy exclusively, others use epoxy and other castable resins only in situations where compression mounts are inadequate, such as with thin, fragile, or friable samples. A very valuable property of epoxies is their excellent fluidity, which permits filling of cavities, cracks, or pores, although vacuum impregnation is usually required to fully accomplish this goal. Cold-setting resins, however, are not foolproof, as illustrated by Fig. 2-9. Occasionally a bad batch of epoxy is obtained, which can produce considerable frustration. Cold-setting resins do have definite shelf lives, which if surpassed, influences casting quality. The odor from many of these resins is obnoxious, and therefore, mounting under a ventilation hood is preferred. Some of these resins produce skin damage if contact is frequent.

Acrylics employ a liquid and a powder that will cure in about half an hour after mixing, producing a milky-white mount. Acrylics do not provide good edge retention. Their chief advantage is a short curing time. As mentioned, acrylics are useful in x-ray diffraction work because spurious signals that could interfere with those from the sample are not produced. Acrylics are simple to use and relatively foolproof, and demounting is simple. A sample is removed from an acrylic mount by immersing the sample in hot glycerin [11]. After a few minutes, the sample is removed from the glycerin and squeezed in a vise to pop out the sample.

Epoxides:

DEFECT	CAUSE	REMEDY
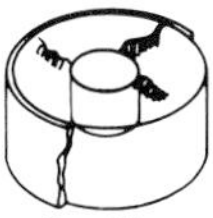 Cracking	Insufficient air cure prior to oven cure. Oven cure temperature too high. Resin to hardener ratio incorrect.	Increase air cure time. Decrease oven cure temperature. Correct resin to hardener ratio.
 Bubbles	Too violent agitation while blending resin & hardener mixture.	Blend mixture gently to avoid air entrapment.
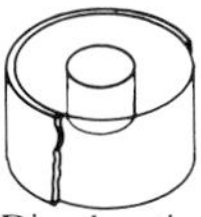 Discoloration	Resin to hardener ratio incorrect. Oxidized hardener.	Correct resin to hardener ratio. Keep containers tightly sealed.
 Soft Mounts	Resin to hardener ratio incorrect. Incorrect blending of resin-hardener mixture.	Correct resin to hardener ratio. Completely blend mixture.

Polyesters:

DEFECT	CAUSE	REMEDY
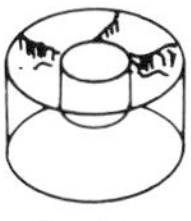 Cracking	Insufficient air cure prior to oven cure. Oven cure temperature too high. Resin to hardener ratio incorrect.	Increase air cure time. Decrease oven cure temperature. Correct resin to hardener ratio.
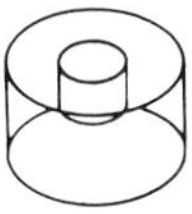 Discoloration	Resin to hardener ratio incorrect. Resin has oxidized.	Correct resin to hardener ratio. Keep containers tightly sealed.
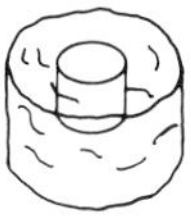 Soft Mounts	Resin to hardener ratio incorrect. Incomplete blending of resin-hardener mixture.	Correct resin to hardener ratio. Completely blend mixture.
 Tacky Tops	Resin to hardener ratio incorrect. Incomplete blending of resin-hardener mixture	Correct resin to hardener ratio. Completely blend mixture.

Acrylics:

DEFECT	CAUSE	REMEDY
 Bubbles	Too violent agitation while blending resin and hardener.	Blend mixture gently to avoid air entrapment.

Figure 2-9 Some cold-mounting defects and their cause and remedy. *(Courtesy of Buehler Ltd.)*

Although referred to as cold-mounting materials, acrylics do generate considerable heat during curing. Nelson conducted an experiment which reveals the extent of the problem and also illustrates how molding technique can influence the magnitude of the exotherm [12]. The four conditions tested were (1) compression-molded Bakelite, (2) acrylic (Kold Mount) cast in a glass mold on a glass plate, (3) acrylic cast in an aluminum mold on an aluminum plate, and (4) epoxy cast in a Bakelite ring form on a pasteboard base. Figure 2-10 shows temperature versus time curves for each mounting technique. As expected, compression mounting of Bakelite produced the highest temperatures, with a maximum of 149.5°C. For Kold Mount cast in a glass ring on a glass plate (poor heat conduction), the maximum temperature was 132°C, only slightly less than with Bakelite. Use of Kold Mount in an aluminum ring on an aluminum plate (good heat conduction) produced a maximum temperature of only 42°C, a vast improvement. The epoxy, although cast under conditions of poor heat conduction, produced a temperature rise of only 7°C.

Baczewski described a procedure for removing samples from an epoxy mount [13]. First, as much of the epoxy as possible is removed by cutting. Then, the sample is placed in a wire basket and the basket lowered into boiling dimethylsulf-oxide (DMSO). DMSO boils at about 190°C. After 1 to 2 min, the basket is removed and quickly plunged into a very cold liquid such as liquid nitrogen or a mixture of dry ice and acetone. After one or more repetitions of this process, any epoxy still adhering to the sample can easily be removed by hand. In using this

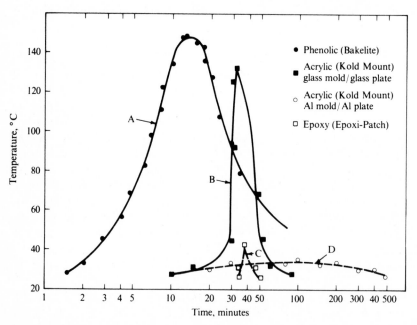

Figure 2-10 Heat generated during curing of various resins. *(From Nelson, Ref. 12, courtesy of Dr. Riederer-Verlag, GmbH.)*

method, one should work under a hood, since the DMSO fumes are toxic, and skin contact with DMSO should be avoided.

2-4.5 Vacuum Impregnation

Vacuum impregnation of epoxy resins is the only satisfactory procedure for mounting porous, fragile, or friable specimens. Procedures can involve a second impregnation step after fine grinding. Vacuum impregnation removes air from pores, crevices, and cracks, thus permitting entrance of the epoxy. As a result, complete bonding can be achieved, which reduces the chance of damage to fragile or friable samples. Insufficient bonding could result in portions of the sample breaking off during grinding or polishing. Filling of pores permits proper retention of pore structure. Polishing experiments with nonimpregnated porous samples have shown that pore size can be enlarged, pore edges can become rounded, and some pores may collapse, with the degree of these problems varying with polishing technique. Open pores or cracks permit entrapment of polishing compounds, solvent, and etchants and cause staining problems.

Vacuum impregnation is commonly used with powder metallurgy specimens, coal or coke, ceramics, and minerals and in corrosion or failure analysis. Equipment requirements are simple. Most of the necessary apparatus is already present in a well-equipped laboratory or can be purchased. Many laboratories are equipped with a house vacuum line which is usually adequate. If none is available, a simple mechanical vacuum pump can be used. A vacuum gauge is useful but not indispensable. The vacuum line can be passed through a dehydrating agent for removal of moisture. A bell jar and base plate or a vacuum dessicator is used to contain the sample under vacuum during impregnation. Optimum results are obtained if the epoxy is added to the mold under vacuum. Nelson and Slepian [14] have described a simple single-sample impregnation system, while Petretzky [15] has described a multiple-sample impregnation system.

The surface of the sample to be mounted is first ground with coarse grit paper to flatten the surface of interest. With some fragile samples, this cannot be done, and a second impregnation step is used after fine grinding. If possible, the sample is cleaned before being placed inside the mold. If the sample is porous or cracked, it is dried for about 15 min at about 150 to 200°F (66 to 93°C) (assuming this produces no damage) to remove moisture. The sample is placed inside the mold, and the mold is placed in the chamber. Nelson and Slepian recommend placing the sample surface that is to be polished face up, with a small spacer block beneath so that the desired surface is slightly below the top of the mold. Block thickness is adjusted so that the overall mount height is ½ to ¾ in and so that about ⅛ in of epoxy will cover the top of the sample. The mold is centered under the tube used to introduce the epoxy. The chamber is evacuated, but the vacuum level should not be high enough to boil the epoxy. After a few minutes the epoxy is added until the mold is nearly full. The vacuum is maintained for a few minutes and then the air is allowed to enter slowly. The sample is removed and allowed to cure in the air.

An alternate procedure is to add the epoxy to the mold under atmospheric pressure and outgas the mount in a vacuum dessicator until all air bubbles are removed. This may require 10 min or more. When air is admitted to the vessel, epoxy is forced into the openings. Some users prefer to use alternate vacuum and air cycles. Another useful procedure is to outgas the epoxy under vacuum for a few minutes before adding it to the mold and then outgas the filled mold. However, these techniques may not be as effective as the first procedure described. The best procedure is to outgas the epoxy and add it to the evacuated mold without going outside the vacuum chamber.

2-4.6 Taper Mounting

Metallographers have used the taper sectioning procedure in conjunction with light microscopy to obtain greater surface structure detail. Samuels used this method extensively in his studies on the influence of grinding and polishing on surface deformation [3]. A taper section is produced by grinding the sample at a small angle to the surface or by slightly raising one end of the sample in the mount, as illustrated in Fig. 2-11. The magnification produced is equal to the cosecant of the taper angle α. For a round sample, a chord can be ground tangentially to the surface as illustrated.

The taper magnification for a rod-shaped sample is the ratio of the bar diameter to the chord length. At the line of intersection between the specimen surface and the plane of polish, the structure is enlarged an amount established by the taper magnification. For a flat specimen, a taper angle α of $5°44'$ produces a 10X enlargement. The taper angle can be determined by placing a piece of shim stock of known thickness under one corner of the sample and then measuring the distance from the shim stock to the opposite corner, as shown in Fig. 2-11. Alternatively, a cut of shallow depth is produced across the sample. A small piece is cut off and it is mounted in the normal manner so that the true depth of the cut can be measured. Then, a taper mount is prepared with the balance of the sample. The apparent depth of the cut on the taper section is measured, and it is divided by the true depth to determine the taper magnification.

2-4.7 Edge Preservation

In many metallographic studies, it is necessary to examine the extreme surface structure. This requires a flat polished surface out to the edge of the sample. The degree of edge retention depends on the mounting material, the use of fillers or plating, and the polishing technique. Schüller and Schwaab measured the edge profile of polished samples mounted in different plastic materials [16]. Their measurements revealed that only a few of the epoxy resins exhibited suitable edge retention. Addition of alumina filler produced excellent results, while the same resin without filler had poor edge retention. Of the compression mounting materials tested, methyl methacrylate (Lucite) produced the poorest results. No direct correlation was observed between mount hardness and edge retention,

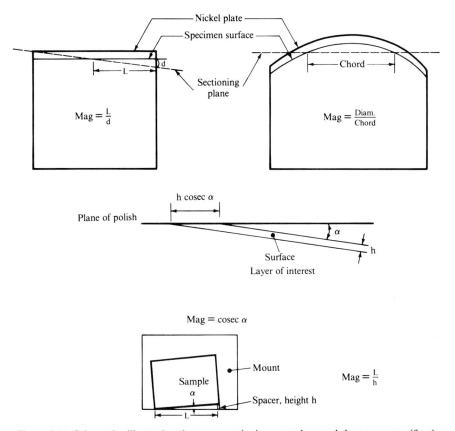

Figure 2-11 Schematics illustrating the taper sectioning procedure and the taper magnification.

although samples with the best edge retention were frequently higher-hardness mounting materials.

Edge retention can be improved through use of a variety of procedures. Typical procedures include use of backup materials near the edge of interest, addition of filler material to castable resins, or plating prior to mounting. Backup material must be similar to the sample and should be placed close to the edge of interest.

Nelson and Slepian [17] published an epoxy-sandwich technique using the stacking method as outlined in Fig. 2-12. Each sample is coated with a metal-filled epoxy [Hysol Epoxy-Patch Kit 6C (aluminum) or 73C (iron), Hysol Corp, Olean, New York] by rolling the epoxy on with a round stick to minimize air entrapment. Stack thickness must be of sufficient thickness for stable polishing. After the stack sets for about half an hour, light pressure is applied to squeeze out excess epoxy. A light weight is placed on the stack, and the stack is allowed to harden for about 24 h. Next, the surface to be polished is ground flat, and the stack is encapsulated in

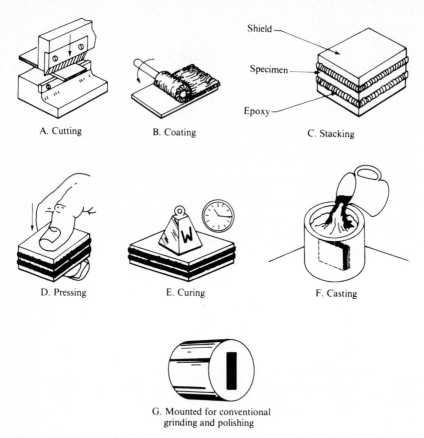

A. Cutting   B. Coating

Shield
Specimen
Epoxy

C. Stacking

D. Pressing   E. Curing   F. Casting

G. Mounted for conventional
grinding and polishing

Figure 2-12 Steps used to prepare epoxy-sandwich mounts. *(From Nelson and Slepian, Ref. 17, courtesy of Dr. Riederer-Verlag, GmbH.)*

any desired mounting material. Results are shown in Fig. 2-13a to d. Figure 2-13a shows an oxide layer on a sample of electrical sheet steel mounted by this method, which has excellent edge retention. Figure 2-13b shows a plated aluminum busbar in a standard thermosetting resin. Note the gap between the plating and the mount. Edge rounding is present but is not noticeable until the same material is prepared by the epoxy-sandwich method, as shown in Fig. 2-13c. Note that the plated layer is more clearly delineated and appears to be thicker in Fig. 2-13c than in Fig. 2-13b. An aluminum foil coated with an organic resin and mounted by the epoxy-sandwich technique is shown in Fig. 2-13d. Again, edge retention is excellent.

A wide variety of mold filler material has been used to improve edge retention including cast iron grit, metal flake, ground glass, and pelletized alumina. The latter is the most popular and is available in white or black and in several sizes and hardness ranges. White −80- to +250-mesh alumina is recommended for surrounding uniformly shaped samples, while the finer −250-mesh particles are

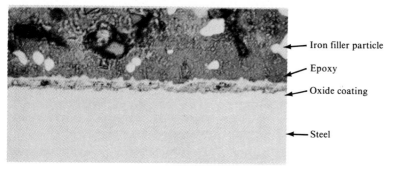

— Iron filler particle

— Epoxy

— Oxide coating

— Steel

A. Oxide coated steel epoxy sandwich mount

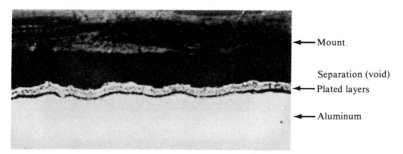

— Mount

Separation (void)
— Plated layers

— Aluminum

B. Plated bus bar - conventional mount

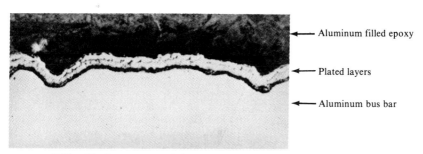

— Aluminum filled epoxy

— Plated layers

— Aluminum bus bar

C. Plated bus bar - epoxy sandwich mount

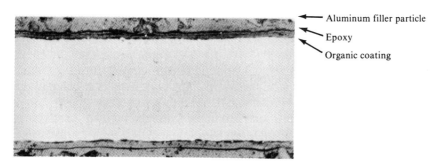

— Aluminum filler particle

Epoxy

Organic coating

D. Organic coated foil - epoxy mount

Figure 2-13 Photomicrographs at $500\times$ magnification illustrating the degree of edge retention achievable with the epoxy sandwich mounting technique. *(From Nelson and Slepian, Ref. 17, courtesy of Dr. Riederer-Verlag, GmbH.)*

preferred with more complicated geometries. Black pelletized alumina is available in two sizes, − 150 and + 150 mesh. Both come in three hardness grades, low-, medium-, and high-fired. Low-fired alumina is recommended for soft metals; and hard-fired is recommended for high-hardness materials. White pelletized alumina comes in the same hardness ranges and the recommendations for its use are the same. Black pelletized alumina dispersed in epoxy that has been dyed black has been shown to produce improved contrast between the sample and mount in work using polarized light and in photomicrography.

Pelletized alumina provides excellent edge retention and is especially useful where plating is inconvenient or impossible to perform. Because of the very high hardness of alumina, grinding and polishing rates are greatly reduced and greater use is made of grinding paper. Automatic grinding and polishing is recommended rather than hand polishing.

Polishing procedures also influence the degree of edge retention. Automatic polishing produces better results than manual polishing. Regardless of the technique used, a low-nap or napless cloth is preferred for rough polishing and fine polishing, although scratching may be more pronounced. The manual polishing technique suggested by Cprek is helpful [18]. In this method, the critical edge is maintained as the trailing edge with respect to the wheel rotation direction during grinding and polishing. In practice, slight shifts in orientation must be used between steps to minimize comet tailing.

Perhaps the oldest technique for edge preservation, and one of the most effective methods, is plating, which can be done electrolytically or can be done with electroless solutions [19–22]. Many metals may be deposited electrolytically, but chromium, copper, iron, nickel, and zinc are the most common in metallographic work. Although it is impossible to electroplate nonconductive surfaces, a host of techniques exist for producing a continuous conductive coating to serve as the basis for a subsequent electrodeposit. One such method is to metallize the surface with silver, as in the Brashear process. More modern techniques (see App. D) are less wasteful of silver and avoid the danger of forming fulminating silver. Electroless copper can also be used to coat nonconductors.

A clean specimen surface is required for the plating to adhere. Many of the cleaning treatments recommended for industrial plating are too harsh for metallographic work. Milder cleaning treatments are recommended and involve use of detergents, solvents, or mild alkaline or acidic solutions. Internal stresses in the electrodeposit also influence adhesion. Shrinkage stresses during mounting have been known to pull poorly adhering platings from the sample surface. Plating residual stresses vary depending on the type of metal deposited, the plating bath composition, and the plating thickness. Electrolytic baths are less effective than electroless solutions in covering and penetrating rough, porous, or irregular surfaces. Electroless solutions are preferred for metallographic work, since penetration is better and residual stresses are low. In addition to edge retention plated surfaces also help to produce good contrast between the sample and the mounting material. Procedures for electrolytic and electroless plating are given in App. D.

2-4.8 Conductive Mounts

Because plastic mounts will not conduct electricity, samples to be mounted and electropolished or examined in the SEM or microprobe are sometimes mounted using thermosetting resins containing a conductive filler such as iron, aluminum, or copper. The best known of these materials is copper diallyl phthalate.

For SEM or microprobe work, carbon can be vacuum-deposited on the surface or a conductive paint can be applied from the edge of the sample surface to the specimen holder. When used near the edge of a mounted sample, some plastics produce undesirable charging effects, which causes poor secondary electron images or interferes with chemical analysis (see Table 2-5). Charging can be reduced by the choice of mounting plastics, plating of the edge, or vapor deposition of carbon.

Table 2-5 Energy-dispersive analysis of common mounting materials†

Mounting material	Al	Si	Ca	Cl	Ti	Cu	Fe	Others
Thermosetting resins								
Bakelite‡	—	200	375	—	—	—	150	Mn:75
Bakelite‡	—	—	—	—	—	—	—	—
Bakelite‡	320	450	975	—	—	110	—	Pb:610, Cr:225
Diallyl phthalate								
Fiber-filled	710	1450	900	250	300	—	—	—
Mineral-filled	200	425	225	125	—	125	—	Mg:200, Zn:75
Thermoplastic resins								
Methyl methacrylate§	—	—	—	—	—	—	—	—
Thermosetting epoxy								
Plastimet	750	4000	300	—	150	—	—	—
Epomet	—	1600	175	350	—	—	—	—
Struers no. 5	225	475	850	—	—	—	50	—
Acrylics								
Kold Mount§	—	—	—	—	—	—	—	—
Epoxy								
Epoxide§	—	90	—	220	—	70	80	S:225
Conductive mounts								
Cu–diallyl phthalate	—	—	—	—	—	1975	100	—
Al-phenolic	8000	—	—	—	—	—	—	—
Fe-Struers no. 1	—	200	—	—	—	—	2250	—
C-phenolic	90	360	375	80	60	40	60	K:110, S:70

Note: Energy-dispersive analysis does not detect elements lighter than sodium.

†Values are counts in 30 s.

‡Bakelite is highly variable in composition, which is probably due to impurities in the wood flour.

§These materials charge badly under the beam and must be coated with carbon (vacuum deposition).

2-4.9 Special Mounting Techniques

It is not uncommon in metallographic work to encounter difficult mounting problems, and there have been many articles describing methods to solve these problems. Many times, edge retention is also an important goal. Fragile particles, for example, are often coated with epoxy prior to mounting or cutting, a method known as prepotting, which is also often used in the preparation of electronic parts. The epoxy-sandwich technique is useful with thin samples.

The mounting of wire, especially to view the transverse plane, is a common problem. One solution has been to fuse tungsten wire inside thick-walled Pyrex capillary tubing prior to mounting [23]. The tubing is heated until it collapses around the wire, thus developing a tight bond. If heat cannot be tolerated, the wire can be placed inside a capillary tube with an inner diameter slightly larger than the wire, followed by vacuum impregnation with epoxy. Some workers have coiled the wire into a spring which is placed longitudinally in the mold and mounted. After polishing, both longitudinal and transverse orientations can be observed.

Mounting of powders can be accomplished in several ways. Jamison and Byron recommend mixing one part of the powder to three parts transoptic powder [24]. This mixture is distributed evenly over the bottom of the mold, and the balance of the mold is filled with transoptic only. Others have coated the particles first with an adhesive before mounting. Wachtell recommends adding the powder particles to a mixture of one-third amber Bakelite and two-thirds pulverized Bakelite powder [25]. This mixture is placed in the bottom of the mold, followed by Bakelite to the required level. Vacuum-impregnated epoxy resins are also commonly used to mount small particles.

2-4.10 Mount Marking and Storage

After mounting, it is common practice to place identifying information on the back side of the mount. If more than one sample is contained in the mount, the sequence for identification is made with reference to a small bent piece of sheet-metal marker. On the rear of the mount, the identifying codes are placed in the same order. Obviously, only a limited amount of information can be placed on the mount. Such information can include a job number and sample codes plus grade or treatment data, as space permits.

With compression mounting plastics, a vibratory engraving tool is generally used to scratch the information onto the plastic. With castable mounts, an engraving tool can be used or a piece of thin cardboard or a metal tag with the information can be inserted inside the top of the mount, assuming the plastic is reasonably transparent. An indelible ink must be used. Any identifying marks on the back of the sample will be visible.

During preparation or examination, samples are usually stored in a dessicator to minimize surface oxidation. Moisture-absorbing material is usually placed in the bottom of the dessicator. Several types of dessicators are available, ranging from simple canisters to elaborate cabinets or vacuum units. Surfaces can also be coated with clear lacquer for extended preservation. The structure can be viewed through the lacquer, or the lacquer can be removed with acetone.

2-4.11 Summary

Specimen mounting is frequently necessary in the preparation of metallographic samples. A host of mounting materials and techniques are available that can usually fill any need. Each material has inherent advantages and disadvantages. The specific needs of the investigation and the nature of the material being mounted will influence the choice of the mounting material. If the mount is used merely to hold the sample and extreme surface examination is not required, any mounting material will suffice, but the least expensive material or the quickest technique is usually chosen. As the requirements become more restrictive, much more thought must be given to the choice of the material and the procedure used in order to optimize sample preparation and minimize subsequent difficulties. Careful planning prior to mounting pays off.

2-5 GRINDING

Grinding is a very important phase of the sample preparation sequence because damage introduced by sectioning must be removed at this phase. If sectioning produces extensive damage, it is usually better to resection the material in an unaffected area with a gentler cutting method. A cutting burn can be very difficult to remove by grinding. Grinding also produces damage which must be minimized so that subsequent grinding with finer abrasives can remove this damage. At the end of the grinding phase, the only grinding damage present must be from the last grinding step. Severe grinding damage cannot be removed by polishing abrasives.

The surface to be prepared is abraded using a graded sequence of abrasives, starting with a coarse abrasive, often in the range of 60 to 180 mesh and then progressing through to 600 mesh or finer in certain cases. A commonly employed grit sequence uses 120-, 240-, 320-, 400-, and 600-mesh abrasive paper. Initial grit size depends on the surface roughness and the depth of the damage from sectioning. Band-sawed surfaces require the coarsest initial grit sizes, generally 60 to 120 grit. Surfaces cut with the abrasive cutoff saw are smoother and have less damage requiring 120 to 240 grits to start the grinding sequence. Surfaces cut with a wire saw or a low-speed diamond saw can be ground initially with 320- or 400-grit paper.

To minimize heat-generated damage and to maximize grinding-paper life, wet grinding should be used. Wet grinding minimizes metal entrapment between abrasive particles (clogging), and thus the abrasive is more fully exposed to the sample, which promotes cutting rather than smearing or burnishing. Sharp cutting minimizes grinding damage while maximizing the rate of metal removal. Wet grinding cools the sample, reducing frictional heat that might alter the true

Figure 2-14 SiC abrasive (arrows) embedded in polished Ti-6Al-4V (verified by microprobe analysis, 750×).

microstructure. Dry grinding, once quite common, is used in only isolated instances today. Water is the most common coolant and lubricant except with materials that react with water. With these materials kerosene or other liquids are used instead. Wet grinding also removes loose abrasive and cutting debris from the grinding surface, thus minimizing the tendency to embed abrasives in the sample surface. As shown in Fig. 2-14, embedded abrasive can be misinterpreted as nonmetallic inclusions. These particles must be removed during subsequent grinding and polishing steps.

The direction of grinding, with reference to the sample, must not be held constant throughout the grinding sequence. For best results, the direction of grinding should be varied by 45 to 90° between steps. If hand grinding is employed, the operator visually inspects the surface to ensure that scratches from the previous step have been removed completely. Figure 2-15 illustrates grinding and polishing scratches present after each step in the polishing sequence. Automatic polishing devices produce a randomly oriented scratch pattern. The time required for each grinding step is usually quoted as at least twice that required to remove all the scratches from the previous step. This will ensure that deformation from the previous step is also removed. Typically, 1 to 2 min is required for each step for most materials.

The applied pressure must also be controlled for best results. For most materials, a moderately heavy pressure should be firmly and evenly applied. Light pressures produce heating without cutting, while very heavy pressure promotes abrasive embedment and gouging. The correct level of pressure does vary with the material being polished. Automatic devices permit reproducible achievement of specific pressures, thus removing some of the "art" required in hand preparation.

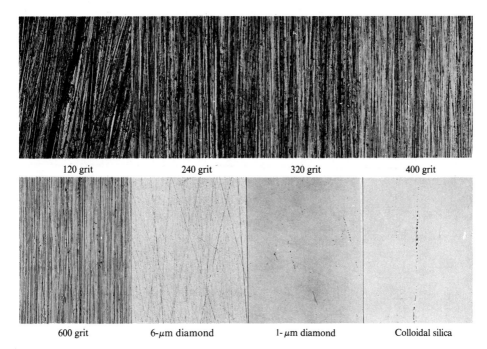

| 120 grit | 240 grit | 320 grit | 400 grit |

| 600 grit | 6-μm diamond | 1-μm diamond | Colloidal silica |

Figure 2-15 Appearance of the surface of austenitic stainless steel at each step of the sample preparation sequence, 90×.

With hand preparation, it is difficult to maintain a uniform pressure. Interrupting grinding to inspect the surface can lead to curvature if the sample is not carefully replaced against the grinding paper. With tall mounts, i.e., those greater than ¾ in high, it is difficult to control the flatness when hand grinding is used.

Between each grinding step the sample surface should be washed briefly under running water and wiped dry for examination. This prevents contamination of the next finer abrasive by loose abrasive from the previous step. With certain samples, it may be necessary to ultrasonically clean the sample between steps, especially if embedment is a problem or the sample is porous. Grinding and polishing wheels can also become contaminated from airborne dust or debris. A clean environment is necessary for good results.

2-5.1 Grinding Media

A variety of grinding media can be employed including silicon carbide, aluminum oxide, emery, diamond, and boron carbide. Graded abrasive is bonded to paper or cloth in a variety of forms, for example, as sheets, belts, or discs of varying size. Alternatively, loose abrasive particles can be applied to a lap for grinding. Each abrasive size and type produces a characteristic scratch and deformation depth.

Figures 2-16*a* and *b* illustrate the appearance of 120- to 600-grit silicon carbide abrasive paper.

Silicon carbide (SiC) is the most popular abrasive because of its very high hardness (Mohs 9.5), reasonable cost, and excellent cutting characteristics. As shown in Table 2-1, the depth of damage after grinding with SiC is less than that produced by emery paper. Scratch depth varies directly with grit size.

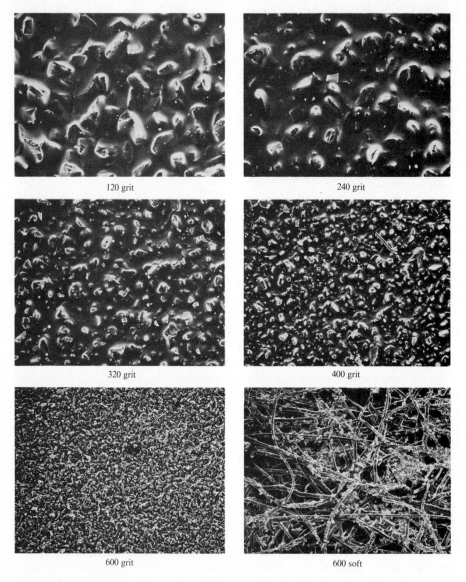

120 grit

240 grit

320 grit

400 grit

600 grit

600 soft

Figure 2-16*a* Appearance of the surface of silicon carbide grinding paper (Buehler Carbimet), 60×.

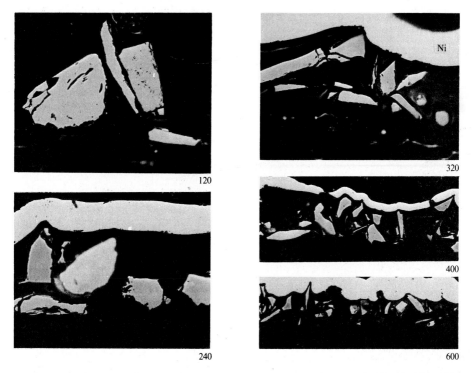

Figure 2-16b Cross-sectional views of silicon carbide grinding paper (Buehler Carbimet). All but 120-grit paper were coated with electroless nickel (white layers), 250×.

Aluminum oxide (Al_2O_3, corundum) waterproof abrasive papers are also made but are not as readily available as SiC. The hardness of alumina (Mohs 9.1) is not quite as great as SiC, but the alumina papers behave in a similiar fashion. Abrasive embedment occurs to some degree with all samples but is in general only a serious problem with soft materials. Thus with soft materials, alumina abrasive paper is preferred to SiC or emery. Abrasive embedment is usually a greater problem with the finer abrasive grades than with the coarser grades. The fine SiC particles often have a needlelike shape rather than a granular shape. Dry grinding promotes abrasive embedment. If embedment occurs with wet grinding, use of a liquid soap or kerosene will reduce the problem but a solid lubricant, such as paraffin wax, is more effective.

Emery is a mixture of aluminum oxide and iron oxide, with a hardness (Mohs 8.0) substantially lower than SiC or alumina. Emery paper of equivalent mesh size feels smoother than other papers because emery particles have smoother surfaces. These smoother surfaces produce much lower cutting rates. Embedment problems are more common with emery than with SiC. Emery papers cannot be lubricated with water, a serious disadvantage. Historically, emery paper was once quite widely used but has been largely replaced with SiC.

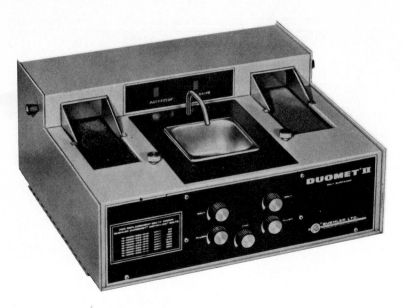

Figure 2-17 The Buehler Duomet II belt surfacer for coarse grinding. *(Courtesy of Buehler Ltd.)*

2-5.2 Equipment

Grinding is often classified as coarse (up to 150-mesh grit size) or fine (180- to 600-mesh grit size). Coarse grinding is generally performed on belt or disc grinders (see Fig. 2-17). Surface grinders employing grinding wheels are also used. For field work, spot grinders are used for grinding and polishing.

Most metallographers prefer to grind samples using mechanically driven grinding paper, 8 to 12 in in diameter, mounted on motor-driven grinder and polisher wheels. These wheels are mounted flush on a table, as illustrated in Fig. 2-18, or on a laboratory bench. In general, a separate wheel is used for each paper grade. Wheels are made of bronze, aluminum, cast iron, copper, lead, or stainless steel. Bronze wheels are most commonly used and can be obtained with a glass facing for grinding semiconductors, where extreme flatness is required.

The grinding paper can be held in place using a tight metal ring around the lap head. Wetting the lap head with water under the paper produces suction and better holding. Alternatively, adhesive-backed paper may be used, but this is generally not required for hand grinding. During use, water is directed onto the disc surface. If the flow rate is too high, the ring can lift up and the paper will stall under the sample. During grinding, the sample is held flat against the disc surface with moderately high pressure and moved slowly from center to edge. If the applied pressure is too high, the grinding paper will not rotate unless adhesive-backed paper is used. Therefore, holding the grinding paper by a ring will prevent application of excessive pressure.

For most work, a rotation speed of 300 to 600 r/min is recommended. Most motor-driven wheels are equipped with two speeds; either low- or high-speed

Figure 2-18 Example of a commercially available polishing table equipped with two 8-in wheels and a sink. *(Courtesy of Leco Corp.)*

wheels can be obtained that cover the range from about 50 to 1200 r/min. Polishing wheels with variable speeds are available from all manufacturers.

Automatic grinding and polishing devices have become very popular, since they reduce much of the tedium associated with sample preparation; produce better edge retention, flatness, and inclusion or graphite retention, require less operator skill, and give better reproducibility. A wide variety of devices are available for attachment to standard grinding and polishing wheels, as illustrated in Fig. 2-19. These devices require standard-size mounted samples. A different

Figure 2-19 Leco VP-50 variable-speed polishing wheel with AP-50 automatic variable-load polishing attachment. *(Courtesy of Leco Corp.)*

Figure 2-20 The Struers Abraplan automatic grinder (left) and Abrapol automatic polisher (right). *(Courtesy of Struers, Inc.)*

approach is provided by the Buehler Minimet, a single-sample automatic grinder and polisher. This device uses mounted samples, with a hole drilled in the back for sample manipulation.

Recently, large self-contained automatic grinding and polishing machines have been developed (see Fig. 2-20). Excellent results can be obtained with these devices by an unskilled operator after a short training period. Most of the micrographs shown in this text were prepared on one of these devices. Because of their high price, only labs with a relatively high sample load can justify their initial cost. However, experience with these units has shown that they do produce a high production rate with exceptional results and a lower consumable cost per sample.

2-5.3 Lapping

Lapping is a technique for preparing surfaces using a disc surface impregnated with a loose abrasive. Laps have been made from wood, Micarta, lead, cast iron, paper, leather, paraffin wax, nylon, or other plastics. Some of these materials are backed by a metal disc. Generally, the lap surface is grooved, often in a spiral pattern counter to the direction of rotation. The abrasive can be pressed into the lap surface or charged as a liquid suspension during lapping.

The sample, if hand held, is placed against the lap surface and rotated in a circular pattern in a direction counter to the rotation direction. Lapping produces finer scratches than disc grinding with the same abrasive type and size, but the surface is generally dull rather than bright. Lapping is noted for producing excellent flat surfaces and good inclusion or graphite retention. The disadvantages are that laps require considerable attention for good results and must be occasionally reground to keep the surface flat.

2-6 POLISHING

After being ground to a 600-grit finish, the sample is polished to produce a flat, reasonably scratch-free surface with high reflectivity, as illustrated in Fig. 2-15. A totally scratch-free surface is not necessary for routine examination; however, any scratches present should be very fine and well dispersed so that the true structure can be observed. If photomicrographs are to be taken, scratches should be eliminated. Very fine scratches can be suppressed if darkroom photographic techniques are employed. Use of staining etchants and examination with anodizing or polarized light require a very high-quality surface and total freedom from scratches. Other artifacts, such as "comet tailing," pitting, pullout, and staining, must be prevented.

Polishing is also classified as coarse or fine. Coarse polishing uses abrasives in the range of 30 to 3 μm, while fine polishing uses abrasives 1 μm and smaller. Rough polishing involves one or more abrasive steps and low-nap or napless cloths. Fine polishing also uses one or more abrasive sizes and employs low-, medium-, or high-nap cloths.

Polishing should be performed in a dust-free environment separated from the sample cutting and grinding areas, since airborne contaminants cannot be tolerated. Cleaning between polishing stages is more critical than between grinding stages because carryover is a bigger problem. Carryover can also be caused by abrasive on the operator's hands; thus, both the sample and the operator's hands should be washed between steps. If automatic devices are used, the fixture must also be washed. The mount or fixture can be held under running water and swabbed with cotton, followed by similar treatment with alcohol. With porous samples or when gaps are present between the sample and the mount, ultrasonic cleaning should be used. Careful cleaning is important if good results are to be obtained and cannot be overemphasized.

As with grinding, the sample orientation should not be held constant, but the problem is even more acute. On a given wheel, the sample orientation must be continuously changed if comet tailing is to be avoided. For hand polishing, the sample is held firmly against the wheel using moderately high pressure and rotated counter to the direction of wheel rotation while moving the sample in a track from center to edge. This practice will prevent comet tailing. Hand polishing is preferred by many metallographers, especially for the final polishing step, however, automatic polishing devices produce excellent results. Generally, the pressure is moderately heavy during the initial polishing period and is gradually reduced toward the end. Some prefer to conclude polishing with the wheel stationary, using a figure eight or circular motion. Final-polishing abrasives are usually mixed as water slurries that are added intermittently during polishing. Coarse polishing employs diamond paste or coarse alumina. Diamond paste or diamond aerosol sprays are used along with a lubricant (extender).

Rough polishing is generally performed at 150 to 600 r/min using 6-μm diamond, or if two steps are required, 9- and 3-μm diamond. Fine polishing uses 1-μm diamond (optional), followed by 0.3- and 0.05-μm alumina slurries. Occasionally, ¼-μm diamond is also employed. For routine examination, a 1-μm diamond finish is often adequate for most samples, particularly hard steels. A commonly employed polishing sequence is 6-μm diamond and 0.3- and 0.05-μm alumina. Other final polishing abrasives can also be used.

Diamond particles have been added most frequently as a paste that is obtained in a syringe in which the paste is a color-coded carrier for the diamond. To charge a new cloth, several strips are applied to the cloth and worked into the cloth with a clear sample or dummy mount or with the fingertips (cleaned first). Liquid extender, either water-soluble or oil-soluble, is squirted or sprayed on the cloth. The cloth should be moistened lightly by the extender. If the cloth is allowed to dry out, lower polishing rates and surface tearing or pullout can occur. Excessive diamond extender can result in loss of diamond as well as a messy operation due to splatter. Some workers have used purified, odorless kerosene as the lubricant. Samuels recommends using a mixture of distilled water and propylene glycol [3]. Prepared extenders can be purchased from commercial suppliers.

The other polishing abrasives are usually applied as water slurries or thick pastes (skid polishing). A typical slurry consists of 1 part abrasive to 10 parts distilled water. The polishing rate of alumina slurries decreases markedly as the pH increases [3]. A pH of 6 to 7 is best to prevent staining. Liquid soaps or detergents are sometimes added to the slurry, but the polishing rate may be reduced. Samuels recommends a one-to-one mixture of soft soap made from coconut oil and water, which improves the polishing rate.

Magnesium oxide (MgO) abrasive is used somewhat differently. The powder is usually added dry to the polishing cloth and then wet with water, producing a thick slurry. Magnesia usage is complicated by formation of carbonates, which will produce scratches. Samuels recommends using propylene glycol to prevent carbonation [3].

Many workers have recommended the use of alternate polishing and etching to remove surface cold-work damage. After final polishing, the sample is etched with a standard etchant and then repolished to remove all traces of the etchant. Repetition of this cycle several times is often recommended. This procedure is generally ineffective for removal of artifacts, since the depth of metal that can be removed by an etch-polish cycle is very small. Also, this practice usually produces relief and loss of edge retention. If artifacts are present, it is better to go back to the rough polishing stage, or farther back if the artifacts are severe.

In a two-phase structure where one phase is somewhat harder, microstructural details can often be observed in the as-polished condition because of relief between the phases. The softer phase polishes more readily than the harder phase, producing depressions and elevations. One can easily determine the relative hardnesses of the phases in this manner. A controlled amount of relief can be useful for examination with differential interference contrast illumination (DIC).

2-6.1 Equipment

Motor-driven wheels, such as those illustrated in Fig. 2-18, or automatic devices such as those shown in Figs. 2-19 and 2-20, can be used for polishing. Lower speeds are usually employed for polishing, typically 50 to 300 r/min, although high-speed (1750 r/min), 4-in diameter wheels have been used for certain metals. Automatic polishing devices are widely used, since they produce excellent flatness and freedom from comet tailing. Several special-purpose devices are available and have proved to be very useful for difficult-to-polish materials.

Vibratory polishing, using the Buehler Vibromet or the FMC Syntron devices (see Fig. 2-21), is an effective final polishing technique that is widely used with metals that are difficult to polish. Vibrations in both the vertical and horizontal directions are produced either by motor-driven eccentric weights (Vibromet) or by electromagnetic forces (Syntron). Samples are placed in weights and then placed face down on the cloth. Inertia from the sample weight produces movement over the cloth and, thus, polishing. The vibrations induce the sample to move about its axis and around the cloth periphery. The vibration amplitude is

Figure 2-21 Syntron vibratory polishers. *(Courtesy of R. S. Crouse, Oak Ridge National Laboratory.)*

adjusted to a level just adequate to produce smooth movement around the bowl. Because the polishing rate is low, several hours may be required, and the method is generally limited to final polishing. Samuels has developed recommended procedures, some involving attack polishing, for a number of metals [3].

2-6.2 Polishing Cloths

The polishing cloth must be able to hold the abrasive against the sample and should not contain any foreign matter that will scratch the sample or dye that will react with the sample. Long life and low cost are practical advantages. Many different fabrics have been used. Historically, cloths were always stretched over the polishing wheel and held in place with a clamp. More recently, some of the more popular cloths have become available with adhesive backing and are quite popular. Changing cloths is much simpler with adhesive-backed cloths, and the risk of ripping a cloth is reduced.

For rough polishing, low-nap or napless cloths are preferred in order to produce maximum abrasive contact, high cutting rates, and low relief. Commonly employed rough polishing cloths include canvas, nylon, silk, or a chemotextile synthetic mixture of rayon and nylon known as Texmet or Pellon. Wheel speeds of 150 to 600 r/min are usually employed.

For fine polishing, either low-, medium-, or high-nap cloths are used. Low-nap cloths are employed where little relief can be tolerated. Medium-nap cloths provide better control of scratching without excessive relief problems and are widely used. The most popular type consists of densely packed, vertical synthetic fibers. Variations of this type include Microcloth (Buehler), Astromet (Precision Scientific), NAP (Struers), and Finale (Jarrett-Scan Dia).

Commonly used polishing cloths were examined in the SEM to illustrate similarities and differences [26] (see Fig. 2-22). The following list describes the more common cloths.

Canvas. Generally 10-oz duck, recommended for rough polishing with coarse Al_2O_3, SiC, or diamond abrasives. It exhibits a loosely woven pattern with numerous free ends.

Nylon. A napless satin weave pattern with a dense, controlled weave recommended for coarse diamond polishing. Each yarn has a controlled diameter, about 100 to 125 μm, and is composed of numerous fine strands. The weave pattern is complex and appears different on each side.

Silk. A napless, pure Japanese silk with a controlled simple weave pattern recommended for coarse diamond polishing and slurry or skid polishing with alumina. Note that the pattern is more open than nylon.

Texmet or *Pellon.* A synthetic, napless chemotextile mixture of rayon and nylon used for rough diamond polishing. Produces good edges, inclusion, and graphite retention. Note the distinct appearance of these cloths.

Billiard. A medium-nap, 21-oz 100 percent virgin wool cloth with a uniformly sheared pile recommended for rough polishing of steels using alumina or other abrasives.

Red felt. A medium-nap, tightly woven 100 percent virgin wool fabric with plucked pile used for the same applications as billiard cloth but gives longer life. Note the very loose, long, tangled fibers.

Selvyt. A medium-nap cotton cloth recommended for rough and final polishing of metals and ceramics using alumina, chromic oxide, or cerium oxide abrasives. Exhibits a rapid wear rate with coarse abrasives, but its softness is beneficial with fine abrasives. Note the very loose, tangled appearance of the fibers.

Synthetic suedes. Medium-nap cloths consisting of rayon or nylon fibers bonded to a cloth or polymer backing. Very popular cloths used for rough and fine polishing with any abrasive. Note the long thin, vertically aligned fibers which may be fluted or smooth. Examples include Microcloth, Glenco, NAP, Astromet, Gamal, and Finale.

Kitten Ear. A high-nap, all-wool broadcloth used for final polishing. Its softness produces high-quality surfaces with fine abrasives, but relief can develop. The fiber pattern is similar to red felt.

Velvet. A high-nap synthetic cloth (Rayvel) consisting of long, smooth vertical fibers. Used for final polishing of soft metals where its softness helps produce deformation-free, scratch-free surfaces. Good for slurry and skid polishing.

Chemomet. A synthetic, napless, microporous, chemically resistant cloth recommended for attack polishing where acid attack deteriorates most other cloths.

The polishing cloth supports the abrasive against the sample and must also contain the abrasive so that the abrasive it not rapidly thrown from the wheel. The weave or nap traps the abrasive. The weave pattern in napless cloths, the nap texture, the fiber length and density, and the resilience of the cloth are important factors that influence cloth performance.

2-6.3 Polishing Abrasives

A number of abrasives have been used in metallography, but the introduction of diamond abrasives in the later 1940s was an improvement of tremendous value. Diamond abrasives are the most widely used rough polishing abrasive, with the other abrasives primarily relegated to fine polishing.

Alumina abrasives e.g., Linde A, B, or C, are the most commonly used fine polishing abrasive. Aluminum oxide can be produced by a variety of techniques [27] and is available for polishing as a powder or premixed suspension in particle sizes of 5-, 1-, 0.3- and 0.05-μm (other sizes are also available). The finest nominal particle size, gamma alumina (γ-Al_2O_3), is softer (Mohs 8.0) than the others (Mohs 9.0), which are alpha alumina (α-Al_2O_3). Gamma alumina has a cubic crystal structure, while alpha alumina is hexagonal. Diamond abrasives have largely replaced use of the coarser aluminas for polishing; thus, Linde A (0.3 μm) and Linde B (0.05 μm) are the most commonly used alumina abrasives.

Nylon

Silk

Canvas

Metcloth

Texmet

Chemomet

Figure 2-22 Appearance of commonly used polishing cloths (Buehler Ltd. cloths shown), $60 \times$.

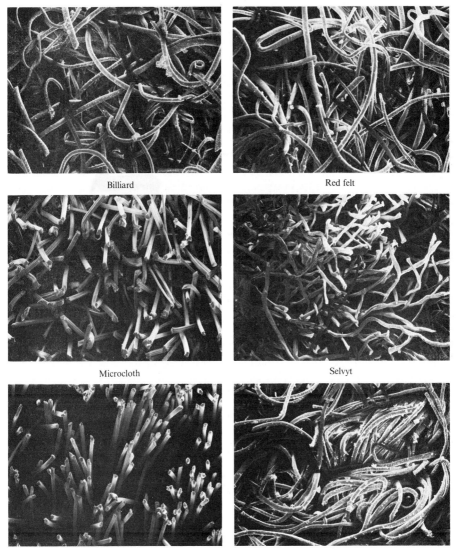

Billiard

Red felt

Microcloth

Selvyt

Rayvel

Kitten Ear

Magnesium oxide is a general-purpose abrasive, but because of the difficulties encountered, it is usually used only for final polishing of aluminum and magnesium alloys. The powder is moistened with water to produce a thick slurry. This slurry, however, has a limited life because the moist MgO carbonates in air and the magnesium carbonate produced causes scratching. The polishing cloth must be washed before and after use and should be treated with and stored in a 2% aqueous HCl solution. Because of this problem, many metallographers prefer to avoid use of magnesia.

Iron oxide (Fe_2O_3), also known as red rouge, or jeweler's rouge, is available in a 3-μm particle size and has been used for rough polishing of steels and cast irons. Chromic oxide (Cr_2O_3) is available in 1-μm and 0.05-μm particle sizes and has been used for rough and final polishing of iron and steel. Cerium oxide (CeO) is available in a 1-μm particle size and has been used for final polishing of low-melting-point metals, soft metals and materials, aluminum, and copper. Mixtures of cerium oxide, alpha alumina, and chromium oxide (C-RO and CER-CRO) and cerium oxide, alpha alumina, and iron oxide (Final-Pol) have been found to be useful final polishing abrasives for many metals [28].

A colloidal suspension of 0.04-μm silicon dioxide developed by Monsanto, known as Syton or Final, is a highly effective final polishing abrasive. This abrasive was used for the final polishing of many of the samples shown in this book. Its use is simple as long as a few precautions are taken. The usual polishing sequence has been automatic polishing with 3-μm diamond on canvas and 1-μm diamond on a synthetic medium-nap cloth, followed by hand polishing for 30 to 60 s with the colloidal SiO_2 solution on a synthetic medium-nap cloth attached to a glass plate. The colloidal silica is excellent for removal of fine diamond scratches and associated deformation damage, producing clear, crisp microstructures. Attack polishing agents can also be employed as needed. The cloth is rinsed after use to prevent crystallization of the abrasive with drying, which will produce scratches when the cloth is used again. If the polishing solution is permitted to freeze, it will be useless. Before the polishing solution is added to a moistened cloth, the top of the container should be wiped to remove any precipitates that might fall on the cloth.

Introduction of diamond abrasives for rough polishing was a highly significant development. Because of the extreme hardness of diamond, it is not only indispensable for preparation of hard metals, carbides, and ceramics but it is also beneficial for softer metals and materials. Only a few materials should not be polished with diamond paste. The polishing rates with diamond abrasives, even when the particle size is small, are equal to or better than other abrasives used for rough polishing. Use of small abrasive sizes is always beneficial because the scratch and deformation depth is reduced. Results with diamond polishing are usually superior in comparisons of surface appearance; edge, graphite, and inclusion retention; and relief control. On the negative side, diamond abrasives are expensive, but most metallographers have found that their cost is justified by the superior results and savings in time.

Diamond can be obtained as a powder in a variety of sizes, but most users prefer to purchase diamond abrasives (90 to $\frac{1}{10}$ μm) as a dispersion in a carrier paste or as an aerosol. The amount of diamond on the cloth is actually rather small considering the high polishing rates obtained. Increasing the amount of diamond on the cloth does not increase the polishing rate [3] except in the case of the use of very coarse diamond for grinding. Quite a few samples can be polished with a single charging before the polishing rate falls significantly. Although polishing debris does build up in the cloth during use, it will not affect the polishing of subsequent samples. Samuels has shown that 6-μm (4- to 8-μm range) diamond produces the highest polishing rate on most materials [3]. Polishing rates of finer diamond sizes, down to the 1-μm range, are slightly lower. Table 2-6 lists polishing rates for a number of metals polished with 6-μm diamond [3].

Mayburg developed an analytical procedure for determining optimum polishing abrasive sizes for minimizing polishing times [29]. It is assumed that the rate of material removal is αS, where S is the size of the abrasive and α is a constant with

Table 2-6 Comparative polishing rates of a number of common metals and alloys

| | Specimen | | | |
Alloy	Condition	Melting range, °C	Hardness, HV	Polishing rate, μm/min
Sb–Sn–Pb eutectic	As-cast	95	11	24
Tin	Annealed	231	9	9
Cadmium	Annealed	321	22	14
Lead	Annealed	327	5	7
Zinc	Annealed	421	50	12
Magnesium	Annealed	650	40	16
Aluminum alloy	Heat treated	580–650	105	13
Aluminum alloy	Annealed	580–610	40	8
Aluminum	Annealed	660	25	9
Brass (40% Zn)	Annealed	900–905	155	15
Brass (30% Zn)	Annealed	915–955	95	14
Silver	Annealed	960	30	12
Copper	Annealed	1083	45	11
Austenitic steel (18% Cr, 8% Ni)	Annealed	1400–1425	170	3
B.S. 970:En9 Steel	Annealed	1425–1450	250	1.2
B.S. 970:En9 Steel	Hardened	1425–1450	800	1.1
B.S. 970:En2A Steel	Annealed	1450–1500	150	1.2
Nickel	Annealed	1452	125	0.3
Titanium	Annealed	1725	275	0.1

Note: Specimens (½ in diameter) polished by hand on a wheel rotating at 250 r/min, covered with a napped synthetic-suede cloth and charged with 4–8-μm diamond abrasive.

Source: From Samuels, Ref. 3.

respect to S whose value depends on the nature of the abrasive and applied pressure. The value of α is assumed to be constant throughout the polishing process. Polishing commences after grinding which produces a surface of roughness S_0 with an abrasive size S_1. Abrasive S_1 removes a depth of at least S_0 in time t_1, that is,

$$S_0 = \alpha S_1 t_1 \tag{2-1}$$

The next polishing step converts the surface with a roughness $\leq S_1$ to one with a roughness $\leq S_2$, thus,

$$S_1 = \alpha S_2 t_2 \tag{2-2}$$

This process is repeated to the final step S_f where

$$S_{f-1} = \alpha S_f t_f \tag{2-3}$$

The total polishing time T is the sum of the individual steps. For minimum T,

$$S_n^2 = (S_{n-1})(S_{n+1}) \tag{2-4}$$

or

$$\frac{S_{n-1}}{S_n} = \frac{S_n}{S_{n+1}} \tag{2-5}$$

or

$$t_n = t_{n+1} \equiv t \tag{2-6}$$

This suggests that the polishing time for each step t should be equal to minimize the total time T; that is,

$$T = ft \tag{2-7}$$

T can be calculated from:

$$T = \frac{1}{\alpha} f \left(\frac{S_0}{S_f} \right)^{1/f} \tag{2-8}$$

The minimum number of steps f_{min} is given by:

$$f_{min} = \ln \frac{S_0}{S_f} \tag{2-9}$$

and for this number of steps,

$$T = \frac{f_{min} e}{\alpha} \quad (e = 2.72) \tag{2-10}$$

Thus, the optimum number of steps is dependent on the initial surface roughness S_0 and the finest available abrasive S_f for the final step.

For example, assume that a sample has been ground through 600-grit SiC paper (about 30-μm size) and will be polished to 1-μm diamond. The initial surface roughness S_0 can be estimated in several ways. The most conservative approach is to simply use the grit size of 600-grit SiC paper. The number of steps is calculated using Eq. (2-9).

$$f_{min} = \ln\frac{30}{1} = 3.4 \qquad \text{or 3 polishing steps}$$

According to Samuels [3] the polishing rate α of steel with 6-μm diamond is about 1.2 μm/min (see Table 2-6). Thus, the total polishing time T for a steel sample can be calculated using Eq. (2-10).

$$T = \frac{(3)(2.72)}{1.2} = 6.8 \text{ min}$$

The polishing rate is thus about 2¼ min for each step. Equations for the first (S_1) and second (S_2) diamond abrasive sizes ($S_f = 1$ μm) can be calculated as:

$$S_1 = (S_0^2 S_f)^{1/3} = [(30^2)(1)]^{1/3} = 9.4 \ \mu\text{m}$$
$$S_2 = (S_0 S_f^2)^{1/3} = [(30)(1^2)]^{1/3} = 3.1 \ \mu\text{m}$$

Thus, the analysis suggests that optimum polishing is achieved with 9-, 3-, and 1-μm diamond for 2¼ min each.

If we desire to use only two diamond polishing steps, the last with 1 μm, T can be calculated using Eq. (2-8).

$$T = \frac{(2)(30/1)^{1/2}}{1.2} = 9.1 \text{ min}$$

The polishing time is thus about 4.5 min for each step. The initial abrasive size S_1, which is calculated using Eq. (2-4), is 5.5 μm. Thus, the analysis suggests polishing with 6- and 1-μm diamond paste for 4.5 min each.

The initial choice of S_0 was rather conservative, based on the measurements of Samuels [3]. Rather than using the size of 600-grit SiC paper for S_0, we could substitute measurements of the total damage depth produced by 600-grit paper. If we found that the total depth of damage was 20 μm, for example, we would again obtain three steps as the optimum sequence and a total polishing time of 6.8 min, as before. Calculations for S_1 and S_2 produce values of 7.4- and 2.7-μm abrasive sizes. Therefore, the only difference would be choice of either 9-μm diamond or 6-μm diamond for the first step. If we found that the total depth of damage was either 10 or 5 μm, calculation shows that only two diamond abrasives are required, with 2¼ min for each. Calculation of S_1 in either instance suggests 3-μm diamond for the initial stage. With a total damage depth of only 2.5 μm, only one diamond step, 1 μm, is required and again the time required is 2¼ min. Thus, if we can determine the total depth of damage after 600-grit SiC grinding and we know the diamond polishing metal removal rate, realistic, useful estimates can be made for the polishing sequence for optimum results.

Buchheit and McCall studied 39 different diamond polishing compounds with sizes ranging from ¼ to 15 μm and investigated factors that influence polishing results [30]. The diamonds in the pastes were either natural, synthetic, or reclaimed. Carriers were water-soluble, oil-soluble, or soluble in both water and oil. Diamond concentrations, reported as light to heavy, ranged from less than

5 wt % to greater than 24 wt %. Particle sizing during manufacture is done by separation procedures, but Buchheit and McCall made actual TEM and SEM measurements of the longest dimension. Their procedure produced greater measurement values, as might be expected, but related better to metallographic performance. A few large sliver (needle or rodlike shape with axial ratios greater than 3:1) particles were found in many of the compounds. The study showed that particle shape was only one of several important characteristics.

Buchheit and McCall studied the polishing characteristics of each compound under controlled conditions and found a wide range of performance [30]. As the diamond concentration in the paste increased, polishing results, based on surface roughness, improved but further increases in concentration produced poorer results, suggesting an optimum concentration for the conditions tested. Diamond shape before and after polishing was essentially identical, indicating that other factors must be responsible for the degradation of polishing performance with time.

McCall and Mantaring evaluated the influence of wheel speed on the metal removal rate (weight loss) as a function of polishing time using 6-μm diamond paste and all other variables fixed [31]. The maximum polishing rate was obtained with a speed of 200 r/min, while the minimum rate was obtained at 510 r/min. As wheel speed was increased from 48 to 200 r/min, the polishing rate increased. The polishing rate also increased as the wheel speed increased from 510 to 1200 r/min, but it decreased as the wheel speed increased from 200 to 510 r/min.

Exner and Kuhn evaluated diamond polishing variables by measuring depth removal using Vickers hardness (HV) impressions [32]. Their study showed that the polishing rate is improved by frequent additions of small amounts of paste compared to one-time charging. With low-nap or napless cloths, the removal rate increased with increasing particle size, while with medium- and high-nap cloths, the maximum polishing rate was obtained with 7-μm diamond. The type of diamond, natural or synthetic, and the diamond shape did not significantly alter the polishing rate. They observed that increases in diamond concentration had only a minor influence on the polishing rate. Increasing the applied pressure increased the polishing rate but the effect was greater for coarse diamond and hard cloths than for fine diamond and soft cloths. Greater pressure, however, did increase the depth of scratches and deformations. The amount of material removed in a given operation was greater for a soft metal than for a hard metal. For example, their work showed that the amount of metal removed from a steel at 200 HV hardness was twice that of a hard metal at 1740 HV.

2-7 GRINDING AND POLISHING THEORY

Our current understanding of the mechanisms of grinding and polishing stems from the work of Beilby. Although Beilby's ideas have been shown to be incorrect, many metallographers are still influenced by his concept of polishing. Beilby's polishing theory stemmed from his study of the influence of etchants on "polished" surfaces. Beilby observed that etching of a surface that appeared to be polished smooth resulted in reappearance of the polishing scratches. Beilby assumed that polishing had smeared materials from high spots over the depressions, bridging them with a thin, smooth skin. The etchant removed this skin, revealing the original depressions associated with grinding scratches. Beilby assumed that the skin produced was amorphous rather than crystalline.

Electron diffraction experiments in the early 1930s revealed that the diffraction rings became more diffuse as the surface was polished. This evidence was claimed as proof for the amorphous metal theory of Beilby, but subsequent workers claimed that these results proved nothing. Most of the polished surfaces examined in these early studies were prepared by burnishing processes rather than by acceptable metallographic methods. While the thickness of the "Beilby layer" was estimated as 5 to 10 nm, the depth of the scratches that this layer was supposed to fill is several orders of magnitude greater.

Beilby's theory was further developed by Bowden and Hughes, who suggested that local surface areas can be heated to their melting points during polishing [33]. They claimed that surface flow, polish, and Beilby-layer formation readily occur on metals, crystals, and glasses as long as the melting point of the abrasive is greater than that of the sample being polished. The relative hardnesses at room temperature were unimportant. Metallographic polishing does not produce surface melting, but the extreme surface layers can reach high temperatures. If the extreme temperatures suggested by Bowden and Hughes was obtained, evidence of this heat would be present, but it is not.

Bowden and Hughes suggested that if the abrasion theory of polishing, which was developed by Newton (1730), Herschel (1830), and Rayleigh (1901), were correct, a polishing abrasive should be able to polish any solid softer than itself. Bowden and Hughes showed that relative differences in hardness at room temperature could not explain polishing behavior. For example, they showed that camphor would polish Wood's metal but not tin, which was softer. They claimed that the ability to polish depended on differences in melting points. This correlation did not hold for materials with a high melting point. Subsequent studies have shown that the ability of an abrasive to polish depends on the relative hardness of the materials at the temperature developed at the surface, which, of course, implies that abrasion occurs.

Mulhearn and Samuels studied the abrasive grinding process by combining theoretical modeling with comparisons to experimental results obtained using silicon carbide papers and abrading metals with a low rate of work hardening [34]. Examination of unused abrasive papers revealed that most of the abrasive particles in the coarser grades (280 mesh or coarser) were roughly equiaxed. With the finer paper grades, particularly 400 and 600 grit, a higher portion of the particles were acicular. Most abrasive particles were almost completely buried in the resin support, although some projected well above the resin (see Fig. 2-16). With the finer grades, a higher proportion of the abrasive protruded above the resin. Grinding debris was in general much finer than the abrasive.

Their theoretical analysis was tested against experimental data using controlled conditions and a range of SiC papers. The number of likely contact particles per unit area for each paper grade was measured by direct observation and by a sectioning method. They found that the density of contacting particles increased substantially with decreasing grit size and also increased with usage, with greater gains for the coarser grits. Examination of cross sections of abrasive papers revealed that the most common contact angle was about 75°. The critical contact angle for cutting was found to be $90°\pm2°$ for the material ground (steel). Measurements were made of the proportion of the particles with attack angles equal to or greater than the critical angle on unused and used paper of different grit sizes. Their results showed that cutting is performed by a relatively small fraction of the particles. Although the number of contacting particles increases with use, the proportion that cut is lower.

Grinding with abrasives produces two types of scratches. The first type is responsible for metal removal and is the result of the favorable contact angles. The second type of scratch does not produce metal removal; it produces ploughing and is responsible for most of the deformation associated with grinding.

Samuel's work on grinding revealed a complex deformation pattern [3]. His work has shown that there is a thin outer fragmented layer where the crystal structure has been broken into many small crystalline subgrains which cohere with each other. The appearance of this zone is consistent with severe plastic deformation, which produces the compressive textures seen in heavy cold rolling. Beneath this layer, the metal deformation is minor but not uniform, being concentrated in bands or rays beneath the surface scratches [3]. Scratch depth and damage depths decrease with decreasing abrasive size. Thus, the grinding and polishing sequence must be carefully controlled to remove the deformation from each prior step. This is complicated by the decrease in abrasion and polishing rates seen, in general, with decreasing grit size. The importance of the excellent polishing rate of diamond abrasives for removing the last remnants of grinding damage is obvious.

Samuels has shown that grinding and polishing produce the same basic phenomena, i.e., production of scratches or grooves, metal removal, and production of a plastically deformed layer [3]. The difference between grinding and polishing is merely the extent of producing these three features. Samuels concluded that the same mechanism operates during grinding and polishing. Therefore, the preceding discussion on the nature of grinding applies also to polishing. The load applied to a polishing abrasive of a particular size establishes the depth and width of scratches, while the attack angle determines whether cutting or ploughing results. The load applied to polishing abrasives is lower than that applied to grinding abrasives, and the particles are smaller; therefore, scratches are shallow and narrow and damage depths are low.

The main difference between polishing and grinding resides in the manner in which the abrasive particles are supported. Samuels has suggested that the abrasive tumbles upon contact with the sample, producing ploughing [3]. After some movement, the particles become embedded in the cloth fibers where the particles either cut or rub the surface depending on the attack angle. The elasticity of the cloth fibers holds the abrasive against the sample. Thus, in polishing, the abrasives are not rigidly held in place and contact pressures are much lower than in grinding. Dynamic observation of diamond polishing by Richardson and Brose [35] confirmed this theory. Examination of used cloths by Richardson et al. revealed extensive abrasion of the polishing cloth (nylon) fibers in diamond polishing, indicating considerable movement between the cloth fibers and the abrasive [26].

The mechanical aspects of the polishing mechanism has been shown by Aghan and Samuels to be relevant to all polishing abrasives regardless of their size [36]. However, there are some polishing situations where the liquid suspension or an etchant added to the slurry contribute significantly to the polishing action, producing greater metal removal. Samuels concluded that the abrasive acts to wipe away protective films that form on the surface and referred to this action as a "wiping-chemical polishing" mechanism [3]. Polishing produces plastically deformed surface layers, similar to those produced by grinding, but the depths are much lower [3]. As in grinding, the deformation is not uniform but is concentrated under the scratches and is responsible for the reappearance and apparent enlargement of polishing scratches after etching.

2-8 ELECTROMECHANICAL POLISHING

Electromechanical polishing, which was developed by Reinacher [37], combines electrolytic etching and mechanical polishing to produce high-quality polished surfaces. Variants of the method include electrolytic lapping and electrovibratory polishing. A suitable electrolyte mixed with an abrasive, generally alumina, is placed in a plastic bowl attached to the polishing wheel. The polishing cloth must have adequate resistance to the electrolyte. Electric contact must be made to the sample. The cloth is attached to a cathode made from a stainless steel plate with an outer lip to contain the polishing solution. The specimen is the anode in normal polarity operation but can be the cathode in reverse polarity operation. In some cases, the polarity is reversed every 1 to 5 s (cyclic polarity). Appendix E lists electrolytes recommended in the literature; other electrolytes are given in the manual for the Struers Relapol. The current density required may need to be found by experimentation. If the center is etched while the edge is polished, the current density is too low. The reverse situation indicates too high a current density, or excessive, uneven etching may also be observed.

Many metals can be polished with this method, although it is most frequently reserved for polishing copper, precious metals, or refractory metals. To use the method, the sample is held against the rotating cloth, generally at low speeds, and moved slightly. With some metals, abrasive is not required, but the polishing action is improved by adding a fine abrasive, usually alumina. In most work, direct current is used, but ac has also been employed. In general, dc is used with noble metals, and cyclic polarity reversal is frequently used for refractory metals. The most commonly used device is the Struers Relapol, but an electromechanical polishing device has recently been introduced for the Buehler Minimet.

2-9 ATTACK POLISHING

Metallographic preparation of many materials is complicated by the removal of the disturbed layer produced by cutting, grinding, and polishing or by the removal of fine scratches. Electropolishing, electromechanical or chemical polishing, or alternate mechanical polishing and etching are frequently used with these materials. Special polishing devices, such as the Fini-Pol or a vibratory polisher, can also be used. An alternate technique is to add a dilute chemical etchant to the polishing media. This technique, known as "attack polishing," "etch attack," or "etch polishing," is extremely useful and applicable to many materials [3, 38, 39]. Addition of a dilute etchant to the abrasive can increase the polishing rate and can change the polishing mechanism to one where dissolution predominates. With some materials a chemical solution which would not ordinarily produce etching attack can be used as an attack-polishing reagent because passivating surface films are removed during polishing.

Attack-polishing techniques can be used as the final step, or two successive steps can be employed. Occasionally, attack polishing is followed by either a chemical polish or an electropolish. Because the polishing mechanism is altered, attack polishing can dramatically reduce or eliminate surface damage. The technique must, however, be carefully controlled for good results. A balance must be maintained between the abrasive solution and the strength of the etchant. If the etchant is too strong, a fast polishing rate can be obtained but pitting, excessive relief, or attack of second-phase particles can occur. In practice, the etchant is added dropwise to the wheel already charged with an abrasive slurry, or the etchant is premixed with the slurry. The latter method allows greater control of the process, assuming that the ratio chosen is proper.

Either manual or automatic polishing can be employed. Bear in mind, however, that many of the solutions are quite corrosive and can damage equipment and injure personnel. Thus, plastic wheels and bowls are preferred, and many automatic devices are suitable. For hand polishing, the operator must protect himself or herself from splashing in addition to wearing thin rubber gloves. Hand polishing is not recommended with the stronger attack-polishing solutions. Reactions can occur between the sample, the wheel, and the abrasive. Therefore, plastic wheels, wax-coated metal wheels, plastic inserted between cloth and wheel, or glass plates are preferred. Cloth life is in general reduced, and the cloth may not be reusable. The cloth should always be washed after use and the operator should make certain that others know that it was used with an etchant. Because of poor cloth life, synthetic cloths, for example, Chemomet or Terylene, are commonly used.

In general, a firm, moderately heavy pressure is used, at least in the initial period. As polishing progresses, the pressure can be reduced. Sometimes, water is added in the latter stages to dilute the etchant. Alternatively, near the end of polishing, the wheel is flushed and polishing is continued for awhile with or without addition of abrasive without the etchant. Since attack polishing can produce excellent results, it should be a useful technique for metallographers, depending on the materials prepared. Appendix F lists details for attack polishing many different materials.

2-10 CHEMICAL POLISHING

Chemical polishing is a method for obtaining a polished surface by immersion in or swabbing with a suitable solution without need of the external electric current used in electropolishing [40–43]. Chemical polishing stems from the use of pickling or brightening solutions used since antiquity. Although secret processes were developed for "bright-dipping" copper and brass in the nineteenth century, the technique did not achieve commercialization until the first process was patented by the Battelle Memorial Institute in 1948.

Since the initial patent, a great many processes have been developed, many of which are suitable for metallographic work. Appendix G lists details of chemical polishing solutions for many materials. The technique is capable of achieving good results on many materials and is particularly useful for those materials that are difficult to polish mechanically. Routine use of chemical polishing by metallographers, however, is limited.

Chemical polishing is generally simple to employ and fast, requiring little physical exertion. Elaborate equipment is not required. Metal removal rates are high enough to remove scratches and deformation from fine grinding. The method is applicable to round or curved surfaces or for simultaneous polishing of all of the sides of a square, rectangular, or flat specimen. Thus, the technique has wide applicability and versatility.

The disadvantages are that a given volume of solution can only polish a limited number of samples. Some solutions must be mixed fresh and must be discarded immediately after use; they cannot be stored as stock solutions. Many of the solutions are somewhat dangerous to use. Most should be used under a chemical hood, with the operator avoiding contact with the solution or it vapors. No universally applicable solution exists; most must be tailored to the specific alloy. Therefore, some experimentation may be required with a new alloy to obtain good results. Figure 2-23 illustrates the tailoring of the composition of a chemical polishing solution to accomodate compositional changes and shows the optimum ratios of oxalic acid (25 g/L) to hydrogen peroxide (100%) as a function of the carbon content of carbon steel [41].

Some solutions are employed at about 100°C, which can produce microstructural alterations in some materials. As with electropolishing, inclusions and pores are preferentially attacked, which is a serious drawback. Both techniques produce edge rounding. As with electropolishing, results are best with pure metals or single-phase alloys, although some chemical polishes work well with two-phase alloys.

Chemical polishing is usually performed in a beaker placed on a magnetic stirring device. The sample is hung in the bath or held with tongs. If stirring is not desired, the sample can be placed on the bottom of the beaker. Some chemical

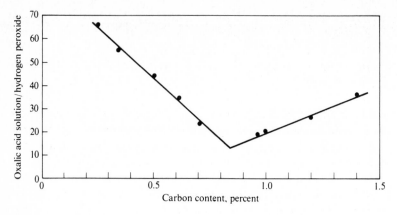

Figure 2-23 Optimum ratios of oxalic acid solution (25 g/1000 mL water) to hydrogen peroxide (100% solution) as a function of carbon content for chemical polishing of carbon steels. *(From Hallet et al., Ref. 41, courtesy of Butterworths Publishing, Inc.)*

polishes work better by swabbing. With these chemical polishes, the solution is placed in a shallow, wide dish. The sample is held with tongs, and the solution is rubbed against the surface using cotton held with tongs. With some samples, the solution volume relative to the sample size is important. Therefore, for best results, attention must be given to technique.

Most samples are ground to 600-grit SiC, although in a few instances a coarser final grind works best. In general, the finer the mechanical finish, the less time is required for chemical polishing and difficulties with pitting and other preferential attack are reduced. A film sometimes forms on the specimen surface, which must be removed by treatment with an appropriate solution. Comments regarding these problems, when available, have been incorporated into App. G.

Chemical polishing is a controlled corrosion process with many similarities to electropolishing. Solutions contain an oxidizing agent, such as nitric acid or hydrogen peroxide, which takes the place of the electric current used in electropolishing. An anion is used to dissolve the film formed at a controlled rate. Experiments have shown that for many metal-polishing solution combinations, a surface film forms during chemical polishing. These films are either oxides or hydroxides, since the solutions are strongly oxidizing. In cases where the sample is immersed in an unstirred solution, a clearly visible viscous layer is present. In some polishing solutions, gas evolution is observed, which is indicative of polishing. While the viscous film theory, which was proposed by Jacquet to explain electropolishing, appears to relate well to many chemical polishing solutions, the action of passivating oxide films has been suggested as a prime factor in chemical polishing of aluminum and other metals that experience passivation. Uniform dissolution of the surface of a particular metal in a specific solution is due to the presence of either a passivating oxide film or a viscous diffusion layer.

2-11 ELECTROPOLISHING

In the years prior to the introduction of diamond abrasives and automatic polishing devices, mechanical polishing was a more tedious process that was truly dependent on the artisan's skill. Attaining high-quality mechanically polished surfaces routinely was difficult even for the most competent metallographers. Hence, the possibility of replacing at least the polishing stages of sample preparation by a relatively simple electrolytic treatment, which appeared to be capable of producing quality surfaces with good reproducibility, was highly attractive. Although there were a few experiments conducted at the beginning of this century, electropolishing was invented by Pierre Jacquet of France in 1929 and was first successfully applied to metallographic sample preparation in 1935.

Electrolytic polishing, or electropolishing, is widely used in research and industry; however, a universally applicable mechanism has not been developed and found acceptable. However, studies have produced considerable insight into the phenomenon. The metal sample to be polished is usually preground by SiC or other abrasives to a 600-grit, or equivalent, finish. The sample is made the anode in an electrolytic cell containing an appropriate electrolyte. The surface is smoothed and brightened by the anodic solution when the correct combination of bath temperature, voltage, current density, and time is employed. The literature on electropolishing is vast, with many electropolishing solutions reported for a wide variety of metals. Many of these electrolytes and the appropriate operating conditions are listed in App. H. References 42 to 44 are general reviews on the subject.

In attempting to duplicate the results of others, the metallographer is faced with control of many experimental variables. Mixing of the electrolytes must be performed with care, since many of these solutions are dangerous, some even explosive. Therefore, before attempting to prepare these solutions, the comments that appear later in this chapter on safety precautions should be read and understood. When in doubt, a chemist or the references listed should be consulted for guidance. Variables that influence electropolishing results include the following:

- Surface area to be polished
- Orientation of sample in bath
- Orientation of cathode in bath
- Choice of cathode material
- Ratio of cathode-to-anode surface area
- Anode-to-cathode spacing
- Depth of sample below solution surface
- Composition of sample, including impurities
- Electrolyte bath age and composition changes
- Bath temperature
- Degree of bath agitation

- Current density and voltage
- Time
- Degree of preliminary mechanical treatment
- Manner of specimen removal from bath
- Washing procedure

The need to control all these variables acts as a mental barrier to many metallographers, which has reduced the utilization of the method.

2-11.1 Advantages

Electropolishing has numerous advantages that make the process quite attractive, but there are also a number of disadvantages which restrict its use. Properly applied, electropolishing can be of great value, since the surfaces so prepared are usually as good as the best that can be obtained by mechanical polishing. When electropolishing is correctly performed, the prepared surfaces are scratch-free and the deformation from cutting and grinding is removed. Hence, the method is ideal for preparation of metals that are difficult to polish mechanically, especially where disturbed metal or mechanical twinning artifacts are problems. These characteristics are valuable for very low load microhardness testing or for TEM thin-foil work. For laboratories that routinely examine the same materials, once the operating conditions are fully established, an inexperienced metallographer can be quickly trained and can obtain excellent results. In some instances, electropolishing can reduce the overall time required for preparation. Etching can often be accomplished in the same electrolyte merely be reducing the applied voltage to about 10 percent of that required for polishing.

2-11.2 Disadvantages

On the negative side, some of the electrolytes are poisonous and highly corrosive and can be explosive. Unfortunately, many publications do not give a full description of the precautions needed for safe use of the electrolytes discussed. Comments pertinent to safe operation are listed in App. H. Other comments are provided in the section on laboratory safety. When using published recommendations for specific electrolytes, it may be necessary to find the optimum conditions irrespective of the published guidelines. For some electrolytes, the bath composition and operating conditions can be varied substantially without impairing results, while other electrolytes must be rigorously controlled within very narrow limits to get satisfactory results.

Electropolishing is best suited for pure metals and single-phase alloys. Electropolishing of multiphase alloys is often quite difficult because of differences in the polishing rates of the constituents. Two types of problems can be encountered [43]. If a second phase is anodic with respect to the matrix, it will be attacked preferentially. If the second phase is cathodic to the matrix, the matrix is preferentially attacked, leaving the second phase in relief, as is observed when electropolishing graphitic cast irons.

In some solutions, e.g., those containing perchloric acid, it is not safe to use plastic mounts. Therefore, working with small samples is more difficult. Since edges are attacked at a faster rate than the interior, surface edges, coatings, cracks, or pores may not be satisfactory for viewing. Many solutions will preferentially attack nonmetallic inclusions. In some instances, the electropolished surface may be passivated and difficult to etch. A few examples of electropolishing artifacts have also been reported.

2-11.3 Equipment

The apparatus required for electropolishing is reasonably simply. Commercially available devices are available for laboratory or field use. Devices have also been introduced that permit *in situ* observation of the electropolishing process. Since the surface area of metallographic samples is reasonably small, the problems encountered in industrial electropolishing of large samples are avoided. Most metallographic samples are limited to a surface area of 1 to 6.5 cm^2.

Because the current density must be controlled, it is generally necessary to measure the sample surface area. Some devices obviate this need by use of orifice masks against which the sample is clamped. The surface area is fixed for a given mask size, and the current density can be established simply by monitoring the current while the voltage is changed. In devices where the entire sample is immersed in the electrolyte, it is usually necessary to mask the surfaces that are not to be polished using insulating tape, paint, etc., since all exposed surfaces will be polished.

Power is usually provided by a rectified power supply. Since the applied voltage sometimes exceeds 100 V, care must be exercised to avoid electric shock. Meters to measure voltage and current are required to control the process. To minimize undesirable etching effects, it should be possible to remove the sample quickly and safely from the solution, often with the current still applied. As shown in App. H, the amount of agitation required varies from none to vigorous depending on the electrolyte. The correct degree of agitation must be obtainable. Some electrolytes are used in a cyclic manner; thus, a timing device to control the polishing cycle is useful. Because the solutions and their fumes are corrosive, it is best to operate the cell under a chemical hood while placing the electric controls and power supply at a distance. The cell must be corrosion-resistant, easy to drain, and clean.

2-11.4 Theory

The operating conditions of a particular sample-electrolyte combination can be evaluated by preparing a plot of the applied voltage versus the current density. The curve of current density versus voltage shown in Fig. 2-24 is typical of mineral

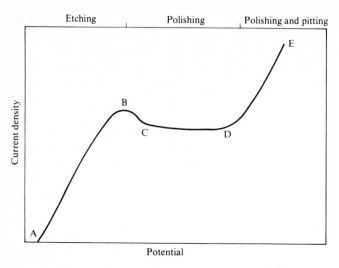

Figure 2-24 Schematic illustrating the classic current density versus voltage relationship for electropolishing solutions.

acids in viscous organic solutions where an ionic film is formed. Polishing occurs on the plateau (C-D), etching occurs at low voltages (A-B), and gas evolution and pitting occur at high voltages (D-E). Optimum polishing generally occurs at C. If the cathode surface area is much larger than the anode surface area, the cathode reaction, i.e., liberation of hydrogen, will not alter the shape of the curve. Processes occurring at the anode are responsible for the shape of the curve of current density versus voltage. To obtain curves of this type, a potentiometric circuit is required. The curve will be different in a series circuit, where an adjustable resistor is used to vary the voltage.

Desirable electrolyte characteristics include the following [44]:

- Should be a somewhat viscous solution
- Should be a good solvent during electrolysis
- Should not attack the sample with the current off
- Should contain one or more large ions, e.g., PO_4^{3-}, ClO_4^{1-} or SO_4^{2-}, or large organic molecules
- Should be simple to mix, stable, safe
- Should be operable at room temperature and be insensitive to temperature changes.

ASTM Standard E3 [44] lists commonly encountered problems in electropolishing and recommendations for their elimination, as shown in Table 2-7.

A unified theory of electropolishing has not been developed. Several mechanisms may be involved, and the relative importance of each may vary depending on the metal being polished and the electrolyte used. Jacquet's initial idea was that differences in resistance in the anolyte layer over projections versus that over depressions, shown by Hickling and Higgins [45] to be about 2.5, was a key factor. This may be so for the initial coarse leveling stage (macropolishing) but not for the final, brightening (micropolishing) stage. Surface brightening has been observed in situations where extensive gas evolution exists, a condition in which a viscous surface layer would exert little influence. In addition, brightening does not always occur when a viscous layer is present.

These factors suggest that some additional important factor exists. Several studies have suggested that the formation of an anode surface film plays an important role in electropolishing. Hoar and Farthing studied the wetting of copper surfaces by mercury in phosphoric acid [46]. They observed that mercury would wet the surface under etching conditions but not under polishing conditions. This difference was attributed to the existence of a surface film on the polishing sample, since it is known that mercury will not wet the surface of copper

Table 2-7 Electropolishing procedural problems and corrections

Trouble	Possible cause	Suggested correction
Center of specimen deeply etched	No polishing film at center of specimen	Increase voltage Decrease agitation Use more viscous electrolyte
Pitting or etching at edges of specimen	Too viscous or thick film	Decrease voltage Increase agitation Use less viscous electrolyte
Sludge settling on surface	Insoluble anode product	Try new electrolyte Increase temperature Increase voltage
Roughness or matte surface	Insufficient or no polishing film	Increase voltage Use more viscous electrolyte
Waviness or streaks on polished surface	Insufficient time Incorrect agitation Inadequate preparation Too much time	Increase or decrease agitation Use better preparation Increase voltage and decrease time
Stains on polished surface	Attack after polishing current is off	Remove specimen while current is still on Try less corrosive electrolyte
Unpolished spots (bullseyes)	Gas bubbles	Increase agitation Decrease voltage
Phases in relief	Insufficient polishing film	Increase voltage Use better preparation Decrease time
Pitting	Polishing too long Voltage too high	Use better preparation Decrease voltage Decrease time Try different electrolyte

samples that are heated in air and as a result become coated with a thin oxide film. Direct experimental proof of the existence of these surface films during electropolishing is difficult to obtain. If these films are present, they must be extremely thin, probably only a few layers of atoms thick. The presence of a thin anode surface film during polishing does provide an explanation for the differences between electropolishing conditions that produce etching versus those that produce brightening.

Olefjord used ESCA (electron spectroscopy for chemical analysis) to study surface films formed on stainless steel during electropolishing [47]. The sample was mechanically polished and then electropolished in a mixture of 13% H_2SO_4, 63% H_3PO_4, and 24% H_2O for 4 min at 25°C, 3 V, and 1 A/cm^2. The potential used was high enough to produce oxygen evolution at the anode. Following electropolishing, the sample was washed in alcohol and dried. ESCA examination of the as-polished surface revealed iron, chromium, oxygen, sulfur, and phosphorus, although the intensities of the iron and chromium were much lower than the other elements. The top layer, therefore, consisted of sulfates and phosphates. This layer was removed by ion milling, which revealed only oxygen, chromium, and iron. Additional ion milling revealed the nickel and manganese present in the bulk sample.

Mathieu et al. employed AES (Auger electron spectroscopy) analysis to examine surface films formed on titanium electropolished in a solution consisting of perchloric acid and acetic acid [48]. Anodic polarization produced an anodic film of TiO_2, which grew at a linear rate with potentials of up to 20 to 22 V where electropolishing began. Prepolishing removal of film was initiated by penetration of ClO_4^- ions through flaws in the film and by reaction of ClO_4^- ions to Cl^- with the simultaneous dissolution of metal. After electropolishing, the anode surface was covered by a thin Cl^--contaminated oxide layer. It could not be determined whether this film was present during electropolishing or only after completion of electrolysis.

2-11.5 Factors Influencing Electropolishing

When the bath temperature rises, the resistance of the bath decreases and the potential required to produce the plateau current density decreases. In addition, the bath viscosity decreases, making it more difficult to maintain a viscous anode layer. Honeycombe and Hughan determined the influence of bath temperature on the plateau current density for copper electropolished in phosphoric acid [49]. They found that the current density for the plateau was essentially constant but the plateau current density varied from 1.86 to 8.06 A/dm^2 as the temperature rose from 4.5 to 70°C. At high bath temperatures, the surface quality decreased; thus, the optimum bath temperature, which must be determined, is the temperature at which the power requirement is minimum and surface quality is maximum. Control of bath temperature is of extreme importance with electrolytes that are explosive. With many samples, lower bath temperatures produce better surface quality, but the temperature cannot be lowered beyond the point where precipitation of solid particles occurs on the anode surface.

In general, the time required to electropolish a sample decreases as the degree of preliminary mechanical polishing increases. However, more time may be required to establish polishing conditions when starting with a fine mechanically polished surface. Indeed, the curves for voltage versus current density will be somewhat different when comparing coarsely ground versus finely polished samples in the same electrolyte. Thus, there appears to be an optimum initial surface roughness. If the initial surface roughness is too coarse, electropolishing times will be long, with excessive metal removal and waviness, and other problems, such as preferential attack of inclusions, may be emphasized. For most work, the optimum surface finish is obtained by grinding to about a 600-grit finish. The time required to electropolish a sample also depends on the metal to be polished and the electrolyte chosen. In general, the higher the plateau current density, the shorter the required time. Some of the electrolytes listed require only a few seconds of operations and can be difficult to control.

2-11.6 Comparison of Mechanically and Electrolytically Polished Surfaces

The quality of electrolytically polished surfaces has been evaluated and compared to those polished mechanically. The best comparison of surfaces produced by both methods has been accomplished by Samuels [50]. Some prior studies had indicated that in certain systems, very fine precipitates are observed after electropolishing but not after mechanical polishing. Samuels examined these systems and found that these precipitates could be observed on properly prepared mechanically polished samples. Samuels also found that with some samples the "precipitates" observed after electropolishing were actually etch pits or grooves.

To obtain artifact-free surfaces, the deformed layer produced by cutting and rough abrasion must be removed. This is true regardless of whether the sample is mechanically or electrolytically polished. This layer is removed only if the process is continued long enough. In many of the references on electropolishing, the pregrind used is rather coarse. Since most of the electropolishing solutions have metal removal rates of about 1 μm/min, it is clear that electropolishing times of up to 60 min or more are required to produce deformation-free surfaces if one starts with a roughly ground surface. If mechanical grinding is continued to a finer state, for example, 600-grit SiC, electropolishing produces deformation-free surfaces in about 15 min. As shown in App. H, much shorter electropolishing times are usually quoted. Therefore, electropolishing does not ensure that deformation-free surfaces will always be produced. Long electropolishing times, however, are not always desired, since surface waviness, edge rounding, and relief may be accentuated. Thus, the preliminary treatment must ensure that the depth of the artifact-containing layer is reduced adequately.

Certain pure refractory metals, e.g., titanium, zirconium, niobium, and uranium, are soft and twin readily at low strain rates. Polishing rates, even with diamond paste, are quite low and artifact-free mechanical polishing of these metals is difficult [50]. Attack polishing, vibratory polishing, or electropolishing can be used to prepare these metals. These three procedures, as well as chemical

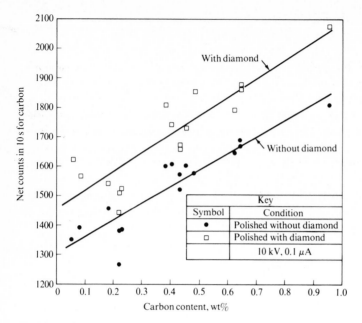

Figure 2-25 Electron microprobe analysis for carbon shows that diamond abrasive is embedded on the surface of steels polished with diamond abrasive.

polishing, are very effective for eliminating fine polishing scratches that often plague metallographers.

Electropolished surfaces are usually free of most of the artifacts commonly encountered with mechanical polishing. Electropolished surfaces generally exhibit slightly better reflectivity than mechanically polished surfaces but are not as flat and often exhibit undulations, dimples, and pimples. Artifact structures resembling furrows or cellular patterns have been observed on electropolished aluminum, iron, and zinc. Both electrolytically and mechanically polished samples exhibit surface contamination. Some of these problems have already been mentioned. Electron microprobe analysis of mechanically polished surfaces of carbon and alloy steels with or without use of diamond abrasives has shown (see Fig. 2-25) that carbon x-ray intensities are higher with diamond polishing than without use of diamond abrasives.

Electropolishing is useful for those metals that are difficult to mechanically polish, but is generally limited to pure metals and single-phase alloys. When edges are to be examined or when inclusions or porosity are of interest, mechanical polishing is preferred. Most two-phase or more-complex alloys must be mechanically polished. Each method has inherent advantages and disadvantages which must be understood before choosing a procedure.

2-12 SPECIFIC POLISHING RECOMMENDATIONS

2-12.1 Universal Methods

Metallographic specimen preparation would be greatly simplified if a universal method were available and applicable to all materials. While several workers have described "universal" polishing procedures, these methods are not truly universal, although they may have wide applicability [51–53]. Thus, a basic technique can be outlined and then modified as required for specific materials and problems.

In general, sample preparation consists of six steps: sectioning, mounting (optional), coarse grinding, fine grinding, rough polishing, and fine polishing. Choice of the initial grinding abrasive size is dependent on the sectioning procedure. Abrasive cutting is most common, and the initial grit size can be 120-, 180-, or 240-grit SiC paper; usually water lubrication is used. A general grinding sequence is 120-, 240-, 320-, 400-, and 600-grit SiC. Between each step, the sample is rinsed under running water and rotated 45 to 90° from the previous orientation, if hand-ground. With automatic grinding, the scratch pattern is random.

Coarse polishing is often done using 6-μm diamond paste on a napfree, low-nap, or medium-nap cloth, depending on the tendency for relief formation. Alternatively, two diamond polishing steps can be used, for example 6- and 1-μm or 3- and 1-μm diamond paste. When a sample is hand-polished, it is rotated clockwise against the counterclockwise wheel rotation to prevent comet tailing. After each step, the sample (and the operator's hands) are washed under running water with cotton, followed by alcohol. If there is danger of abrasive entrapment, ultrasonic cleaning is necessary. Water should never be allowed to dry on the sample surface between steps. Drying is facilitated by spraying the surface with alcohol and placing the sample under a stream of hot air. Drying with compressed air is not recommended, since the air can be contaminated with oil or particulate matter.

If a single diamond polishing stage is employed, two final polishing steps produce best results. In general, 0.3- and 0.05-μm alumina slurries are most commonly employed. If two diamond polishing stages are used, a single 0.05-μm alumina polish suffices. Choice of the final polishing abrasives and polishing method involves considerable personal preference and is frequently dictated by the nature of the material being polished.

Other final polishing methods may be desired to facilitate removal of fine polishing scratches and to produce sharp definition of the microstructure. Vibratory polishing, attack polishing, or electromechanical polishing procedures can be chosen. Where best suited, chemical or electrolytic polishing can be employed in place of rough and fine polishing.

2-12.2 Common Problems

Several problems are repeatedly encountered by metallographers, such as edge retention, polishing of coated samples, and inclusion and graphite retention.

Procedures to produce good edge retention have already been discussed. These same techniques are required for coated samples, but additional problems are encountered. Specific procedures are required for maximum retention of graphite or inclusions.

Coatings A wide variety of coatings and coating processes have been used with metals and other materials. Some specific information [54–61] has been published regarding metallographic preparation techniques for coated samples, although the majority of these studies pertain to coated steels. Mechanical polishing is the preferred method, since edges are rounded by electropolishing. With all samples, the edge must be protected by mounting. With some samples, the surface can be plated with electroless nickel, but the pretreatment step and the solution must not affect the coating. Electroless nickel cannot be used directly on galvanized (zinc-coated) steels. An intermediate flash coating, for example, a coating of copper, is required before use of electroless nickel. Some mounting materials, particularly the compression mounting epoxies, provide adequate flatness without plating, especially if automatic polishing is used. If microprobe work is to be done near the coated edge, however, these materials produce interfering x-ray signals. Compression mounting can be damaging to some soft coatings, e.g., tin, and cold-setting resins are required. Here again, automatic polishing can provide significantly better edge flatness than hand polishing, thus eliminating the need for plating. Use of nap-free cloths for rough polishing and low- or medium-nap cloths for final polishing is recommended to control rounding and relief. Polishing times should be held to a minimum. Staining can occur after final polishing if tap water is used. Cold distilled water or alcohol can be used to avoid staining.

Taper sections are occasionally used in the study of coatings by light microscopy to provide higher magnification. Davies and Hoare used either electrolytic copper or iron (see App. D) for protection of tinplate in taper sections [54]. Iron plating was preferred. Diamond and alumina polishing was performed on Selvyt cloth. Earlier work by Hoare used magnesia as the final abrasive [55]. Romig and Rowland used alumina on a velvet cloth for final polishing of tin-plated specimens [56].

Rowland and Romig have published details of their procedure for polishing galvanized steels [57]. A commercial grade of alumina abrasive was found to be too alkaline for polishing galvanized steel; it caused staining of the zinc coating. Since they could not control the pH of this abrasive, alumina was prepared from a sulfate of aluminum. The sulfate remaining was removed by use of hot distilled water, and the pH had to be controlled to prevent staining. This study showed that a pH of 7.0 to 7.6 was necessary to reproducibly produce artifact-free surfaces. Final polishing was conducted with the pH-controlled alumina abrasive on a silk-velvet cloth for 30 to 60 s and with use of fairly heavy hand pressure. The washing technique after polishing was also critical, since staining resulted if tap water, distilled water, or ethanol were used prior to etching. They recommended swabbing with amyl alcohol, blow-drying, etching, rinsing with amyl alcohol and then ethanol, and finally drying. Modern alumina abrasives eliminate the pH problems originally encountered [58].

Preparation of porcelain-enameled steel requires particular care in the sectioning and mounting stages. To prevent damage to the coating, it is best to support the sample with metal clamps prior to abrasive cutting. Alternatively, a low-speed diamond saw can be employed. If the enamel-to-steel bond is not strong, or if the sample is curved, the specimen can be potted in epoxy before sectioning. A wide variety of mounting materials can be employed, depending on the quality of the coating. Polishing is straightforward using the general procedure just described. If the coating is porous, vacuum impregnation with epoxy resin after fine grinding helps to maintain the pore size and prevents bleed-out.

The study of anodized surface layers on aluminum is a particularly challenging problem because of the thinness of the coating and the lack of contrast between the specimen and the coating. Keller and Wilcox have described three methods for examining anodized films on aluminum [59]. The first method employs the traditional mounted and polished cross section. Bright-field examination reveals little detail, but crossed polarized examination is useful. The second procedure is to anodize the surface of a completely polished sample and examine this layer with bright- and dark-field illumination. The third method is to prepare a thin section by grinding away most of the aluminum substrate and polishing to reveal the coating under transmitted light. This method reveals details of the film microstructure but is rather difficult and tedious.

Atkinson and Godden [60] suggested an alternate method [61] to improve the image contrast of cross sections of anodized samples. Two procedures were used. The first method used vapor deposition of a thin semitransparent layer of aluminum on the polished cross section to improve bright-field image contrast. In the second method, a completely opaque, thick aluminum layer was deposited as a vapor onto the anodized surface prior to mounting. After polishing, a thin, semitransparent aluminum layer was deposited as a vapor on the polished surface. Use of the two-stage metallization treatment produced best contrast.

Edge retention is not a problem in preparing materials with hard coatings, but attention must be given to the sectioning and mounting procedures. Sectioning is performed with SiC or diamond wheels. Cutting is always in the direction of the sample bulk, never the reverse, because the tensile stresses developed can break or pop the coating off the substrate. If a plating is used, it should exhibit contrast with the coating. A hard, adherent mounting material should be used. Polishing must be performed in a manner to minimize relief.

Graphite and inclusion retention Retention of graphite in cast iron is a common polishing problem that has received considerable attention. Some success has been reported using electropolishing solutions, but electropolishing is, in general, not the best approach. Several workers have obtained satisfactory results using electromechanical polishing as the final polishing step. Most samples, however, have been done by mechanical polishing.

Coarse grinding is a critical phase. If the soft graphite is lost during coarse grinding, it cannot be recovered in subsequent steps and leaves an open or collapsed cavity. SiC papers are preferred to emery because the improved cutting of SiC produces less damage. Fresh paper should always be used.

Automatic grinding and polishing generally produce results that are superior to hand polishing, since the applied pressure is more even. The omnidirectional grinding and polishing pattern also helps. Diamond abrasives produce superior results to those obtained with coarse alumina. A napless cloth is best for rough polishing. Samuels recommends a cotton drill cloth and heavy pressure for diamond polishing and a Selvyt cloth with magnesia for final polishing [3].

Figure 2-26 illustrates graphite retention in flake, compacted, and spheroidal graphite samples. These specimens were prepared by automatic grinding and

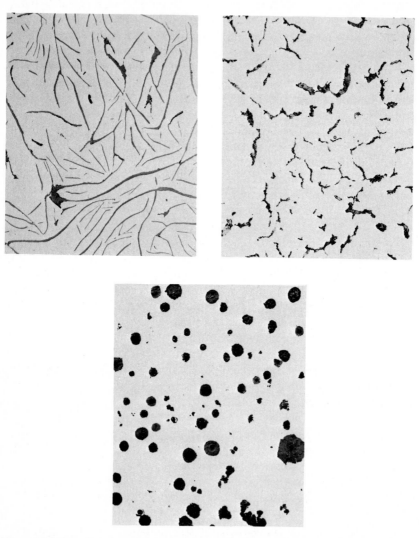

Figure 2-26 Examples of graphite retention in cast-iron samples polished automatically as described in the text. Top left, flake graphite; top right, compacted graphite; bottom, nodular graphite; 65×.

polishing using the following sequence: 120-, 240-, 320-, 400-, and 600-grit SiC paper with heavy pressure and water lubrication, 3-μm diamond on canvas with high pressure and lubrication, 1-μm diamond on a synthetic suede cloth with medium pressure and lubrication, and hand polishing on Microcloth (stationary) with colloidal SiO_2 polishing solution. In the diamond polishing steps, one should avoid using a worn cloth.

Inclusion retention is a simpler problem, since the inclusions are significantly harder than graphite; indeed, some types are harder than the metal matrix [62]. The soft inclusions, such as sulfides, are observed as depressions, while the very hard inclusions, such as aluminates, stand proud above the surface. If hand polishing is employed, best results are obtained if the sample is hardened before polishing. This step is often unnecessary with automatic devices. Electropolishing generally produces preferential attack at inclusions and should be avoided.

The polishing procedure recommended for graphite retention works very well for inclusion retention and produces minimal relief. Figure 2-27 shows examples of inclusion retention in steels polished as described for graphite retention.

Polishing of free-machining steels or other metals containing large amounts of sulfides and lead or bismuth is probably the most difficult inclusion polishing and

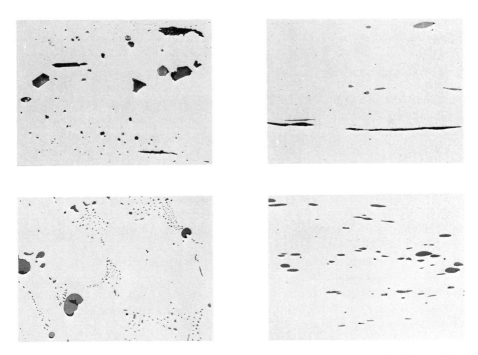

Figure 2-27 Example of inclusion retention in steels polished automatically as described in text. Top, oxides in as-cast (left) and wrought (right, silicates and sulfides) samples; 240$\times$. Bottom, sulfides in as-cast (left) and wrought (right) free-machining steel samples; 120$\times$.

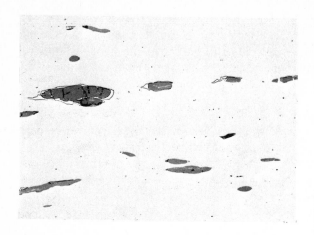

Figure 2-28 As-polished free-machining steel treated with bismuth, 150×. *(Courtesy of V.E. McGraw, Bethlehem Steel Corp.)*

retention problem because of the softness of these materials and their tendency to smear. In resulfurized leaded steels, lead or bismuth is generally observed to be attached to the manganese sulfides, as shown in Fig. 2-28.

Chalfant has shown that control of the pH of the final alumina abrasive is critical [63]. She has recommended final polishing with Microcloth and a weak solution of gamma alumina abrasive with a pH of 7.0. Final polishing should reveal lead as off-white particles with distinct black boundaries.

2-12.3 Metals

Specific recommendations regarding the polishing of many metals and alloys can be found in the literature [3, 64, 65]. The following section is a summary of pertinent comments.

Aluminum Although polishing of high-purity aluminum is rather difficult, polishing of alloys or cold-worked samples is considerably simpler [3, 65, 66]. Cutting and grinding must be carefully performed to minimize surface deformation. Some workers prefer to add liquid soap to the water lubricant during grinding [66]. The usual sequence of SiC grinding papers can be augmented by a final grind with new soft 600-grit SiC or a finer grit paper.

Polishing using bronze or copper wheels can produce undesirable galvanic reactions; thus, aluminum wheels are preferred. If the alloy contains hard second-phase particles, which is common, a napless cloth is used for rough diamond polishing. Microcloth and cerium oxide, CER-CRO, or Rayvel or Kitten Ear and magnesium oxide are commonly used for final polishing. Vibratory polishing or use of the Fini-Pol permit scratch-free surface preparation. Polishing times should be held to a minimum to control relief if hard phases are present (see Fig. 2-29). A very high quality surface polish is required if anodizing is to be used. After polishing, a thin, transparent oxide film forms which can make etching difficult.

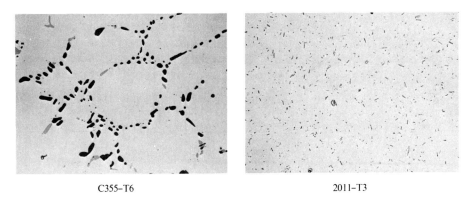

C355–T6   2011–T3

Figure 2-29 Microstructure of as-polished cast (left) and wrought (right) aluminum alloys, 300×.

Antimony and bismuth Antimony is a hard, brittle, extremely friable metal; thus, considerable care must be exercised during its sectioning. Prepotting prior to sectioning can be very helpful. Bismuth is soft but brittle and not as friable as antimony. Although sectioning of bismuth must be done with care, polishing is not too difficult. Pure antimony is rarely encountered; however, pure bismuth is occasionally prepared. Both are more common as alloying elements in other metals.

Loading up of grinding paper is a common problem, even when generous amounts of water are applied to the grinding paper. Most critical is the last step in which two sheets of 600-grit paper may be required. Once loading occurs, one should not continue to grind because damage results. Diamond polishing is not very successful with these metals [65]. Bismuth can be successfully prepared by attack polishing [64]. Rough polishing is accomplished by alternate deep etching and polishing with coarse alumina on a synthetic cloth followed by vibratory polishing with a Rayvel cloth and a magnesia slurry [65]. Both metals can be electropolished. Figure 2-30 shows an as-polished bismuth alloy.

Beryllium Preparation of beryllium samples presents an acute health hazard because of the extreme toxicity of the grinding dust. Wet cutting and grinding is usually adequate to prevent air contamination. Many procedures have been developed [38, 67–70], which are thoroughly reviewed by Price and McCall [70]. Beryllium is a moderately difficult metal to polish because of the ease of forming deformation twins during grinding. Most workers recommend light pressures during grinding.

Beryllium is a difficult metal to etch; however, because of its close-packed hexagonal crystal structure, the microstructure can be vividly revealed in polarized light, as described in Chap. 4. However, a very high quality surface is required to obtain good response. The usual sequence of SiC grinding papers are employed, although some [67] claim that grinding beyond 400 grit is unnecessary,

Figure 2-30 Microstructure of as-polished bismuth (80%)-manganese (20%) alloy, 150×. *(Courtesy of M. A. Rodriguez, Bethlehem Steel Corp.)*

while others [69] recommend grinding up to soft 600-grit SiC. Some workers [38] have used high-speed (1750 r/min) wheels throughout grinding and polishing, but most use normal wheel speeds. Udy et al. [67] claim that grinding papers must be lubricated with kerosene rather than water, while others claim that water is satisfactory. Thus, considerable variation in technique exists. Several workers recommend etching between each grinding step using an etchant consisting of either 150 mL water, 5 g sulfamic acid, and 5 drops HF (etch for 1 min) (Kuhn in Ref. 70) or 19% aqueous H_2SO_4 (etch for 10 to 15 s) (Dingle and Moore Calabra and Jackson in Ref. 69).

Mechanical polishing is often accomplished with the aid of attack polishing solutions (see App. F), although Kaufmann et al. prepared samples mechanically without recourse to attack polishing [68]. Vibratory polishing has also been used with or without attack polishing. Chemical polishing has limited applicability, but electropolishing is very common and quite successful.

Cadmium, lead, tin, and zinc In their pure forms, these metals are all quite soft and difficult to polish. Cadmium and zinc are prone to mechanical twinning grinding damage. Tin is less susceptible to twin formation, but recrystallized surface layers can form during grinding. Pure tin flows under the pressure used for compression mounting; thus, cold-setting resins must be used. Pure lead recrystallizes below room temperature; therefore, grain size is usually of little interest. Alloys of these metals are harder and less difficult to prepare, as illustrated in Fig. 2-31.

These metals can be cut with a microtome, thus eliminating the need for coarse grinding. Since they are soft, copious lubrication is required to minimize loading of the abrasive paper. Cadmium can be chemically or electrolytically polished and both techniques are useful.

Pb: 15% Sb, 5% Sn   Pb: 12.5% Sb

Figure 2-31 Microstructure of as-polished lead alloys, 120×.

Lead and its alloys are commonly encountered by metallographers. Slepian and Blann have described a polishing procedure using the Automet automatic polishing attachment [71]. After cutting with a hacksaw or shearing, samples were mounted using cold-setting resins. Surfaces were filed smooth and then ground using 320-, 400-, and 600-grit SiC paper with low pressure, short times, and copious lubrication. Between steps, the sample holder was cleaned ultrasonically in water and a detergent (Alconox). Three steps were employed for polishing: 9-μm diamond on duck cloth, 1-μm alumina on Microcloth, and either cerium oxide or colloidal silica on Microcloth. Pressures were slightly higher than for grinding. After the last step, the samples were vibratory-polished for about 20 min using colloidal silica on Microcloth. Chemical polishing of lead has also been used.

Pure tin can be handled in the same manner as lead. Eyre used Selvyt cloth and gamma alumina for the final polishing step [72]. Electropolishing is frequently used for preparing tin samples. Zinc can be prepared in the same manner as lead and tin. Both chemical and electrolytic polishing procedures are common.

Chromium, molybdenum, and tungsten Polishing of these metals is complicated by abrasion damage in the outer fragmented layer and the low polishing rates in rough polishing. Therefore, additional rough polishing with diamond abrasives must be done in order to remove grinding damage. Final polishing is commonly performed by attack polishing (see App. F). Yih and Wang have described a two-stage attack polishing procedure for tungsten [73]. Other procedures use a single attack polishing step. Electromechanical polishing procedures are also common. Electropolishing is widely used to prepare these three metals.

Cobalt, manganese, nickel, and iron These metals are relatively easy to polish, although cold working from cutting and grinding can be troublesome with the purer metals. Nearly any mounting procedure can be employed unless edge retention is needed. Grinding is performed with the usual sequence of 120- to 600-grit SiC papers. Austenitic stainless steels and nickel are quite sensitive to grinding damage. Each step must be thoroughly completed before the next is begun.

Diamond compounds are widely used for rough polishing, using either a single-step or two-stage process. The coarser diamond is used with a low-nap or napless cloth such as canvas, nylon, or synthetics (Texmet or Pellon). The fine diamond step, when used, generally employs a medium-nap cloth, such as Microcloth. Final polishing uses two steps or a single step. Most abrasives can be used. For the softer metals and alloys, vibratory polishing or the Fini-Pol are useful for controlling surface distortion. Chemical and electrolytic polishing are also used, and the latter is quite popular with austenitic stainless steel and nickel.

Copper Specimen preparation of copper alloys is not particularly difficult, although considerable effort can be required to remove fine scratches. Surface damage from cutting or grinding does not produce troublesome artifacts. Grinding and rough polishing of single-phase alloys requires thorough execution, especially for high-alloy types such as cartridge brass. Removal of fine-polishing scratches in pure copper and single-phase alloys is difficult but can be accomplished by attack polishing. Most of the copper alloys shown in this book were attack polished. Beta alloys are relatively easy to polish. Some copper alloys contain large amounts of lead. The polishing procedure described for leaded steels works well for leaded copper, although the pressures used are lighter. Etching prior to fine diamond polishing is also useful. Vibratory polishing is also popular for finishing copper alloys, and chemical or electrolytic polishing are common.

Germanium and silicon Germanium and silicon are often encountered in solid-state devices, often as single crystals. Germanium is easy to polish. Thick sections of silicon present little difficulty, but thin sections are very friable and require considerable care in handling [64]. This entails careful sectioning and mounting, light grinding pressures, and hard, napless cloths. Diamond abrasives are quite useful.

Silicon is present in most steels as a deoxidizer and presents no polishing problems at this concentration. However, in electrical sheet steels containing several percent silicon, staining during final polishing is a commmon problem, especially if warm tap water is used. Therefore, samples should be washed in cold distilled water or with alcohol.

Indium and thallium Both indium and thallium are very soft and have low melting points. Pure indium is soft enough to be cut with the fingernail. However, pure indium is seldom encountered, and its alloys are harder. Both metals can be cut with a microtome. Compression mounting materials should be avoided. Both metals will be slowly attacked by cold water containing oxygen; thus water is avoided during preparation. Sections that have been cut with a microtome can be polished directly on Selvyt cloth with alumina abrasives and a heavy liquid soap. Electropolishing has been used to prepare indium and indium-thallium alloys.

Magnesium Pure magnesium is difficult to polish because it is very soft, mechanical twinning may be produced during cutting and abrasion, and it is attacked by many dilute organic acids. Pure magnesium is slowly attacked by water, while many magnesium alloys are rapidly attacked. Fine magnesium dust is a fire hazard; therefore, wet grinding is necessary. The less-reactive alloys can be ground and polished using distilled water, while kerosene is often used for the more reactive alloys. Oberländer and Lillerud have recommended grinding with 320- to 1000-grit SiC paper using a mixture of one part glycerin and three parts alcohol as the lubricant to prevent corrosive attack [74]. Three stages of diamond polishing were used: 6-μm diamond on Pellon, 3-μm diamond on silk, and 1-μm diamond on velvet. Final polishing was performed using alumina in three parts alcohol and one part glycerin. Pepper used 6-μm and 1-μm diamond on Microcloth followed by final polishing with 1/4-μm diamond on Microcloth with a cream lubricant [75]. The cream consisted of 6 mL triethanolamine in 75 mL water stirred into 12.5 g stearic acid at 80 to 90°C. After cooling, the solution was whipped to a smooth consistency with 100 mL of oil extender. The 1/4-μm diamond was added to Microcloth, then a few drops of oil extender were added, and this was followed by a small amount of the cream. This slurry was worked into the nap and polishing was conducted at 500 r/min. After polishing, the sample was swabbed with methylated spirits to remove residual cream and oil. Attack polishing and chemical and electrolytic polishing have also been used to prepare magnesium alloys.

Niobium, tantalum, and vanadium Pure niobium is soft and ductile and cold-works readily; thus distortion-free microstructures are difficult to prepare. Alloyed niobium is harder and more easily prepared. Grinding and polishing steps must be thoroughly executed to remove prior abrasion damage. Hard niobium carbides are often present in less-pure grades, producing relief problems. SiC papers are used for grinding. Anderson [64] recommends repeating the final 600-grit step. Diamond polishing is often followed by attack polishing.

Tantalum is quite similar to niobium but is softer and more difficult to prepare. Polishing is conducted in the same manner as niobium, using attack polishing as the final step, or followed by a chemical polish. In some cases it is necessary to polish the sample mechanically after chemical polishing which is then followed by a second chemical polish. Electrolytic polishing is also used.

Pure vanadium is soft and ductile, but if hydrogen is present, which is common, it is brittle. Vanadium is not very difficult to prepare and polishes somewhat like austenitic stainless steel. Single-phase alloys are often electropolished. Kallfass and Hörz recommend mounting single-phase vanadium alloys in cold-setting resins because of the risk of altering the structure [76]. They recommend grinding pure vanadium, niobium, tantalum, and their alloys through 1200-grit SiC abrasive papers. If specimens have been doped, they recommend dry grinding with the very fine papers. For doped and aged niobium and tantalum samples, they recommend vibratory polishing with alumina for 10 to 20 h after fine grinding. For vanadium, electropolishing is preferred.

Precious metals Pure gold and silver are very soft and difficult to polish. Some of the platinum metals are difficult to polish; others are reasonably easy. Gold alloys are harder than pure gold and less difficult to polish. Gold is usually ground and polished using standard procedures and then electropolished. These electrolytes are rather difficult to use and are sometimes followed by polishing with magnesia on velvet.

Silver is susceptible to damage during cutting and grinding and has a strong tendency to embed abrasives. Calabra has described a technique for preparing silver samples [77]. Grinding is carried through to 600-grit soft SiC paper using water as the coolant. Fresh papers should be employed, since smearing and surface damage results from using worn papers. Calabra cautions against cleaning ultrasonically because prolonged cleaning causes cavitation and damages the surface. This is a common problem with all soft metals. Ultrasonic cleaning, if needed, should not exceed 30 s. After grinding, samples are electromechanically polished. This technique is widely used with precious metals and is highly effective.

Piotrowski and Accinno have prepared an excellent review of metallographic techniques for precious metals [78]. Specimen sectioning uses abrasive cutoff wheels where the wheel hardness is matched to that of the sample. For iridium and ruthenium, they recommend cutting with a diamond wheel. To achieve suitable bonding, they recommend vacuum impregnation with epoxy. Coarse grinding employs water-cooled 80-, 120-, and 180-grit SiC belts. Fine grinding uses 220-, 320-, 400-, and 600-grit SiC at 280 r/min. Hand grinding of high-hardness ruthenium and osmium can result in multiplanar surfaces. Special fixtures were designed to prevent specimen rocking during grinding. This problem can also be eliminated by use of automatic devices.

Rough polishing, except for gold and gold alloys, is conducted on nylon on a brass wheel with 6-μm diamond and oil extender. Wheel speeds of up to 1150 r/min are used along with high pressures. Specimens must be moved continually to prevent comet tailing. Polishing time varies with the metal being prepared. Rough polishing with 5-μm alumina on Kitten Ear cloth is used for gold samples. Light pressure and wheel speeds of 250 r/min are employed.

Fine polishing is conducted using 1-μm diamond on Microcloth. Ruthenium and osmium are polished at 550 r/min or greater, while 550 to 250 r/min or less is used for the other softer metals. Final polishing, except for gold, uses ¼-μm diamond. For gold, final polishing uses 1-μm alpha alumina at 160 r/min and very light pressure, followed by vibratory polishing with gamma alumina (500 mL alumina to 250 mL distilled water). The above procedures are adequate for the harder precious metals and gold, but electromechanical or electrolytic polishing is preferred for finishing the softer metals. Attack polishing is also used with the platinum metals.

Radioactive metals Pure uranium is a ductile, malleable metal. Uranium, its compounds, and other radioactive metals are highly toxic and must be prepared in specially designed hot cells, as described in Chap. 4. Alpha uranium is very susceptible to mechanical deformation; therefore, mechanical polishing generally produces twinning and deformation band artifacts. Because the structure of alpha uranium is orthorhombic, polarized light is usually employed (see Chap. 4) to study its grain structure, which is fortunate, since grain boundary etching is difficult. Grinding is performed with water-cooled SiC paper to 600 grit. This is generally followed by electropolishing, although attack polishing is also used.

Plutonium, an extremely poisonous metal, is also prepared by remote handling to protect the metallographer. Sectioning is performed with abrasive cutoff wheels. Samples are cold-mounted, and a brass screw is placed in the back of the mount to produce a conductive path for electropolishing. Samples are ground with water-cooled SiC paper through 600 grit, which is followed by diamond polishing on nylon in four steps from 15 to 1 μm, and then the samples are electropolished. Cochran states that water should be avoided in preparing most plutonium compounds because of their hydroscopic nature [79]. Vibratory polishing has also been employed for both rough and final polishing.

Richter has described a preparation procedure for neptunium [80]. Samples were mounted in a cold-setting resin and ground on SiC papers (180 to 600 grit), followed by rough polishing with 6-μm diamond paste on nylon cloth. This was followed by electropolishing. Thorium is a soft, malleable, moderately poisonous radioactive metal [64]. Water must be avoided during the preparation of thorium samples, and kerosene is preferred. Electropolishing is used as the final preparation step.

Rare earth metals Metallographic sample preparation of the rare earth metals cannot be generalized because of the variable characteristics of these metals. Love points out that europium oxidizes in air about as rapidly as sodium; lanthanum and cerium form an oxide surface film within a few minutes, while yttrium and high-atomic-number rare earths remain bright for many days [81].

Sectioning can be performed with a hacksaw and an oil lubricant. Samples must be kept cool [81], especially the low-atomic-number rare earths, since excessive heating can ignite chips as well as produce disturbed surfaces. Abrasive cutoff wheels can be employed; however, the water coolant corrodes the more reactive rare earths to a substantial depth. Some of the rare earths, e.g., yttrium, require cold-setting resins for mounting, since compression mounting will produce twin artifacts. Grinding must employ mineral oil, kerosene, or diethylene glycol rather than water. Of these, kerosene is the most satisfactory. Yttrium and rare earths of higher atomic number can be sectioned using water as the coolant. Many of the rare earths are sensitive to grinding damage.

Polishing is done at low wheel speeds and with very light pressure in several steps, each of short duration. Diamond abrasives are frequently employed. Roman used 9- and 3-μm diamond on Metcloth followed by chemical polishing if the inclusion content was low [82]. Acetone is used to clean samples rather than water. For samples with higher inclusion content, fine polishing is performed with 1- and ¼-μm diamond prior to chemical polishing.

Dobbins has described procedures for preparing holmium [83]. Samples were ground on 240- to 600-grit SiC paper lubricated with kerosene and paraffin. A three-stage diamond polishing sequence was employed with 6-, 3-, and 1-μm diamond on Metcloth with ethyl alcohol as the lubricant. This was followed by a short final polish with a high-speed wheel and gamma alumina in water on a synthetic suede cloth. This treatment oxidized the surface sufficiently to reveal the structure under polarized light. Chemical polishing, in place of the final alumina polish, produced similar results.

Selenium and tellurium These metals and their compounds are extremely toxic and must be handled with care. Both have low melting points and are rather friable; therefore, low-exotherm, cold-setting resins must be used for mounting. Cutting and grinding must be carefully performed using low pressures.

Sodium Sodium is a very soft metal which is highly reactive. Handling of sodium should be avoided, since the heat produced by reaction with moisture on the skin can produce ignition. Sodium is normally stored under kerosene. Bender has described a procedure to prepare sodium for metallographic examination [84]. Samples are sectioned with a knife and mounted in Wood's metal (melting point of 70 to 72°C) using an aluminum ring die and holding the temperature at 72°C to prevent melting of the sodium (melting point of 97.7°C). Because sodium floats on the liquid Wood's metal, it is held down with an aluminum peg until freezing occurs. Solidification is conducted in a glove box evacuated and filled with helium. The mounted samples are cooled to liquid nitrogen temperature and immediately ground with 320-grit SiC paper lubricated with kerosene. The samples are cleaned in methyl chloroform, refrozen, and ground with 600-grit SiC. The cleaning and refreezing steps are repeated, followed by 6-μm diamond polishing on Texmet. The samples are etched with 3% HCl in methyl chloroform, refrozen, polished with 1-μm diamond, cleaned, and allowed to thaw. By avoiding water and using an inert atmosphere, oxidation effects can be inhibited long enough to permit examination.

Titanium Pure titanium is a soft, ductile metal, but the addition of impurities or alloying elements makes it harder and less ductile. Specimen preparation of titanium, especially pure titanium, is difficult with standard methods [38, 85]. Twin artifacts can be produced during sectioning, and excess heat can produce phase changes, especially if beta phase is present. Mounting in Bakelite is not recommended because of the possible absorption of hydrogen. If hydrides are present, the high temperatures used with compression mounting materials can cause the hydrides to go into solution, and they will precipitate on cooling in a different form. If the hydride phase is of interest, use low-exotherm, cold-setting resins.

Grinding is performed using the normal sequence of SiC papers and water lubrication. Polishing can be conducted using a variety of techniques and is a critical step that is rendered difficult because of the low polishing rates obtained. Alternatively, rough polishing can be done by attack polishing and 600-grit

Carborundum abrasive powder. Etching between polishing steps helps remove the disturbed metal surface layer. Mechanical polishing consists of three or four steps, generally incorporating several grades of diamond paste and one or more attack polishing steps. Electropolishing is often used as a final polishing operation after grinding to a 600-grit surface finish.

Zirconium and hafnium Zirconium and hafnium are soft, ductile metals that are rather difficult to prepare by standard methods because of the ease with which they form mechanical twins during cutting and grinding. Polishing rates are also low, and removal of fine scratches by mechanical polishing is difficult. Since compression mounting pressures are great enough to produce twinning, cold-setting resins are preferred. Sectioning, mounting, and grinding must be carefully controlled [86, 87].

The usual sequence of SiC grinding papers are used. Smearing and flow can occur during grinding and polishing. Copious water cooling is used, generally with longer grinding periods. Only fresh paper should be used. Some workers prefer using kerosene and paraffin wax to lubricate the finer paper grades. Swab etching between grinding steps has also been used. If samples are finished mechanically, attack polishing is a necessity.

Because of the artifact problems, chemical and electrolytic polishing procedures are widely used. Chemical polishing is quite common and considerably simpler to employ than electropolishing. Chemically polished surfaces respond well to polarized light (see Fig. 3-73 in Chap. 3). Reproducibility of electropolishing results has been claimed to be a problem. Polishing of hafnium is done in the same manner as zirconium.

2-12.4 Borides and Carbides

Sintered carbides and borides are extremely hard materials requiring different procedures than those used for metals. With some samples special abrasive cutoff wheels are used for sectioning; however, diamond wheels are preferred. Grinding with emery or silicon carbide paper is not recommended because very little material will be removed before the paper wears out. Diamond abrasives are used, almost exclusively, for all stages of preparation.

Hand grinding is a very tiring chore; automatic devices are definitely preferred. Several procedures have been used to hold the diamond abrasives during rough and fine grinding, such as diamond on cast-iron or cedar wheels, rosewood rods, and resin- or metal-bonded diamond laps. Depending on the smoothness of the cut, preparation commences with 60-, 45-, or 30-μm diamond discs. With automatic devices, relatively high pressures and short times (1 to 2 min) are used with a wheel speed of about 300 r/min and copious water cooling. Coarser grits may be required if an as-sintered surface is being ground.

Rough polishing is generally conducted using 6- or 3-μm diamond paste on nylon, Texmet, or Pellon cloths. Polishing times of 1 to 2 min are used with very high pressure and low (150 r/min) wheel speeds. Final polishing frequently uses

1-μm diamond paste on a low-nap or napless cloth with high pressure for about 1 min. Some prefer to finish samples with ¼-μm diamond paste on Microcloth. These procedures are necessary to minimize relief in cemented carbides in which the binder, generally cobalt, is much softer than the carbides. Examples of tungsten carbide–cobalt samples are given in Chap. 3.

2-12.5 Carbonaceous Materials

In recent years, the metallographic preparation of pyrolytic graphite and coal or coke has received considerable attention. Polishing of these materials requires different procedures because of their softness. Most work is conducted in reflected light, usually with oil immersion objectives, although some thin sectioning has been performed.

Techniques for polishing pyrolytic graphite have been described by Coons [88] and Brassard and Holik [89]. Coons used a high-speed diamond saw to cut samples. Sectioning with a hacksaw or bandsaw was not recommended. Lucite was used to mount samples by allowing the powder to become plastic before application of pressure to prevent crushing, buckling, or delamination. The applied pressure was about half that normally used. Samples were ground with 240- and 320-grit SiC paper followed by 0, 3/0, and 4/0 emery paper. Rough polishing was done using heavy hand pressure with 1-μm diamond paste on Microcloth for 2 to 3 min. Final polishing was performed with the Curtiss-Wright Burrell automatic polisher ("iron cross"), a forerunner of the Leco Fini-Pol device. C-RO polishing compound was applied to Microcloth plus a fair amount of 5% aqueous CrO_3 (attack polish). Polishing required about 10 min.

Brassard and Holik mounted samples in epoxy and used 240-, 400-, and 600-grit SiC paper lubricated with water for grinding [89]. Rough polishing was performed with 1-μm aluminum oxide abrasive on felt lubricated with soapy water. Moderate to heavy pressure was applied. Vibratory polishing with 0.1-μm alumina on Microcloth for 30 min completed the process. For sections parallel to the basal plane, magnesium oxide abrasive on Microcloth and very light pressure on a 200 r/min wheel were used. Porous samples were vacuum impregnated.

Polishing of coal and coke involves two basic sample preparation procedures, i.e., use of either lump samples or crushed pellets. Since coal is a very heterogeneous material, it is rather challenging to obtain representative samples for reflectivity analysis and maceral (coal constituents) point counting. Guidelines are provided in Ref. 90 and in ASTM D2797. Blocks of coal or coke can be cut to size with a diamond saw followed by vacuum impregnation with epoxy.

In order to produce representative pellets, a large quantity of the wet or damp coal or coke is dried and then subjected to a series of crushing, sieving, and splitting operations to produce a small quantity of −20-mesh material suitable for mounting [90]. Mounting involves mixing of 5 to 10 volume percent of epoxy (colored black) with a small quantity of coal. The epoxy must be thoroughly mixed with the grains. This mixture is placed in a steel mold that is used with a simple laboratory mounting press plus a mold release agent. The mold assembly is subjected to a pressure of about 4600 lb/in² for 3 to 5 s, and the pressure is then

Vitrinite and semifusinite (white)

Figure 2-32 Microstructure of coal, 150×.

released. This process is repeated about 20 times to remove entrapped air and form a dense compact. Finally, the sample is removed from the mold and allowed to cure.

Automatic grinding and polishing devices are preferred [90]. Grinding commences with 240-grit SiC water-cooled paper for 2 min at a low speed, about 150 r/min. This is followed in similar fashion with 400- and 600-grit SiC paper. After ultrasonic cleaning, the samples are rough-polished with 3-μm alumina on Texmet or Pellon. Polishing begins at zero pressure. Low pressure is applied and then increased after the cloth begins to discolor. Polishing is halted after 2 min.

Final polishing is performed by applying a sheet of adhesive-backed Texmet to a wheel and covering it with two layers of silk [90]. A 1:1 mixture of 0.05-μm alumina and water is applied to the wheel. The same pressure application method is used as for rough polishing. After 2 min, the polishing solution is flushed off and polishing is continued for another minute. Other procedures using diamond paste for rough polishing have been employed. Figure 2-32 shows the microstructure of a coal sample.

2-12.6 Ceramics

Sample preparation of ceramic materials is performed in the same manner as borides and carbides. Vacuum impregnation with epoxy is widely employed with ceramics. Since ceramic materials are quite brittle, care is required in sectioning. Since most are quite hard, diamond cutoff wheels are used. SiC grinding paper is employed with some ceramics, although metal-bonded diamond discs have wider applicability and are very effective. A recent innovation in fine grinding is the introduction of a steel-mesh cloth (Struers DP-NET) with either 6- or 3-μm diamond spray and a wheel speed of 150 r/min. This step is used after rough grinding on coarse metal-bonded diamond discs. Figure 2-33 shows the microstructure of MgO.

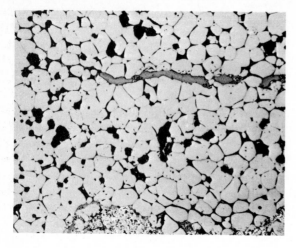

Pitch-bonded MgO

Figure 2-33 Microstructure of as-polished ceramic sample, 75×.

2-12.7 Composites

Polishing of composites generally requires careful control of relief. Thus, low-nap or napless cloths are preferred. Automatic devices are often preferred over hand polishing. For sectioning, embedding in epoxy will prevent damage to the composite. Fiber-reinforced composites present problems because of the vast difference in properties between the matrix and fiber. Thin cutoff wheels, light pressure, and copious cooling are required.

Grinding can usually be performed with water-cooled SiC papers in the usual grit sequence. Sometimes, grits finer than 600 are used. Rough polishing is commonly done using nylon, Texmet, or Pellon, while final polishing employs softer synthetic cloths.

2-12.8 Minerals

Minerals are commonly examined either using polished opaque specimens and reflected light or using thin sections and transmitted light. If the thin section is polished, it can be examined with both reflected and transmitted light [91, 92]. Thus, a wide range of techniques are used to prepare minerals, and the choice is influenced by the extreme range of sample characteristics and mixtures that are encountered. Sectioning is generally performed using diamond cutoff wheels, which produce a flat, smooth surface and eliminate the coarser grinding steps needed to flatten samples. Vacuum impregnation with epoxy is probably the most common mounting procedure, a necessity for filling cracks often present in minerals. A second impregnation step on the rough-polished surface is also required with many samples. Either water-cooled SiC paper or metal-bonded diamond discs are used for grinding, depending on specimen hardness. Since the cut surfaces are reasonably smooth, grinding can commence with 240-grit SiC. Rough polishing is generally performed with one or more grades of diamond paste using low-nap or napless cloths. Fine polishing is frequently conducted using 0.3-μm alpha alumina and 0.05-μm gamma alumina, although most final polishing abrasives can be used. For some ores, a satisfactory final polish is obtained with 1-μm diamond paste.

The petrographic thin-section technique was developed by Sorby in 1850, and the same basic procedure is still used today. To prepare a thin section, two parallel cuts are made about ⅛ in (3 mm) apart. It may be necessary to pot the sample in epoxy in order to hold the sample and to reduce fracturing during cutting. The sectioned sample should measure about ½ by 1 in (12 by 25 mm). A few grinding machines can grind both sides simultaneously while maintaining exact parallel dimensions. Alternatively, the sample can be held against a rotating wheel or lap by hand to grind the surfaces. Next, the sample is cemented to a glass slide, placed in a petrographic slide holder, and ground with 320- and 600-grit SiC or a medium-grade diamond disc until the sample is about 50 μm thick. This is followed by hand grinding with 5- to 10-μm alumina on a slowly rotating wheel until the thickness is about 30 μm. A cover glass is glued onto the top surface of the sample, or a clear, colorless acrylic spray is used. Additional information can be obtained, especially if some of the structure is opaque, if the top surface is polished to a fine finish so that the sample can be examined with both reflected and transmitted light.

Recently, techniques have been developed to prepare ultrathin, 1- to 5-μm thick, doubly polished thin sections which provide vastly improved transparency and resolution. This technique has been described by Beauchamp and Williford [92]. They employed a unique mounting procedure that is critical to successful implementation of the technique. The sample is placed in a Silastic mold and partly filled with epoxy (Maraset 655 and 555 catalyst, Marblette Corporation). While the sample is being impregnated with epoxy in a vacuum chamber, a portion of the same batch of epoxy is filled with 0.3-μm alumina powder and stirred. When outgassing is completed, the sample is removed from the vacuum chamber and glass beads are carefully placed around the sample perimeter. The mold is then filled with the epoxy-alumina mixture and cured overnight at 80°C. The glass beads and alumina help maintain sample flatness. The alumina settles to the bottom of the mount and serves as a reference for thickness control during thinning.

Depending on the sample hardness, the exposed (first) side is ground flat either with a 120-grit SiC belt or on a 45-μm diamond-bonded wheel. Then, it is ground sequentially with 30-, 15-, and 9-μm diamond-bonded wheels, with water cooling. A fixed abrasive is preferred over loose abrasive because the depth of subsurface fracturing is reduced and a flatter sample can be obtained, which is critical in ultrathinning. Polishing is conducted with a vibratory polisher using water-dispersed diamond slurries on Pellon. Samples are placed in 800- to 1100-g weights and run overnight.

After a satisfactory polish has been obtained on the first side, the mount is clamped in a diamond saw and sliced parallel to the first side to produce a thickness between 1 and 3 mm. The polished surface is cemented to the well side of a standard petrographic slide with the mounting epoxy. The glue line is outgassed under vacuum and worked down by pressing on the section. The glue is allowed to cure overnight at 80°C. After curing, the sample should be slowly cooled to ambient temperature to avoid thermal shock problems.

The second side is polished in the same way as the first. Rough thinning is stopped when light can just be seen through the alumina. Lapping is continued with a 15-μm diamond wheel until the sample is 15 to 20 μm thick. The alumina is highly translucent at this point. Thinning is continued with a 9-μm diamond wheel or with 3- or 1-μm diamond paste on a vibratory polisher. The second side must be completely polished, with only a few micrometers thickness remaining. Doubly polished ultrathin sections can be examined with either transmitted or reflected light using bright-field, polarized, or interference contrast illumination and produce much information, as demonstrated by the work of Beauchamp and Williford [92].

2-12.9 Polymers

Recent studies have shown that the properties of polymers are controlled not only by their composition and the size of their molecules but also by the structure produced by the arrangement of the macromolecules. Samples can be prepared using several techniques. Thin foils can be made directly from the melt, but the structure observed is not representative of bulk samples. Thus, examination of thick polished samples using reflected light or thin sections using transmitted light is most common [93, 94].

Specimen mounting is generally done with cold-setting resins, chiefly epoxy. Polishing of bulk specimens is done using traditional metallographic methods for soft materials. Wet grinding is performed using 240- to 600-grit SiC papers followed by diamond polishing with 6- or 3-μm paste on a synthetic cloth. Finer diamond abrasives can also be used. Vibratory polishing with alumina is a popular finishing step.

Holik et al. have described a technique for preparing thin sections of polymeric materials [93]. A thin sample is cut and mounted in epoxy. Polyester resins are not recommended because they tend to swell and craze the specimen. After curing, the sample is ground with 240-, 400-, and 600-grit aluminum oxide paper discs followed by grinding with 8- and 3-μm aluminum oxide–coated polyester discs. Water is used as the coolant during grinding. Next, the samples are polished with 1- and then 0.3-μm alumina-water slurries on nylon. Final polishing employs 0.05-μm alumina on Microcloth. Overpolishing must be avoided to minimize relief.

The polished face is now ready for mounting on a glass slide so that the opposite face can be polished. Most of the mount is cut away, leaving an epoxy border around the sample for containment. This slice is reduced in size to fit on the slide, and the polished surface is glued to the slide. The sample is placed in a petrographic sample holder to facilitate grinding and polishing. The grinding process is repeated on the top side until the sample is 100 to 125 μm thick. This surface is polished as before to produce a thickness of 25 to 75 μm. Linke and Kopp have described a similar method for producing thin sections of polymers [94]. Figure 2-34 shows an example of a polymer structure.

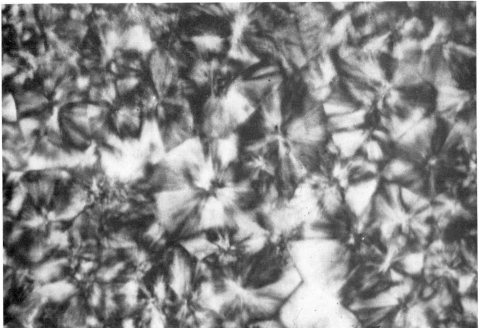

Figure 2-34 The structure of polyamide. Top, polished bulk sample etched with xylol, photographed with interference contrast illumination. 100×. Bottom, thin section examined in transmitted polarized light, 100×. *(Courtesy of W. U. Kopp, K & B Grubbs Instrument GmbH & Co. KG.)*

2-13 SAFETY

The metallographic laboratory is a relatively safe working environment, but there are many potential hazards. With use of good common sense and adherence to simple guidelines, these hazards can be minimized. Every metallographer should be familiar with the dangers inherent to the materials used in the laboratory. Information is available in the literature [95–99] to supplement the comments given here. The paper by Anderson [95], "Safety in the Metallographic Laboratory," should be read by all metallographers and consulted regularly. Likewise, the book by Sax [96] should be accessible for ready reference whenever dealing with unfamiliar chemicals or solvents.

Safe working habits begin with good housekeeping and cleanliness habits. A neat, orderly laboratory promotes safe working habits, while a sloppy, messy work area invites disaster. Good working habits include such obvious, common-sense items as washing the hands after handling chemicals or before eating. Simple carelessness can cause accidents, for example, failure to clean glassware after use can cause an accident for the next user. Another common problem is burns due to failure to properly clean acid spills or splatter.

Many of the chemicals used in metallography are toxic, corrosive, flammable, or potentially explosive. Therefore, only small quantities that are likely to be used within a reasonably short time should be stored. Flammable solvents must be protected from heat; metal cabinets close to the floor are ideal. Bottles of strong acids or bases should not be stored on a shelf where they can fall and break. Oxidizable materials should not be stored in the same cabinet with oxidizing agents.

Most reagents, chemical or electrolytic polishing electrolytes, and solvents should be used under a ventilation hood designed for use with chemicals. Many of the chemicals used in metallography can cause serious damage on contact. It is best to assume that all chemicals are toxic and all vapors or fumes will be toxic if inhaled or will be damaging to the eyes. A hood will prevent the working area from being contaminated with these fumes. However, you will not be protected when your head is inside the hood. In most cases, a protective plastic or shatterproof glass shield can be drawn across the front of the hood for further protection from splattering or any unexpected reactions. Most hoods contain a sink for washing and for disposal of solutions. Disposal is sometimes a serious problem. When in doubt about the safety of a procedure, a chemist or the cited references should be consulted. Strong acids should be highly diluted with water before being poured down the drain. This dilution step is necessary because one never knows what chemicals may be in the drain system and it also extends the life of the plumbing. Chemical polishing solutions or etchants containing substantial hydrofluoric acid (HF) are particularly harsh on plumbing. Disposal of chemicals, such as anhydrous aluminum chloride or metallic sodium, that react violently with water are a serious problem. Many hoods contain adequate shelf area for storage of small (50 to 500 mL) bottles of acids and stock etching solutions. Bottles should always be identified with neat, legible, permanent labels.

All laboratories should be equipped with a shower and an eyewash for emergency use. This equipment should be near the work area so that the injured can reach it quickly and easily. Fire alarms and fire extinguishers (CO_2 type) should be available and tested periodically.

Sample preparation devices used in metallographic laboratories are generally quite safe to use. Information supplied by the manufacturer usually describes safe operating procedures. It is good laboratory practice to prepare a job safety analysis detailing potential hazards and describing the safe operating procedure for each piece of equipment. This information should be provided to all users.

Bandsaws or abrasive cutoff saws are commonly used by metallographers. The cutting area of bandsaws is exposed and a potential danger. Your hands should never be used to guide the workpiece during cutting. A guiding device or block of wood should always be used between the workpiece and your hands. After cutting is completed, the saw should be turned off before samples near the blade are removed. Samples should be handled carefully, since considerable heat can be generated. In addition, sharp burrs are often present, which should be carefully removed by filing or grinding. Abrasive cutoff saws are safer to use because the cutting area is usually closed off during use. The chief danger is from flying pieces from a broken wheel. Fortunately, the closed cover contains these pieces within the cutting chamber. Wheel breakage usually occurs when the part is not firmly clamped in place or if excessive pressure is applied, a bad practice from the standpoint of specimen damage as well.

The dust produced during grinding of metals is always dangerous. For certain metals, like beryllium, magnesium, lead, manganese, and silver, the dusts are extremely toxic. Wet grinding is preferred both for dust control and for preventing heat damage to the sample. Bench grinders must be firmly mounted to prevent sudden movement. Care must be exercised to avoid grinding one's fingers or striking the edge of a grinding belt, which will cause painful lacerations. Dust can also be generated on low-speed grinding wheels, but this is less of a problem as the grit size becomes finer. With nearly all samples, wet grinding is preferred and produces best results. For routine handling of dangerous metals, grinding should be done wet under a ventilation hood. Waste must be handled carefully. Radioactive materials require special remote-handling facilities and elaborate safety precautions.

A drill press is frequently used in the laboratory. Drilling holes in thin samples requires secure clamping, since the sample can be grabbed by the drill and spun around, inflicting serious lacerations. Hair, ties, and shirt cuffs can become tangled in a drill, inflicting serious injuries. Safety glasses should always be worn when using drill presses or when cutting or grinding. Mounting presses or laboratory heat-treatment furnaces present potential burn hazards. Gloves should be worn when working with these devices. It is also good practice to place a "hot" sign in front of a laboratory furnace when it is in use.

While the metallography laboratory is generally a fairly safe place, it is rather rough on clothing. A laboratory coat is useful for protecting the operator's clothing but provides little safety protection from acids. Lab coats should be changed regularly. For handling acids, a rubberized or plastic-coated apron provides much better protection. The former is rather hot and heavy, while the latter is generally more comfortable. Many types of gloves are available and are useful for handling bulk samples and for working with hot material or hazardous solutions. Lightweight surgeons' gloves are very popular for attack polishing, since the operator retains the ability to "feel" the sample. These gloves should always be checked for holes, since they are easily punctured. Thicker rubber gloves are often used for handling samples during macroetching, chemical polishing, pickling, etc. The gloves should always be checked first for small holes or cracks. Since the operator's hands generally perspire when using rubber gloves, it is sometimes difficult to tell if the moisture is due solely to perspiration or to leakage. Gloves can impart a false sense of security, and in many cases, there may be better techniques available that make the use of gloves unnecessary. A chemical face shield is useful when handling large quantities of hazardous liquids.

It is occasionally necessary to heat solutions during their preparation or use. Although bunsen burners are commonly employed for this purpose, it is better to use a hot plate or water bath and thus avoid the use of an open flame. If a bunsen burner is used, the flame should never be applied directly to a flask, beaker, or dish. A plain or asbestos-centered wire gauze should always be placed between the flame and the container.

Most laboratories mix commonly used reagents in quantities of 250 to 1000 mL and then store them as stock reagents. Many reagents can be safely handled in this manner. It is best to store only those reagents that are used regularly. Glass-stoppered bottles are commonly used as stock reagent bottles. If these bottles are opened regularly, the stopper will not become "frozen." However, if they are used infrequently, a frozen stopper often results. They can usually be loosened by holding the neck of the bottle under a stream of hot water. If thermal expansion does not free the stopper, the stopper can be gently tapped with a piece of wood. Glass bottles with plastic screw-on tops can be used so long as the solution does not attack the plastic. These bottles are useful for holding solutions, such as nital, that can build up gas pressure within a tightly stoppered bottle. A small hole can be drilled through the cap top to serve as a pressure relief vent. Tightly stoppered bottles of nital and some other solutions have exploded as the result of pressure buildup. One should make certain that the reagent is safe to store and store only small quantities. All bottles should be clearly labeled. Polyethylene bottles are required for etchants containing hydrofluoric acid, which attacks glass.

Most recipes for etchants or electrolytes list the ingredients by weight if they are solids and by volume if they are liquids. In a few cases, all amounts are given in weight percentages. In most metallographic studies, the compositions of reagents are not extremely critical. An ordinary laboratory balance provides adequate weighing accuracy, while graduated cylinders provide acceptable accuracy for volumetric measurements. These devices should be cleaned after use to prevent accidents to the next user. For weight measurements, a clean piece of filter paper should be placed on the balance pan to hold the chemical, to protect the pan surface, and to facilitate transfer to the mixing beaker. A large graduated beaker is usually employed for mixing solutions. Again, when using HF, all containers should be made of polyethylene. With some chemicals, the mixing order is important, especially when dangerous chemicals are used. When water is specified, distilled water should always be used, since most tap water contains minerals or may be chlorinated or fluorinated. Tap water can produce poor results or unexpected problems. Cold water should always be used, never warm or hot water, which can cause a reaction to become violent. In mixing, one should start with the solvents, such as water and alcohol, then dissolve the specified salts. A magnetic stirring device is of great value. Then, the dangerous chemicals, such as acids, should be added carefully and slowly while the solution is being stirred. Whenever sulfuric acid (H_2SO_4) is specified, it should be added last. It should be added slowly while stirring, and it should be cooled, if necessary, to minimize heating. If sulfuric acid is added to water without stirring, it can collect at the bottom of the beaker and enough local heating can occur to throw the contents out of the beaker.

Reagent-grade chemicals or solvents of highest purity should always be used for metallographic work. Although these grades are more expensive, the amounts used are small and the gain in safety and reliability more than compensates for the cost difference. Since chemicals may deteriorate during storage, only reasonably small quantities should be purchased. Since light can accelerate deterioration of some chemicals, they should be stored in a closed metal cabinet.

The metallographic literature contains references to a great many formulas for etchants, chemical polishes, and electrolytes that are extremely dangerous. In many of these references, no comments are included regarding safe handling procedures or potential hazards. Fortunately, metallographic applications involve small quantities of these solutions, and accidents do not usually produce catastrophic results. However, even with small solution volumes considerable damage can be, and has been, done. Anderson cites numerous examples of such problems [95].

2-13.1 Solvents

Numerous organic solvents are employed in metallography for cleaning or in chemical or electrolytic polishing solutions or etchants, in which they are used to control ionization or the speed and mode of attack. Commonly employed solvents include water, acetone, benzene, ethyl ether, ethylene glycol, glycerin, kerosene, petroleum ether, trichloroethylene, butyl cellosolve, and alcohols, such as amyl alcohol, ethanol, methanol, and isopropyl alcohol. Most are flammable and their vapors can form explosive mixtures with air. They should be kept closed when not in use and should be stored in a cool place away from heat and open flames.

Acetone (CH_3COCH_3) is a colorless liquid with a fragrant mintlike odor. It is volatile and very flammable and a dangerous fire hazard. It is an irritant to the eyes and the mucous membranes.

Benzene (C_6H_6) is a clear, colorless liquid. Its vapors are very toxic. The liquid is highly volatile, and it is a potential fire and explosion hazard. Benzene accumulates in the body and can cause serious injury to the blood. Its use is often prohibited.

Ethyl ether ($C_2H_5OC_2H_5$) can form peroxides, which can explode if heated to about 100°C. Static electricity can cause ignition and explosion of the vapors. Containers should be electrically grounded. Petroleum ether is somewhat similar but less dangerous.

Butyl cellosolve ($C_4H_9OCH_2CH_2OH$) is a colorless liquid with a rancid odor that is used in electropolishing solutions. Although flammable, it is not a dangerous fire hazard. Its vapors irritate the mucous membranes, eyes, skin, and respiratory tract.

Carbitol (diethylene glycol monoethyl ether) is a colorless, viscous solvent that is compatible with water and is used in electropolishing solutions. It irritates the skin, although not as badly as glycerin. It is a moderate fire hazard and is poisonous if ingested.

Ethylene glycol ($HOCH_2CH_2OH$) is a colorless liquid with a sweet taste. It is about as toxic as methanol but is not as readily absorbed in the body. It is flammable and is a moderate fire hazard.

Glycerin (glycerol) ($CH_2OHCHOHCH_2OH$) is a colorless or pale yellow, odorless, syrupy liquid with a sweet, warm taste. It is relatively nontoxic and nonvolatile but can cause iritis (inflammation of the iris). It is combustible and is a moderate fire hazard. Glycerin should never be used in anhydrous solutions containing nitric and sulfuric acids, since nitroglycerin can form. Glycerin is often added to aqua regia. This mixture decomposes readily and should be discarded immediately after use. This etchant should not be allowed to stand for more than about 15 min after mixing.

Kerosene is occasionally employed in grinding samples and with diamond paste as a lubricant. Only the deodorized form should be used for metallographic purposes. It is flammable, but the vapors do not readily explode. Contact can cause dermatitis and other problems.

Trichloroethylene ($CHCl{=}CCl_2$) is a stable, colorless liquid with a chloroformlike odor. At ambient temperatures it is nonflammable and nonexplosive but becomes hazardous at higher temperatures. In the presence of strong alkalies, with which it can react, it can form explosive mixtures. It is toxic when inhaled or ingested, which may cause acute poisoning.

Toluene ($C_6H_5CH_3$) is a solvent similar to benzene. It is flammable and is a dangerous fire hazard. Its vapors are toxic. Xylene [$C_6H_4(CH_3)_2$] is a colorless solvent used to remove oil or grease. It is flammable and is a dangerous fire and explosive hazard. It is not as toxic as benzene or toluene. Its vapors are poisonous.

Amyl alcohol ($CH_3(CH_2)_3CH_2OH$) is a colorless liquid with noxious odor. It is flammable and is a moderate fire hazard. It is very toxic, and its fumes are irritating to the eyes and upper respiratory tract.

Ethyl alcohol (CH_3CH_2OH), or ethanol, is a colorless, inoffensive solvent commonly used in metallography. Ethanol is hydroscopic and rapidly absorbs up to 5% water from the air. The denatured version is less expensive and contains 5% absolute methanol. Denatured ethanol is suitable for any recipe requiring ethyl alcohol. It is a dangerous fire hazard, and its vapors are irritating to the eyes and upper respiratory tract. High concentrations of its vapor can produce intoxication. Because ethanol is completely burned in the body, it is not a cumulative poison like methanol. Solutions containing additions of up to 2% nitric acid (nital) can be safely mixed and stored in small quantities. Higher concentrations result in pressure buildup in tightly stoppered bottles. Explosions of 5% nitric acid in ethanol have occurred as a result of failure to relieve the pressure [95]. If higher concentrations are desired, they can be mixed daily, placed in an open dish, and used safely. The etch should be discarded at the end of the day. Pouring a small amount of concentrated nitric acid into a bottle containing a small quantity of aged nital can result in formation of nitrous oxide fumes and spewing of the liquid from the bottle.

Methyl alcohol (CH_3OH) is an excellent, nonhydroscopic solvent, but it is a cumulative poison. Ingestion or absorption damages the central nervous system, kidneys, liver, heart, and other organs. Blindness has resulted from severe poisoning. It is particularly dangerous because repeated low-level exposures can also cause acute poisoning as a result of accumulation. Thus, whenever possible, ethanol should be used. When using methanol, one should always work under a ventilation hood. Mixtures of methanol and sulfuric acid can form dimethyl sulfate, which is extremely toxic. Solutions of methanol and nitric acid are more stable than mixtures of nitric acid and higher alcohols. Mixtures of up to 5% nitric acid are safe to use and store in small quantities. Mixtures with more than 5% nitric acid if heated are subject to violent decomposition. Mixtures of 33% nitric acid in methanol have decomposed suddenly and violently [95].

Isopropyl alcohol ($CH_3CHOHCH_3$) is a clear, colorless liquid which, like ethanol, does not accumulate in the body, although it does have a strong narcotic effect. It is a flammable liquid and is a dangerous fire hazard. It is toxic but not highly dangerous because of its good warning properties.

2-13.2 Acids

Both inorganic and organic acids are common constituents in chemical and electrolytic polishing solutions and in etchants. The inorganic, or mineral acids, include the very familar acids such as hydrochloric, nitric, perchloric, phosphoric, and sulfuric. In general, the mineral acids are highly corrosive and poisonous. They should be stored in a cool, well-ventilated location away from potential fire hazards and, of course, away from open flames. They should not be stored in a location that receives direct sunlight. When the pure acids contact metals, most liberate hydrogen gas—a fire and explosion hazard. The organic acids are naturally occurring substances in sour milk, fruits, and plants and include the following acids: acetic, lactic, citric, oxalic, and tartaric.

Hydrochloric acid (HCl), which is widely used in metallography, is a colorless gas or fuming liquid with a choking odor. It is very dangerous to the eyes and irritating to the nose and throat. It attacks the skin strongly.

Nitric acid (HNO_3), which is also widely used in metallography, is a colorless or yellowish fuming liquid which is highly toxic and dangerous to the eyes. If it contacts organic material or other easily oxidizable materials, it can cause fires and possibly explosions. When it reacts with other materials, toxic oxides of nitrogen are produced. The oxides, which vary with the conditions, include nitrous acid, nitrogen dioxide, nitric oxide, nitrous oxide, and hydroxylamine. A commonly encountered problem involves pouring nitric acid into a graduated cylinder which contains some methanol or ethanol from prior use. The brown fumes given off are quite harmful. Mixtures of nitric acid and alcohols higher than ethanol should not be stored. Mixtures of concentrated nitric and sulfuric acids are extremely dangerous, while strong mixtures of nitric acid and glycerin or glycols can be explosive. Aqua regia, a mixture of one part nitric acid and two to four parts hydrochloric acid, forms several products including nitrosyl chloride, an exceptionally toxic gas. Aqua regia is a popular etchant but must be used with care under a hood.

Several etchants containing nitric acid have been reported to be quite unstable. Satz reported that the mixed acids in glycerol etchant (20 mL HF, 10 mL HNO_3, and 30 mL glycerol) are unstable if allowed to stand (after 18 h at 20°C, after 8 h at 30 to 35°C, or after 1 min at 100°C) [100]. If stainless steel is immersed in the solution, a violent bubbling reaction will occur at 20°C after 3 to 4 h. The reagent should be used fresh and discarded promptly after use. Warren reported a similar problem with an etch consisting of 20 to 30 mL HCl, 10 mL HNO_3, and 30 mL glycerol when left at room temperature for 2 to 3 h [101]. Fox and Frant reported that a closed bottle containing 40 mL acetic acid, 40 mL acetone, and 40 mL nitric acid used to etch nickel exploded 4 h after preparation [102]. Lane and Durmann reported that a mixture of 10 mL nitric acid, 10 mL acetic acid, and 20 mL acetone reacted spontaneously about 2 min after mixing, with evolution of heat and nitrous and nitric oxide fumes [103]. This problem can be controlled by cooling the acid mixture and then slowly pouring it into the acetone cooled with a cold-water bath. The solution should be kept cold and discarded immediately after use.

Bubar and Vermilyea reported that a chemical polishing solution for zirconium containing 5 parts lactic acid, 5 parts nitric acid, 2 parts water, and one part hydrofluoric acid is unstable and should not be stored [104]. Lactic acid and nitric acid react autocatalytically, producing heat and gas some time after mixing. The pressure from the evolution of gas was high enough to rupture the plastic container. Green reported a similar storage explosion of a chemical polishing solution for niobium and tantalum which consisted of 50 mL lactic acid, 30 mL nitric acid, and 2 mL hydrofluoric acid [105].

Fuming nitric acid is nitric acid with additional NO_2 and N_2O_4. It is more toxic and more reactive than ordinary nitric acid. Although recommended in certain etching and chemical polishes, it is extremely hazardous to use and is not recommended.

Sulfuric acid (H_2SO_4) is a colorless, oily liquid which is highly corrosive and dangerously reactive and is a strong oxidizing agent. It reacts with water and organics, with evolution of substantial heat. Thus, one should add sulfuric acid very slowly to water with constant stirring. If added without stirring, it will produce a pocket of steam in the bottom of the vessel, throwing the contents out of the vessel. Contact with the concentrated acid produces rapid destruction of tissues and severe burns. Repeated contact with dilute solutions produces dermatitis, while repeated inhalation of the vapors can lead to chronic bronchitis.

Hydrofluoric acid (HF) is a clear, colorless, fuming liquid or gas with a sharp, penetrating odor. It is very dangerous to the eyes, skin, and upper respiratory tract. Although it is a relatively weak mineral acid, it will attack glass or silicon compounds, and because of the toxicity of its fumes and drastic attack on the skin, it is very dangerous to handle. Fluorides in general are very toxic, almost as dangerous as cyanides.

Orthophosphoric acid (H_3PO_4), the most important acid of phosphorus, is not as dangerous as nitric, sulfuric, or hydrofluoric acids. Phosphoric acid is toxic and corrosive and is a dangerous fire hazard. Reactions with metals are not usually dangerous. Skin contact should be avoided. Phosphoric acid can react with certain organic compounds forming organophosphorus nerve-gas-type compounds that are extremely toxic.

Perchloric acid ($HClO_4$) is one of the strongest known acids. Since concentrations greater than about 72% are extremely unstable, commercially available perchloric acids come in concentrations of 70 to 72% or less. In this form, contact with perchloric acid will cause irritation and burns, while its fumes are highly irritating to the mucous membranes. In contact with organic or other easily oxidized materials, it can form highly unstable perchlorates, which can ignite or cause explosions. One should never electropolish samples mounted in Bakelite or other plastics in perchloric acid solutions. Regular use of perchloric acid requires special fume hoods with a waterfall type of fume washer to remove the perchlorate fumes before they can enter the exhaust system.

Perchloric acid is very useful in electropolishing solutions. The mixture of perchloric acid and acetic anhydride, which was developed by Jacquet, is difficult to prepare and highly explosive [106, 107]. Jacquet has reviewed the accidents involving perchloric acid and has described safety procedures [106]. The worst accident occurred on February 20, 1947, in an electroplating factory in Los Angeles. In this accident 17 people were killed and 150 were injured. Medard, Jacquet, and Sartorius have prepared a ternary diagram showing safe compositions of perchloric acid, acetic anhydride, and water (see Fig. 2-35). Anderson, however, states that accidents have still occurred with solutions in the "safe" region of this diagram [95]. Thus, electropolishing solutions composed of perchloric acid and acetic anhydride are not recommended. Indeed, many companies forbid the use of such mixtures, and some cities have banned their use. Electropolishing solutions of perchloric acid and alcohol, with or without organic additions, and mixtures of perchloric acid and glacial acetic acid are safe to use. Nevertheless, in using these "safe" mixtures, one should follow the formula instructions carefully, mix only small quantities, keep the temperature under control, and avoid evaporation. These solutions should not be stored.

Comas et al. have studied the hazards associated with mixtures consisting of

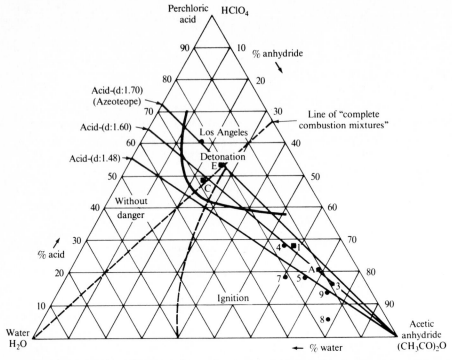

Figure 2-35 Ternary diagram showing safe and dangerous combinations of perchloric acid, acetic anhydride, and water. Points 1 to 9 represent electrolyte compositions suggested by Jacquet. Point A is the composition at which all the water is from the perchloric acid. Point C is a mixture representing complete combustion. Point E and "Los Angeles" (see text) represent compositions that produced explosions. *(From Jacquet, Ref. 106, courtesy of Metal Finishing, Metals and Plastics Publications, Inc.)*

butyl cellosolve and from 10 to 95% of 70% perchloric acid [107]. Mixtures with 60 to 90% acid were explosive at room temperature. Acid concentrations of 30% or less were inflammable but were judged to be safe to use as long as the operating temperature does not exceed 20°C.

Bismuth, or metals containing bismuth, should never be electropolished in perchloric acid solutions because an explosive compound is formed. Anderson suggests that arsenic, antimony, and tin may also be incompatible with perchloric electrolytes [95].

Acetic acid (CH_3COOH) is a clear, colorless liquid with a pungent odor. It is a good solvent and is not easily oxidized or decomposed. Although it is flammable, it is not easily ignited. Contact with the skin results in serious burns. Inhalation of the fumes irritates the mucous membranes. Anderson states that acetic acid is a good solvent for nitric acid and that a 50% solution can be prepared, but not stored, without danger [95]. Sax, however, states that mixtures of nitric and acetic acids are dangerous [96].

Acetic anhydride [(CH$_3$CO)$_2$O], or acetic oxide, is a colorless liquid with a very strong acetic odor. It is very damaging to the eyes and dangerously reactive with water or sulfuric acid. Dawkins reported an accident involving a mixture of chromium trioxide and acetic anhydride that had been used for electropolishing [108]. A 100-g quantity of CrO$_3$ was dissolved in 200 mL of water. The solution was cooled to ambient temperature and 700 mL of acetic anhydride was added in a slow stream with constant stirring. The beaker became warm to the touch. After about 20 s, the solution erupted from the beaker.

Citric acid [C$_3$H$_4$(OH)(COOH)$_3$·H$_2$O] comes as colorless, odorless crystals that are water-soluble. No unusual problems are encountered except for occasional allergic reactions. Lactic acid (CH$_3$CHOHCOOH) is a yellow or colorless thick liquid. It is damaging to the eyes.

Oxalic acid (COOHCOOH·2H$_2$O) comes as transparent, colorless crystals. It is poisonous if ingested and irritating to the upper respiratory tract and digestive system if inhaled. Skin contact produces caustic action and will discolor and embrittle the fingernails. It is not compatible with nitric acid.

Picric acid [(NO$_2$)$_3$C$_6$H$_2$OH], or trinitrophenol, comes as yellow crystals that are wet with 10 to 20% water. When picric acid is dry, it is a dangerous explosive. It is toxic and stains the skin. Picrates, which are metal salts of picric acid, are explosive. When picrates are dry, they can detonate readily, possibly spontaneously. One should purchase small quantities and store them in a safe, cool place. Picric acid is nearly insoluble in water. The maximum solubility of picric acid in ethanol is about 6 g per 100 mL. Picral can be stored safely. During use, the solution should not be allowed to dry out. The etching residue should be discarded at the end of the day to avoid potential explosions.

Tartaric acid [HOOC(CHOH)$_2$COOH] is a relatively weak acid. It is flammable and is a moderate fire hazard. It should not be stored near powerful oxidizing agents.

2-13.3 Other Chemicals

Bases, such as ammonium hydroxide (NH$_4$OH), potassium hydroxide (KOH), and sodium hydroxide (NaOH), are commonly used in metallography. Ammonium hydroxide is a minor fire and explosive hazard, while sodium and potassium hydroxide are not flammable. Sodium and potassium hydroxides are strong bases and will destroy tissue, causing severe burns. They are also very dangerous to the eyes. Inhalation irritates and injures the upper respiratory tract, while ingestion causes serious damage to the digestive system. Potassium and sodium hydroxide are obtained as solid pellets. When they are added to water, much heat is liberated. They should never be dissolved in hot water, since the heat liberated can produce boiling and splattering of the solution.

Hydrogen peroxide (H$_2$O$_2$) is available as a liquid in concentrations of either 3 or 30%. The 3% solution is reasonably safe to use, while the 30% solution is a very powerful oxidant whose effect on the skin is about as harmful as that produced by contact with sulfuric acid. Hydrogen peroxide by itself is not combustible, but if brought in contact with combustible materials, it can produce violent combustion. Hydrogen peroxide is very damaging to the eyes. Because release of oxygen can cause high pressures to develop within the container, the container caps are vented.

Bromine (Br_2) is commonly used in deep-etching solutions. It is a very corrosive, dangerous liquid that should only be handled by well-qualified personnel. Its vapors are extremely irritating to the eyes, skin, and mucous membranes. Skin contact produces deep, penetrating burns that are slow to heal. Contact with organic matter can cause fires.

Chromic acid (H_2CrO_4) is formed when chromium trioxide (CrO_3) is dissolved in water. CrO_3 is used in electropolishing solutions (see previous comment about explosive nature of mixtures with acetic anhydride), and dilute aqueous solutions are widely used for attack polishing. Since it is a powerful oxidant, one should always wear gloves when using it for attack polishing or use automatic devices.

Potassium permanganate ($KMnO_4$) is another powerful oxidant used in etchants. It is a dangerous fire and explosion hazard. Ingestion produces serious damage. $KMnO_4$ and sulfuric acid should never be mixed together because a violent explosion can result. Potassium dichromate ($K_2Cr_2O_7$) is another powerful oxidant that is also used in etchants.

Cyanide compounds are occasionally used in metallographic applications. Potassium cyanide (KCN) and sodium cyanide (NaCN) are extremely dangerous, while potassium ferricyanide ($K_3Fe(CN)_6$), although poisonous, is reasonably safe to use. NaCN and KCN vapors are intensely poisonous. Poisoning can also result from skin contact with NaCN or KCN. They are particularly hazardous when brought in contact with acids or acid fumes because of liberation of hydrogen cyanide, which is extremely toxic and highly flammable.

A number of nitrates, such as ferric nitrate [$Fe(NO_3)_3 \cdot 6H_2O$], lead nitrate [$Pb(NO_3)_6$], and silver nitrate ($AgNO_3$), are employed by metallographers. Since they are powerful oxidizers, they pose a dangerous fire hazard. Most are poisonous and corrosive.

2-13.4 Summary

In general, the metallographic laboratory is a reasonably safe environment. However, depending on the materials being prepared, dangerous situations can arise. Some hazards, such as the preparation of radioactive or reactive metals, are quite obvious, while others are not. In the preceding discussion, some of the potential hazards that can be encountered are summarized; others undoubtedly exist that are not included.

Most accidents can be prevented by simple commonsense rules. It is best to assume that all metal dust and all chemicals are hazardous. Inhalation of dust and fumes, ingestion, or bodily contact should be minimized or totally avoided. Personnal protective equipment is very useful, but it should not be used as a substitute for good laboratory technique. The use of such equipment does not guarantee freedom from injury.

The metallographic literature is filled with references to the use of many dangerous materials, often without any mention of the dangers involved or safe handling procedures. This is unfortunate because the unwary may be injured. Many of us are tempted to experiment when a recommended procedure does not work as claimed. The development of electrolytes, chemical polishing agents, or etchants should be left to those who are fully versed in the potential dangers. Metallographic laboratories should all have some of the referenced safety publications readily available in the laboratory and these safety publications should be consulted when working with new or infrequently used materials.

2-14 SUMMARY

Preparation of samples for light microscopy requires a carefully planned and executed sequence of events tailored to the problems specific to the material being studied. A wide range of techniques are available for polishing metals, ceramics, minerals, and polymers. Each step builds on the previous one, and each must be properly executed.

This chapter has described the damage that is produced during cutting, grinding, and polishing, damage which must be removed by the next step if artifact-free surfaces are to be obtained. Damage in each step must be minimized. With certain samples, the mounting technique can also produce problems; thus, the mounting material and method must be tailored to the material and technique employed. There are few short cuts that can be taken without producing poor or even false results.

The development of automatic preparation devices has greatly simplified sample preparation. An inexperienced technician can be quickly trained to use these machines and can produce satisfactory results. Thus, much of the "art" previously required to obtain quality results is unnecessary. The availability and relative ease of use of automatic preparation devices does not, of course, mean that skilled metallographers are no longer required, but does show that new personnel can be quickly assimilated into the laboratory. Automatic grinding and polishing devices also produce excellent results, frequently better than can be done by hand.

Mechanical polishing can be considered the starting point in sample polishing. The basic sequence of 120- to 600-grit SiC paper for grinding is generally followed by one or two rough polishing steps, usually on napless or low-nap cloths. Final polishing involves use of a fine diamond paste and/or one or more fine abrasives, usually on medium-nap cloths. The final polishing procedure is modified to accommodate the particular material or the specific needs. Specialized final polishing procedures, such as vibratory polishing or attack polishing, are employed as required. With some samples, chemical or electrolytic polishing offers certain advantages, and where applicable, these methods can produce excellent results. In establishing a preparation sequence, the metallographer must be familiar with the specific problems that can be encountered with a given material. If this information is not available, the preparation sequence can be established initially by comparing techniques for materials with similar hardness, crystal structure, or composition. The initial results may need modification. With some materials, considerable information can be obtained with the sample in the as-polished condition, and etching or other similar processes are not needed.

REFERENCES

1. Kehl, G. L.: *The Principles of Metallographic Laboratory Practice,* 3d ed., McGraw-Hill Book Company, New York, 1949.
2. Richardson, J. H.: *Optical Microscopy for the Materials Sciences,* Marcel Dekker, Inc., New York, 1971.
3. Samuels, L. E.: *Metallographic Polishing by Mechanical Methods,* 2d ed., American Elsevier Publishing Company, Inc., New York, 1971; 3d ed., American Society for Metals, Metals Park, Ohio, 1982.
4. McCall, J. L., and W. M. Mueller (eds.): *Metallographic Specimen Preparation,* Plenum Press, Plenum Publishing Corporation, New York, 1974.
5. Szirmae, A., and R. M. Fisher: "Specimen Damage During Cutting and Grinding," *Am. Soc. Test Mater., Spec. Tech. Publ. 372,* 1964, pp. 3–9.
6. Wellner, P.: "Investigations on the Effect of the Cutting Operation on the Surface Deformation of Different Materials," *Prakt. Metallogr.,* vol. 17, 1980, pp. 525–535.
7. Nelson, J. A., and R. M. Westrich: "Abrasive Cutting in Metallography," *Metallographic Specimen Preparation,* Plenum Press, Plenum Publishing Corporation, New York, 1974, pp. 41–54.
8. Nelson, J. A., and W. U. Ahmed: "The Significance of the Coolant/Lubricant in Low Speed Saw Sectioning," *Prakt. Metallogr.,* vol. 13, 1976, pp. 297–305.
9. Stevens, D. W., and R. N. Gillmeister: "Ultramicrotomy of Engineering Materials for Microscopy Analysis," *Microstructural Science,* vol. 5, Elsevier Publishing Company, New York, 1977, pp. 277–285.
10. Miley, D. V., and A. E. Calabra: "A Review of Specimen Mounting Methods for Metallography," *Metallographic Specimen Preparation,* Plenum Press, Plenum Publishing Corporation, New York, 1974, pp. 1–40.
11. Nelson, J. A.: "Modern Methods and Materials for Metallographic Mounting," *Microstructural Science,* vol. 4, Elsevier Publishing Company, New York, 1976, pp. 327–338.
12. Nelson, J. A.: "Heating of Metallographic Specimens Mounted in 'Cold Setting' Resins," *Prakt. Metallogr.,* vol. 7, 1970, pp. 188–191.
13. Baczewski, A.: "Removal of Epoxy Embedment," *Metallography,* vol. 3, 1970, pp. 481–482.
14. Nelson, J. A., and R. M. Slepian: "The Application of Vacuum Impregnation to Five Metallographic Mounting Problems," *Prakt. Metallogr.,* vol. 7, 1970, pp. 510–521.
15. Petretzky, P. B.: "A Production Method for the Vacuum Impregnation of a Large Number of Metallographic Specimens," *Microstructural Science,* vol. 5, Elsevier Publishing Company, New York, 1977, pp. 273–276.
16. Schüller, H.J., and P. Schwaab: "Investigations on Mounting Media," *Prakt. Metallogr.,* vol. 7, 1970, pp. 679–690.
17. Nelson, J. A., and R. M. Slepian: "The Epoxy-Sandwich Technique for Preserving Thin Coatings During Specimen Preparation," *Metallography,* vol. 1, 1969, pp. 425–429; *Prakt. Metallogr.,* vol. 6, 1969, pp. 112–117.
18. Cprek, E. R.: "Polishing Technique for Obtaining Flat Edges on Sectioned Metallographic Specimens," *Trans. Am. Soc. Met.,* vol. 55, 1962, pp. 369–372.
19. Krieg, A.: "Processing Procedures," *Am. Soc. Test. Mater., Spec. Tech. Publ. 265, Symp. on Electroless Nickel Plating,* 1959, pp. 21–37.
20. Pinkerton, H. L.: "Preparing Nonconductors for Electroplating," *Modern Electroplating,* 2d ed., John Wiley & Sons, Inc., New York, 1963, pp. 604–617.

21. Rodgers, T. M.: *Handbook of Practical Electroplating,* The Macmillan Company, New York, 1959.
22. Jenkinson, E. A.: "The Iron-Plating of Specimens for Microscopical Examination," *J. Iron Steel Inst.,* vol. 142, no. II, 1940, pp. 89P–94P.
23. Wolff, U. E., and L. B. Fradette: "Mounting Thin Tungsten Wire and Sheet," *Met. Prog.,* vol. 76, Aug. 1959, pp. 111–112.
24. Jamison, H. M., and E. S. Byron: "Preparation of Iron Powder Compacts and Powders for Microscopic Examination," *Met. Prog.,* vol. 51, 1947, pp. 437–440.
25. Wachtell, R.: "Metallographic Technique for Mounting Porous Compacts," *Powder Metall. Bull.,* vol. 4, no. 4, 1949, pp. 126–128.
26. Richardson, J. H., W. De La Torre, and H. E. Mendoza: "An SEM Study of Polishing Cloths," *Microstructural Science,* vol. 3B, Elsevier Publishing Company, New York, 1975, pp. 551–566.
27. Charvat, F. R., P. C. Warren, and E. D. Albrecht: "Linde Alumina Abrasives for Metallographic Polishing," *Metallographic Specimen Preparation,* Plenum Press, Plenum Publishing Corporation, New York, 1974, pp. 95–107.
28. Coons, W. C.: "The Evaluation of Final Polishing Abrasives," *Metallographic Specimen Preparation,* Plenum Press, Plenum Publishing Corporation, New York, 1974, pp. 109–120.
29. Mayburg, S.: "Optimum Abrasive Sizes for Minimizing the Polishing Times of Semiconductors," *J. Electrochem. Soc.,* vol. 116, 1969, pp. 509–510.
30. Buchheit, R. D., and J. L. McCall: "Diamond Compounds for Polishing Metallographic Specimens," *Metallographic Specimen Preparation,* Plenum Press, Plenum Publishing Corporation, New York, 1974, pp. 77–94.
31. McCall, J. L., and R. M. Mantaring: "Effect of Wheel Speed and Amount of Extender in Metallographic Polishing with Diamond Compounds," *Microstructural Science,* vol. 4, Elsevier Publishing Company, New York, 1976, pp. 319–326.
32. Exner, H. E., and K. Kuhn: "Investigation of the Rate of Removal of Material by Diamond Polishing," *Prakt. Metallogr.,* vol. 8, 1971, pp. 453–469.
33. Bowden, F. P., and T. P. Hughes: "Physical Properties of Surfaces. IV. Polishing, Surface Flow and the Formation of the Beilby Layer," *Proc. R. Soc., London,* Ser. A, vol. 160, no. A903, 1937, pp. 575–587.
34. Mulhearn, T. O., and L. E. Samuels: "The Abrasion of Metals: A Model of the Process," *Wear,* vol. 5, 1962, pp. 478–498.
35. Richardson, J. H., and R. A. Brose: "Dynamic Observation of Polishing Using the SEM," *Microstructural Science,* vol. 4, Elsevier Publishing Company, New York, 1976, pp. 281–284.
36. Aghan, R. L., and L. E. Samuels: "Mechanisms of Abrasive Polishing," *Wear,* vol. 16, 1970, pp. 293–301.
37. Reinacher, G.: "Metallographic Preparation of Noble Metals by Electropolishing," *Z. Metallkunde,* vol 48, 1957, pp. 162–170.
38. Buchheit, R. D., C. H. Brady, and G. A. Wheeler: "Procedures for the Metallographic Preparation of Beryllium, Titanium, and Refractory Metals," DMIC Memo. no. 37, Battelle Memorial Institute, Defense Metal Information Center, Columbus, Ohio, Oct. 26, 1959.
39. Haddrell, V. J.: "An Attack-Polishing Technique for the Metallographic Preparation of Magnesium and its Dilute Alloys," *J. Inst. Met.,* vol. 92, 1963–1964, p. 121.
40. Chia, K.: "Chemical Polishing in Metallography," *Prakt. Metallogr.,* vol. 8, 1971, pp. 26–39.
41. Hallett, A. R., I. Posener, and L. W. Graham: "Metallographic Chemical Polishing of Steel: Variation in Solution Composition with Carbon Content," *Research,* vol. 9, no. 11, 1956, p. S39.
42. Jacquet, P. A.: "Electrolytic and Chemical Polishing," *Met. Rev.,* vol. 1, pt. 2, 1956, pp. 157–238.
43. McG. Tegart, W. J.: *The Electrolytic and Chemical Polishing of Metals in Research and Industry,* Pergamon Press Ltd., London, 1956.
44. American Society for Testing and Materials Standard E3, "Standard Methods of Preparation of Metallographic Specimens."
45. Hickling, A., and J. K. Higgins: "The Rate-Determining Stage in the Anodic Dissolution of Metals (During Electrolytic Polishing of Copper)," *Trans. Inst. Met. Finish.,* vol. 29, 1952–1953, pp. 274–301.

46. Hoar, T. P., and T. W. Farthing: "Solid Films on Electropolishing Anodes," *Nature*, vol. 169, no. 4295, 1952, pp. 324–325.
47. Olefjord, I.: "ESCA Studies on Films Formed on Stainless Steels During Oxidation and During Electropolishing," *Scand. J. Metall.*, vol. 3, 1974, pp. 129–136.
48. Mathieu, J. B., H. J. Mathieu, and D. Landolt: "Electropolishing of Titanium in Perchloric Acid-Acetic Acid Solutions," *J. Electrochem. Soc.*, vol. 125, 1978, pp. 1039–1043.
49. Honeycombe, R. W. K., and R. R. Hughan: "Electrolytic Polishing of Copper in Orthophosphoric Acid," *J. Counc. Sci. Ind. Res.* (Aust.), vol. 20, 1947, pp. 297–305.
50. Samuels, L. E.: "A Critical Comparison Between Mechanical and Electrolytic Methods of Metallographic Polishing," *Metallurgia*, vol. 66, no. 396, 1962, pp. 187–199.
51. Coons, W. C.: "A Universal Metallographic Polishing Procedure," *Met. Prog.*, vol. 49, 1946, pp. 956–959.
52. Cannon, H. S.: "A Universal Polishing Method," *Met. Prog.*, vol. 67, April 1955, pp. 83–86.
53. Samuels, L. E.: "The Use of Diamond Abrasives for a Universal System of Metallographic Polishing," *J. Inst. Met.*, vol. 81, 1952–1953, pp. 471–478.
54. Davies, J. E., and W. E. Hoare: "Metallography of Electro-Tinplate," *J. Iron Steel Inst.*, vol. 168, 1951, pp. 134–140.
55. Hoare, W. E.: "Tin-Iron Alloy in Tinplate with Notes on Some Imperfections," *J. Iron Steel Inst.*, vol. 129, no. 1, 1934, pp. 253–271.
56. Romig, O. E., and D. H. Rowland: "Metallography of Tin and Tin Coatings on Steel," *Met. Alloys*, vol. 13, 1941, pp. 436–443.
57. Rowland, D. H., and O. E. Romig: "The Metallography of Galvanized Sheet Steel Using a Specially Prepared Polishing Medium and Controlled pH," *Trans. Am. Soc. Met.*, vol. 31, 1943, pp. 980–997.
58. Rowland, D. H.: "Metallography of Hot-Dipped Galvanized Coatings," *Trans. Am. Soc. Met.*, vol. 40, 1948, pp. 983–1011.
59. Keller, F., and G. W. Wilcox: "Anodically Oxidized Aluminum Alloys—Metallographic Examination," *Met. Alloys*, vol. 10, 1939, pp. 187–195.
60. Atkinson, J. T. N., and C. A. Godden: "Novel Metallographic Techniques, Particularly as Applied to the Study of Aluminum," *Can. Min. Metall. Bull.*, vol. 55, no. 604, 1962, pp. 587–590.
61. Godden, C. A.: "Metallic Films Aid Study of Oxide Coatings," *Met. Prog.*, vol. 79, Jan. 1961, pp. 121–122.
62. Brandenburg, C. F.: "Present Methods of Metallographic Specimen Preparation for Retention and Identification of Inclusions in Steel," *Am. Soc. Test. Mater., Spec. Tech. Publ. 285*, 1960, pp. 29–36.
63. Chalfant, G. M.: "Revealing Lead Inclusions in Leaded Steels," *Met. Prog.*, vol. 78, Sept. 1960, pp. 77–79.
64. Anderson, R. L.: *Revealing Microstructures in Metals*, Westinghouse Res. Lab., Sci. Paper no. 425-0000-P2, Dec. 22, 1961.
65. Hamilton, R. I., and E. F. Connors: "The Preparation of 'As-Polished' Metallographic Finishes in Non-Ferrous Metals," Dept. of Mines and Tech. Surveys, Mines Branch, no. IC 176, Ottawa, June 1965 (reprinted July 1977).
66. Hoeg, R.: "New Reproducible, Automatic Preparation Method for Aluminum and its Alloys," *Prakt. Metallogr.*, vol. 16, 1979, pp. 301–302.
67. Udy, M. C., G. K. Manning, and L. W. Eastwood: "Metallographic Examination of Beryllium Alloys," *Trans. Am. Inst. Min. Metall. Eng.*, vol. 185, 1949, pp. 779–784.
68. Kaufmann, A. R., P. Gordon, and D. W. Lillie: "Metallography of Beryllium," *Met. Prog.*, vol. 56, 1949, pp. 664–665.
69. Calabra, A. E., and R. J. Jackson: "Metallographic Techniques for Vacuum-Cast Rolled Ingot Beryllium Sheet," *International Metallographic Society Proceedings*, First Annual IMS Technical Meeting, Nov. 11–13, 1968, Denver, Colo., pp. 63–70.
70. Price, C. W., and J. L. McCall: "A Review of Metallographic Preparation Procedures for Beryllium and Beryllium Alloys," DMIC Memo. no. 237, Battelle Memorial Institute, Defense Metal Information Center, Columbus, Ohio, June 1, 1978.

71. Slepian, R. M., and G. A. Blann: "Improved Metallographic Preparation of Lead and Lead Alloys," *Metallography,* vol. 12, no. 3, 1979, pp. 195–214.
72. Eyre, B. L.: "The Preparation of Tin and Tin Alloys for Micro-Examination," *Metallurgia,* vol. 58, no. 346, 1958, pp. 95–106.
73. Yih, S. W. H., and C. T. Wang: "Metallographic Preparation of Tungsten, Its Alloys, and Tungsten Carbides," *Tungsten, Sources, Metallurgy, Properties and Applications,* Plenum Press, Plenum Publishing Corporation, New York, 1979, pp. 437–440.
74. Oberländer, B., and K. P. Lillerud: "Structural Development of Magnesium Alloys," *Prakt. Metallogr.,* vol. 17, 1980, pp. 473–478.
75. Pepper, R. T.: "A New Metallographic Technique for Magnesium Alloys," *Trans. Am. Inst. Min. Metall. Eng.,* vol. 218, 1960, p. 374.
76. Kallfass, M., and G. Hörz: "Specimen Preparation and Metallographic Studies in the Alloy Systems of the Va Metals Vanadium, Niobium, and Tantalum with Nitrogen, Oxygen, or Carbon," *Prakt. Metallogr.,* vol. 17, 1980, pp. 61–77.
77. Calabra, A. E.: "A Rapid and Reliable Metallographic Technique for Silver," *Microstructural Science,* vol. 1, Elsevier Publishing Company, New York, 1974, pp. 25–37.
78. Piotrowski, T., and D. J. Accinno: "Metallography of the Precious Metals," *Metallography,* vol. 10, 1977, pp. 243–289.
79. Cochran, F. L.: "Preparing Plutonium for Optical Microscopy: A Precis," *Microstructures,* vol. 1, no. 2, 1970, pp. 27–34.
80. Richter, A. E.: "A Note on the Metallography of Neptunium," *International Metallographic Society Proceedings,* First Annual IMS Technical Meeting, Nov. 11–13, 1968, Denver, Colo., pp. 179–180.
81. Love, B.: "Metallography of the Rare-Earth Metals," *The Rare Earths,* John Wiley & Sons, Inc., New York, 1961, pp. 215–224.
82. Roman, W. A.: "The Metallographic Preparation of Some Rare-Earth Metals," *J. Less-Common Met.,* vol. 10, 1965, pp. 150–152.
83. Dobbins, A. G.: "Metallographic Preparation of Holmium," Union Carbide Corp., Rep. Y-1618, Oak Ridge, Tenn., May 28, 1968.
84. Bender, J. H.: "A Technique for the Metallographic Preparation of Metallic Sodium," *International Metallographic Society Proceedings,* First Annual IMS Technical Meeting, Nov. 11–13, 1968, Denver, Colo., pp. 33–36.
85. McQuillan, A. D., and M. K. McQuillan: "Metallographic Techniques for Titanium and Its Alloys," *Titanium,* Academic Press, Inc., New York, 1956, pp. 447–458.
86. Cain, F. M.: "A Simplified Procedure for the Metallography of Zirconium and Hafnium and their Alloys," *Zirconium and Zirconium Alloys,* American Society for Metals, Cleveland, 1953, pp. 176–185.
87. Bölsing, R., and G. Dressler: "The Metallography of Zirconium and Zirconium Alloys," *Prakt. Metallogr.,* vol. 6, 1969, pp. 706–710.
88. Coons, W. C.: "A Rapid Method for Polishing Pyrolytic Graphic," *Met. Prog.,* vol. 81, June 1962, pp. 83–85.
89. Brassard, T. V., and A. S. Holik: "Preparing Various Graphites for Metallographic Examination," *Met. Prog.,* vol. 81, May 1962, pp. 109–111.
90. Cole, D. L., and R. G. Moses: "Preparation and Polishing of Coal and Coke for Petrographic Analysis," *Bitum. Coal Res. Inc. Tech. Rep.* Monroeville, Pa., July 30, 1965, revised February 1979.
91. "Petrographic Sample Preparation," *AB Met. Dig.,* vol. 12/13, no. 1, Buehler Ltd., Evanston, Ill., 1973.
92. Beauchamp, R. H., and J. F. Williford: "Metallographic Methods Applied to Ultrathinning Lunar Rocks, Meteorites, Fossils, and Other Brittle Materials for Optical Microscopy," *Metallographic Sample Preparation,* Plenum Press, Plenum Publishing Corporation, New York, 1974, pp. 233–249.
93. Holik, A. S., et al.: "Grinding and Polishing Techniques for Thin Sectioning of Polymeric Materials for Transmission Light Microscopy," *Microstructural Science,* vol. 7, Elsevier Publishing Company, New York, 1979, pp. 357–367.

94. Linke, U., and W. U. Kopp: "Preparation of Polished Specimens and Thin Sections of Plastics," *Prakt. Mettalogr.*, vol. 17, 1980, pp. 479–488.
95. Anderson, R. L.: "Safety in the Metallographic Laboratory," Westinghouse Res. Lab. Sci. Paper no. 65-1P30-METLL-P2, March 29, 1965.
96. Sax, N. I.: *Dangerous Properties of Industrial Materials,* 5th ed., Van Nostrand Reinhold Company, Inc., New York, 1979.
97. National Research Council: *Prudent Practices for Handling Hazardous Chemicals in Laboratories,* National Academy Press, Washington, D.C., 1981.
98. Steere, N. V.: *Handbook of Laboratory Safety,* The Chemical Rubber Company, Cleveland, 1967.
99. Proctor, N., and J. Hughes: *Chemical Hazards in the Workplace,* J. B. Lippincott Company, Philadelphia, 1978.
100. Satz, L. H.: "Discard this Etchant Promptly," *Met. Prog.*, vol. 62, Aug. 1952, p. 96.
101. Warren, D.: "More on Hazardous Etchants," *Met. Prog.*, vol. 62, Dec. 1952, p. 122.
102. Fox, H. A., and M. S. Frant: "Some Reagents Explode," *Met. Prog.*, vol. 80, July 1961, p. 114.
103. Lane, G. D., and G. J. Durmann: "Some Reagents Explode," *Met. Prog.*, vol. 80, Nov. 1961, p. 118.
104. Bubar, S. F., and D. A. Vermilyea: "Explosion of a Chemical Polishing Solution," *J. Electrochem. Soc.*, vol. 113, 1966, p. 519.
105. Green, W. V.: "An Unstable Chemical Polishing Reagent," *J. Less-Common Met.*, vol. 9, no. 2, 1965, pp. 155–156.
106. Jacquet, P. A.: "The Safe Use of Perchloric-Acetic Electropolishing Baths," *Met. Finish.*, vol. 47, 1949, pp. 62–69.
107. Comas, S. M., R. Gonzalez Palacin, and D. Vassallo: "Hazards Associated with Perchloric Acid-Butylcellosolve Polishing Solutions," *Metallography*, vol. 7, 1974, pp. 47–57.
108. Dawkins, A. E.: "Chromic Acid-Acetic Anhydride 'Explosion,'" J. Iron Steel Inst., vol. 182, 1956, p. 388.

THREE

MICROSTRUCTURE

3-1 INTRODUCTION

Accurate, sharp delineation of the true microstructure of materials is of great importance in the characterization of the composition, structure, and properties of materials. With materials whose constituents exhibit large differences in light reflectivity after polishing, the desired microstructure, or certain features of the microstructure, can be observed in the as-polished condition under bright-field illumination without recourse to subsequent treatments such as etching. Constituents that differ in reflectivity from one another or from the matrix by at least 6 to 8 percent in the as-polished condition can be distinguished clearly. Smaller differences in reflectivity can be accentuated and made visible by the use of vapor-deposited interference films or by the use of phase-contrast illumination. Inclusion phases in metals exhibit maximum contrast with the matrix in the as-polished condition. If the constituents differ significantly in hardness from the matrix, relief polishing can be used along with oblique light or interference-contrast illumination to view the structure without etching. A number of examples of structures that are observable in the as-polished condition are presented in Chap. 2.

Anisotropic metals, such as beryllium, uranium, or zirconium, can be examined using crossed-polarized light without recourse to etching. Isotropic metals do not respond to polarized light, although with some isotropic metals polarized light reveals additional detail when these metals are etched with certain etchants. Some of the anodizing techniques used on isotropic metals (such as aluminum) require subsequent examination of the metal with polarized light. In some metals, certain phases or constituents, such as sigma phase in stainless steel, are anisotropic while the matrix is isotropic, and thus phase discrimination and identification are aided by the use of polarized light. Additional details on the use of polarized light are provided in Chap. 4.

3-2 ETCHING

For many materials, the microstructure is revealed only by application of an appropriate etchant. To obtain a sharply delineated contrasty condition, the polished surface must be free of any artifacts, as is described in Chap. 2. The sample must be thoroughly cleaned before etching, a satisfactory etchant must be selected and prepared, and the etching technique must be carefully controlled. Following etching, the sample must be washed free of any residue and dried. At this point, the sample can be examined and photographed, if desired, using the techniques described in Chap. 4.

Many techniques are available to produce an "etched" condition suitable for structure examination. Standard chemical etching solutions are most commonly employed, but other methods are also used such as anodizing and electrolytic and potentiostatic etching. Techniques using heat, such as heat tinting or thermal etching, are useful and have wide applicability. The depositing of interference films is also used to make microstructural constituents more visible; these films are produced by heat tinting but can also be made by other methods, for example, by gas contrasting, by tint etching, or by vapor deposition of a nonabsorbing material with a high refractive index. These techniques as well as others are discussed in this chapter, and examples that illustrate their use are also provided.

3-2.1 Etching Theory

Etching is basically a controlled corrosion process resulting from electrolytic action between surface areas of different potential [1–5]. The myriad chemical solutions (see App. I) used for etching have been developed primarily by trial and error, with some aid provided perhaps by knowledge of the corrosion behavior of the material in question. Etching occurs by electrolytic action at structural variations on the sample surface. Electrolytic activity results from local physical or chemical heterogeneities which render some features anodic and others cathodic under the specific etching conditions.

Chemical etchants produce metallographic contrast either by crystal faceting (that is, grains etch at different rates because of variation in their crystallographic orientation) which produces steps at grain boundaries and reflectivity differences or by grain- or phase-boundary etching, which produces grooves. Selective phase dissolution is more difficult to obtain, since it requires a preferential chemical reaction. Selective etching can be obtained by roughening of the phase of interest or by preferential staining of the phase.

Established chemical etchants have certain common features. Chemical etchants usually have three main components: a corrosive agent (such as hydrochloric, sulfuric, phosphoric, or acetic acid), a modifier (such as alcohol or glycerin) that reduces ionization, and an oxidizer (such as hydrogen peroxide, Fe^{3+}, or Cu^{2+}). In some etchants one component serves two of these functions, such as nitric acid in nital. In electrolytic etchants, the applied current acts as the oxidizer. Because etching involves controlled dissolution, oxidation must be controlled. The oxidizer provides this control by absorbing electrons. Small changes in the oxidizing power of a reagent can markedly alter the dissolution rate. Since the dissolved oxygen in tap water will increase the dissolution rate, it is always best to use distilled water in preparing etchants.

With pure metals and single-phase alloys, a potential is produced between differently oriented grains, between grain boundaries and grain interiors, between impurity phases and the matrix, or at concentration gradients in the single-phase alloys. With two-phase or multiphased alloys, potential differences are also present between phases of different composition. These potential differences are used to produce controlled dissolution.

Microstructure is revealed by selective dissolution of the structure, starting at the surface and proceeding inward. Differences in the rate of attack reveal the structure. Besides selective dissolution, preferential staining or coloring of phases or constituents occurs with certain reagents. In a two-phase alloy, the potential of one phase is higher than that of the other phase; i.e., it is anodic with respect to the other phase (cathodic). During etching, the more electropositive anodic phase is attacked while the electronegative cathodic phase is not appreciably attacked. As the potential difference between the two phases increases, etching time must be carefully controlled to avoid overetching. Because of the magnitude of the potential between different phases, duplex alloys usually etch more rapidly than pure metals or single-phase alloys.

The unetched cathodic phase will stand in relief and appear bright, especially if its size is reasonably large. The anodic phase is recessed below the original plane of polish and can appear to have a rough surface depending on the etchant and the alloy composition. Surface roughness will make the anodic constituent appear dark under bright-field illumination.

If etching is continued beyond the time required to delineate the structure clearly, the phase that was initially anodic may undergo a change in potential, perhaps by deposition of reaction products or formation of other anodic protective layers. If this occurs, the phase that was originally cathodic can undergo dissolution, resulting in a poorly resolved overetched structure. Thus, etch time must be carefully controlled, especially for examination at high magnification, where the depth of field is extremely small. As a rule of thumb, as the magnification increases, the degree of etch attack must be reduced. At low magnifications, a deeper, more contrasty etch is desirable.

The etching response of pearlite in steel is a classic example of the etch response of a two-phase mixture. The cementite lamellae are cathodic to the ferrite lamellae, with a substantial potential difference. Etching with 4% picric acid in alcohol (picral) produces a slow, uniform, smooth dissolution of the ferrite lamellae, with the cathodic cementite lamellae in relief. If the interlamellar spacing is small, light scattering from the etched structure will make the pearlite appear dark and look like a single phase. Picral etching produces uniform etching and darkening of the pearlite colonies. Etching with 2 to 3% nitric acid in alcohol (nital), however, produces a wide range of gray-level contrast because of the orientation sensitivity of nital (see Fig. 3-1). Etch attack in the lighter pearlite

Figure 3-1 Pearlite in steel (AISI 1060) is revealed completely by 4% picral (right) but not by 2% nital (left) because of the sensitivity of nital to orientation (600×).

colonies is superficial compared to that in the dark areas. There is the danger that some of the light etching areas may be mistaken for ferrite. Examination of coarse pearlite at high magnification reveals that the cementite lamellae are not attacked but appear outlined because of dissolution of the ferrite lamellae. The brightness of both ferrite and massive cementite are similar, and one must know that the discontinuous phase is cementite and the continuous phase is ferrite in order to interpret the structure without recourse to selective stain etchants (see Fig. 3-37, which appears later in this chapter.)

Etching of single-phase pure metals and alloys takes place without the aid of the large potential differences present in duplex alloys. The potential differences between grain boundaries and grain interiors are smaller and exert less influence on etch response. Impurities that segregate to the grain boundaries can significantly alter etch response. In single-phase metals and alloys, a particular etchant can either attack the grain boundary or preferentially dissolve differently oriented grains (faceting), which produces grain contrast etching. An etchant that etches the grain boundary can also produce grain contrasting with longer etch times. Etchants that produce grain contrast are sensitive to the difference in dissolution rates of the differently oriented grains at the specimen surface. Vertical light striking the grain facets will be reflected at different angles, producing gray level contrast in the differently oriented grains.

Thus, when single-phase metals are etched to produce faceting, some grains appear bright and lustrous while the remaining grains are darkened to varying degrees. This phenomenon, sometimes called "grain-oriented luster," is not due to compositional differences that lead to selective staining but to the angle of the etched grain with respect to the incident illumination. Those grains perpendicular to the incident light appear bright and lustrous, while those angled to the incident light appear dark. The darkness of the grains depends on the angle of the grain facet. If the etchant roughens the surface, this feature will be more easily observed on the angled grains.

Many chemical etchants are mixtures of acids with a solvent such as water. During etching, the atoms on the anodic surface are transferred to the etching solution as cations. However, before these atoms are transferred to the solution, [3], they are adsorbed onto the metal surface:

$$M_{lattice} \rightarrow M_{ad}$$

These atoms are mobile and are transferred to the etching solution as follows: Water molecules become bound to the metal cation by ion dipole forces, and the metal cation is hydrated [3]:

$$M_{ad} \rightarrow M_{aq}^{n+} + ne^-$$

Finally, the cation is removed from the surface into the solution after hydration is completed. The metal being etched does not always react with the etchant to produce hydration. Instead, complexly bound ions or relatively insoluble metal compounds may be formed and precipitated onto the metal surface.

Etching involves three types of action. If cations are formed, an acceptor for the electrons must exist for the process to continue. In the etching of a nonprecious metal in a nonoxidizing solution, metal dissolution produces hydrogen, which acts as an electron acceptor. Changes in the acid concentration will accelerate or retard etching.

Hydrogen is not liberated when more-noble metals are etched. The etchant must be formulated so that the electrons released are consumed by reduction of oxygen in acid or alkaline-to-neutral solutions. Therefore, etchants for more-noble metals must contain oxidizers that release oxygen, such as nitric acid, chromic acid, picric acid, iron chloride, persulfates, or peroxides. Since most etchants contain oxidizers, they can be used to etch nonnoble and noble metals.

In general, the composition of chemical etchants is not critical. The success of an etchant can be influenced, however, by the order in which the chemicals are mixed, by the purity of the chemicals, or by changes due to aging. Most chemical etchants contain a solvent used to dissolve the etching agent. Chemical additions can be made to influence ionization or decomposition of the active agent. In some instances, a concentrated acid or a mixture of two acids, e.g., aqua regia, are employed for etching. Unfortunately, the function of each component in an etching reagent cannot always be determined with certainty. Also, when a given etchant, for example Murakami's reagent, is used to etch different metals, the etch components can have different roles with different metals.

In recent years, extensive use has been made of the addition of wetting agents to etchants, particularly for revealing prior-austenite grain boundaries in steel. The wetting agent zephiran chloride (benzalkonium chloride) has been added to picral for many years to improve etch response. Addition of wetting agents lowers the surface energy at the etchant-sample interface, thus influencing etching action. Nelson has evaluated the influence of wetting agents on etching response using three etchants, five wetting agents, and four types of steels containing a variety of microstructural constituents [6]. Four different responses were obtained as the wetting agent concentration was increased:

- Noticeable sharp improvement up to a maximum, higher concentrations producing no effect

- Slight gradual improvement up to a maximum, higher concentrations being detrimental
- Little or no value
- Detrimental in any concentration or damaging with increasing concentration

Additions of zephiran chloride to picral improved etching speed (approximately double) at 8 drops per 30 mL picral. Further additions of up to 90 drops per 30 mL picral produced little change in the rate of attack. Zephiran chloride addition to picral also improved structure delineation. Tergitol additions to picral worked well on ferrite-pearlite or bainitic structures but poorly on martensite and left a greasy residue on the sample.

Aqueous picric acid, which is a slow etch, was even slower when wetting agents were added. Although addition of Tergitol increased the rate of attack, the results were still very poor. Wetting agents were not useful with aqueous picric acid, except for additions of sodium tridecylbenzene sulfonate, which produced attack of prior-austenite grain boundaries in all but the ferrite-pearlite sample. The etching properties of aqueous sodium bisulfite was not improved by the addition of wetting agents; zephiran chloride did increase the rate of attack but etch quality decreased.

Nelson's study revealed that wetting agents do act differently and are not interchangeable [6]. The etching results obtained with some etchants can be improved, but etching results can also be impaired by the addition of wetting agents. Thus wetting agents cannot be used indiscriminantly but must be carefully evaluated. While etch time can often be shortened by the use of a wetting agent, the reverse can also occur.

A number of researchers have developed techniques to measure the solution potential of the local anodic and cathodic surface areas in a particular solution. Dix used a microcapillary technique with $0.1 N$ KCN in the study of Al-Cu alloys and found that the grain boundaries averaged about 91 mV anodic to the grain centers, with a maximum difference of 200 mV [7].

Budd and Booth have summarized studies measuring solution potentials [8]. Numerous attempts have been made to define the influence of grain orientation on solution potential. Results of a number of studies indicate that the potential varies only slightly with grain orientation, although the methods used in the studies make the results questionable. Cold working has been found to render an area more anodic.

Kehl and Metlay made potential measurements of the alpha and beta phases in an alloy of 60% Cu and 40% Zn (Muntz metal) using nine different etchants [1]. A difference of 0.01 to 0.03 V was consistently observed between the alpha and beta phases with beta always anodic to alpha. All the etchants tried, except an aqueous solution of NH_4OH and H_2O_2, preferentially attacked and darkened the beta phase. The aqueous NH_4OH and H_2O_2 etch attacked the alpha phase, but the potential measurements were considered to be an "informed guess" because of the rapid and erratic measurements caused by gas evolution. Kehl and Metlay also made measurements on a single-phase alloy of 90% Cu and 10% Zn, which revealed that the grain boundaries are anodic to the grain centers. Tests on an alloy of cadmium and bismuth, which consisted essentially of two pure-metal phases, revealed that cadmium was 0.735 V anodic to bismuth, using an etchant that preferentially darkens cadmium.

3-2.2 Etching Technique

Chemical etching of specimens is a straightforward, simple procedure that is easily mastered. Results with commonly used etchants on familiar metals are usually predictable and reproducible, even with minor variations in etch composition, temperature, or time. Results with selective etchants or tint etchants require careful attention to technique and can be unpredictable at times. The sequence of mixing these etchants can be important. Also, the quality of the polish can influence etch response.

When an unfamiliar metal or alloy is to be etched, one must first select an appropriate reagent. This can be done by consultations with other metallographers or by reference to etchant compilations [9–14], as given in App. I. It is usually best to start with a commonly used general etchant of simple and safe composition before trying selective etchants or more complex or dangerous solutions. The overall structure of the metal should be evaluated prior to using selective etchants.

Although the compositions of most etchants are usually not highly critical, it is best to follow closely the directions provided by prior users. However, compositions of staining reagents and anodizing solutions are usually quite critical, and the directions must be followed closely to obtain the anticipated results. Chemical reagents are usually mixed in small quantities, generally 50 to 200 mL, and are placed in shallow dishes or beakers. If the reagent can be stored safely, stock solutions, typically 500 to 1000 mL, can be prepared as discussed in the section on laboratory safety in Chap. 2.

Chemical etchants are used either by immersing the sample and gently agitating it or by swabbing the sample, usually at room temperature. The sample is grasped with tongs, never with the fingers, and lowered into the solution. The sample should be gently agitated so that the reaction products do not settle on the surface and produce uneven, "muddy" etching. Although some recommend etching upside down to minimize deposition of reaction products, the progress of etching cannot be followed, which results in poor control. If surface deposition is a serious problem, a magnetic bar can be used to stir the solution during etching. As a rule, swabbing should not be used unless specified in the literature for the etch. With swabbing, there is a danger of scratching the surface, particularly with soft metals. Some use cotton-tipped wood or paper rods for swabbing, while others prefer to grasp a large wad of cotton with tongs, saturate the cotton with the etch, and rub it against the sample, which is held with another pair of tongs over a watch glass to catch any drippings. The cotton should be recharged regularly with fresh etchant until the desired contrast is obtained. Swabbing is preferred for those etchants with which the deposition of reaction products or staining is a problem, as with titanium alloys.

Etching time is usually determined empirically, although in well-defined situations, as in electrolytic etching, the specified times generally produce acceptable results. If the polished surface is faceup in the reagent, the surface can be observed, permitting etching to be halted at the proper time. With a little experience, one can gauge the proper degree of etching by the surface dulling or coloration produced. If etching does not occur upon immersion, the sample should be removed and held under hot water for a few seconds; the sample should then be dried, and the etchant tried again. A sample that is wet with water and is placed in an alcoholic solution will produce poor etch results. If the level of etch is inadequate, it is sometimes necessary to repolish the sample before reetching it for a longer time. Many times, the sample can be etched longer without repolishing; however, overetched samples must be repolished and etched for a shorter time.

Control of the etch time is important in obtaining a sharp, crisp image that permits resolution of fine detail. If an etchant is strong and produces rapid etching, that is, an etching time of less than a few seconds, good results can be quite difficult to obtain consistently and a milder etch may be preferred for better control. Etchants that require 20 s or more to develop the structure usually provide the needed control for etching. Underetching fails to reveal all the detail, while overetching obscures detail.

3-2.3 Etching Problems

The quality of the polish influences the development of the true microstructure. A faulty preparation can lead to misinterpretations of the structure, as illustrated in Fig. 3-2. Likewise, if the surface is not properly cleaned after polishing, etch

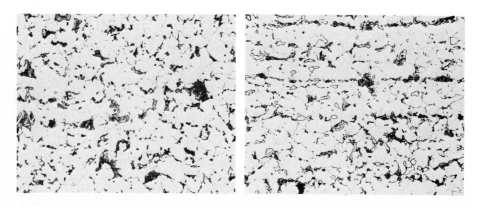

Figure 3-2 Sample preparation can alter the microstructure, as demonstrated by these two micrographs of dual-phase sheet steel. Shearing (left) transformed the retained austenite to martensite, while abrasive cutting (right) did not (retained austenite are small, outlined white particles). Etchant was 20% sodium metabisulfite, 600×. *(Courtesy of A. O. Benscoter, Bethlehem Steel Corp.)*

attack will be uneven and the structure will be obscured. In general, wiping of the surface with moist cotton under running water is adequate, although ultrasonic cleaning, especially if cracks or pores are present, is preferable.

Staining of the surface during etching or afterward as the result of bleed-out is a commonly encountered, frustrating problem. Gifkins has introduced a very useful technique for cleaning etched samples that employs EDTA (ethylene-diaminetetra-acetic acid) [15]. Gifkins' initial experiments with EDTA involved prevention of tarnish on lead samples. He found that a saturated EDTA solution could be substituted for acetic acid in the usual chemical polishing solution for lead and that EDTA would remove the tarnish formed on the surface after chemical polishing. A few drops of the concentrated EDTA solution removed the tarnish without altering the surface finish. EDTA apparently complexes with metal ions, removing only tarnish oxides. Gifkins also showed that cracked steel specimens could be etched stain-free by adding a few drops of concentrated EDTA to the etchant (nital in his illustration). Gifkins also used EDTA additions to alcoholic ferric chloride to etch alpha brass creep specimens. Without EDTA, staining occurred where slip was intense. Stains can also be removed after etching by ultrasonic cleaning with a dilute EDTA solution.

Figure 3-3 shows a carbon steel sheet sample which had a stained surface after etching. Ultrasonic cleaning in a 3% aqueous EDTA solution removed the stain. When the sample was removed from the cleaning solution, it was rinsed first with water and then with alcohol before drying. Another example is a cast-iron sample that was etched in boiling alkaline sodium picrate to preferentially stain the cementite in the ternary Fe_3C-Fe_3P-ferrite eutectic. Pitting attack resulted which could not be removed except by repolishing. Since repolishing and reetching produced similar stains and pits, the sample was repolished and etched with 2% EDTA added to the boiling alkaline sodium picrate solution, and excellent results were obtained (see Fig. 3-4).

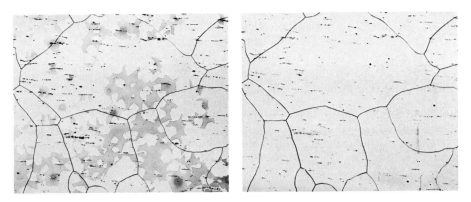

Figure 3-3 Etching of sheet steel with nital, Marshall's reagent, and nital produced a stained surface (left) which was removed (right) by ultrasonic cleaning in 3% aqueous EDTA followed by water rinse, alcohol rinse, and drying (110×). *(Courtesy of A. O. Benscoter, Bethlehem Steel Corp.)*

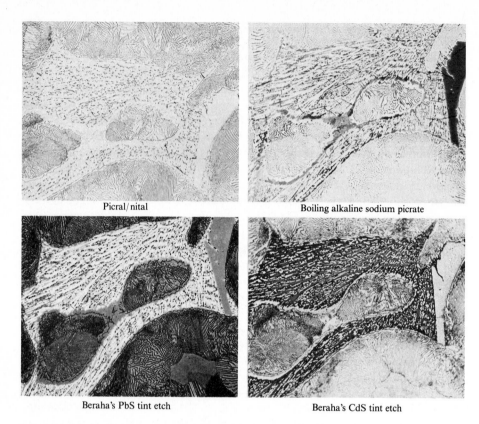

Picral/nital

Boiling alkaline sodium picrate

Beraha's PbS tint etch

Beraha's CdS tint etch

Figure 3-4 Ternary eutectic of iron phosphide, iron carbide, and ferrite in gray cast iron etched with different reagents (300×). Etching with picral and nital outlines eutectic, reveals location of ferrite in eutectic, and etches pearlitic matrix. Boiling alkaline sodium picrate (1 min) colors cementite only. Beraha's lead sulfide tint etch (90 s, after nital preetch) colored cementite pale blue and phosphide yellow. Beraha's cadmium sulfide tint etch (80 s, after nital preetch) colored phosphide brown, cementite tan-yellow, and ferrite blue.

Figure 3-5 *(inside back cover)* Influence of etch time on coloration of lath martensite, sample from an alloy of Fe and 4.9% Mn that has been tint-etched with Beraha's aqueous 3% $K_2S_2O_5$ and 10% $Na_2S_2O_5$ reagent, 50×. *(Courtesy of A. O. Benscoter, Bethlehem Steel Corp.)*

3-2.4 Tint Etching

In recent years, considerable progress has been made in the development of immersion etchants that produce color contrast, often selectively, that are visible under bright-field illumination. In many cases, further enhancement is obtained with polarized light. These reagents, known as tint etchants, are usually acidic with water or alcohol solvents and are chemically balanced to deposit a thin (40 to 500 nm) film of oxide, sulfide, complex molybdate, elemental selenium, or chromate. Coloration is produced by interference, as in heat tinting or vapor deposition of compounds with a high index of refraction (Pepperhoff method), which is discussed later. All these staining reagents are applied by simple immersion of the sample in the reagent. In most cases, the surface is not actually etched beneath the interference film.

As discussed in the sections on heat tinting and on the Pepperhoff method, the film thickness controls the color of the film and the colors of each phase viewed under the microscope. Crystallographic orientation also influences the observed colors. A stable film is deposited if the reactive solution is properly balanced so that the corrosion products on the surface are not redissolved and transferred into the solution.

Beraha classified tint etching systems as anodic reagents that precipitate a thin film on the anodic constituents and produce coloration of only these areas, cathodic reagents that precipitate a thin film on the cathodic constituents and thus color only these areas, or complex reagents that precipitate a film by a complex reaction [16]. The type of tint etchants developed by Klemm and Beraha are the complex type and are listed in App. I under the applicable metal.

Sodium metabisulfite ($Na_2S_2O_5$), potassium metabisulfite ($K_2S_2O_5$), and sodium thiosulfate ($Na_2S_2O_3$) are common ingredients in some of the more popular tint etchants. In an aqueous solution, the metabisulfite salt decomposes on contact with the metal surface, producing SO_2, H_2S, and H_2 and a characteristic odor [16]. On passivated surfaces, e.g., stainless steel, SO_2 depassivates the surface, while the H_2S provides sulfur ions, which combine with metallic ions from the sample, e.g., iron or nickel ions, to produce the sulfide staining film. The thiosulfate ion decomposes in a similar manner. Analysis of the surface films produced by these reagents reveals the presence of oxide, sulfide, and sulfate compounds [17, 18]. Addition of hydrochloric acid to these solutions permits their use on stainless steels and heat-resisting alloys containing substantial chromium. The anodic microconstituents, i.e., ferrite and austenite, are colored, while the cathodic constituents, i.e., carbides and nitrides, are bright and unaffected. Furthermore, because of orientation differences, the anodic phases are colored with various tints.

Beraha developed a tint etch containing selenic acid, alcohol, and hydrochloric acid, which are used in varying proportions depending on the application. Selenic acid is reduced to elemental selenium and is deposited on the cathodic areas in the microstructure, producing colors that vary with the thickness of the film on the constituents. The alcohol suppresses ionization and polarization at the microelectrodes, premitting preferential deposition on the cathode areas. By altering the amount of selenic acid and hydrochloric acid in the tint etch (see App. I), a wide range of iron-based alloys can be selectively tint-etched.

Beraha also developed tint etchants containing sodium molybdate ($Na_2MoO_4 \cdot 2H_2O$), which produces molybdic acid (H_2MoO_4) in an acidic solution. Molybdic acid is partially reduced, producing a blue color in the solution. The molybdate solution is reduced at the cathodic microconstituents, which precipitates a complex molybdate film on these areas. The colors produced depend on time, the film thickness, and the ability of the cathodic areas to reduce the molybdate. The molybdate reagent is acidified with nitric acid for coloring cast iron and steels or with hydrochloric acid for aluminum alloys. Coloration of steels is further enhanced by additions of a minor amount of ammonium bifluoride (NH_4FHF) (see App. I).

Beraha also developed a complex aqueous thiosulfate solution containing lead acetate and citric acid, which has wide applicability. This reagent deposits a lead sulfide film and is very useful for copper-based alloys, for preferential staining of cementite or phosphide, or for coloring sulfide inclusions in steel. The lead sulfide film is formed as follows: The citric acid makes the solution slightly acidic. Because excess thiosulfate is used, lead thiosulfate precipitates and dissolves to form a complex solution. Citric acid reacts with the metal surface and produces metal ions that decompose the lead thiosulfate complex, producing lead cations (Pb^{2+}). These cations precipitate as PbS on the sample surface. Deposition of PbS depends on the rate of attack by citric acid on the microconstituents, that is, the rate at which the metal ions from the sample decompose lead thiosulfate and produce lead ions.

Beraha developed a chromating reagent for tinting copper and aluminum alloys. The reagent can use either chromium trioxide (CrO_3) or a dichromate salt. The fundamental reaction in these reagents is partial reduction of Cr^{6+} to Cr^{3+} and the production of a complex film containing both ions. The particular solution suggested by Beraha uses CrO_3, which results in rapid attack and coating. If desired, the reaction can be retarded by increasing the water content. Preetching with a general-purpose reagent is also recommended.

The tint etchants listed in App. I are easily prepared by dissolving the salts in the specified solvents, that is, water or alcohol. Whenever fluorine ions are present, polyethylene beakers should be used rather than glass beakers. A few of the reagents must be aged for at least 24 h in a dark bottle in a cool, dark location. Some of the reagents, e.g., those containing sodium or potassium metabisulfite, liberate sulfur dioxide and hydrogen sulfide, producing a strong odor near the beaker. It is recommended that these reagents be used under a hood, although the intensity of the odor is not strong. Plastic tongs rather than metal ones should be used with the reagents for stainless steel and heat-resisting alloys. While the staining reagents are not particularly dangerous, it is best to avoid contact with them. Selenic acid is corrosive and highly toxic, being rather similar to sulfuric acid; it should be handled with extreme care.

In using tint etchants, a light preetch with a general-purpose chemical etchant usually improves image sharpness. Tint etchants are almost always used at room temperature with immersion of the sample, never with swabbing, which prevents film formation and promotes etching. The sample is placed in a beaker containing about 100 mL of solution and gently agitated while the sample is observed. The solution is usually agitated for 20 to 40 s and then allowed to remain motionless until the desired macroscopic color is obtained, which is usually violet. Then the sample is grasped carefully with tongs, removed from the solution, washed under running water, rinsed with alcohol, and dried under warm air. One should never touch the surface film.

Tint etchants require a very high-quality polished sample for best results. Surfaces that appear to be scratch-free in the as-polished condition can exhibit extensive scratching after tinting. The interference film will vividly reveal even the most minute scratches present on the surface. Color photography is ideal when the expense is justified, but good results can be obtained with black-and-white film. If the surface has a variety of shades of red, orthochromatic film will not reveal this detail; panchromatic film is required.

Figure 3-5 (see p. 174 and inside back cover) shows the microstructure of an alloy of Fe and 4% Mn that has been heat-treated to form massive martensite. The ten micrographs illustrate the influence of etch time on coloration; Beraha's tint etch (3 g $K_2S_2O_5$, 10 g $Na_2S_2O_3$, and 100 mL H_2O) was used. The photomicrographs were made by immersing the objective lens into the solution during etching (the lens was carefully cleaned and dried upon removal). Coloration began after 10 to 15 s, with optimum results after about 65 s.

As discussed previously, Fig. 3-4 shows the ternary Fe_3C-Fe_3P-ferrite eutectic in a gray cast-iron sample that has been etched with different selective etchants, including several of Beraha's tint etchants. Etching with nital and picral revealed the outline of the ternary eutectic and the fine ferrite particles but did not etch the phase boundary between cementite and phosphide. Beraha's tint etchants selectively colored the phosphide and cementite phases, although the colors obtained were not always those claimed [19]. The ferrite phase in the eutectic was not always revealed clearly. Murakami's reagent (10 g KOH, 10 g $K_3Fe(CN)_6$, and 100 mL H_2O) did not produce visible etching at room temperature. However when this reagent was used boiling, after 10 s, only the phosphide was colored light brown; after 2 min, cementite was lightly colored yellow and the phosphide was dark brown. Use for 1 min of boiling alkaline sodium picrate to which 2% EDTA had been added colored only the cementite. Heat tinting (750°F, 10 min) colored cementite deep blue and phosphide light tan. Other examples of the use of tint etchants appear throughout this chapter.

3-2.5 Electrolytic Etching

As described in Chap. 2, many electropolishing solutions can be used to etch samples simply by reducing the applied voltage at the end of polishing to about one-tenth the polishing voltage and maintaining this lower level for several seconds or more, or by short-circuiting the electrodes at the end of the polishing cycle. Appendix H outlines the use of these electropolishing solutions for etching. Not all the electropolishing solutions produce good etching results.

Many of the solutions developed that are ideal electrolytic etchants do not produce useful polishing at higher voltages. As long as samples are polished beforehand, these solutions can be used to etch samples with good results. For revealing certain structural characteristics, such as dislocations, an electrolytically or chemically polished surface is usually desired for best results.

In electrolytic etching, the applied potential takes the place of the oxidizer used in a chemical reagent. Thus, most electrolytic reagents are rather simple in composition, being acidic, alkaline, or salt solutions. The sample is nearly always the anode, although a few cathodic etching solutions have been developed. Also, direct current is nearly always used, although a few solutions require alternating current. With electrolytic etching, the etching process is controlled by varying the etching voltage and time. Usually the sample can be etched, examined, and reetched successfully without repolishing—a practice that is not always feasible with chemical reagents.

Electrolytic etchants are often employed for selective etching of specific constituents or grain boundaries. Some electrolytic etchants attack the sample surface nonselectively, but many are quite specific in their attack and are quite useful for phase identification. Electrolytic etchants have been widely used in the study of stainless steels, as is discussed later in this chapter. They are simple to use, are generally quite safe, and generally produce excellent results that are frequently superior to chemical etchants. Appendix I lists electrolytic etchants for various metals and alloys, and examples of the use of these etchants are given later in this chapter.

3-2.6 Anodizing

Anodic oxidation, or anodizing, is an electrolytic etching process for depositing an oxide film on the metal surface that is often epitaxial to the underlying grain structure. It is similar in nature to heat tinting or tint etching in that an interference film is produced on the metal surface. However, with some samples, polarized light must be used to obtain the desired structural information, irrespective of the crystal structure of the underlying metal. In general, surfaces that have been electropolished produce the best results, and anodizing has been used with aluminum, copper, niobium (columbium), titanium, uranium, and zirconium.

Anodizing was first applied to the study of the grain structure of aluminum. Although aluminum has a cubic crystal structure and is, therefore, isotropic, the oxide film produced permits the grain structure to be observed under crossed-polarized illumination. If the film is thin, interference colors are produced and physical or chemical inhomogeneities can be observed. Generally, however, thicker films are produced, and the interference effect is not used. The optical anisotropy effect produced by thick films has been ascribed to the surface structure of the oxide film, although Jacquet [20] has claimed that the effect is due to the submicroscopic profile of the interface of the metal and oxide (see discussion in later section on chemical etchants that render cubic metals responsive to polarized light).

Although anodizing has in general been employed with isotropic metals, it is also useful for studying anisotropic metals, such as uranium and zirconium, in which certain chemical and structural effects can be enhanced for observation. Anodizing techniques for different metals are listed in App. I and further discussed in later sections on the specific metals.

3-2.7 Potentiostatic Etching

The potentiostat, which was originally developed for the study of certain corrosion processes, provides the metallographer with a highly controlled, selective electrolytic etching technique. A third electrode, a reference electrode (frequently a saturated calomel electrode), is employed to maintain a constant potential during etching. Current passes only between the polished sample (anode) and the platinum cathode and is controlled by the potential difference between the reference electrode and the specimen.

A potentiostat consists of a two-stage balanced dc amplifier which permits the current to be controlled in both directions. Any deviation from the desired constant potential imposed by the potentiostat is amplified and compensated for in order to maintain a constant potential at the sample surface. The procedure for making potentiostatic measurements is described in American Society for Testing and Materials (ASTM) Standard G5. Etching phenomena can be studied by slowly varying the potential and recording the polarization curves in both directions.

The nature of the polarization curves of a polished metal surface depends on the temperature and composition of the electrolyte, the alloy composition, and the amount and nature of the phases present. Thus these curves are developed under specific conditions so that selective etching conditions can be established. Examination of the polarization curves permits establishment of the potential ranges in which anodic dissolution of the phases occurs. Each phase has a characteristic polarization curve, and examination of these curves and comparison to polarization curves of a multiphased alloy containing these phases enables determination of a specific potential or range of potentials that will preferentially attack each desired phase. To produce clear phase discrimination, the ratio of the solution rate of the desired phase to that of the other phases present should be as high as possible. Thus, in a two-phase alloy, the differentiation ratio is the ratio of the current per unit surface area for the desired phase to that of the other phase at the applied potential. The relative amounts of the phases do not affect the differentiation ratio.

The optimum procedure for determining selective etching potentials is to obtain independent polarization curves for each phase present in the alloy. This, however, is frequently impossible, since the phases may not be separable. However, continuous recording of the polarization curve for the multiphase alloy can be used to develop the required information. Alternatively, by choosing alloys of somewhat similar composition and subjecting them to specific heat treatments to obtain single-phase conditions, or large amounts of a desired phase, the required individual polarization curves can be developed.

The study by Greene et al. on the potentiostatic etching of tin-zinc alloys provides considerable insight into potentiostatic etching and its potential value [21]. This system is ideal for study because the phases consist of pure tin and pure zinc whose polarization characteristics have been well defined. The tin dissolution products are colorless, while the zinc dissolution products are dark and insoluble; thus, staining versus nonstaining etching results can be compared.

Potentiostatically determined anodic polarization curves for tin and zinc in 1 N sodium hydroxide are shown in Fig. 3-6. The dotted region of the curves indicates loss of potentiostatic control. Because tin and zinc form a heterogenous alloy system, i.e., neither is soluble in the other, these curves are indicative of the dissolution rates for the two phases in tin-zinc alloys. Zinc is selectively dissolved at potentials below -1.10 V versus the saturated calomel electrode (SCE) and at potentials more positive than -0.7 V versus the SCE. Tin will be selectively

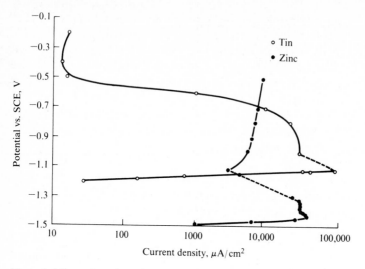

Figure 3-6 Potentiostatic anodic polarization curve for tin and zinc in 1 *N* NaOH at 25°C. *(From Greene et al., Ref. 21, courtesy of Pergamon Press.)*

attacked between -1.10 and -0.7 V versus the SCE. The highest differentiation ratios occur at -1.45 V for zinc and at -1.10 V or at potentials more positive than -0.50 V for tin.

Greene et al. showed (see Fig. 3-7) that an alloy of 50 wt % zinc and 50 wt % tin can be preferentially etched potentiostatically at -1.45 and -0.60 V versus SCE for zinc and at -0.95 V versus SCE for tin. Selective etching of tin roughens the surface and makes it appear dark. A differentiation ratio of at least 5 was required for selective etching of tin for good results; lower ratios did not produce adequate contrast. Selective etching of zinc could be obtained with lower differentiation ratios because of the production of dark corrosion products. Measurements of the depth of etching of the tin phase revealed that etching must be continued to a depth of 2.5 μm to produce acceptable contrast at 100X magnification. Less metal removal is needed for producing contrast at the zinc phase because of the colored corrosion products.

The potentiostatic etching method provides the unique advantage of selective etching of desired microstructural constituents with very high reproducibility. Thus, the method is ideal for phase identification and quantitative metallography. Specific etching instructions for using this method with a variety of alloys are given in App. I.

3-2.8 Polarized-Light Etchants

Metals with cubic, isotropic crystal structures do not respond to crossed-polarized light in the as-polished condition. As discussed in the previous section, anodized surface films on cubic metals, such as aluminum, are usually examined under polarized light to reveal grain contrast. Tint-etched samples and heat-tinted samples can be examined with bright-field illumination, although polarized light often enhances the color contrast. There are also a number of chemical etchants

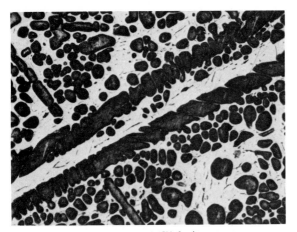

Zn darkened, –1.45V, 3 min

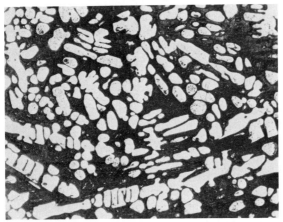

Sn darkened, –0.95V, 3 min

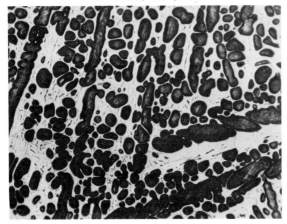

Zn darkened, –0.60V, 3 min

Figure 3-7 Examples of selective etching of an alloy of Sn and 50% Zn using potentiostatic etching with 1 *N* NaOH (potentials versus standard calomel electrode. 75×). *(From Greene et al., Ref. 21, courtesy of N. D. Greene, Univ. of Connecticut, reproduced courtesy of Pergamon Press.)*

which render the surface of many metals active to polarized light even though the metals are isotropic. Mott and Haines [22] have summarized the preparation procedures for examining many anisotropic metals, alloys, and intermetallic phases with polarized light and have also reviewed the use of polarized light to study both anisotropic and etched metals or anodized isotropic metals [23].

In 1924, Jones demonstrated that deeply etched isotropic metal surfaces (steels, brasses, aluminum bronze, cupronickels, bismuth, nickel, and aluminum) respond to polarized light, and in 1935, Baeyertz demonstrated that etched pearlite responds to polarized light, while no effect is observed in the as-polished condition. In a study of deformed Monel metal in which the structure was revealed with a standard grain contrast etch, Woodard obtained an intensity contrast pattern with polarized light that was attributed to differences in crystalline orientation [24]. Woodard suggested that the contrast etchant produced an anisotropic surface film much like that produced by anodizing.

Perryman and Lack conducted an experiment to determine if the polarization response was due to surface contour effects or to the presence of an anisotropic surface film [25]. Electrolytically polished zinc and cadmium (both anisotropic), electrolytically polished and anodized aluminum (isotropic), and Monel (isotropic) treated by Woodard's method were examined before and after vacuum deposition of a thin film (80 nm) of silver on the polished surfaces. If the polarization effects were due to optical anisotropy, the optically isotropic silver film would render the surface inactive to polarized light. However, if the polarization effects were due to surface roughness, the silver film would not impair polarization effects because it would reproduce the surface roughness. Before deposition, all four samples responded to polarized light. After deposition, the optically anisotropic zinc and cadmium did not respond to polarized light, as expected. However, both the anodized aluminum and the etched Monel still responded to polarized light. Thus, polarization effects on anodized aluminum and etched Monel must be due to surface roughness effects and not the presence of an anisotropic surface film. These surface roughness effects could be observed with phase-contrast illumination and by electron microscopy and were not present on the as-polished aluminum and Monel samples.

3-3 HEAT TINTING

If a polished metal sample is heated in air at a relatively low temperature, the surface will be oxidized. In a multiphased alloy, the oxidation rates of the constituents can vary depending on their composition, producing variations in oxide thickness and characteristic colors. Interference colors are obtained once the film reaches a certain thickness, generally about 30 nm. Thinner oxide films are invisible without special examination methods.

The colors produced by a film of suitable thickness are caused by interference between light rays reflected from the inner and outer film surfaces. Recombination of two waves with a phase difference of 180° causes light of a certain wavelength to disappear, and the reflected light exhibits the complimentary color. Interference results when the oxide thickness is an odd multiple of one-quarter the wavelength of a component of the incident light wave. The critical factor is the wavelength of light in the oxide, which is influenced by the refractive index of the oxide film. Relationships between film thickness and interference colors have been determined for iron, steel, nickel, and copper.

Research at Oak Ridge National Laboratory, reported by Gray et al., has vividly demonstrated that crystallographic orientation also influences oxidation rates [26]. Using single-crystal spheres of copper, they demonstrated that oxidation at 250°C occurred fastest on certain crystallographic faces, with the rate of oxidation decreasing in the following order: (100), (210), (110), (311). Figure 3-8, which is from their study, shows oxidation patterns on single-crystal spheres of copper and copper containing 0.1% aluminum (both cubic) and zirconium and hafnium (both hexagonal close-packed). The patterns due to oxidation for cubic metals are quite different than the patterns for hexagonal close-packed metals.

Several methods have been used to produce suitable oxide films by heat tinting. These methods include heating on a hot plate or on a sheet placed over a bunsen burner, flotation on molten tin, or heating in a laboratory furnace. Regardless of the technique used, the polished surface is placed face up and must be kept clean during oxidation. With these methods, heating times of up to about 20 min are generally used. With the first three methods, heating is continued until a violet or purple macroscopic color is observed. The temperature is not controlled, except with molten tin. If a laboratory furnace is used, both temperature and time are fixed in order to provide better control. Heating in an induction coil

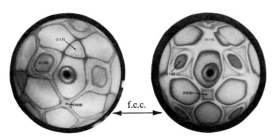

Cu, 250°C–30 min.–O_2 Cu-0.1 w/o Al, 250°C–30 min.–O_2

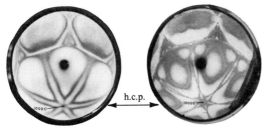

Zr, 360°C–15 min.–air   Hf, 500°C–20 hrs.–steam

OXIDIZED SINGLE CRYSTAL SPHERES

Figure 3-8 Patterns developed on face-centered cubic and hexagonal close-packed single crystals by heat tinting, which demonstrates the sensitivity of oxidation to crystal orientation. *(From R. J. Gray et al., Ref. 26, courtesy of Plenum Press.)*

produces rapid oxidation, generally in 5 to 10 s, although control of the process can be rather difficult.

Light preetching with a general-purpose reagent often helps in obtaining sharper images. Heat tinting can produce striking color effects and can be quite useful for phase identification, since certain constituents oxidize more readily than others. The examination of the microstructure of many ferrous and nonferrous metals and alloys can be made easier by the use of heat tinting. However, this process should not be employed if heating produces phase changes or other effects such as precipitation. Despite the simplicity of heat tinting and the excellent results that can be obtained, metallographers use the method infrequently. The infrequent use of this method is probably due to the claim that the method is difficult to control and not reproducible. However, if a laboratory furnace is used to control both temperature and time, excellent reproducibility can be obtained with commonly encountered materials.

Heat tinting is not useful for carbon and low-alloy steels because the ferrite phase oxidizes rapidly and the film produced is thick and obscures details. Cementite also oxidizes rapidly so that both are colored. While pearlite can be colored nicely, no advantage is gained compared to standard etchants. Heat tinting has been used to study the microstructure of cast iron [27]. The procedure recommends immersing the polished sample in a 50% NH_4OH solution for a few seconds. This prevents the graphite from absorbing the etchant and from producing staining during heat tinting. Next, the sample is etched either in 2% H_3PO_4 or in nital, washed, and dried. The sample is heated on a hot plate to about 575°F (302°C) until the surface is colored purple. The ternary Fe_3C-Fe_3P-ferrite eutectic appears yellowish red, graphite appears blue with slight purple coloring along the edges, ferrite appears blue and white, and pearlite appears red and purple.

Heat tinting is quite useful for high-alloy steels and stainless steels. Depending on the alloy content (primarily chromium), temperatures from 700 to 1380°F (371 to 750°C) have been employed. Heat tinting is quite useful with tool steels in which the matrix can be colored, leaving the carbides white for measurement of the amount and size of the carbides.

Considerable use of heat tinting has been made in the study of the microstructure of stainless steels. Emmanuel heat-tinted an alloy of 25% Cr and 20% Ni at 1200°F (649°C) for periods of up to 20 min [28]. Austenite passes through temper colors ahead of ferrite, while the carbides resist oxidation longest. After a 20-min period, austenite was colored mottled green, sigma phase was orange, and the carbides remained white. Figure 3-9 shows a heat-tinted stainless steel sample.

Weeton and Signorelli used heat tinting for phase identification in a wrought cobalt-based alloy, Stellite 21 [29]. Samples were preetched electrolytically with 5% aqueous HCl and then heated until the surface was dull red in color. Sigma phase was medium brown, $Cr_{23}C_6$ was white, and M_6C was dark.

Heat tinting has also been used for titanium and its alloys. For all alpha alloys, heat tinting can produce better grain contrast and grain boundary delineation than chemical etching. Heat tinting at 896°F (480°C) for 2 h has been used to distinguish between primary and secondary alpha phase. In alpha-beta alloys, the beta phase has been reported to darken before the alpha phase.

Figure 3-9 Heat tinting at 1100°F (593°C) for 5 min was used to color phases in austentic stainless steel weld metal (preetched with Vilella's reagent). Austenite colored (blue) more rapidly than delta ferrite (cream-white), 150×.

Figure 3-10 (*inside front cover*) Examples of gas contrasting to reveal microstructure. Top: AlSi$_{12}$CuNi cast alloy, oxygen gas, Fe electrode, 1.8 kV at 55 Pa, 300×; bottom: 25 Be-45Ni-30Co (at. %), oxygen gas, Fe electrode, 2 kV at 55 Pa, 115×. (*Courtesy of G. Petzow, Max-Planck Institut für Metallforschung.*)

Heat tinting has been widely used in the study of the microstructure of sintered carbides. Franssen heat-tinted samples at 1470°F (800°C) for 90 to 120 s [30]. Tungsten carbide was colored blue, titanium carbide was colored brown to red, and cobalt was colored reddish black. Heat tinting at 660 to 750°F (350 to 400°C) for 30 to 45 min produced the following colors: tungsten carbide was white or faintly blue, cobalt was clear but outlined, and the solid solution of tungsten carbide (WC) and titanium carbide was light brown. W$_2$C is colored but WC is not.

Chaporova heat-tinted alloys of tungsten carbide and cobalt (WC-Co) and of tungsten carbide, titanium carbide, and cobalt (WC-TiC-Co) at 750°F (400°C) for 15 min in a muffle furnace [31]. This treatment outlined and colored the cobalt phase, leaving the carbide lightly colored. Bleecker heat-tinted WC-TiC-Co samples at 500 to 600°F (260 to 316°C) for 10 min [32]. Co was darkened, TiC was yellowish brown, and WC was unaffected. Powers and Loach preetched sintered carbides electrolytically with 5% sodium carbonate and then heat-tinted them for about 5 min at 900°F (482°C) [33]. The following colors were produced: WC was gray, TaC was yellow, Co was blue, and eta phase was brown and deep purple.

3-4 THERMAL ETCHING

If metals and ceramics are heated to high temperatures in a vacuum or in an inert atmosphere in which stable compounds cannot form on the surface, grooves will be produced at the crystal boundaries. Some metals, when heated in certain inert atmospheres, also develop striations on the grain surfaces, with their form and direction a function of crystal orientation. A similar effect is observed when non-cubic metals, such as Sn, Zn, or Cd, are heated in an inert atmosphere, but the effect is due to thermal fatigue rather than thermal etching. Grains in noncubic metals expand and contract anisotropically, producing lines at the grain boundaries during heating and cooling as a result of the anisotropic dimension changes. Thermal etching occurs in materials whose grains expand and contract uniformly.

Thermal etching was first demonstrated by Osmond in 1888, while Oberhoffer in 1909 was the first to use a vacuum for thermal etching. Early workers believed that a gas, such as chlorine, was required in small amounts to promote etching, but this was shown to be unnecessary by subsequent studies. Grain-boundary grooving was originally attributed to selective evaporation at the grain boundaries but is now believed to occur by the transfer of atoms or ions from one part of the surface to another, probably by surface migration, producing an equilibrium structure of minimum free energy.

Thermal etching has been used to study grain growth in many metals. The technique has been used with iron and steel to study the alpha-to-gamma phase transformation and the formation of martensite and bainite. Thermal etching was introduced by O'Neill in 1937 and by Day and Austin in 1940 for the determination of the austenite grain size of steels. Thermal etching occurs during hot-stage microscopic examination, as discussed and illustrated in Chap. 4. Thermal etching is a very effective technique for grain-boundary delineation in ceramics. Other uses include delineation of dislocations in silver, revealing the distribution of impurities, and determination of grain-boundary energy as a function of grain orientation.

3-5 GAS CONTRASTING

In 1973, Bartz described a color contrasting method that required relatively simple, inexpensive equipment which permitted *in situ* observation during coloration [34]. This gas contrasting technique has wide applicability and is quite reproducible. The commercially available Leitz gas contrasting device can be used to apply this technique to a variety of samples. The sample is placed in a small vacuum chamber fixed to the stage of an upright microscope. A two-stage mechanical pump is used to produce a vacuum of about 10^{-3} mmHg (0.1 Pa). After evacuation of the chamber, needle valves are opened, permitting pure or mixed gases to enter the chamber. During this period, the vacuum pump remains in operation to maintain a gas pressure of 10^{-2} to 1 mmHg (1 to 100 Pa). The polished surface is then moved to the contrasting position in front of a gas-discharge electron gun operating at a potential of 0.5 to 4 kV with the sample as the anode in the circuit. A film forms on the sample surface during the gas discharge, producing color contrast between different constituents. During the gas discharge, the surface temperature rises until it reaches an equilibrium level that depends on the applied potential. Temperatures of up to 392°F (200°C) have been measured. If such temperatures cannot be tolerated because of phase changes or precipitation, lower potentials less than (<1.4 kV) can be used. Alternatively, higher potentials can be used cyclically to minimize heating.

The obtainment of specific color contrast effects requires production of a certain film thickness, which is a function of time, voltage, the spacing between the sample and the electron gun, the type of gas, and the gas pressure. The time required decreases with increasing potential and decreasing spacing. The coating time t can be calculated using Eq. (3-1) [35]:

$$t = \frac{A}{kV - B} \qquad (3\text{-}1)$$

where A is 4.4 min and B is 0.3 kV. Contrast effects can be changed by varying the time or the cathode material. In general, optimum contrast is obtained when the macroscopic surface color is red to blue, as in heat tinting or in the Pepperhoff vapor-deposition method. Typically, times of 3 to 20 min are required using potentials of 1.5 to 2.5 kV and sample-to-gun spacings of 5 to 10 mm.

The gas pressure influences coating time and coating area (generally 1 cm^2). High gas pressure (50 Pa) reduces contrasting time, but the area coated is reduced. If the coated area is inadequate, lower pressures can be used. Although most early work employed an iron cathode, Exner and Roth experimented with Ag, Au, Cu, In, Pb, and Pt cathodes [35]. In general, only a few cathode materials produced significant differences if the coating time is adjusted. They also reported that changes in the gas used produced no significant differences. Typically, argon, air, or oxygen is used. The time required for contrasting can be significantly influenced by the gas used. The use of noble-metal cathode and inert gases reduced the coating time by at least a factor of 3 [35].

Exner and Roth investigated gas contrasting of many materials and have listed useful recipes and results [35]. Successful gas contrasting of carbon and low-alloy steels required a preetch with a 10% ferric chloride solution and results showed little advantage over the traditional chemical etchants. Excellent contrast was obtained on preetched high-alloy steels and on cast irons. Use of gas contrasting to show phase discrimination in aluminum alloys is simple and reliable and avoids the problem of repolishing between use of selective chemical etchants that heavily attack a given constituent. Gas contrasting of hard-metal alloys and carbides has been quite useful. Most metals can be successfully contrasted. Figure 3-10 (see p. 185 and inside front cover) shows examples of the use of gas contrasting to reveal microstructure.

3-6 VAPOR-DEPOSITED INTERFERENCE FILMS

In 1960, Pepperhoff demonstrated that microstructural contrast could be developed without etching by using vacuum deposition of a suitable material onto the sample surface to produce a thin, low-absorption, dielectric film with a high refractive index. In the as-polished condition, small differences in intensity and in optical phase angles usually exist between the microstructural constituents so that the microstructural constituents are either invisible or barely visible under bright-field illumination. Sometimes interference-contrast or phase-contrast illumination can produce images where none are visible with bright-field illumination. The introduction of a thin interference film amplifies these minor differences by successive light reflection at the specimen surface, rendering the structure visible in the same manner as in heat tinting or gas contrasting.

When a polished sample that is coated with an interference film is examined with monochromatic light, the light waves reflected at the top and bottom of the interference film recombine and form reflected light. Some of the light striking the sample is reflected by the air and film interface, while some is refracted on entering the film and is reflected by the film and sample interface. This light is partly reflected and partly refracted at the film and air interface, with the refracted beam superimposed on the light that was initially reflected at the air and film interface. This process occurs continuously between the film surfaces. Contrast increases as the amount of reflected light is reduced by interference.

Maximum contrast between two constituents is obtained by deposition of a material whose film has a high refractive index (n_s). A wide range of materials has been used. ZnTe, TiO_2, ZnSe, and ZnS are some of the more popular vapor-deposited materials. ZnSe and TiO_2 are slightly absorbent, while ZnS is perfectly transparent. The high refractive index of the deposited film increases the brightness contrast between the phases and also increases the phase displacements between the waves reflected from the constituents producing color differences. Phase-contrast discrimination with interference films is more sensitive than phase-contrast illumination.

Good sample preparation procedures with particular attention to cleanliness is imperative for best results. Introduction of a slight amount of relief during final polishing, or a light preetch, are useful for obtaining better resolution of details. Residues left on the surface from polishing, cleaning, or handling must be removed. Vapor deposition is generally conducted under a vacuum of about 10^{-3} to 10^{-5} mmHg, with the sample about 10 to 15 cm from the deposition material. The compound should be evaporated slowly while being observed. As the film thickness increases, the macroscopic surface color changes in the following sequence: yellow, green, red, purple, violet, blue, silvery blue. Evaporation should be halted when the surface color is purple to violet, although with a few samples a green or red color has produced excellent results. To obtain a uniform film thickness, the sample is placed perpendicular to the flow of evaporated material and the sample can be slowly rotated. It sometimes helps to angle the sample surface so that a range of film thicknesses and colors is obtained. In this way, the conditions for best color contrast can be established in a single experiment.

Maximum contrast between structural features is obtained when the observation occurs at the interference minimum. This occurs when the reflection minimum lies in the green-yellow portion of the spectral region, i.e., when the macroscopic surface color is purple to violet in white light. Samples can often be viewed under bright-field illumination without the use of a green filter, although the use of a green filter may increase contrast differences. Kohlhaas and Fischer have shown that the use of a continuous-band interference filter can further enhance contrast between phases and is especially useful for black-and-white photography [36]. The filter is moved across the light path until the wavelength producing minimum reflectivity for a given phase is obtained. Alternatively, one can try placing filters of different colors in the light path to increase contrast between the constituents.

In general, as the reflectivity of the polished surface increases, the refractive index of the deposited film must increase for proper contrast development. Thus for high-reflectivity metals, materials with n_s values equal to or greater than that of ZnSe must be used. Oxides and sulfides exhibit low reflectivities, and contrast can be obtained with materials with n_s values as low as that of PbF_2.

To obtain maximum contrast, the reflected wave from one constituent must undergo extinction by interference and produce zero reflectivity while the reflectivity of the other constituent must be as high as possible. For maximum contrast, the optical constants, that is the refractive index and absorption coefficient for the different phases, should be known. Bühler and his associates have developed the needed information for several systems. Bühler and Kossel determined optical constants (absorption coefficients and refractive indexes) for carbides in ferritic and austenitic steels [37]. This information was then plotted on graphs that showed the relationship between the absorption coefficient as a function of the refracting indexes of commonly used vapor-deposited films, as shown in Fig. 3-11. This graph shows that the carbides have zero reflectivity if platinum oxide or lead oxide are used. The contrast between the carbide and the matrix decreases as the refractive index of the deposited film decreases.

With metals, i.e., samples that exhibit high reflectivity or are strongly absorbing substrates, the deposited material must have a very high refractive index and must be nonabsorbing. ZnTe, ZnSe, TiO_2, and ZnS are commonly used for coating metals because of their high n_s values. Optical constants for aluminum and some common intermetallic phases have been developed [37]. Zogg et al.

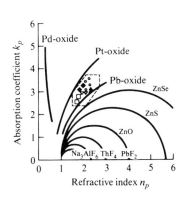

Layer	n_s	k_s
Pd-oxide	2.75	0.6
Pt-oxide	2.75	0.25
Pb-oxide	2.67	0.1
ZnSe	2.65	—
ZnS	2.36	—
ZnO	2.0	—
PbF_2	1.7	—
ThF_4	1.5	—
Na_3AlF_6	1.35	—

$\lambda = 500 - 500$ nm

•— $M_{23}C$	▽— M_6C
○— $M_2[C,N]$	◆— M_2C_3
▲— $M_6[C,N]$	□— NbC

Figure 3-11 Optical constants of carbides and carbonitrides and common vapor-deposited compound. *(From Bühler and Kossel, Ref. 37, courtesy of Dr. Riederer-Verlag, GmbH.)*

have shown the usefulness of vapor-deposited ZnTe for identification of constituents in aluminum alloys [38].

The Pepperhoff interference film method has been applied to the study of a very wide range of materials, as summarized in Ref. 39. It is a simple technique to employ but does require use of a vacuum evaporator. Striking results can be obtained, and the method is useful for phase identification and image analysis.

Figure 3-12 shows the as-polished structure of a 70% alpha alumina and 30% TiC cermet cutting tool. Microprobe analysis revealed discrete particles of the WC-Co grinding media used to size the raw materials. A number of etching techniques were tried to bring out the entrapped WC-Co grinding media, but all were unsuccessful. As shown in Fig. 3-12, vapor deposition of ZnSe reversed the contrast between the TiC and the Al_2O_3 and clearly revealed the entrapped WC-Co grinding media (colored orange).

3-7 MAGNETIC "ETCHING"

Researchers studying magnetic materials have employed a number of methods to examine magnetic domain structures [40, 41] in order to relate metallographic and domain structure to properties such as core loss, permeability, and magnetostriction. Factors such as the domain wall spacing and mobility and grain misorientation have been shown to be important variables. Techniques used to observe magnetic domains include the Bitter technique, magneto-optic Kerr and Faraday effects, Lorentz microscopy, and x-ray topography.

The Bitter method is quite commonly used because of its simplicity. This technique initially employed finely ground particles of gamma ferric oxide suspended in ethyl acetate. Since the initial work by Bitter, researchers have prepared true colloidal (i.e., permanent) suspensions of gamma ferric oxide or

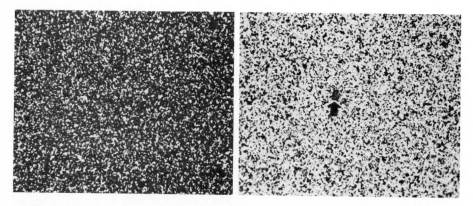

Figure 3-12 Use of vapor-deposited ZnSe to reveal entrapped WC-Co grinding media (flakes from ball milling of raw materials). As-polished (left) condition reveals only the TiC (white) and Al_2O_3. Vapor deposition of ZnSe reverses the color contrast of the major phases and reveals the entrapped grinding media (arrow), colored orange (600×).

have used a commercially prepared colloidal magnetic suspension known as Ferrofluid (Ferrofluidics Corp., Nashua, New Hampshire 03061). The Bitter method has also been used to detect ferromagnetic phases in austenitic materials (see discussion later in this chapter under "Etchants for Stainless Steels").

To use the Bitter technique, samples must be carefully prepared to eliminate artifact structures and residual stresses. Electropolishing is generally preferred. A drop of the colloidal suspension of magnetic iron oxide is applied to the sample surface. The particles are attracted by stray magnetic fields, thus outlining domain structures. The sample is observed with either bright-field or dark-field illumination. A magnetic coil or yoke is used to alter the magnetic structure. Examination can be made using magnifications of up to several hundred fold; if replicas are prepared, electron microscopy [42] can be used or optical microscopy at high magnification can be performed if the suspension is dried after application ("dry Bitter technique") [43]. The Bitter technique is limited to observation of static or slowly changing domain structures.

Scortecci and Stagno have shown that the domain structure of ferrite in carbon steel can be revealed by electropolishing [44]. Jacquet's electropolishing solution (300 mL acetic acid and 27 mL perchloric acid) was used at 150 A/dm^2 (40 V dc) for 5 min with a stainless steel cathode. The patterns were not visible after mechanical polishing but were revealed after the electropolishing solution had been used for at least 50 samples.

3-8 ION-BOMBARDMENT ETCHING

Ion-bombardment etching is a special metallographic technique used primarily with materials that are difficult to etch by chemical methods [45, 46]. Ion etching is not a new technique; it was first demonstrated by Grove in 1852. However, except for a few studies, for example, that of Smith in 1927, it has not been used as a metallographic tool until the development of interest in radioactive materials and composites.

The development of structure by ion etching results from the energy and angular distribution of the impinging ions as well as the compositional and orientation differences on the sample surface. Sputtering produces different metal and compound removal rates, which depend on the atom bonding, the gas ion employed, and the bombardment energy. As the bombardment energy increases, the depth of penetration increases and the sputtering yield increases. Very high bombardment energy, however, results in implantation of the bombarding gas ions.

Three modes of ion etching are used [47]:

- Physical sputtering with an ion beam
- Physical cathodic sputtering by gas discharge ion bombardment
- Chemical sputtering by activated gas discharge

Physical sputtering with an ion beam under a strong vacuum at a preset impingement angle for the gas ions is employed for ion thinning of foils that are used for transmission electron microscopy (TEM) or for depth-profile studies using techniques such as Auger analysis. Ion thinning of TEM foils is generally used on materials that cannot be satisfactorily thinned chemically or electrolytically. Ion etching at low sputtering rates is often used to clean samples prior to chemical analysis of the surface.

Cathodic sputtering by a gas discharge to accelerate the ions above the specimen (cathode) uses dc potentials of up to about 5 kV under vacuum. A high-frequency field can be applied, using external electrodes to stabilize the gas discharge. Chemical ion etching, or reactive sputtering, usually employs oxygen and in general is used only for organic specimens, particularly polymers. The structures developed, however, are influenced by the impingement angle.

Vacuum cathodic etching has proved useful for developing the microstructures of aluminum and cast iron. In steels, the sputtering rates for ferrite and cementite are nearly identical; thus the technique offers no advantage over chemical etchants for steels. However, with composite materials, coatings, dissimilar welds, etc., it is often difficult to completely reveal the structure by chemical etching. One component may be satisfactorily etched, while the other is unaffected or overetched. Vacuum cathodic etching is quite useful for revealing the structure of metals that are difficult to etch and has been used on radioactive materials and on ceramics. The etches are stain-free, and fine polishing scratches are removed. Disadvantages of this method are that samples mounted in plastics are unsuitable, since the glow discharge will decompose the plastic and produce contaminating films on the surface. Considerable heat can be generated during etching. Ion-bombardment etching of low-melting-point metals can produce cone-shaped artifacts on the etched surface. Cone formation seems to be more common when argon or neon gases are used. Thus, it can be difficult to interpret the microstructure when such features are present. Boundaries between phases with different removal rates can be widened unnaturally. Surfaces etched by ion bombardment usually exhibit a flat etch contrast. Grain and phase boundaries are revealed strongly. The process, as illustrated in Fig. 3-13, usually requires 1 to 10 min, although times of up to an hour are sometimes used. An expensive apparatus is also required.

3-9 DISLOCATION ETCH PITTING

While the modern era of dislocation etching can be traced to the work in 1949 of Shockley and Read, the development of etch figures on minerals began with the work of Daniell in 1817. Honess listed many of the etchants used for minerals in his classic book written in 1927. Etch figures were used to study crystal symmetry; however, the technique was supplanted by the development of x-ray diffraction methods.

The introduction of the concept of dislocations in the 1930s to provide an understanding of plasticity, strength, the structure of grain boundaries, and many other phenomena prompted development of many techniques for detecting

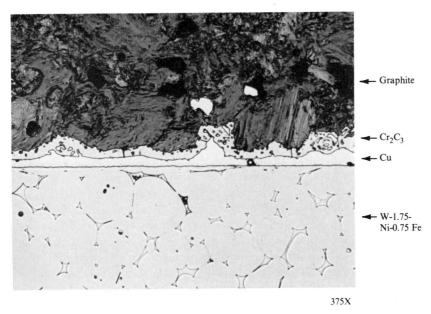

Graphite

Cr$_2$C$_3$

Cu

W-1.75-Ni-0.75 Fe

375X

Figure 3-13 Vacuum cathodic etching (2 min, 2500 V, xenon gas at 100 torr) of A7-J graphite brazed to W-1.75Ni-0.75Fe. *(Courtesy of R. S. Crouse, Oak Ridge National Laboratory.)*

dislocations. Investigations of the properties of single crystals have relied upon the measurement of dislocation content, or density, dislocation distribution, and substructure.

Many techniques have been used to detect dislocations and determine dislocation density. Of these, etch pitting is the simplest, most widely employed method. Etch pitting can be applied to crystals that can be cleaved or cut and polished to expose low-index crystal planes. Because dislocations are regions of disorder, they can be revealed through the use of an etchant that preferentially attacks these locations. The etchant should attack only dislocations and should attack all of the dislocations that emerge at the surface. Because bulk samples are used, dislocations within the sample cannot be revealed. Successive polishing and etching can be used to study dislocations within the crystal.

Dislocations have also been studied by precipitation decoration. Alloys of aluminum containing 4% copper have been studied by this method. The method is based on the observation that precipitation occurs preferentially at dislocations. The internal configuration of dislocations within crystals can be examined using decoration methods.

The first deliberate use of etch pits to reveal dislocations was performed by Horn and by Gevers and his coworkers in 1952. These studies provided the first direct proof that dislocations could be revealed by etching. Both studies used silicon carbide crystals etched in fused borax.

Etch pits are formed by immersing a suitably prepared crystal into a specific liquid or gas at ambient or elevated temperatures for a certain time period. If the conditions have been chosen and executed properly, small pits are observed on the surface of the crystal where dislocations are present. In addition to chemical etching, dislocations can be revealed using electrolytic etching, thermal etching, preferential oxidation, or ionic bombardment. These methods have been summarized in a number of reviews [48–51] and are listed in App. J.

In metals, segregation of impurities or Cottrell atmosphere formation at dislocations is required for reliable etch-pit formation. In ionic crystals, however, impurities do not appear to be important. On a freshly cleaved face, newly formed (fresh) dislocations as well as grown-in (old) dislocations can be revealed. Some etching solutions attack only fresh dislocations, while other etchants attack only old dislocations. In general, fresh dislocations are more easily revealed, probably because of the strain field associated with the fresh dislocation.

The shape of an etch pit is determined by the ratio of the lateral displacement of the surface steps (v_1) to the rate at which the pit deepens (v_n). If the ratio of v_1/v_n is small, i.e., less than 10, a well-defined pit results. A successful etch-pitting solution produces ratios less than 10. In general, v_1 can be lowered by adding impurities to the solution. In etching some samples, for example, in etching LiF, the concentration of the active "poison" is very important, while in others it is not.

The crystallographic orientation of the surface often has a substantial effect on etching response. Close-packed planes are usually the easiest to etch, while only some high-index planes can be etched. In many samples etch pits are produced only over a limited range of orientations near the close-packed planes.

Because the low-index planes are easiest to etch-pit, it is not surprising that etch-pit morphology is a function of crystal symmetry. For example, etch pits on a (111) close-packed plane of a face-centered cubic metal appear as triangular-based pyramids, and the exposed pit surfaces are {111} planes. In a body-centered cubic metal, etch pits on a (111) plane will appear as triangular-based pyramids with {110}-faced sides, while pits on {100} surfaces will appear as squares, and pits on {110} surfaces will appear as rectangles. Figure 3-14 shows an example of dislocation etch pits.

Many investigators have evaluated the relationship between the number of etch pits and the dislocation density, and have shown that there is a one-to-one correlation between etch pit density and dislocation density. Achievement of a one-to-one correlation depends on the etch composition, surface quality, and orientation. It must be mentioned, however, that etch pits can also occur at precipitates and inclusions; thus, care is required in interpreting results. Also, etch pits can be used to estimate the dislocation density only when it is relatively low. Higher dislocation densities can be estimated by using electron metallographic techniques. One can also sometimes differentiate between edge and screw dislocations because edge dislocations usually produce deeper etch pits than screw dislocations.

3-10 CORROSION TESTS

Since etching is basically a selective corrosion process, it is not surprising that etchants are commonly employed to study the corrosion resistance of metals. In addition, etching solutions are widely employed to evaluate the coating weight,

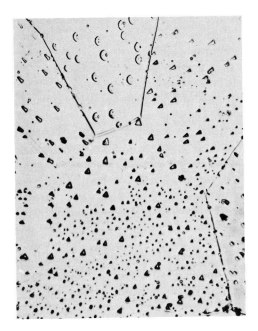

Figure 3-14 Dislocation etch pits in an Fe-Si alloy electrical sheet steel. Sample was chemically polished, etched in 1% nital for 1 min, and then etched in ½% nital for 5 min (750×).

thickness, and quality of coated metals. Many of these corrosion tests are used to evaluate stainless steels and other corrosion-resistant materials.

One of the best-known tests is the electrolytic etching of stainless steels with oxalic acid, a quick screening test for detecting susceptibility to intergranular attack that was developed by Streicher [52, 53]. After etching, the sample is examined at 250 to 500X to see if any grains are surrounded by carbides. If such grains are present, the material must be tested using other more time-consuming etch tests. Samples are classified into one of seven possible categories as described in ASTM Specification A262. Susceptibility to intergranular corrosion attack is indicated by the presence of pronounced "ditches" at the grain boundaries.

Microscopic examination after controlled etching experiments has been employed to evaluate the tendency toward pitting corrosion. Pitting attack involves simultaneous cathodic and anodic reactions. Anodic behavior of a passive metal surface is influenced by surface preparation. Bianchi et al. have employed a series of chemical etchants for evaluating the pitting susceptibility of stainless steels [54]. Their work indicates that chemical etchants reproduce actual corrosion conditions better than potentiostatic etchants.

3-11 SPECIFIC ETCHING RECOMMENDATIONS

3-11.1 Metals

Over the past century a large number of etching techniques have been developed for many metals and alloys. The majority of these techniques use chemical etchants, which are often preferred because of their simplicity. In more recent years, numerous tint etchants and electrolytic and potentiostatic etchants have also been developed, and these formulations have proved to be most valuable. Appendix I lists these formulations by metal and by type of reagent. Space does not permit complete documentation of the source of these reagents; however, the names of the etch developers and subsequent users have been included where possible, particularly with reagents frequently referred to by the originator's name. For many reagents, it is difficult to trace the formulation to its origin.

Aluminum and alloys As is discussed in Chap. 2, examination of as-polished aluminum alloys reveals the presence of intermetallic precipitates and inclusions and other details such as porosity or cracks. Etchants reveal the precipitates more clearly and often bring out some not observable in the as-polished condition; a dilute aqueous HF etch is commonly used (see Fig. 3-15). Double-etching techniques ("sequence etching") are often employed without repolishing. Etchants that reveal grain structure are usually applied last.

Pure aluminum is attacked by dilute aqueous solutions containing either HCl or HF but not by dilute H_2SO_4 or HNO_3 [10]. Aluminum is also attacked by caustic solutions such as aqueous NaOH. The intermetallic constituents are often quite reactive, and anomalous etching effects can be encountered.

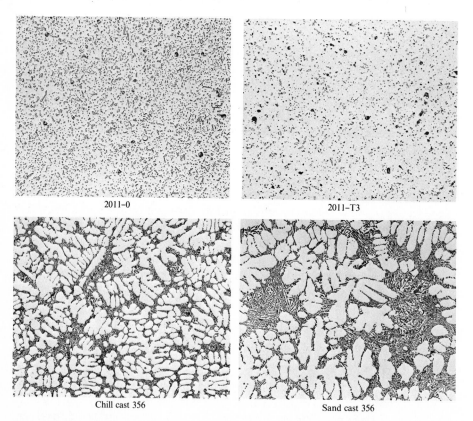

2011–0

2011–T3

Chill cast 356

Sand cast 356

Figure 3-15 Wrought (top, $300\times$) and cast (bottom, $60\times$) aluminum alloys etched with 0.5% aqueous HF. *(Top photos are courtesy of R. D. Buchheit, Battelle Memorial Institute.)*

Etching to reveal grain boundaries can be quite difficult with some alloys and treatment conditions. Anodizing techniques are commonly employed to reveal the grain structure, usually with the aid of polarized light. Some methods [55–57] are applicable only to high-purity aluminum (see Fig. 3-16), while Barker's method [58] (see Fig. 3-17) and Cole and Brooks' methods [59] are widely applicable.

Keller's reagent and several modifications are widely used as general-purpose etchants for aluminum alloys (see Fig. 3-18). Keller's etch will reveal the grain boundaries in 2XXX and 7XXX series wrought aluminum alloys as well as in aluminum and copper and aluminum and zinc castings. Keller's reagent reveals the grain boundaries of 2011 alloy in the T3 temper but not in the annealed condition. Keller's reagent is also used to examine cold-worked alloys and recrystallized alloys, to detect preferred orientation, and to differentiate between tempers, primarily with the 2XXX series of aluminum-copper alloys.

Graff and Sargent developed a new etchant for alloys that are difficult to etch for grain structure or in which recrystallization is incomplete [60]. Figure 3-19 shows an example of the use of this etch. Klemm has shown how a modified Murakami's etch will reveal grain boundaries and precipitates in eutectic aluminum solid-solution castings with high silicon content [61]. A useful compilation of etching techniques for aluminum alloys has been published by the American Society for Metals (ASM) [62].

Aside from the anodizing techniques, only a few general color etching methods have been developed for aluminum alloys. Beraha has developed an aqueous chromating solution containing CrO_3, HCl, and sodium sulfate [63]. The acid attacks the surface selectively, producing etching, while a thin chromate coating is precipitated nonuniformly on the surface. The coating thickness varies, producing different color contrasts. Beraha has also developed a color etchant useful for phase discrimination that does not color the matrix [64]. This reagent

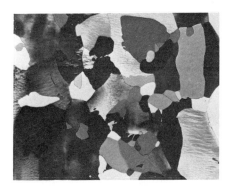 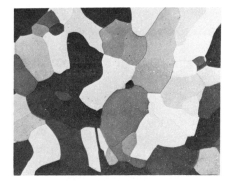

Figure 3-16 Superpure aluminum anodized using the method of Hone and Pearson (Ref. 56), polarized light, 32×. Left, held 6 min at 375°C, partly recrystallized. Right, held 2 h at 375°C, fully recrystallized. *(Courtesy of E. C. Pearson, Alcan International Ltd.)*

Figure 3-17 (*inside back cover*) Pure aluminum anodized with 3% fluoboric acid, 25 to 30 V dc, 60 to 80 s, sensitive tint, 15×. *(Courtesy of R. S. Crouse, Oak Ridge National Laboratory.)*

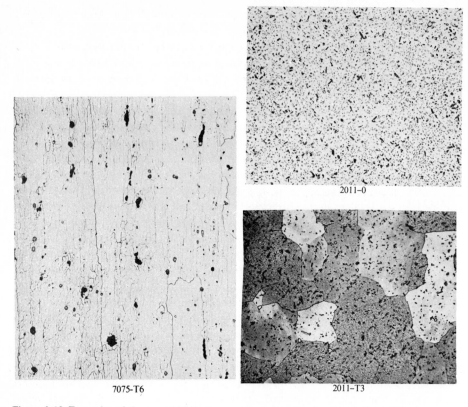

2011–0

7075-T6

2011–T3

Figure 3-18 Examples of the use of Keller's reagent on wrought aluminum alloys (300×).

Figure 3-19 The Graff-Sargent etch used on aluminum alloy 7075-T6, 375×.

and the other color etchants e.g., that of Gerstlauer and Franchini [65], all use molybdate solutions for coloration.

Etching response has been widely employed to identify precipitate phases in aluminum alloys [66–68]. Appendix I lists etchants used for this purpose and resultant color and attack responses. Mondolfo [66] has prepared a very detailed summary of the color of common constituents and their reaction to different etchants (see Table 3-1). These procedures are still useful, although electron microprobes and scanning electron microscopes with energy dispersive analysis capability are now available and are widely used for phase identification.

Antimony and bismuth Etchants employed for revealing the microstructure of antimony and bismuth and their alloys are listed in App. I. Antimony is attacked by mineral acids, while bismuth is readily attacked by nitric acid and by halogen acids if oxygen is present [10]. Examination with polarized light is useful. Figure 3-20 illustrates the microstructure of antimony and bismuth alloys.

Beryllium For most metallographic examinations, the grain structure of properly polished beryllium can be observed with polarized light, as discussed in Chap. 4. However, a number of etchants have been developed and are listed in App. I. One of the earlier etchants, a 5% aqueous solution suggested by Kehl, produces inconsistent results. Heat tinting reveals the grain structure but also produces etch pits which do not appear to be related to the crystal structure [69]. Vacuum cathodic etching has produced satisfactory results. Several electrolytic methods have been developed, and these appear to produce better results than chemical etchants. Etchants for beryllium appear to offer little advantage over use of polarized light.

Cadmium, lead, tin, and zinc Cadmium is attacked by most mineral acids [10]. Cadmium and its alloys (see Fig. 3-21) have not received much attention from metallographers and only a few etchants have been developed. Examination with polarized light is frequently used. Lead and lead alloys are often examined

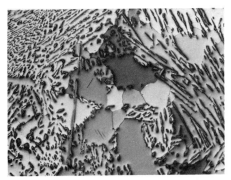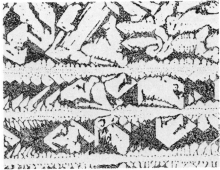

Figure 3-20 Left, as-cast alloy of Sb and 2% Ni etched with 70 mL water, 30 mL HCl, and 5 mL H_2O_2 (30%) viewed in crossed-polarized light ($60\times$); right, as-cast alloy of Bi and 10% Cd after attack polishing ($60\times$).

Table 3-1 Etching characteristics of constituents in aluminum alloys

Constituent	Not etched	25% Fe(NO₃)₃ 30 s, by swabbing	20% H₂SO₄ 160°F, 30 s, by immersion	25% HNO₃ 160°F, 40 s, by immersion	0.5% HF 15 s by swabbing	10% NaOH 160°F, 5 s, by immersion	Acid mixture of 0.5% HF, 1.5% HCl, 2.5% HNO₃, 15 s, by immersion
Bi	Gray to black	Black	Black	Black	Black	Black	Black
Pb	Gray to black	Black	Black	Black	Black	Black	Black
Si	Slate gray	Unattacked	Unattacked	Unattacked	Lighter	Unattacked	Unattacked
Co₂Al₉	Pale violet	Unattacked	Unattacked	Unattacked	Light brown	Light brown	Light brown
CrAl₇	Gray	Unattacked	Unattacked	Unattacked	Unattacked	Light brown to blue	Unattacked
CuAl₂	Pale pink	Dark brown to black	Lighter	Black	Unattacked	Light to dark brown	Unattacked
FeAl₃ and Fe₂Al₇	Purplish gray	Unattacked	Black	Unattacked	Light to dark brown	Dark brown	Slightly darkened
Mg₅Al₈	Pale ivory	Unattacked	Black	Unattacked	Unattacked	Light to dark brown	Black
MnAl₆	Pale blue	Unattacked	Unattacked	Unattacked	Slightly darkened	Brown to blue	Unattacked
NiAl₃	Yellowish gray	Unattacked	Unattacked	Unattacked	Brown to blue	Dark brown to blue	Brown to black
TiAl₃	Gray	Unattacked	Unattacked	Unattacked	Darkened	Light brown	Darkened
Mg₂Si	From blue-gray to blue or black	Black	Black	Black	Dark brown, eaten	Brown	Black
MgZn₂ and MgZn₅	Light gray	Black, eaten	Black, eaten	Black, eaten	Brown	Unattacked	Black, eaten
AlCoFe	Pale violet	Unattacked	Unattacked	Unattacked	Dark brown to black	Brown	Dark brown to black
(CrFe)Al₇	Gray	Unattacked	Unattacked	Unattacked	Light brown	Dark brown to black	Light brown
AlCrMg	Pale gray-yellow	Unattacked	Unattacked	Unattacked	Light brown	Light brown	Light brown
α(AlCrSi)	Gray	Unattacked	Unattacked	Unattacked	Light brown	Light brown	Light brown

β(AlCrSi)	Light gray	Unattacked	Unattacked	Unattacked	Unattacked	Unattacked	Unattacked
(CuFe)Al₃	Light yellowish gray	Unattacked	Unattacked	Unattacked	Brown	Dark brown to blue	Black
Cu₂FeAl₇	Light gray	Unattacked	Unattacked	Unattacked	Unattacked	Light brown	Light brown
ω(AlCuFe)	Gray	Unattacked	Light brown	Unattacked	Light brown	Unattacked	Brown
Cu₂Mg₂Al₅	From pale brown to black	Black	Black	Black	Black	Black	Black
CuMg₄Al₆	From pale to dark brown	Black	Black	Black	Black	Black	Black
AlCuMn	Brown gray	Unattacked	Unattacked	Unattacked	Brown to blue	Light brown	Black
(CuNi)₂Al₃	Gray	Unattacked	Unattacked	Brown	Light brown	Light brown	Brown to black
AlCuNi	Gray	Unattacked	Unattacked	Black	Unattacked	Unattacked	Unattacked
(FeMn)Al₆	Gray	Brown to black	Unattacked	Unattacked	Brown to blue	Brown to blue	Darkened
FeNiAl₉	Gray	Unattacked	Unattacked	Unattacked	Dark brown to blue	Light brown	Dark brown to blue
α(AlFeSi)	Gray-violet	Unattacked	Black	Unattacked	Light brown	Dark brown	Brown
FeSiAl₅	Light gray	Unattacked	Unattacked	Unattacked	Unattacked	Light brown	Dark brown
δ(AlFeSi)	Very light gray	Brown to black	Unattacked	Unattacked	Light brown	Unattacked	Light brown
Mg₃Zn₃Al₂	Light gray	Unattacked	Black	Black	Brown to black	Unattacked	Black
α(AlMnSi)	Gray	Unattacked	Light brown	Unattacked	Light brown	Unattacked	Light brown
δ(AlMnSi)	Light gray	Unattacked	Unattacked	Unattacked	Slightly darkened	Slightly darkened	Slightly darkened
AlCrFeSi	Gray	Unattacked	Black	Unattacked	Light brown	Light brown	Light brown
AlCuFeMn	Gray	Unattacked	Brown to blue	Unattacked	Dark brown to blue	Unattacked	Dark brown to blue
AlCuFeNi	Light brown-gray	Unattacked	Unattacked	Unattacked	Brown to blue	Brown to blue	Brown to blue
AlCuFeSi	Light gray	Unattacked	Light brown to black	Unattacked	Dark brown	Light brown	Dark brown
CuMg₅Si₄Al₄	Gray	Unattacked	Unattacked	Dark blue to black	Dark brown to black	Unattacked	Black
AlFeMgSi	Very light gray-blue	Unattacked	Unattacked	Unattacked	Unattacked	Unattacked	Unattacked
α(AlFeMnSi)	Gray	Unattacked	Black	Unattacked	Dark brown	Dark brown	Light brown
δ(AlFeMnSi)	Light gray	Unattacked	Unattacked	Unattacked	Light brown	Light brown	Light brown

Source: From Mondolfo, Ref. 66.

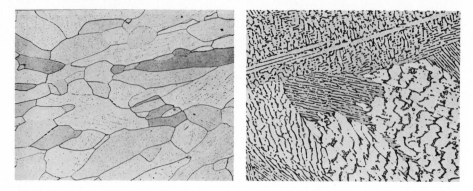

Figure 3-21 Left, as-cast cadmium etched with 2% nital, 30×; right, as-cast alloy of Cd and 10% Bi etched with 2% nital, 60×.

microscopically, and a number of useful etchants have been developed [70]. Pure lead is attacked slowly by hydrochloric acid and rapidly by nitric acid [10]. A mixture of three parts acetic acid to one part hydrogen peroxide is commonly used for lead alloys. Figure 3-22 illustrates three lead alloys etched with a commonly used etchant. The aqueous ammonium molybdate-citric acid etch produces low contrast between the matrix and the precipitates but gives an idea of the grain structure, especially in the low-Sb alloy. Because lead samples tarnish readily, they should be examined shortly after etching. Etchants for lead are given in App. I.

Tin and its alloys have received some attention by metallographers. Tin is attacked by the common mineral acids and by caustic solutions. Insoluble oxides can form on the surface and obscure the microstructure [10]. Some tin alloys are anisotropic and will respond to polarized light.

Pure zinc is attacked slowly by all acids [10]. Many of the commonly used aqueous reagents contain CrO_3, a strong oxidizer which is activated by additions of sodium sulfate (Na_2SO_4). Several variations of this etch are commonly used

Pb-12Sb-3Sn   Pb-12.5Sb   Pb-6.5Sb

Figure 3-22 Three lead alloys etched with ammonium molybdate, citric acid, and water (10:10:100), 90×.

depending on the alloy composition. To avoid irregular etching, it is recommended that the surface be wet with water before immersion [71]. To avoid staining problems, the sample should be rinsed in 20% aqueous CrO_3 after etching and then rinsed with water and alcohol. Although most examinations are made in bright-field illumination, grain boundaries are usually ill-defined, and better definition of the grain structure is provided by polarized light. Figure 3-23 illustrates the microstructure of common zinc die-casting and sand-casting alloys. Etching with the Palmerton reagent produced some coloration, which could be emphasized with polarized light. This etch is quite satisfactory for low-magnification studies but is not particularly good for high-magnification examination. Tint etching with Klemm's reagent produced equivalent results for the diecast alloys but spectacular coloration on the sand-cast alloy which could be further emphasized by polarized light, as shown in Fig. 3-24. Gennone and Kersey have described an aqueous etchant containing sulfuric and hydrofluoric acids that is said to reveal the grain boundaries in zinc [72].

Chromium, molybdenum, and tungsten The refractory metals chromium, molybdenum, and tungsten are common metallographic subjects [73, 74]. Chromium is attacked very slowly by dilute nitric acid and somewhat more rapidly by dilute hydrochloric or sulfuric acid. Molybdenum resists attack by hydrochloric or sulfuric acid, while hydrofluoric acid produces pitting and dilute nitric acid produces rapid attack with pitting. Tungsten resists attack by mineral acids, but is attacked slowly by mixtures of nitric and hydrofluoric acids. Tungsten is attacked by boiling hydrogen peroxide. Chromium, molybdenum, and tungsten are attacked by alkali solutions containing an oxidizer; thus, Murakami's reagent and its many modifications are frequently employed. Wolff described an anodizing method applicable to tungsten, niobium, and tantalum-tungsten alloys [73]. Figure 3-25 shows the microstructure of annealed iodide chromium after elec-

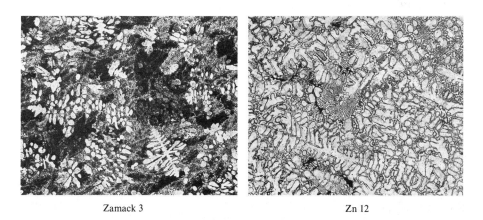

Zamack 3   Zn 12

Figure 3-23 Palmerton reagent used to reveal the structure of two Zn alloys, 60×.

Figure 3-24 (*inside back cover*) Klemm's I tint etch used to reveal the microstructure of gravity-cast Zn 12. *Top*, bright field; *bottom*, polarized light, same areas (50×).

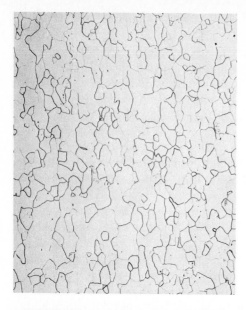

Figure 3-25 Iodide chromium electrolytically etched with 10% oxalic acid (fully annealed, 1000°C, 1 h), 75×. *(Courtesy of R. D. Buchheit, Battelle Memorial Institute.)*

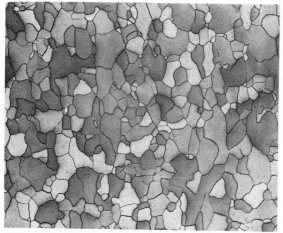

Figure 3-26 Molybdenum (after annealing, 1400°C, 30 min) etched with Murakami's reagent, 75×. *(Courtesy of R. D. Buchheit, Battelle Memorial Institute.)*

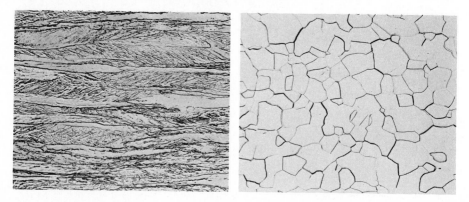

Figure 3-27 Tungsten (cold-worked (left) and annealed, (right) 1800°C, 1 h) etched with Murakami's reagent, 150×. *(Courtesy of R. D. Buchheit, Battelle Memorial Institute.)*

trolytic etching in 10% oxalic acid. Figures 3-26 and 3-27 show the structures of annealed molybdenum and tungsten, respectively, after etching with Murakami's reagent. Appendix I lists etchants for chromium, molybdenum, and tungsten.

Hasson developed tint etchants for molybdenum which are sensitive to grain orientation [75, 76]. The original solution [75] was modified [76] to produce faster etching by dissolving the $FeCl_3$ in water rather than in alcohol. After etching for 40 to 50 s, grains of different orientation are selectively colored: (100) golden yellow, (110) deep blue, (111) deep blue to violet, (112) light to very light blue, and (114) to (118) golden yellow. Figure 3-28 (see below and inside back cover) shows the microstructure of molybdenum etched with a solution of water, hydrogen peroxide, and sulfuric acid. Lehwald and coworkers developed a tint etchant for tungsten that is also sensitive to grain orientation [77].

Cobalt and manganese Cobalt is attacked readily by dilute nitric acid and less rapidly by dilute hydrochloric or sulfuric acids, but not by caustic solutions. Pitting is a commonly encountered problem with many etchants. Morral has compiled an extensive list of reagents for cobalt and its alloys [78]. Figure 3-29 shows the structure of an alloy of cobalt and 15% tungsten after solution annealing in the alpha-phase region and after aging in the region of the alpha plus epsilon phase.

Young has described etching methods for delineating oxide and sulfide phases in cobalt [79]. These etchants color the matrix phase brown but do not affect the oxides and sulfides. Weeton and Signorelli [29] have described different procedures for identifying sigma phase and carbides in wrought Stellite 21 (Co, 0.3% C,

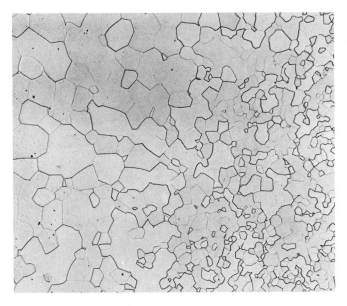

Figure 3-28 Molybdenum etched with a solution of H_2SO_4, H_2O_2 (30%), and H_2O (1:2:7). (***Inside back cover***) Immersion produces a delicate color tint ($32\times$); (***above***) swabbing produces a grain boundary etch ($37\times$). (*Courtesy of R. S. Crouse, Oak Ridge National Laboratory.*)

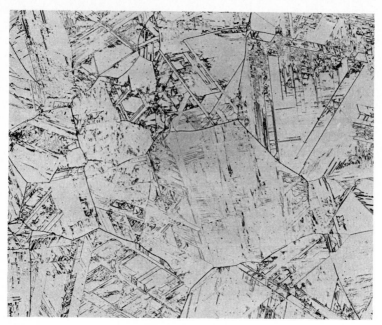

Solution treat (ST)
1400 °C, 1 h-water quench

Figure 3-29 Alloy of cobalt and 15% tungsten etched in nitric acid, hydrogen peroxide, and lactic acid (10:10:80), 250×. *(Courtesy of R. D. Buchheit, Battelle Memorial Institute.)*

3% Ni, 5.5% Mo, 0.3% Fe, 0.45% Si, and 0.55% Mn); these procedures are listed in Table 3-2. Beraha has developed a tint etch for cobalt-based alloys [80].

Manganese is a rather reactive metal and is attacked slowly by cold water and rapidly by hot water. Acids and alkalis attack Mn and form a MnO_2 surface film which obscures the microstructure. Although Mn alloys are easily etched, pure or very high Mn alloys are difficult to etch because of film formation. When a film is formed, repolishing is required. Anderson has developed an etch for Mn and high-Mn alloys which removes the Mn ions by a complexing process [10]. Ultrasonic agitation is useful for promoting even attack and complexing. Kennon et al. have developed an electrolytic etch for Mn-Cu alloys [81].

Copper and alloys Metallographic examination of as-polished samples of copper or copper alloys is conducted to detect shrinkage cavities or porosity in castings or inclusions in wrought alloys. Polarized light is used to identify Cu_2O inclusions, which appear bright ruby red in polarized light; other inclusions that have a similar morphology and color to Cu_2O inclusions when viewed under bright-field illumination do not respond to polarized light. Most microstructural examinations of Cu and its alloys require etching.

The most commonly employed etchant for copper and brass is the mixture of equal parts of ammonium hydroxide (NH_4OH), 3% hydrogen peroxide (H_2O_2), and water (optional). These components can be mixed in several other ratios (see App. I), but all are applied by swabbing. The grain structure of alpha brass is

Table 3-2 Staining and heat tinting procedures for identification of sigma phase and carbides in Stellite 21, wrought Co alloy

Coloring process	Method	Purpose	First etchant		Staining method		Colors of minor phases obtained by previous investigators
			Solution	Method	Solution	Method	
1	Etch	To stain sigma phase	8% oxalic acid; 92% water	Electrolytic etch; 8–10 s; 6 V; room temperature	5 g KMnO$_4$; 5 g NaOH; 90 mL water	Immerse 10–20 s; room temperature	Sigma: bright green or red to purple
2	Etch	To differentiate between carbides and sigma phase	10% NaCN; 90% water	Electrolytic etch; 10–20 s; 1.5 V	Murakami's 10 g K$_3$Fe(CN)$_6$; 10 g KOH; 100 mL water	Immerse 2–4 s; room temperature	Carbides: straw to yellow-brown or buff Gamma (sigma): grey to blue or greenish grey
3	Etch	To identify carbides	2% chromic acid; 98% water	Light electrolytic etch	1 part (20% KMnO$_4$, 80% water); 1 part (8% NaOH, 92% water)	Immerse 7 s; room temperature	Cr$_{23}$C$_6$: brown Cr$_7$C$_3$: pale yellow to light tan M$_6$C: red, green, yellow, blue (also reticulation)
4	Heat tint	To identify carbides and sigma phase	5% HCl; 95% water	Light electrolytic etch; 1 s; 5V		Heat polished specimen to dull red Held at temperature until surface becomes colored Air-cooled or Hg-quenched	Sigma: dark medium brown Cr$_{23}$C$_6$: white M$_6$C: dark Note M$_6$C and sigma cannot be differentiated in same structure

Source: From Weeton and Signorelli, Ref. 29

Figure 3-30 Microstructure of annealed cartridge (alpha) brass at 60×. Left, swabbed with equal parts NH$_4$OH and H$_2$O$_2$ (3%); right, tint-etched (color) with Klemm's I reagent.

Figure 3-31 (*inside front cover*) Electrolytic tough pitch copper (top) and alpha brass (bottom) tint-etched with Beraha's lead sulfide reagent after a light preetch, 50×.

usually revealed by grain contrast, which is good for low-magnification grain comparison ratings but is not always satisfactory for high-magnification work. These reagents also reveal coring segregation in cast alloys.

Greene and Teterin have described how the NH$_4$OH-H$_2$O$_2$-H$_2$O etchants operate [82]. Ammonium hydroxide acts as the corrosive electrolyte, while the hydrogen peroxide produces the correct etching potential. Addition of water slows down the corrosive action to control the speed of the reaction. While copper and zinc form soluble complexes with ammonium ions (NH$_4^+$), some insoluble reaction products are formed which deposit on the surface obscuring the etch results. Swabbing removes these products and produces better results than immersion. Because hydrogen peroxide is unstable in alkaline solutions, the etch has a limited life. Thus, use of a freshly made solution is needed for best results. Also, because the ammonia vapors are irritating, the etch should be used under a hood. This etchant produces strong grain contrast in alpha brass, as shown in Fig. 3-30. Klemm's I tint etch also produces excellent results, as shown in this figure.

Beraha developed several tint etchants for copper and its alloys [63, 83]. His lead sulfide tint etch produces excellent results, as illustrated in Fig. 3-31. Both samples were preetched lightly before tinting. The citric acid in this etchant does not go completely into solution, but the undissolved chemicals did not harm the etch results with these samples. Coloration effects can be enhanced slightly with polarized light.

Slepian and Prohaska have examined the grain-boundary etching response of a number of commonly employed reagents for copper and copper alloys [84]. Etching of electrolytic tough pitch copper produced only partial grain-boundary etching. The NH$_4$OH-H$_2$O$_2$-H$_2$O etchant produced pitting with no grain contrast. Of the six standard etchants tried, best results were obtained with acidified alcoholic ferric chloride. This reagent attacked the twin boundaries more readily than the grain boundaries and produced some grain contrast. A new etchant consisting of ferric nitrate, hydrochloric acid, and water produced excellent twin- and grain-boundary etching and light grain contrast.

Kehl and Metlay [1], as discussed earlier in this chapter, examined the response of different etchants on alpha-beta brass (Muntz metal). The beta phase was anodic to the alpha phase in all reagents tested. All the regeants tested, except NH_4OH and H_2O_2, attacked the beta phase preferentially and darkened it, leaving the alpha phase light. Figure 3-32 shows the structure of alpha-beta brass etched with Klemm's reagent.

A number of etchants have been used to reveal the structure of aluminum bronze—an interesting alloy because of the variations in microstructure that can be obtained. Figure 3-33 shows the structure of this alloy (ASTM B148 Grade 9C) after etching with an aqueous solution of $FeCl_3$, CrO_3, and HCl. Furnace cooling from 1750°F (954°C) produced a coarse primary α grain size, the eutectic $\alpha + \gamma_2$ structure, and δ particles (Fe). The standard heat-treatment practice, which consists of water quenching from 1600°F (871°C) and aging at 1000°F (538°C) followed by water quenching, produced the grain boundary α, β' (martensite), and δ particles. The prior β grain boundaries are decorated by the grain boundary α phase.

Copper-beryllium alloys can be solution-annealed and aged, producing alloys of rather high strengths. Figure 3-34 illustrates the microstructure of a wrought alloy of Cu and 2% Be after annealing and after precipitation hardening. Etching (swabbing) with aqueous 3% ammonium persulfate and 1% ammonium hydrox- ide reveals the grain structure in the annealed sample and vividly reveals the aged structure.

A few tint etchants have been developed for copper and its alloys, as listed in App. I [63, 83, 85]. As demonstrated in the examples, Klemm's I reagent and Beraha's PbS tint etch produce excellent results and should be used to a greater extent than they are by metallographers. They are safe to use and can be stored without danger.

Several electrolytic reagents have also been developed for Cu and its alloys.

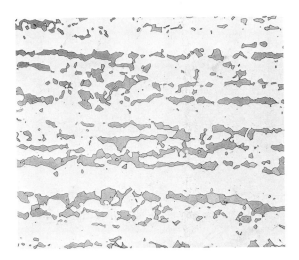

Figure 3-32 Microstructure of alpha-beta brass (alloy of Cu and 40% Zn) tint-etched with Klemm's I reagent (beta phase colored), 150×.

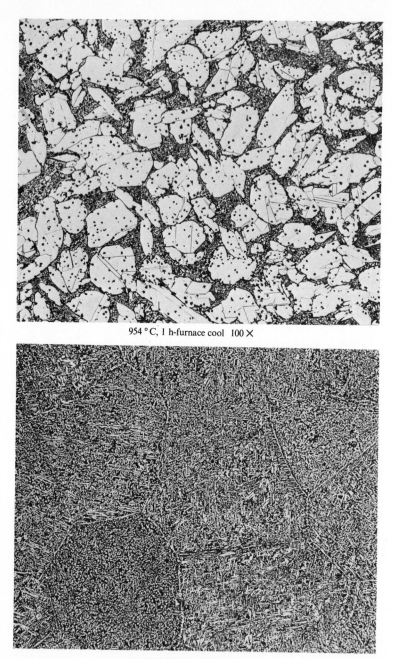

954 °C, 1 h-furnace cool   100 ×

871 °C, 1 h-water quench
538 °C, 1 h-water quench
100×

Figure 3-33 Aluminum bronze (ASTM B148 Grade 9C) etched with a solution of FeCl$_3$, HCl, CrO$_3$, and H$_2$O (20:5:1:100).

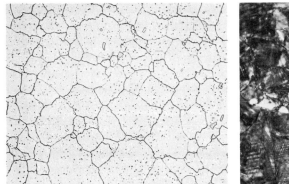

Figure 3-34 Microstructure of beryllium-copper alloy revealed by swabbing with aqueous 3% ammonium persulfate and 1% ammonium hydroxide. Left, solution-annealed, twins not attacked [70 HRB (Rockwell hardness on the B scale), 300×]; right, solution-annealed and aged [41 HRC (Rockwell hardness on the C scale), 600×].

The aqueous 1% CrO_3 electrolytic etch developed by Coons and Blickwede has been used with aluminum bronze and Cu-Be alloys [86]. An electrolytic aqueous sodium thiosulfate etch, which was developed by Jacquet and modified by Samuels [87], has been used to reveal deformation in alpha brass and is claimed to be able to reveal as little as 0.1 percent compressive deformation. The tint etchants are also quite sensitive for revealing cold work. Electrolytic etching has also been used to develop the grain structure of Cu-Ni alloys, as illustrated in Fig. 3-35.

Germanium and silicon Microstructural examination of germanium and silicon has gained considerable attention since the electronics industry has begun to make greater use of microscopy. While much of the attention has traditionally centered on dislocation etching, general etchants to reveal the microstructure of polycrys-

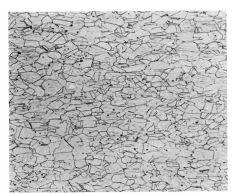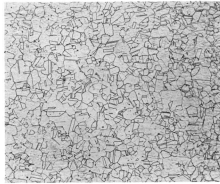

Figure 3-35 The microstructure of an alloy of Cu and 30% Ni electrolytically etched with a solution of acetic acid, nitric acid, and water (5:10:85), 150×. Left, cold-worked; right, annealed. *(Courtesy of R. D. Buchheit, Battelle Memorial Institute.)*

talline materials have been developed. Germanium is not attacked by cold mineral acids except for nitric acid. Hot sulfuric acid and hot 50% nitric acid produce attack, as does hot hydrogen peroxide. Silicon is also quite inert but is attacked by alkaline solutions and by mixtures of nitric and hydrofluoric acids [10].

Indium and thallium Indium and thallium and their alloys are infrequent subjects for metallographic examination and only a few etchants have been developed. Indium is slowly attacked by dilute HCl or H_2SO_4 at room temperature but is rapidly attacked by concentrated HCl or by dilute HNO_3 when heated. Caustic alkali solutions do not attack indium. Thallium, however, is attacked by all dilute mineral acids, with nitric acid producing rapid attack [10].

Iron and steels The microstructure of iron and steel has been documented more thoroughly than any other metal because of the commercial significance of these alloys. Because a wide variety of iron and steel alloys has been developed and because their properties can be varied extensively through heat treatment, it is not surprising that many different etchants have been formulated for specific alloys and conditions (see App. I.).

Although many different etchants have been developed, two are most frequently employed—nital, introduced by Boylston, and picral, introduced by Igevski. Nital has been used in concentrations from 0.5 to 10%, but 2 to 3% is most common (see safety comments about storing nital in Chap. 2). Picral is generally used at a 4% concentration with addition of about 0.25 to 1% zephiran chloride (wetting agent). Nital is more commonly used, but picral produces superior results for certain structures. Nital etches ferrite grain boundaries, while picral does not. Figure 3-36 illustrates differences in etch attack of nital and picral on a low-carbon sheet steel. Picral attacks the phase boundary between ferrite and cementite but not the boundaries between ferrite grains. Nital attacks both ferrite grain boundaries and the ferrite-cementite phase boundaries. If the size, shape, and distribution of the cementite is of interest, picral produces the best results.

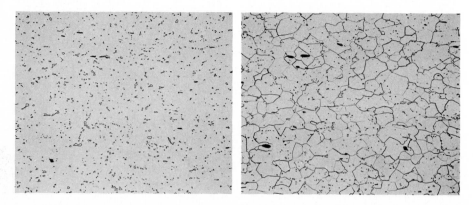

Figure 3-36 The microstructure of AISI 1008 sheet steel revealed with 4% picral (left) and 2% nital (right), 300×.

However, if the ferrite grain size is of interest, nital is preferred, although not all the ferrite grain boundaries are clearly etched because of the orientation sensitivity of nital.

For carbon steels in the as-rolled or normalized condition, nital may be preferred, since it reveals the structure of the ferrite grains as well as the structure of the pearlite, although some of the pearlite colonies will be quite light. (See Fig. 3-1.) However, if the percentage of pearlite is to be measured, picral is preferred, since measurement of the volume fraction is not altered by etch time and by detection of ferrite grain boundaries (using image analysis) after about 10 s of etching [88].

For spheroidized carbide structures, the sensitivity of nital to orientation and the etching of ferrite grain boundaries by nital can produce misleading results. Figure 3-37 shows spheroidized annealed AISI (American Iron and Steel Institute) W2 C-V tool steel etched with four reagents. The sensitivity of nital to orientation produced faint etching at the carbide and ferrite interfaces within certain grains, while etching with picral clearly revealed all the carbides. Neither etch, however, is useful for quantitative metallography by image analysis, since only the interfaces are detectable. Figure 3-37 shows how the cementite can be

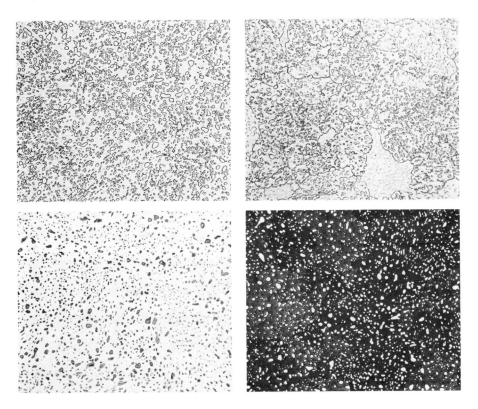

Figure 3-37 Microstructure of AISI W2 C-V tool steel (spheroidize annealed) revealed using 4% picral (top left), 2% nital (top right), boiling alkaline sodium picrate (bottom left), and Klemm's I tint etch after a light picral preetch (bottom right), 600×.

darkened preferentially with boiling alkaline sodium picrate or the ferrite darkened preferentially with Klemm's I tint etch. Both images are excellent for image analysis.

Nital rarely delineates all the ferrite grain boundaries in low-carbon steels. This problem is more acute when the material has been hot-rolled using a low finishing temperature, e.g., 1500 to 950°F (816 to 510°C), which retards recrystallization. Nital is rather poor for such samples. Hawkins [89] has shown that Marshall's reagent (1 part of a solution of 8 g oxalic acid, 5 mL H_2SO_4, and 100 mL H_2O plus 1 part of 30% H_2O_2) can produce exceptional results as an etchant for such steels. Figure 3-38 illustrates two regions of grain structure in a low-carbon hot-band steel that was warm-rolled, i.e., the finishing temperature was quite low. Etching with nital revealed only traces of a few grain boundaries, while the entire grain structure was revealed by a 3-s etch in Marshall's reagent followed by a 20-s etch with nital. In fully recrystallized carbon steels, Marshall's reagent reveals the grain structure evenly and fully while darkening cementite. Marshall's reagent attacks inclusions so the duration of etching must be kept short, generally only a few seconds. It is usually best to hold the sample vertically in the etch. After immersion, the sample should be rinsed in water, rinsed in alcohol and then immersed in nital to increase the attack at the grain boundary. This latter etch is not always necessary. If visible vigorous attack does not occur when the sample is immersed in Marshall's etch, the sample should be etched for 2 to 3 s in nital and then transferred directly to the Marshall's etch. This will activate the surface.

Picral is also preferred to nital for etching bainitic structures, although the difference in etch attack is not as dramatic as with pearlite or spheroidized carbide. Figure 3-39 illustrates the microstructure of lower bainite isothermally formed in AISI 5160 alloy steel etched with 2% nital or 4% picral. The best delineation is with picral, although the characteristic 60° angular pattern of lower bainite is most clearly revealed by nital. Picral would be preferred if the structure is to be studied by TEM replication.

Nital and picral are also used to study the structure of martensite. While either

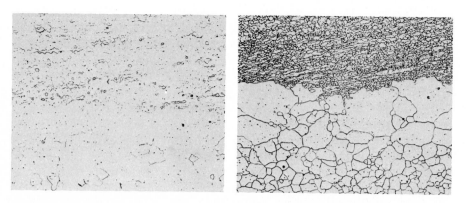

Figure 3-38 Microstructure of warm-rolled hot-band steel (0.02C-0.13P-0.2Ti) etched with 2% nital (left) and with Marshall's reagent (3 s) followed by nital (20 s), (right), 300×, same area. *(Courtesy of A. O. Benscoter, Bethlehem Steel Corp.)*

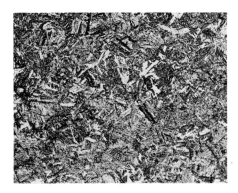

Figure 3-39 Lower bainite in isothermally transformed AISI 5160 alloy steel etched with 2% nital (left) or 4% picral (right), 250×.

etch can be used with tempered martensite, picral reveals little detail in as-quenched martensite, while nital is satisfactory. If diffusion-controlled transformation products are present with as-quenched martensite, these can be revealed more clearly with picral. The appearance of as-quenched martensite is markedly influenced by carbon content, changing from lath to plate martensite with increasing carbon content. The appearance of either type is more easily observed if the size of prior-austenite grains is coarse. Polarized light can enhance images of etched as-quenched martensite.

Solution-annealed austenitic manganese steel (Hadfield's) is shown in Fig. 3-40. A short nital etch followed by tinting with 20% aqueous sodium metabisulfite produces excellent color contrast. This etch is also useful for measuring decarburization in these steels, which is discussed in Chap. 6. Etching with picral also produces excellent grain contrast and coloration. Etch attack at the grain boundary in solution-annealed samples can be obtained with equal parts of HNO_3, HCl, and H_2O, although this etch is sensitive to orientation, and some boundaries are

2% Nital/20% $Na_2S_2O_5$(75X)

Figure 3-40 Microstructure of solution-annealed Hadfield Mn austenitic steel.

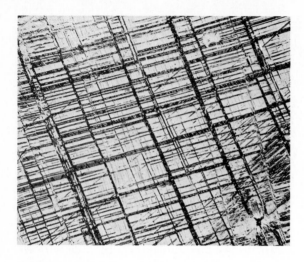

Figure 3-41 Microstructure of explosively hardened Hadfield Mn steel (sheet martensite) revealed using 2% nital followed by 20% aqueous sodium metabisulfite, 375×.

heavily attacked while others are not attacked. Figure 3-41 illustrates explosively hardened austenitic manganese steel preetched with nital and tint-etched with 20% sodium metabisulfite, which reveals epsilon martensite.

Dual-phase steels High-strength low-alloy dual-phase sheet steels have received considerable attention recently because of their interesting properties. Selective etching is used widely in development studies on these alloys. While the phases present can be revealed by the commonly used nital or picral etchants, the results are not particularly useful for quantification of the phases present. The special etching procedures published by La Pera [90], and Marder [91] produce selective phase discrimination. The alkaline chromate etch of Lawson et al. [92] is used to differentiate between "new" and "old" ferrite produced by the intercritical heat treatment used on these alloys.

A study by Marder and Benscoter showed that good agreement between manual point counting and image analysis measurements of the amount of second phases can be obtained by the use of 10% aqueous sodium metabisulfite [93]. The correlation was not as good using La Pera's etch. Figure 3-42, which is from this study, shows samples with low and high percentages of second-phase constituents etched with 10% aqueous sodium metabisulfite and with La Pera's etch, which is a mixture of 4% picral and 1% aqueous sodium metabisulfite. Note that the etch contrast is reversed when samples etched with these two reagents are compared.

Temper embrittlement etchants The phenomenon of temper embrittlement in alloy steels was studied for many years using special etching reagents, particularly before the development of scanning electron microscopes and Auger analysis. While early studies attributed the embrittlement to precipitation of carbide at the grain boundary, it is now recognized that embrittlement is due to segregation of impurities such as phosphorus, antimony, arsenic, and tin to the prior-austenite grain boundaries. Early studies noted that the prior-austenite grain boundaries in

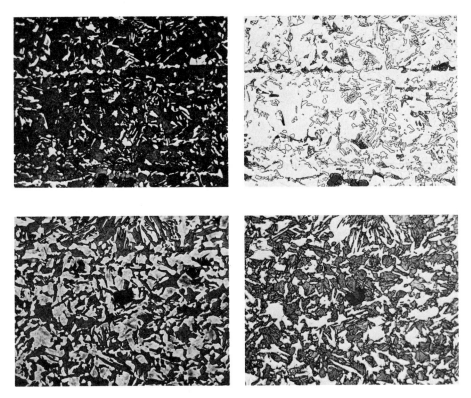

Figure 3-42 Microstructure of dual-phase low-carbon sheet steel with low (top) and high (bottom) martensite contents etched with Le Pera's reagent (left) and 20% $Na_2S_2O_5$ (right), 500×. *(From Marder and Benscoter, Ref. 93, courtesy of Elsevier Science Publishing Co., Inc.)*

embrittled steels were more easily and more clearly delineated than those in similar nonembrittled steels. As is noted in a later section on the use of etchants to reveal prior-austenite grain boundaries, metallographers sometimes subject samples to an embrittlement cycle to permit better delineation of the prior-austenite grain boundaries.

The first etchant deliberately formulated to reveal temper embrittlement was developed by Cohen et al. in 1947 [94]. Their first attempt used saturated alcoholic picric acid, but an etch time of 20 to 30 h was required. They then investigated wetting agents to improve etching response. A small amount of zephiran chloride (benzalkonium chloride) was found to be useful, and after some experimentation, a solution of etheric picric acid and aqueous zephiran chloride was developed. Ether is saturated with picric acid, and zephiran chloride is added to water. The two solutions are mixed and stored overnight in a tightly stoppered bottle to prevent ether evaporation. The solution separates into two layers, and the top layer, consisting of picric acid in ether plus some zephiran chloride, is decanted into a beaker and diluted one-third with ether. The sample is etched by immersion for 1 to 15 min. If the sample was temper-embrittled, the prior-austenite grain boundaries will be revealed along with the microstructure. Light repolishing with the final abrasive removes much of the structure etching and improves the visibility of the grain boundaries.

This work prompted McLean and Northcott [95] to explore the use of other wetting agents with the etch developed by Cohen et al. They also tried wetting agents with saturated alcoholic and saturated aqueous picric acid, with 2% nital, and with a solution of acetic acid, water, and ether. Although the study showed that etching could reliably detect temper embrittlement, not all the etchants tried were successful. Nital, for example, did not reveal grain boundaries in embrittled samples. Saturated aqueous picric acid revealed grain boundaries in embrittled steels but additions of 1% aryl EPG (wetting agent) did not increase either the rate of etching or the quality of delineation. Saturated alcoholic picric acid revealed grain boundaries in only a few samples and wetting agents were not helpful. The etheric picral solution was capable of discriminating between embrittled and nonembrittled chromium steel samples.

Rucker prepared two charts illustrating varying degrees of grain boundary delineation obtained using the etheric picric acid etchant of Cohen et al. and a modified reagent claimed to be more useful [96]. Rucker also etched samples with the modified etheric picric acid solution and then with nital to reveal the relationship of the transformation structure to the prior-austenite grain boundaries. Rucker found that 80 to 100 percent of the boundaries were revealed in embrittled samples but only 0 to 20 percent of the prior-austenite grain boundaries were revealed in nonembrittled samples.

Numerous studies have shown that aqueous picric acid solutions containing a wetting agent (frequently sodium tridecylbenzene sulfonate) can reveal prior-austenite grain boundaries in steels that have been quenched or quenched and tempered. This effect is due to segregation of phosphorus to the grain boundaries not only during tempering in the critical embrittling region but also during austenitization. Although aqueous picric acid will reveal prior-austenite grain boundaries in both embrittled and nonembrittled samples, Preece and Carter showed that there is a clear difference in the appearance of the boundaries using electron microscopy even though optically they appear similar [97].

Recent studies using controlled additions of impurities to alloy steels have shown that phosphorus must be present for saturated aqueous picric acid containing a wetting agent to delineate grain boundries [98]. Experiments in which tin [99] or antimony [100] in alloy steels free of phosphorus was segregated to the grain boundaries showed that grain boundary delineation did not occur even if the steels were embrittled if saturated aqueous picric acid was used.

The following example illustrates the use of etchants to detect temper embrittlement: Three laboratory ingots of AISI 4140 alloy steel were prepared from the same melt but contained the following different phosphorus contents: 0.004, 0.013, and 0.022 for ingots A, B, and C, respectively. Wrought samples were heat-treated and subjected to a step-wise cooling embrittlement cycle that produced these properties:

Properties of AISI 4140 samples

Ingot	% P	Hardness HRC†	Tensile strength		Transition temp. (50% FATT)	
			ksi	MPa	°F	°C
A	0.004	33	149.5	1030.8	−95	−71
B	0.013	33.5	155.4	1071.5	−38	−38
C	0.022	35.5	159.4	1099.1	+85	+29

†Rockwell hardness on the C scale.
FATT = fracture appearance transition temperature.

Scanning electron microscope (SEM) fractography of impact specimens revealed no intergranular fracture in the A sample, considerable intergranular fracture in B, and predominantly intergranular fracture in C. Etching of these samples with nital, picral, or Vilella's reagent did not reveal the grain boundaries in any sample. Etching with the temper embrittlement etchants of Cohen et al. or Rucker revealed prior-austenite grain boundaries in all three samples. Etching with saturated aqueous picric acid containing sodium tridecylbenzene sulfonate also revealed the prior-austenite grain boundaries, as shown in Fig. 3-43. The three samples were deembrittled by tempering at 1150°F (621°C) followed by water quenching. They were reetched with the etheric picric acid solution of Cohen et al. and with the saturated aqueous picric acid solution. No grain boundaries were visible using the etheric picric acid solution, as expected. However, with the saturated aqueous picric acid solution no grain boundaries were visible in sample A, a few were visible in sample B, and most were visible in sample C. The results suggest that some phosphorus was still present in the grain boundaries in samples B and C, with more in C because of its higher phosphorus content.

Prior-austenite grain-size etchants Because the properties of heat-treated steels are influenced by grain size produced during austenitization, considerable effort has been exerted to develop procedures for revealing the location of the prior-austenite grain boundaries. As is discussed in Chap. 6, there are many procedures that can be used to decorate austenite grain boundaries if the sample can be heat-treated, carburized, or oxidized. However, in many instances, as in failure analysis, the sample cannot be subjected to these processes and the prior-austenite grain structure must be revealed in the as-received condition by etching alone, perhaps aided by a temper to improve etch response without altering the grain size.

Many etchants have been used to reveal prior-austenite grain boundaries. Unfortunately, no single etchant is capable of revealing prior-austenite grain boundaries in all samples. In practice, considerable trial and error is involved in many attempts to bring out the grain boundaries sufficiently to permit grain size measurements, and in some cases, all attempts result in failure.

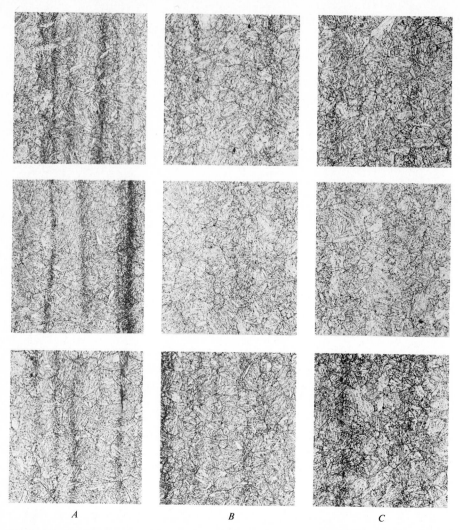

Figure 3-43 Samples that were subjected to stepwise cooling embrittlement cycle and etched with the special etchants of Cohen et al. (top), Rucker (middle), and with saturated aqueous picric acid (bottom), 275×.

Prior-austenite grain boundaries in fully martensitic samples can be revealed with simple etchants, such as nital, in only a few steels, e.g., in highly alloyed tool steels in the as-quenched or lightly tempered condition. Tool steels such as AISI A2 or D2 can be successfully etched with 2 to 10% nital if tempering is 600°F (316°C) or lower, while high-speed steels can be successfully etched using tempers of about 950°F (510°C) or lower depending on the grade.

One of the first etchants to be widely used for revealing prior-austenite grain size was the solution developed by Vilella containing 1 g picric acid, 5 mL HCl, and 100 mL ethanol [101]. When this etch works, it usually produces grain contrast, although in a few samples it produces grain-boundary etching, as shown in Fig. 3-44. To obtain the best grain contrast, several polish and etch cycles may be needed. This etch often produces unsatisfactory results, but if the sample is tempered, an idea of the grain size can occasionally be obtained.

Several etchants containing ferric chloride have been suggested. Miller and Day used a 5% aqueous solution for low-carbon martensitic steels [102]. The best results are obtained on lightly tempered samples. An aqueous solution of 1% $FeCl_3$ and 5% HCl occasionally produces grain-boundary etching in medium-carbon alloy steels, as illustrated in Fig. 3-44. Prior-austenite grain boundary delineation in hardened low-carbon steels has been obtained using Marshall's reagent, as shown in Fig. 3-45. Some success has been obtained using 20% aqueous sodium bisulfite on low-carbon heat-treated plate steels (see Fig. 3-44).

In 1955, Bechet and Beaujard published results obtained with a saturated aqueous picric acid solution (the solution used in temper embrittlement studies) containing 0.5% Teepol (sodium alkylsulfonate), a wetting agent [103]. This solution has since been found to be the single most effective etchant for revealing

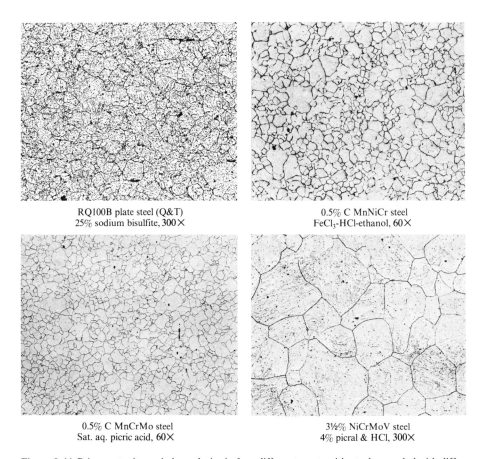

RQ100B plate steel (Q&T)
25% sodium bisulfite, 300×

0.5% C MnNiCr steel
FeCl₃-HCl-ethanol, 60×

0.5% C MnCrMo steel
Sat. aq. picric acid, 60×

3½% NiCrMoV steel
4% picral & HCl, 300×

Figure 3-44 Prior-austenite grain boundaries in four different martensitic steels revealed with different etchants.

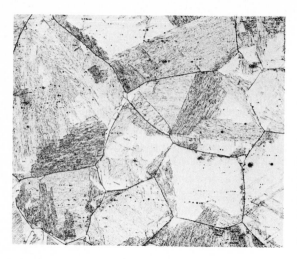

Figure 3-45 Prior-austenite grain boundaries in a martensitic low-carbon sheet steel revealed by etching with Marshall's reagent, 15 s, 150×. *(Courtesy of A. O. Benscoter, Bethlehem Steel Corp.)*

prior-austenite grain boundaries. When etching is successful, grain-boundary attack is obtained, never grain contrast. This reagent was tried on AISI 8620, 4140, and 5160 in the as-quenched condition and after tempering at 400, 800, and 1200°F. Grain boundaries were not revealed in any of the AISI 8620 samples. For the AISI 4140 and 5160 samples, grain-boundary attack was obtained in the as-quenched condition and after tempering at 400 and 800°F (294 and 427°C) but not after tempering at 1200°F (649°C). This etch works well irrespective of the grain size of the sample. Tempered martensite and tempered lower bainite respond equally well.

A wide variety of wetting agents have been used with saturated aqueous picric acid. Skuin, for example, compared samples etched using Teepol or Wofacutan (a hand detergent) as the wetting agent and reported better results with Wofacutan [104]. Dreyer et al. used sodium tridecylbenzene sulfonate (the wetting agent used in all the studies reported in this book) as the wetting agent at 1 g per 100 mL of etchant [105]. Etching times were usually less than 15 min. For steels with higher than usual silicon contents, such as modified AISI 4340, an addition of 0.5 g copper chloride per 100 mL of etchant was found to be helpful. If a copper film forms, it can be removed with ammonia.

Nelson evaluated five wetting agents—zephiran chloride, Tergitol p-28, Triton X-100, Aerosol-22, and sodium tridecylbenzene sulfonate—with several etchants, including saturated aqueous picric acid [6]. Nelson found that aqueous picric acid without a wetting agent was an excellent general-purpose etchant for steels. The addition of sodium tridecylbenzene sulfonate produced extensive etching of the grain boundaries, while development of the general structure was suppressed. The other wetting agents were much less effective or completely ineffective for revealing prior-austenite grain boundaries.

The addition of small amounts (a few drops to a few milliliters per 100 mL of etchant) of hydrochloric acid has been found to produce grain-boundary etching with saturated aqueous picric acid in samples that otherwise would not respond.

For example, AISI 4340 samples were etched with addition of 1% HCl. Without the HCl, the etchant was ineffective.

Grain boundary delineation is always easiest if the steel has been temper-embrittled. Some phosphorus segregates to grain boundaries during austenitization, and additional segregation occurs during aging between about 662 and 1067°F (350 and 575°C). The presence of phosphorus at the austenite grain boundaries has been shown to promote grain-boundary etching with saturated aqueous picric acid [98]. In alloy steels that are free of phosphorus but contain tin [99] or antimony [100] that are subjected to embrittlement treatments, the aqueous saturated picric acid solution does not produce grain-boundary etching. In commercial alloy steels, phosphorus is a common impurity and is usually present in sufficient quantity to permit embrittlement in instances where etching does not bring up the boundaries in the as-received condition.

Grange demonstrated the value of temper embrittlement for revealing austenite grain boundaries in difficult samples [106]. Samples containing either martensite or pearlite and ferrite were embrittled for 16 h at 950°F (510°C). After polishing, they were etched in boiling saturated aqueous picric acid and lightly repolished. The austenite grain boundaries were revealed even in the ferrite-pearlite samples. This is the only technique that works with these structures.

Selective carbide etchants Many of the commonly employed etchants for steels outline the carbide phases in steel. These etchants, however, are not selective in their attack. Numerous studies, principally on highly alloyed steels, have used selective etchants to determine the types and amounts of the various carbides present. These etchants [107–110] are listed in App. I, and their particular responses are summarized in Table 3-3.

In most quantitative measurements of carbides, the first step is to determine the total quantity of all carbides present. The best approach is to select a reagent or method that darkens the matrix and leaves the carbides unaffected. In many steels, the matrix can be darkened by etching with 8 to 15% aqueous sodium metabisulfite (for as-quenched martensite matrixes) or Klemm's I reagent (for ferrite matrixes), as demonstrated in Fig. 3-37. Several of Beraha's tint etchants also color the matrix, leaving the carbides bright. Heat tinting colors cementite readily but not alloy carbides. A light preetch with a general-purpose reagent helps to improve carbide resolution after heat tinting. Depending on the alloy content, the matrix will be darkened by heating in air between 900 and 1200°F (482 and 648°C) for about 5 min.

Knowledge of the steel composition will provide an idea of the types of equilibrium carbides that might be encountered. After the total volume fraction of carbides is determined, the sample is repolished and subjected sequentially to the selective carbide etchants listed in Table 3-3.

Oxygen enrichment etchants Two etchants have been developed to detect oxygen enrichment in steel samples [111, 112]. These etchants are employed to reveal oxygen that is picked up from hot working, welding, cutting, etc. Thus, they are

Table 3-3 Responses of selective carbide etchants

Etchant	Fe$_3$C	Fe$_2$MoC	Mo$_2$C	M$_6$C	MC	M$_{23}$C$_6$	M$_7$C$_3$	Fe$_3$Mo$_2$
Alkaline sodium picrate[1]	Colored dark brown	Colored dark brown	NA†	Colored dark brown	NA	NA‡	NA‡	Colored brown
Aq. CrO$_3$, electrolytic	NA	NA	Outlined in black	NA	Dark gray to black	Outlines (Fe,Cr)$_{23}$C$_6$	Outlined and attacked	NA
Alkaline H$_2$O$_2$	NA	Outlined in black	Outlined in black	Outlined and colored				NA
Murakami's[2] (20°C)	NA	Yellow to light brown	Dark brown to black	Outlined black, colored brown		Faintly attacked	Attacked	Colored brown
Alkaline KMnO$_4$	NA	Outlined in black, colored brown	Colored dark brown	Outlined, colored brown	NA	Mo-type, NA; Cr-type attacked		Colored brown
Alkaline sat. KMnO$_4$	NA	NA	Attacked	Outlined, colored brown	NA	Faint coloring	Attacked	NA

†NA: not attacked
‡Lower chromium carbides are attacked.

Note: (1) Alkaline sodium picrate colors phosphide (Fe$_3$P) more readily than Fe$_3$C. Iron tungstide (Fe$_3$W$_2$) and iron tungsten carbide (Fe$_4$W$_2$C) are colored more rapidly than Fe$_3$C. (2) Murakami's reagent used boiling up to 15 min colors Fe$_3$C black. At room temperature, it colors iron tungsten carbides in several minutes. Prolonged etching at room temperature can color Fe$_3$C very lightly.

useful in quality control and failure analysis. Both etchants are used boiling until the surface is darkened. The oxygen-enriched area appears white against the darkened (colored) matrix structure, as illustrated in Fig. 3-46.

Inclusion etchants One of the oldest methods for identifying inclusions in steel uses the etching schemes based on the work of Comstock (ASTM E3) and Wohrman. Although subsequent development of the electron microprobe or energy-dispersive SEM analysis has largely replaced use of such etching schemes, selective inclusion etching is commonly used for both identification and contrast enhancement in image analysis.

A variety of etching techniques has been developed to preferentially attack or stain sulfides or lead particles, as listed in App. I. The oldest method is that of Whitely, which was developed in 1920 and later modified by Künkele [113]. A few drops of Künkele's solution are applied to the sample and spread over the surface. When the surface becomes black, it is rinsed with water, rubbed with moist cotton to remove the thin silver film, rinsed with alcohol, and dried. Sulfide inclusions are surrounded by a halo. Wallner [114] recommends following this treatment with an etch for 3 to 5 s in Oberhoffer's reagent (see Chap. 1), rinsing, and drying. This process increases the contrast around the sulfide inclusions.

Several simple immersion etches, e.g., dilute aqueous CrO_3, dilute aqueous H_2SO_4, and dilute aqueous oxalic acid, attack sulfide inclusions. Figure 3-47 shows sulfide-aluminate inclusion stringers in which immersion in 1.5% aqueous CrO_3 has preferentially attacked the sulfides.

Whiteley developed a technique in which a Selvyt polishing cloth is soaked in aqueous 5% silver nitrate and the polished surface of the sample is rubbed against

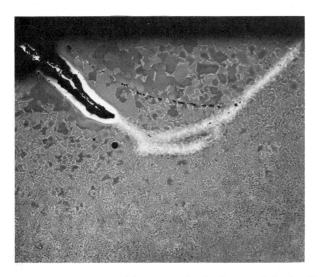

Figure 3-46 Oxygen enrichment at a forging lap revealed using Fine's alkaline chromate etch (16 g CrO_3, 80 g NaOH, and 145 mL water), 37×.

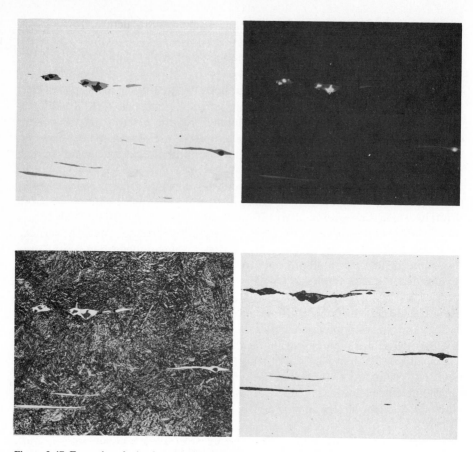

Figure 3-47 Examples of selective techniques applied to sulfide-aluminate inclusions in a resulfurized aluminum-killed alloy steel. Top left, as-polished; top right, ZnSe applied to as-polished surface; bottom left, preetched with nital, then tint-etched with Beraha's lead sulfide etch; bottom right, etched with aqueous 1.5% CrO_3 for 2 min, 300×.

the cloth [115]. Silver is transferred to cover MnS and FeS inclusions with a white film. The contrast between the white inclusions and the matrix is very low. This method was used by Raghupathy and Srinivasan to determine the volume fraction of sulfides [116]. In the as-polished condition, the total inclusion content can be measured by image analysis. After treatment by Whiteley's method, the volume fraction of the oxides alone can be measured, and the volume fraction of sulfides is determined by the difference between the two measurements.

Vapor deposition of compounds with a high refractive index, such as ZnSe, can be used to increase the contrast between the matrix and inclusions, as illustrated in Fig. 3-47. Tint etchants have also been used to aid in inclusion identification. While many of the tint etchants developed by Beraha alter the color of the inclusions, his lead sulfide tint etch [80, 117] was specifically formulated for this purpose. This etch, which is illustrated in Fig. 3-47 for MnS, colors the sulfide a brilliant white against the preetched (nital) matrix microstructure. This etchant is simple to use and is excellent for image analysis.

A number of special etching methods have been developed to selectively attack lead inclusions [118, 119]. In free-machining steels, lead particles are usually associated with the sulfide inclusions and appear white in the as-polished condition. Recent studies of lead inclusions have frequently used back-scattered electron images in the SEM, which produces excellent image contrast against the steel matrix and sulfide inclusions.

Etchants for oxide scales Oxidation of pure iron in the range of 1832 to 2372°F (1000 to 1300°C) produces three oxides, Fe_2O_3 (hematite), Fe_3O_4 (magnetite), and FeO (wustite). Hematite is anisotropic and responds well to polarized light. Magnetite is isotropic and is dark under polarized light. Wustite is unstable below 932°F (500°C) and transforms to magnetite and alpha iron. With rapid cooling, this transformation can be suppressed. Wustite at room temperature is isotropic. A tetragonal FeO phase has been reported when iron is supersaturated with oxygen. This phase is slightly anistropic, resulting in a weak response to polarized light. Hussey et al. have demonstrated that chemical and electrolytic reagents can be used to preferentially etch specific scale phases [120]. Ion beam etching is also quite successful. Hurdus and Tomlinson have listed reagents for distinguishing between Fe_3O_4 and Fe-Cr spinel phases on oxidized chromium ferritic steels [121]. Edstron has shown that dilute HCl in alcohol will attack FeO but not Fe_3O_4 [122].

Etchants for stainless steels Iron-based alloys with enhanced corrosion resistance due to the addition of chromium (11% or greater) are produced in both cast and wrought forms in a wide range of compositions and microstructural forms, including ferrite, martensite, austenite, precipitation-hardened, and duplex combinations. Microstructural complexity is further increased by welding, by high-temperature exposure, or by the addition of elements such as Mo, Ti, Nb, or N. The complexity of these alloys and the commercial importance of stainless steels have fostered extensive development of many etching techniques for revealing the general structure and for preferentially discriminating phases.

Polarized light has limited usefulness with stainless steels except for detection of sigma phase, which has a tetragonal crystal structure. Under cross-polarized light and sensitive tint, sigma phase appears lemon yellow or blue when the stage is rotated, while the cubic ferrite or austenite phases remain maroon or magenta. Chi phase is body-centered cubic and does not respond to polarized light. In the as-polished condition, inclusions can be observed under bright-field illumination, while carbides and sigma phase can be observed with differential interference contrast illumination, especially if some relief is introduced.

Heat tinting [27, 28] is a useful technique for revealing the structure of stainless steels. The sharpness of the phase delineation is improved if the sample is given a light preetch in a general-purpose acid etchant, e.g., dilute aqua regia or Vilella's reagent. Heat tinting can be conducted between 932 and 1292°F (500 and 700°C), but 1200°F (649°C) has been most commonly employed, with times up to

20 min. Austenite is colored more rapidly than ferrite (see Fig. 3-9), and carbides resist coloration longest. After a 20-min period, austenite is colored a mottled blue-green, sigma phase is colored orange, and carbide stays white (uncolored).

Three basic types of reagents are commonly employed for etching stainless steels:

- Concentrated or dilute acid etchants applied by immersion or swabbing of the sample
- Alkaline ferricyanide etchants used at room temperature or heated and applied by immersion of the sample
- Electrolytic etchants

Tint etchants are available, but their use has been minor. The acid etchants usually attack phase boundaries and leave constituents such as carbides and sigma phase in relief without differentiation, except by morphology. Thus, acid etchants are ideal for revealing the grain structure and phases present. Sequential etching, heat tinting, vapor deposition, and magnetic colloidal solutions have been used for phase identification. Figures 3-48 to 3-51 illustrate the microstructure of common stainless steels revealed by general-purpose etchants, and App. I lists etchants for stainless steels.

The alkaline ferricyanide reagents, which were developed originally by Murakami in 1918 and subsequently modified by Burgess and Forgeng in 1938 as well as others (see App. I), has been widely used in metallography not only for stainless steels but also for many metals and carbides. The colors produced vary with etch composition, temperature, time, and phase orientation, and make color discrimination somewhat unreliable unless conditions are rigorously controlled. Etch response, however, is more reliable and accounts for the popularity of Murakami-type reagents.

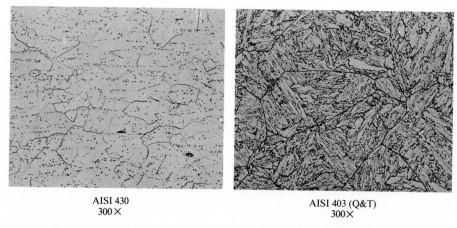

AISI 430
300×

AISI 403 (Q&T)
300×

Figure 3-48 Microstructure of common ferritic (left) and martensitic (right) stainless steels etched with HCl, HNO$_3$, and H$_2$O (1:1:1) (AISI 430) and with picral and HCl (AISI 403).

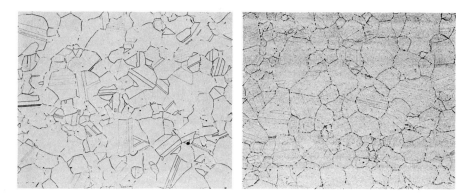

Figure 3-49 AISI 310 austenitic stainless steel etched with aqua regia. Left, solution-annealed; right, sensitized; 60×.

Potassium ferricyanide reacts with potassium hydroxide and produces potassium ferrocyanide [123]:

$$2K_3Fe(CN)_6 + 2KOH \rightarrow 2K_4Fe(CN)_6 + H_2O + \tfrac{1}{2}O_2$$

According to Kegley [123], the ferricyanide acts as an oxidizer, however, whether or not a particular constituent is etched depends on the passivation response of the constituent by either nascent oxygen or excess alkali. Kegley has demonstrated how variations in KOH or $K_3Fe(CN)_6$ affect the room temperature etching response of the alkaline ferricyanide etch, as shown in Fig. 3-52. With the standard Murakami etch (10 g KOH, 10 g $K_3Fe(CN)_6$, and 100 mL H_2O), alloy

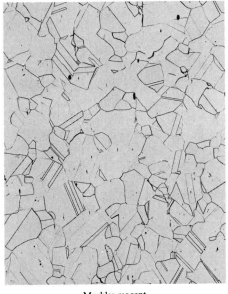

Marbles reagent

Figure 3-50 AISI 316 austenitic stainless steel (solution-annealed), 75×.

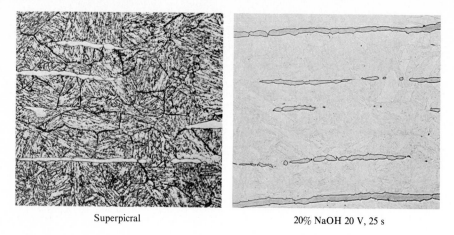

Superpicral   20% NaOH 20 V, 25 s

Figure 3-51 17-4PH stainless steel containing martensite and delta-ferrite stringers, 320×.

carbides are etched at room temperature in 7 to 15 s while sigma is only lightly attacked after 3 min. At higher KOH and $K_3Fe(CN)_6$ levels, sigma phase is attacked preferentially to carbide at room temperature. When the standard Murakami etch is used boiling (for 2 min or more), ferrite, carbide, and sigma phase are attacked, although some workers have reported that sigma phase is not attacked.

The modified Murakami solution of Burgess and Forgeng (30 g KOH, 30 g $K_3Fe(CN)_6$, and 60 mL H_2O) acts in the opposite way to the standard room temperature Murakami's etch. With this modified etch, room temperature etching (for 3 to 5 s) reveals sigma phase while carbide is unattacked, as indicated by Kegley's diagram. If this modified etch is used boiling (for 10 to 60 s), both sigma

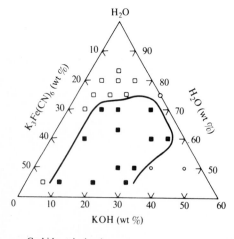

□ Carbide etched only
■ Sigma etched
○ Specimen not etched

Figure 3-52 Room temperature etching response of sigma phase and carbide in different concentrations of Murakami-type reagents. *(From Kegley, Ref. 123, courtesy of International Metallographic Society.)*

phase and ferrite are colored and the carbides are slightly attacked. Kegley has shown that if 100 mL rather than 60 mL of water is used to prepare this modified etch, ferrite is not as readily attacked, thus permitting a clearer distinction between ferrite and sigma phase (sigma phase is black and ferrite is slightly darkened by etching for 2 min with boiling etchant).

Although the alkaline ferricyanide solutions are widely used for discriminating between austenite, ferrite, sigma phase, and carbide, the sharpness, resolution, and uniformity of phase delineation usually is not as good as can be achieved by electrolytic etching. In addition, the selectivity of electrolytic etchants is excellent, making them ideal for quantitative metallography, especially when performed by image analysis.

Electrolytic etching can be accurately controlled by time, voltage, current density, and solution composition. Thus, a high degree of reproducibility is obtainable. In addition, etches can usually be superimposed without staining problems. Since the applied potential takes the place of chemical oxidizers, the composition of electrolytes is usually simple.

A 10% aqueous oxalic acid solution is widely used to reveal carbides and grain structure in austenitic stainless steels [124]. Carbides, if present, are usually observed after etching with oxalic acid for 15 to 30 s at 6 V dc, while the austenite grain structure in carbide-free samples is revealed by etching for 15 to 60 s. Thus, the oxalic acid etch is often used as a test for sensitization, i.e., carbide precipitation at the grain boundary. Electrolytic oxalic acid will outline delta ferrite in austenitic grades when it is present (see Fig. 3-53). A 10% aqueous sodium cyanide electrolytic etch is also used to detect carbide precipitation at grain boundaries [125]. If carbides are not observed after 5 min of etching at 6 V dc, sensitization has not occurred. This etch will also outline delta ferrite, if it is present.

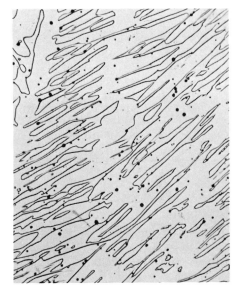

Figure 3-53 Delta ferrite in AISI 312 weld metal revealed using 10% oxalic acid, 6 V dc, 10 s, 750×.

A classic study of the electrolytic etching of stainless steels is that of Gilman [126]. Gilman evaluated the electrolytic etching response of a number of hydroxide solutions (sodium, potassium, barium, lithium, strontium, tetramethyl, and ammonium hydroxides) of different strength and of a number of salt solutions in which the anion forms an insoluble ferric compound including several acetates (ammonium, cadmium, chromium, and lead acetate), sodium oleate, potassium ferricyanide, and potassium thiocyanate.

The simple hydroxide electrolytic solutions stain constituents in the same manner as Murakami's reagent, alkaline sodium picrate, or Groesbeck's reagent. Gilman made the following observations about the color staining of constituents by hydroxide solutions [126]:

- Slight repolishing removes the color, leaving the phases outlined black.
- As etching time increases, the observed colors go through a definite sequence beginning with yellow, then green, red, blue, and finally reddish brown (stays this color with further etching).
- The macroscopic specimen color is usually not the same as the microscopic colors of the constituents.
- Wetting of the sample with water or alcohol produces complimentary colors.
- Before coloration, a constituent acquires a pale-gray cast.

These colors are produced by interference as occurs with tint etchants, heat tinting, or the Pepperhoff vapor-deposition method. Gilman stated that the craze and crack appearance of the stained sigma phase is due to dark lines formed in the thick films rather than to cracking in the sigma phase, as was previously suggested.

Gilman observed that sigma phase is attacked preferentially to carbide only by the strong hydroxide solutions [126]. Weak hydroxide solutions attack carbides much more rapidly than sigma phase; this effect was most extreme with ammonium hydroxide, the weakest base tested. For example, with AISI 314 stainless steel in concentrated NH_4OH at 6 V dc for 30 s, carbides at the grain boundary were blue while other carbides were black and sigma phase was not colored. Sigma phase was etched at 6 V dc after 40 s. At 1.5 V dc, the carbides were completely etched in about 40 s and sigma phase remained uncolored after 3 min.

With strong bases, changes in concentration altered the mode of attack. For example, with 10 N KOH, sigma phase was colored more rapidly than carbide. Etching at 3 V dc for 0.4 s colored sigma phase pinkish brown, while etching for 1.2 s colored sigma phase green and brown and the carbides remained white. With 0.1 N KOH, both sigma phase and carbide were colored. Etching at 3 V dc for 25 s outlined and colored carbides blue and sigma phase pale yellow. After 50 s, the carbides were pink and sigma phase was blue.

With intermediate-strength bases, a change in voltage altered the rate of attack. Aqueous saturated barium hydroxide was the most useful intermediate-strength base. At low voltages, carbides were attacked more readily than sigma phase, while at higher voltages, both were attacked about equally.

Gilman assumed that the effect of hydroxide content on the relative rates of attack on carbides or sigma phase is due to passivation effects. Sigma phase is believed to be more active (less noble) than carbides in concentrated hydroxide solutions. In dilute hydroxide solutions, however, sigma phase apparently becomes passive and is attacked much more slowly than carbide. The carbides are active at either concentration.

Gilman assumed that in hydroxide solutions, ferric hydroxide precipitates on the carbide and sigma phases, producing interference films. He hypothesized that stains could be formed using salt solutions in which the anion forms an insoluble ferric compound. Gilman tested this idea using electrolytic solutions of several acetates, sodium oleate, potassium ferricyanide, and potassium thiocyanate. All produced staining of one or more constituent, although results with sodium oleate were uneven.

Electrolytic solutions of lead acetate and cadmium acetate produced excellent results [126]. A 10% aqueous lead acetate solution at 6 V dc for 0.6 s colors sigma phase dark blue, austenite light blue, and carbide tan. These colors are intense and relatively pure. A light preetch in an acid etchant is required for best results. A 10% aqueous cadmium acetate solution at 6 V dc for 0.6 s outlines carbides and with more time attacks carbides. The rest of the structure is unaffected. At 1.5 V dc for 15 s $M_{23}C_6$ carbide is colored dark blue, sigma phase is not attacked, and austenite is colored pale yellow.

For phase identification, Gilman recommended the following sequence without repolishing between etches [126]:

1. Preetching with Vilella's reagent (1 g picric acid, 5 mL HCl, and 100 mL alcohol) to outline the phases present
2. Electrolytic etching in 10 N KOH at 3 V dc for 0.4 s, which is just long enough to color sigma phase but not carbides
3. Electrolytic etching with concentrated NH_4OH at 6 V dc for 30 s to color carbides

Dulis and Smith conducted a comprehensive review of the effect of most of the common stainless steel etchants on austenite, sigma phase, carbides, and ferrite on nine common austenitic stainless steels [127]. Dulis and Smith recommended the following etching sequence to differentiate between ferrite, sigma phase, and carbide:

1. Etch with Vilella's reagent to reveal all constituents.
2. Etch with Murakami's reagent at room temperature to stain carbides but leave sigma phase and ferrite unaffected.
3. Etch electrolytically with aqueous CrO_3, which severely attacks carbides and sigma phase but not ferrite.

They noted that carbides in stabilized austenitic grades containing titanium or niobium were not consistently attacked by Murakami's reagent. These carbides can be distinguished from sigma phase by their slow rate of attack in electrolytic

CrO_3 as well as by their finer size. They also noted that in room temperature etching with Murakami's reagent of alloys containing 25% Cr and 20% Ni, sigma phase and carbides were attacked in some samples. The carbides in this grade were not attacked by electrolytic CrO_3. Thus, Dulis and Smith concluded that whenever possible other identification methods, e.g., x-ray diffraction, should be applied as well for confirmatory identification.

Slattery and O'Riordan used the etching response in electrolytic 10% oxalic acid at 5 V dc to differentiate phases in AISI 316 stainless steel [128]. After the samples were polished to introduce some relief, samples were examined with interference-contrast illumination, which permitted observation of delta ferrite, sigma phase, chi phase, and $M_{23}C_6$ carbides. Samples were etched electrolytically and examined as follows:

- Carbides are dissolved in 0 to ½ s.
- Sigma phase was outlined in 0 to ½ s and dissolved in ½ to 1 s.
- Chi phase was outlined after 5 to 20 s.
- Ferrite was outlined after 10 to 30 s.

These response times are somewhat more rapid than reported by others, possibly as a result of the relief polishing.

Delta ferrite in martensitic or austenitic stainless steels can be preferentially colored by electrolytic etching with 20% aqueous NaOH at 20 V dc for 5 s. The ferrite is colored tan and outlined, precisely and uniformly. Results are excellent and highly suitable for image analysis. Figure 3-51 illustrates the microstructure of 17-4PH martensitic stainless steel containing delta-ferrite stringers. The ferrite-martensite structure was examined using standard chemical etchants and two electrolytic solutions. Both electrolytic reagents preferentially colored the ferrite phase, but the delineation was sharper and more uniform with 20% NaOH than with 10 N KOH (not shown). The chemical etchants revealed the structure well but did not produce a sample that was suitable for image analysis.

An example of the use of etching techniques for phase identification in a complex austenitic stainless steel is provided by the study of Hattersley and Hume-Rothery [129]. They studied the phases present in austenitic grades containing 17 to 34% Cr, 24 to 30% Ni, and up to 2% Ti at temperatures between 1202 and 2102°F (650 and 1150°C). The etchants used and their influence on the microstructural constituents are listed in Table 3-4.

The grain size of austenitic stainless steels can be estimated by the use of comparison charts. If actual measurements are desired, the twin boundaries must be ignored (in structure-property correlations, better correlations are obtained if all boundaries are considered). The general etchants delineate both grain and twin boundaries, but all boundaries may not be attacked. Some errors can be produced with these etchants because of the limited attack, especially if image analysis is performed. Better etching response can usually be obtained if the sample is sensitized by heating at 1200°F (650°C) prior to polishing and etching with a reagent sensitive to carbides.

Bell and Sonon developed an electrolytic etching procedure to preferentially etch grain boundaries but not twin boundaries in solution-annealed austenitic stainless steels [130]. The electrolyte consists of 60% HNO_3 and 40% water. Prior to immersion, the voltage is set at 1 V dc (no load). The sample is immersed into the solution using insulated tongs, with the sample parallel to an austenitic stainless steel strip cathode (2.5 by 7 cm) with a spacing of about 3.2 cm. The voltage is adjusted to produce a current density of about 8 to 9 mA/cm². Figure 3-54 shows their recommendations for current settings and surface area for different austenitic grades. Etching is conducted for 2 min and followed by water and alcohol rinses and drying. Etching can be repeated if the initial results are too light. If annealing twins are being delineated, light polishing on a stationary final wheel is used to remove the twins without affecting the more deeply etched grain boundaries. If this does not work, the sample is repolished and the etching procedure repeated.

Stephenson and Patchett evaluated the electrolytic etching procedure of Bell and Sonon using sheet samples of AISI 304 and 316 stainless steel plus the more highly alloyed austenitic alloys listed in Table 3-5 [131]. For 304 and 316 stainless steels, they obtained comparable results but needed higher current densities to etch the grain boundaries with a 2-min etch. Their experiments with the more highly alloyed austenitic alloys revealed that use of a platinum cathode produced better results and also reduced etching times. A more dilute electrolyte was required to obtain etching of only grain boundaries in some of these alloys, while other alloys required use of HCl rather than HNO_3, as shown in Table 3-5. Figure 3-55 illustrates the use of this technique on AISI 304 stainless steel. In this example, the 60% HNO_3 electrolyte was used at 0.6 V dc for 2 min at 20°C with a

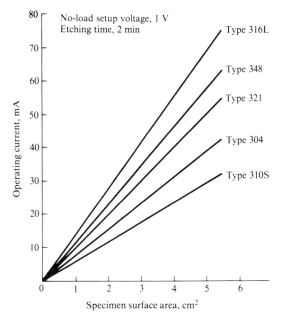

Figure 3-54 Recommended current settings for grain-boundary etching of various austenitic stainless steels using the method of Bell and Sonon. *(From Bell and Sonon, Ref. 130, courtesy of Elsevier Science Publishing Co., Inc.)*

Table 3-4 Identification of constituents in Cr-Ni-Ti stainless steels by etching

Etchant	Effect on						Use
	γ	α	σ	α′	Ni₃Ti(η)	M₂₃C₆	
"Glyceregia" 1 part HNO₃ 2 parts HCl 2 parts glycerol	Lightly attacked	Heavily attacked	Heavily attacked	Attacked	Outlined in alloys free from *large* amounts of other second phases	Outlined but not attacked	Detecting presence of second phase; identification of M₂₃C₆
10 *N* KOH solution (used electrolytically with stainless steel cathode at about 2 V)	Unattacked	Stained yellow to bronze but generally less deep than σ phase	Stained deep yellow to bronze	Outlined and stained pale blue	Not revealed	Outlined and stained a very pale yellow after σ and ferrites have been depicted	Differentiating between σ, α′, and M₂₃C₆ and to some extent between α and σ; does not reveal presence of η

Etchant							
10% oxalic acid solution (used electrolytically with Pt cathode at about 3–4 V)	Moderately attacked	Heavily outlined and shown white in contrast to austenite Prolonged etching resulting in formation of deep, nonreflecting cavities	Heavily outlined and shown white in contrast to austenite Prolonged etching resulting in formation of deep, nonreflecting cavities	Lightly outlined	Outlined even in presence of large quantities of other second phases	Outlined before general structure is revealed	Detecting presence of second phases and in particular the presence of η
Citric acid and potassium iodide solution: 45 g citric acid 30 g potassium iodide 6 g HCl made up to 90 mL with water; used electrolytically with stainless steel cathode at about 2 V	Attacked	Outlined but not attacked (or only lightly attacked)	Outlined but not attacked (or only lightly attacked)	Outlined but not attacked (or only lightly attacked)	Outlined but not attacked (or only lightly attacked)	Outlined but not attacked	Measuring concentration of second-phase content in surface of x-ray specimens

Source: From Hattersley and Hume-Rothery, Ref. 129.

Table 3-5 Electrolytic etching procedures for revealing grain boundaries without attacking twin boundaries in austenitic alloys

Alloy	Acid Type	Concentration, %	Counter electrode material	Voltage, V	Current density, mA/mm²	Etching time, s	Comments
304 stainless	HNO_3	60	316	1.1	1.38	120	Flow lines emphasized at high current
	HNO_3	60	Pt	0.4	0.55	45	
316 stainless	HNO_3	60	316	1.1	0.75	120	Flow lines emphasized at high current
	HNO_3	60	Pt	0.4	0.66	45	
Incoloy 825	HNO_3	20	316	1.5	1.38	120	
	HNO_3	20	Pt	1.4	0.69	30	
Avesta 254 SLX	HNO_3	20	316	1.6	0.82	120	Flow lines and twins at high current and higher acid concentration
	HNO_3	20	Pt	1.0	0.41	120	
Avesta 254 SMO	HNO_3	20	Pt	0.45	0.40	180	Some boundaries faint, flow lines and twins at high current and higher acid concentration
Hastelloy B2	HNO_3	2	Pt	1.1	0.60	60	Very sensitive to acid concentration
Nyby 1803 MOT	HCl	30	Pt	1.3	0.50	5–15	Very sensitive to time
Nyby 2502 MONIT	HCl	50	Pt	1.2	0.75	5–15	Very sensitive to time
Hastelloy G	HCl HNO_3 HCl	25, and 5 50	Pt †	1.55	3.38 0.10	120 300	Faint; twins
Hastelloy C-276	HCl HNO_3 HCl	25, and 5 50	Pt †	1.55	5.18 0.10	120 900	Faint; twins

†Potentiostat
Source: From Stephenson and Patchett, Ref. 131.

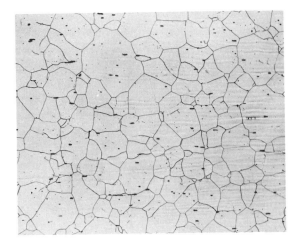

Figure 3-55 Example of grain-boundary etching without twin-boundary etching in AISI 304 austenitic stainless steel using Bell and Sonon's 60% HNO$_3$ aqueous etch, Pt cathode, and 0.6 V dc for 2 min (75×).

Figure 3-56 (*inside front cover*) AISI 316 austenitic stainless steel tint-etched using Beraha's reagent, 65×. *(Courtesy of J. R. Kilpatrick, Bethlehem Steel Corp.)*

platinum cathode. In a few grains, twins were faintly visible and alloy segregation was revealed. The etch attacked the inclusions but this did not obscure the excellent delineation of the grain boundaries. This technique should prove quite valuable for measuring grain size, since the grain structure is very well delineated without interfering twin boundaries.

The use of color metallographic techniques to study stainless steel has largely been associated with staining of sigma phase, carbides, or ferrite by reagents described previously. However, heat tinting colors matrix phases (see Fig. 3-9), and Beraha's tint etchants can also be used [16]. Figure 3-56 illustrates tint etching of stainless steel.

Several workers have shown that the magnetic colloids used to develop Bitter patterns can be used to detect ferromagnetic constituents, such as delta ferrite, in austenitic stainless steels. Gray and his associates have made extensive use of a ferromagnetic colloidal solution, Ferrofluid, to detect ferromagnetic constituents in stainless steels [132, 133]. Ferrofluid contains magnetic particles (smaller than 30 nm) in either an organic or an aqueous colloidal suspension. Particle density is reportedly 10^{18} particles per cubic centimeter. A very small amount of fluid, about ¼ drop (5 μL measured in a micropipette), is applied to the polished sample surface with a syringe. Accurate measurement is not essential, but only a small part of a drop should be used for best results. Since a disturbed metal surface will influence results, a high-quality polish is needed; thus, samples are often electropolished. If mounting material is used, it must be quite dense or the colloid will be absorbed. Bakelite is not recommended, but epoxy is satisfactory. An ultrasonically cleaned cover slip is placed over the colloid and carefully pressed against the specimen surface. The Ferrofluid layer must be transparent to observe the pattern formed by the deposit when it is placed in a magnetic field. Resolution suffers if the layer is too thick.

The sample is placed on a metallograph inside a large coil magnet. Several coil types and sizes have been used by Gray and coworkers to study ferromagnetic constituents. Because delta ferrite is ferromagnetic while sigma is paramagnetic, the magnetic colloid will be attracted to the delta ferrite when the magnetic field is applied momentarily. Such results can also be obtained by holding a permanent magnet behind the sample.

Ferrofluid has been used by Gray et al. to study delta ferrite in austenitic stainless steels. Figure 3-57 shows detection of a small amount of delta ferrite in cast austenitic CF-8 (equivalent to wrought AISI 304). As a result of the magnetic flux lines, many agglomerated particles about 0.5 μm in size were distributed uniformly in the nonmagnetic austenite phase, except in areas where delta ferrite was just below the surface. With the magnetic field off, wavy bands were formed by the colloid in a north-south direction as a result of the earth's magnetic field. Rotation of the stage caused these bands to break up and re-form in the north-south direction. In another sample of austenitic CF-8 containing a large amount of delta ferrite, use of Ferrofluid revealed a "coral-type" domain pattern in the delta ferrite (see Fig. 3-58). The sharpness of the pattern was due to the use of a large magnetic coil operating at 4 A. These patterns are not observable if ordinary etching methods are used.

As this section demonstrates, the microstructure of iron-based alloys is extremely diverse and has been studied using a wide range of techniques. The technique employed depends on the alloy composition, the heat treatment, and the purpose of the study. Although the most commonly employed are chemical etchants, tint etchants, heat tinting, vapor deposition, and electrolytic etchants offer substantial benefits and should be considered for appropriate samples.

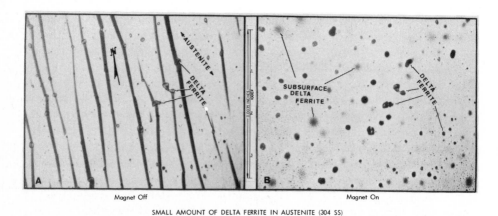

Magnet Off Magnet On

SMALL AMOUNT OF DELTA FERRITE IN AUSTENITE (304 SS)

Specimen was heat treated, 1950°F (1066°C) for 1 hr ⟶ water quench, to convert most of the massive delta ferrite to austenite. Note the banding (A) due to earth's magnetic field. Subsurface delta ferrite is evident (B) by concentrated agglomerates of colloid.

Figure 3-57 Detection of small amounts of delta ferrite in an austenitic stainless steel using Ferrofluid. *(Courtesy of R. J. Gray and R. S. Crouse, Oak Ridge National Laboratory.)*

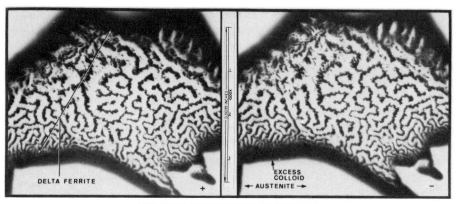

"CORAL" TYPE DOMAIN PATTERNS ON DELTA FERRITE

The magnetic regions, or domains, are made up of millions of atoms (actually electrons). The introduction of a magnetic field produces a net magnetism related to each individual domain. A ferromagnetic material (e.g., delta ferrite) exhibits the strongest net magnetism of all types of materials. The application of a ferromagnetic colloid, Ferrofluid, maps the domain pattern of the substrate.

Figure 3-58 Use of Ferrofluid to reveal the substructure of delta ferrite in austenitic stainless steel. *(Courtesy of R. J. Gray and R. S. Crouse, Oak Ridge National Laboratory.)*

Magnesium and alloys Etchants for magnesium and its alloys are relatively simple in composition and not overly active, since all mineral acids and most organic acids will attack magnesium and magnesium alloys [10]. Many of the etchants developed [134–137] are modifications of nital or picral that contain other solvents such as water or ethylene glycol (see App. I). Simple dilute aqueous solutions containing an organic or mineral acid will etch these metals. A few selective etchants have been developed to preferentially attack common constituents, such as $Mg_{17}Al_{12}$, Mg_2Si, Mg_7Zn_3, or MgZn. For general work, the "glycol" etchant is commonly employed. Figure 3-59 shows the microstructure of a broken die-cast Mg alloy wheel etched with the glycol etch and with an etch of acetic acid and picral. The massive white phase is $Mg_{17}Al_{12}$, the smaller gray (blue)

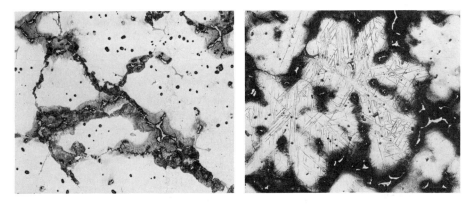

Figure 3-59 Microstructure of a die-cast Mg alloy revealed using the glycol etch (left) and an etch of acetic acid and picral (right), $60\times$.

particles are Mg_2Si, and the lamellar eutectic is a mixture of solid-solution alpha and beta Mg_2Al_3. The glycol etch did not reveal the mechanical twins which were visible after etching with the acetic-picral etch but was a more suitable etch for the eutectic.

Oberländer and Lillerud found that etched image contrast could be improved by vacuum deposition of a thin layer of carbon on the sample surface [137]. To control deposition, a sheet of white paper is placed in the vacuum chamber with the sample, and carbon deposition is halted when the desired gray level is obtained. Color differences in the solid-solution alpha phase were found to correlate to compositional variations in the matrix phase.

Nickel and alloys Nickel resists attack by alkaline solutions, is slowly attacked by dilute HCl or H_2SO_4, and is dissolved readily in dilute HNO_3. Consequently, etchants for nickel and its alloys are rather strong solutions. If the nickel concentration is high, it can be difficult to etch nickel samples. Grain-boundary attack is relatively easy to obtain, but grain contrast ("facet" etching) is difficult. Use of electrolytic etchants is quite popular.

Of the immersion echants, Kalling's no. 2 ("waterless" Kalling's), the 92:5:3 mixture of HCl, H_2SO_4, and HNO_3, and several variants of "glyceregia" are popular and widely used, particularly for superalloys. Many etchants have been developed for nickel and nickel alloys. Beland [138] has described procedures for pure nickel, while Kotval [139], Kohlhaas and Fischer [140], and others [9–14] have compiled lists of reagents suitable for nickel and its alloys. Lund and Wagner have reviewed procedures for identifying constituents in superalloys [141].

Figure 3-60 shows the microstructure of 200 Ni (99.4% Ni) etched with equal parts of acetic acid, nitric acid, and water. Only part of the austenitic grain structure is revealed. Figure 3-61 shows the microstructure of a single-phase alloy

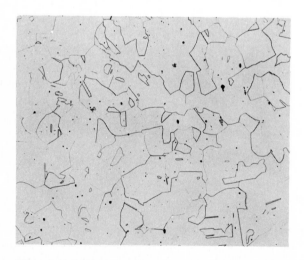

Figure 3-60 Microstructure of 200 nickel revealed using equal parts of acetic acid, nitric acid, and water, 75×. *(Courtesy of R. D. Buchheit, Battelle Memorial Institute.)*

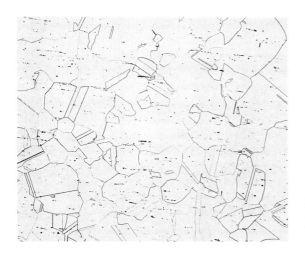

Figure 3-61 Microstructure of an alloy of Ni and 50% Fe etched with saturated aqueous ammonium persulfate, 75×.

of Ni and 50% Fe etched with saturated aqueous ammonium persulfate. Again, not all the grain boundaries are revealed.

Figure 3-62 illustrates the microstructure of two superalloys, Pyromet X-750 (Ni, 0.04% C, 0.2% Mn, 0.2% Si, 15% Cr, 2.5% Ti, 0.7% Al, 1% Nb, 7% Fe) and Pyromet 31 (Ni, 0.04% C, 0.1% Mn, 0.2% Si, 22.7% Cr, 2% Mo, 2.5% Ti, 1.5% Al, 15% Fe, 1.1% Nb, 0.005% B), both in the solution-annealed and aged conditions. Etching with Kalling's no. 2 revealed the grain and twin boundaries. Pyromet 31 etched more readily than X-750 in which some of the grain boundaries were not etched. Etching with Beraha's tint etch (to 100 mL of a solution of 1 part HCl and 2 parts H_2O, add 1 g potassium metabisulfite; 1 g $FeCl_3$ also added for X-750) produced excellent coloration and complete development of the grain structure in both samples.

The microstructure of nickel-base superalloys is quite complex. Strengthening is obtained by precipitation of gamma prime (Ni_3Al) or eta (Ni_3Ti). Several types of carbides, borides, and TiN can be present. Gamma prime is rather small and is best observed by electron metallographic methods, except when the alloys are overaged. Several etchants preferentially attack gamma prime or leave it in relief. Gamma-prime particles have cubical to spherical shapes. Eta is formed in alloys with high Ti/Al ratios and is acicular in appearance. Eta coarsens more rapidly than gamma prime and coalesces into larger particles. In alloys containing niobium (columbium), such as Inconel 718, acicular Ni_3Nb is observed. Carbides in nickel-based superalloys are of the following types: MC, $M_{23}C_6$, M_6C, or M_7C_3. These can usually be selectively etched using the preferential etchants listed under iron and steel in App. I.

Niobium, tantalum, and vanadium Niobium (columbium) resists attack by all mineral acids except hydrofluoric acid. Thus, most chemical etchants for niobium contain HF and must be handled with great care. Addition of nitric acid apparently accelerates the attack. Other etchant components are used to control

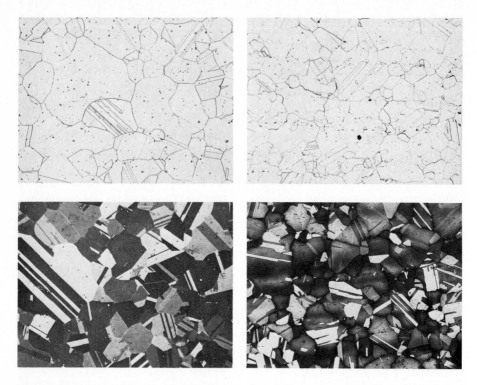

Figure 3-62 Microstructure of nickel-based superalloys (solution-annealed and aged) Pyromet 31 (left) and Pyromet X-750 (right) revealed using Kalling's no. 2 (top) and using Beraha's tint etch (bottom), 60×.

Figure 3-63 (***inside front cover***) Illustration of Picklesimer's anodization technique for revealing the microstructure of a Nb-Nb$_3$Sn "Kunzler-type" alloy (top, 27 V dc, 510×) and a Nb-Sn diffusion couple aged at 900°C (bottom, 28 V dc, 680×). (*Courtesy of M. L. Picklesimer and L. Schrader, Oak Ridge National Laboratory, reproduced courtesy of the American Institute of Physics and Microscope Publications.*)

formation of insoluble complexes or inhibit pitting [10]. Mixtures containing HF, HNO$_3$, and other chemicals or solvents are unstable and should usually be used fresh and discarded within about 1 h after mixing. Forgeng has reviewed etching procedures for niobium and tantalum [142].

Eary and Johnston have examined the etching characteristics of niobium in depth [143]. If the sample exhibits any degree of passivity toward the etchant, attack occurs preferentially at locations without passive film protection, e.g., at pores or impurities. The speed of attack varies with alloy content, pure samples being attacked much more slowly. The characteristics of any solvents used also affect the attack rate.

Niobium, like chromium and aluminum, is protected by a tight oxide film, Nb$_2$O$_5$, which is attacked by HF; however, HF does not attack the metal beneath the oxide. Eary and Johnston experimented with an acidified ferric chloride solution [143]. This solution did not break down the Nb_2O_5 surface film. However, if HF was added, the solution etched niobium. Experiments showed that there was a critical minimum amount of HF (4%) needed for etching. Increasing the HF content beyond this level did not increase the attack rate. Some excess HF is needed to ensure breakdown of the oxide film. In nonacidified ferric chloride solutions, the critical amount of HF required was greater (5.8%).

Anodizing procedures are frequently employed for preferential color staining of Nb and its alloys. These reagents produce a thin interference film; colors are visible under bright-field illumination and can be enhanced with polarized light. Appendix I lists a number of anodizing solutions as well as electrolytic etchants that do not color the microstructure. Crouse [144] has used the cumulative anodizing etch of Ence and Margolin that was developed for titanium to identify phases in Nb.

Picklesimer has developed an anodizing solution applicable to niobium, tantalum, and zirconium [145, 146]. Figure 3-63 illustrates Picklesimer's application of this technique to Nb-Sn alloys. The first example shows a "Kunzler-type" superconducting Nb-Nb_3Sn wire made by filling a Nb tube with a mixture of Nb and Sn powder to make Nb_3Sn plus 10% excess Sn. The tube was swagged and drawn and then reacted at 1832°F (1000°C) for 18 h and quenched with water. The sample was vibratory polished, chemically etched, and anodized in Picklesimer's solution at 27 V. Anodizing reveals several phases not visible with chemical etching. The Nb cladding is blue, the Nb powder particles containing Sn in solution are blue, the red and yellow particles are intermetallic compounds of Nb and Sn, the small, clear, yellow particles are Nb_2N, the small green to green-yellow particles are a terminal Sn-rich phase, and the black areas are voids. The second example is a Nb-Sn diffusion couple aged 16 h at 1652°F (900°C) and quenched with water. The sample was polished and anodized at 28 V. Four intermediate phases were produced in the sample, three of which formed at this temperature. The pure Nb cladding is blue, phase 1 is blue purple, phase 2 is purple, and phase 3 is brown. The area coded L is a tin-rich phase which was liquid at the aging temperature and appears white to very light yellow. The tin content of the phases and their melting points increased in the order 1 to 3.

Tantalum is very similar to niobium and is also resistant to all mineral acids except HF. As with niobium, addition of nitric acid to HF increases the rate of etch attack on tantalum. Thus etchants for tantalum are quite similar to those for niobium. Formation of etch pits is common with many of these etchants. The comments describing the etching of niobium apply equally to tantalum. Figure 3-64 shows the structure of fully recrystallized tantalum etched chemically in a 2:1 mixture of 20% ammonium bifluoride and nitric acid.

Vanadium is attacked readily by nitric acid, resists attack by dilute hydrochloric and sulfuric acids, and is attacked slowly by hot sulfuric acid. Mixtures of HF and nitric acid, with additions of water, lactic acid, or glycerin as solvents, are commonly used to etch vanadium and its alloys.

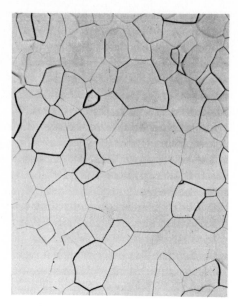

Figure 3-64 Microstructure of fully recrystallized tantalum etched with 20% ammonium bifluoride and HNO₃ (2:1), 75×. *(Courtesy of R. D. Buchheit, Battelle Memorial Institute.)*

Precious metals The precious metals (gold and silver and the platinum metals—ruthenium, rhodium, palladium, osmium, iridium, and platinum) are occasionally examined by metallographers. Gold is not attacked by mineral acids but is etched by nascent chlorine in aqua regia and by a few very strong oxidizers [10]. Gold alloys are easier to etch than pure gold. Since etching residues can produce explosive compounds, it is unwise to experiment with unproven etchants without full knowledge of the chemistry of the reaction products. Figure 3-65 shows the microstructure of a gold tube etched with equal parts of HCl and HNO₃.

Silver is attacked by HNO₃ and by hot sulfuric acid but not by cold sulfuric acid or by the halogen acids. Silver is attacked by alkaline cyanide solutions, and several etchants of this type have been developed. These etchants must be used under a hood with extreme care because of the possible evolution of deadly hydrogen cyanide. Like the reaction products from the etching of gold, those from the etching of silver are often explosive. Oxalates, nitrites, and silver chlorite are explosive but do not detonate when wet. Reagents in which these products can form should be discarded immediately after use. Figure 3-65 also shows the microstructure of an alloy of Ag, 40% Au, and 10% In etched with a mixture of equal parts of 10% aqueous NaCN and 10% aqueous ammonium persulfate.

Ruthenium is also extremely resistant to mineral acids and is not attacked by aqua regia. Fortunately, ruthenium has a hexagonal close-packed crystal structure and can be examined with polarized light. Electrolytic etchants are commonly employed for etching ruthenium and its alloys.

Rhodium is also resistant to mineral acids and is not attacked by aqua regia. Electrolytic etching is generally employed. Figure 3-66 shows the structure of an as-cast alloy of Rh, 54% Ni, and 3% W exhibiting a duplex precipitate structure

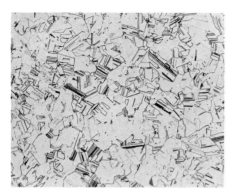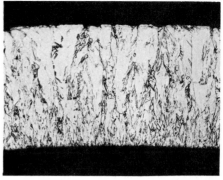

Figure 3-65 Microstructure of an alloy of Ag, 40% Au, and 10% In (left) etched with equal parts of 10% NaCN and 10% ammonium persulfate (90×) and the microstructure of a gold tube (right) etched with equal parts of HCl and HNO₃ (150×). *(Courtesy of R. D. Buchheit, Battelle Memorial Institute.)*

consisting of rhodium plates in a Ni-W matrix. The sample was etched by swabbing with equal parts of nitric and acetic acids.

Palladium, unlike the other platinum metals, is attacked by nitric acid, aided by oxygen or nitrogen oxide compounds. Aqua regia etches palladium very slowly but is unsuitable as a metallographic etchant. Chemical and electrolytic etchants have been developed for palladium. Figure 3-66 also shows two examples of the microstructure of palladium alloys. An arc weld of Pd and 25% Ag using argon gas is shown after etching by immersion in equal parts of 10% aqueous KCN and 10% aqueous ammonium persulfate. The second example is an as-cast alloy of Pd and 0.1% Si containing large grains of Pd in a brittle low-melting point eutectic of PdSi. This sample was etched with the same reagent as the previous palladium alloy.

Osmium resists attack by mineral acids and is not attacked by aqua regia. Electrolytic etching is preferred. Osmium has a hexagonal close-packed crystal structure, and can be examined by use of polarized light without recourse to etching. Figure 3-66 also shows the microstructure of vacuum-arc-melted pure osmium photographed in polarized light.

Iridium is resistant to attack by all acids and bases. Only electrolytic etching produces useful etch results. Figure 3-66 also shows the microstructure of an as-cast alloy of Ir, 10% Ta, and 10% Hf. The microstructure consists of an interdendritic structure of Ir in an Hf-Ta matrix. The sample was electrolytically etched at 4 V ac in HCl and water (2:1) and was photographed with oblique light.

Platinum is resistant to mineral acids but can be etched with hot aqua regia. Electrolytic reagents produce good results. Figure 3-66 also shows the microstructure of a magnetic alloy of Pt and 24% Co quenched from 1832°F (1000°C) and ordered at 1112°F (600°C) for 50 min. The single-phase structure was etched electrolytically at 3 V ac in a mixture of HCl and NaCl. The microstructures shown in Fig. 3-66 are from the excellent review of techniques for precious metals by Piotrowski and Accinno [147]. Etching techniques for these metals are listed in App. I.

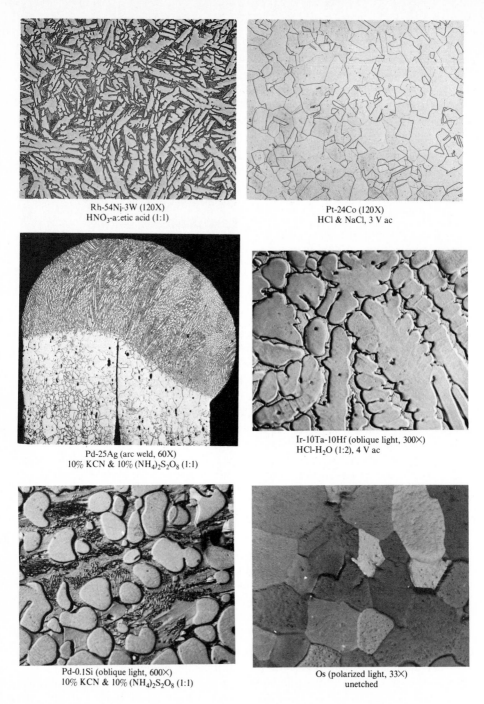

Rh-54Nj-3W (120X)
HNO₃-acetic acid (1:1)

Pt-24Co (120X)
HCl & NaCl, 3 V ac

Pd-25Ag (arc weld, 60X)
10% KCN & 10% (NH₄)₂S₂O₈ (1:1)

Ir-10Ta-10Hf (oblique light, 300X)
HCl-H₂O (1:2), 4 V ac

Pd-0.1Si (oblique light, 600X)
10% KCN & 10% (NH₄)₂S₂O₈ (1:1)

Os (polarized light, 33X)
unetched

Figure 3-66 Examples of the microstructure of precious metals of the platinum family. *(From Piotrowski and Accinno, Ref. 147, courtesy of T. Piotrowski, Englehard Ind. Div, Englehard Corp., reproduced courtesy of Elsevier Science Publishing Co., Inc.)*

Radioactive metals Since World War II, considerable attention has been given to the metallography of radioactive metals [148–150]. Appendix I lists etching techniques for uranium, plutonium, thorium, and neptunium. These metals should only be handled by those thoroughly familiar with their radioactive and toxic characteristics and in properly constructed shielded laboratories. Since uranium has an orthorhombic crystal structure and is strongly anisotropic, examination of properly polished samples with polarized light reveals the structure extremely well, as demonstrated by the example in Chap. 4. Since etching of uranium is not simple, examination with polarized light is highly useful.

Uranium is attacked easily by HCl and HF, is attacked slowly by dilute H_2SO_4, but is not attacked by dilute HNO_3 [10]. Uranium alloys, particularly U-Nb alloys, have been known to explode during or after immersion in strong oxidizers, such as nitric acid. Uranium is quite active chemically, which makes it difficult to reveal the grain boundaries by etching. The surface should be examined shortly after polishing, since several hours of oxidation in air will obscure the structure. Some of the etchants that have been developed reveal the grain structure by preferential oxidation. Heating at 212°F (100°C) in air has been used to identify phases. For example, in a study of U-Si alloys, Wyatt used heat tinting to selectively color phases: U_3Si_2 was white, U_3Si was gray, and UO_2 was dark gray [149]. The microstructure of uranium viewed in polarized light is shown in Chap. 4. Figure 3-67 shows the microstructure of uranium carbide.

Pure plutonium is difficult to etch chemically, but satisfactory results can be obtained with many Pu alloys. In many Pu alloys, certain phases can be observed

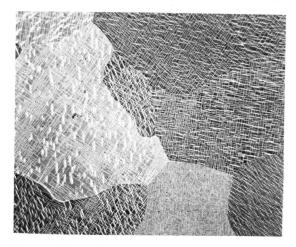

Figure 3-67 Microstructure of uranium carbide etched with equal parts of HNO_3, acetic acid, and water, 190×. *(Courtesy of R. D. Buchheit, Battelle Memorial Institute.)*

Figure 3-68 (*inside front cover*) Microstructure of thorium dicarbide (as-cast) etched with equal parts HNO_3 and H_2O for 45 min, polarized light, 280×. *(Courtesy of R. S. Crouse, Oak Ridge National Laboratory.)*

Figure 3-69 (*inside front cover*) Microstructure of cerium dicarbide etched with equal parts HNO_3, acetic acid, and water, polarized light, 70×. *(Courtesy of R. S. Crouse, Oak Ridge National Laboratory.)*

Figure 3-70 (*inside back cover*) Microstructure of yttrium (as-cast) etched with equal parts of acetic, phosphoric, and nitric acids, sensitive tint, 25×. *(Courtesy of R. S. Crouse, Oak Ridge National Laboratory.)*

as-polished. Pu_2C_3, for example, oxidizes in air more readily than PuC. All the phases in Pu are reactive and oxidize in air. Since Pu tends to form insoluble compounds with strong acids, etching presents problems. Exposure to aqueous solutions must be minimized. Electrolytic etching has in general provided best results for Pu and its alloys. As the result of selective surface oxidation, these etchants reveal the structure under bright-field illumination or under polarized light. According to Rencken, the true structure of alpha plutonium is not revealed by examination of oxidized surfaces with polarized light [150]. Vacuum cathodic etching has been commonly used to reveal the structure of radioactive metals. This technique is useful for Pu but is rather slow. Heating must be minimized because alpha plutonium transforms to beta plutonium at about 248°F (120°C). The microstructure of delta plutonium is shown in Chap. 4.

Only limited metallographic work has been done on thorium and neptunium. Thorium is attacked by water and dissolves in HCl. The alloys of thorium are less reactive. Figure 3-68 (see p. 249 and inside front cover) shows the microstructure of thorium dicarbide.

Rare earth metals The rare earth metals, particularly lanthanum and cerium, and scandium and yttrium which are similar to the rare earths, have been examined occasionally by metallographers. These metals are rather reactive, and their structures can often be revealed by oxidation in air. Many of these metals can be etched with nital. Koch and Picklesimer have developed an anodizing technique for Ce and La [151]. The anodic oxide film produced protects the surface from oxidation, permitting lengthy examination without interference from oxidation. Dobbins has used vacuum cathodic etching to reveal the structure of holmium [152]. Figure 3-69 (see p. 249 and inside front cover) shows the microstructure of etched cerium dicarbide examined with polarized light, while Fig. 3-70 (see p. 249 and inside back cover) shows the microstructure of etched as-cast yttrium viewed with sensitive tint.

Selenium and tellurium Selenium is oxidized by nitric acid producing selenous acid. Selenium is attacked by strong alkali solutions, by strong sodium sulfide solutions, and by aqua regia but not by the halogen acids [10]. Tellurium is not attacked by dilute HCl or H_2SO_4 but is oxidized by HNO_3, by concentrated H_2SO_4, and by hot concentrated alkaline solutions [10]. Tellurides exhibit quite different characteristics than tellurium. Tellurides are attacked by dilute HCl and produce hydrogen telluride, which dissolves in water and forms a strong acid [10].

Titanium and alloys Microscopy has played an important role in the development of titanium alloys. Titanium is attacked by HCl, HF, H_2SO_4, and HNO_3. The adherent oxide film on the surface of Ti and Ti alloys requires strong etchants [153–157]. Thus, most etchants for Ti contain HF and HNO_3 in water, glycerin, or lactic acid. When these two acids are present, HF attacks the surface while HNO_3 brightens it. Kroll's reagent, a dilute aqueous solution containing HF and HNO_3, is one of the oldest and most commonly used etchants. Kroll's reagent reveals the structural details and with some samples, will reveal the grain boundaries. To minimize staining problems that might obscure the microstructure, Kroll's reagent and similar etchants should be applied by swabbing. In general, swabbing produces a brighter etch with these alloys. In some etchants, hydrogen peroxide is added to reduce staining. Appendix I lists etchants for Ti and its alloys.

The Remington A etch, similar in action to Kroll's reagent, contains HF and HNO_3 in glycerin and is also applied by swabbing. The Remington B etch does not contain nitric acid for brightening. This etch can be used advantageously with alpha-beta alloys, since the alpha phase is darkened while the beta phase is outlined.

Horn investigated etching of Ti alloys with solutions containing only HF in water or in organic solvents [157]. She found that titanium hydride can be formed at preferred lattice sites with such etchants. In alloys containing metals nobler than Ti, the nobler metal precipitated rather than titanium hybride. The presence of oxidizing acids, e.g., HNO_3, in the etchant usually inhibits nitride formation.

A popular aqueous etchant containing potassium hydroxide and hydrogen peroxide also stains the alpha phase but does not affect the beta phase. HNO_3 and HF are also added to lactic acid and applied by swabbing. At the higher HF levels, this etch also produces some chemical polishing action during etching, which can be helpful in obtaining well-defined structures.

For alpha-phase Ti, etching with aqueous 0.5% HF stains the alpha grains preferentially. This etch is used by immersion. Kroll's reagent frequently produces similar results when used by immersion. Since the alpha phase has a hexagonal close-packed crystal structure, it responds to polarized light, as demonstrated in Chap. 4. The beta phase has a body-centered cubic crystal structure and is dark under polarized light. If the stage is rotated under crossed polarizers, the alpha grains exhibit alternating light-dark contrast while beta grains remain dark at all angles of rotation. This effect is usually best observed in unetched samples when both phases are present. A sensitive tint plate is useful in conjunction with polarized light. For alpha-phase alloys, etching can enhance results obtained with polarized light if the alpha phase is equiaxed but not when it is acicular.

Heat tinting in air at 752 to 1300°F (400 to 704°C) has been used by several experimenters and found to be quite effective for phase discrimination and delineation. This technique should be used only when it will not alter the structure of the sample. Heat tinting can produce excellent coloration effects in Ti samples and gives best structure resolution when preceded by a light etch with a general-purpose etchant.

Although a few tint etchants have been developed, electrolytic anodizing solutions have been more commonly used for selective phase coloration. Jacquet developed the first anodic oxidation technique for Ti in 1951. The cumulative etch anodizing method of Ence and Margolin [153] has been widely employed, and modified versions of this etch have been used [155, 156, 158]. The colors of the interference films produced are quite sensitive to crystal orientation and phase composition.

Figure 3-71 illustrates the microstructure of a near-alpha Ti alloy containing 6% Al, 2% Sn, 4% Zr, and 2% Mo either (1) forged (954°C) in the alpha-beta

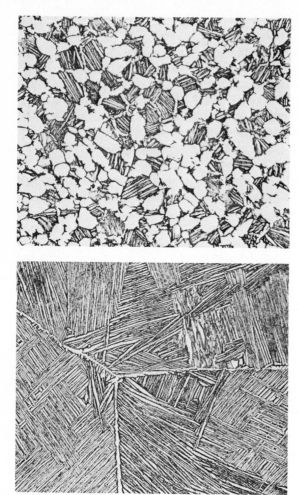

Figure 3-71 Microstructure of Ti-6242 forged in the alpha-beta region and annealed in the alpha-beta region (top) and forged in the beta region and annealed in the beta region (bottom) etched with Kroll's reagent, 375×.

region and annealed (968°C) in the alpha-beta region or (2) forged (1038°C) in the beta region followed by annealing (1024°C) in the beta region. The structures are shown at 375X after etching by swabbing with Kroll's reagent. The first condition produced a mixture of equiaxed alpha and an alpha-beta eutectoid. The second heat treatment produced acicular alpha and prior-beta grain boundaries decorated with alpha. A dilute 0.5% HF etch produced similar results when used by swabbing. Immersion etching with either reagent did not produce comparable crisp delineation. Figure 3-72 shows the structure of alpha-beta alloy of Ti containing 6% Al and 4% V delineated by four different treatments. The "basket-weave" structure results from nucleation and growth during transformation of beta to alpha in a Widmanstätten pattern, with the alpha phase growing on preferred crystallographic planes of the parent beta phase. Some beta appears to be retained between the alpha grains. Kroll's reagent (swabbed) and a solution of

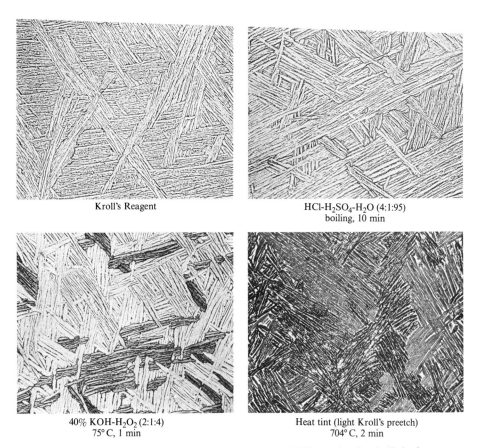

Kroll's Reagent

HCl-H₂SO₄-H₂O (4:1:95)
boiling, 10 min

40% KOH-H₂O₂ (2:1:4)
75° C, 1 min

Heat tint (light Kroll's preetch)
704° C, 2 min

Figure 3-72 Microstructure of an alloy of Ti, 6% Al, and 4% V illustrating the classic basket-weave structure that was etched with three reagents and heat-tinted, 300×.

4 mL HCl, 1 mL H_2SO_4, and 95 mL water (immersed 10 min in boiling solution) produced similar results. Use of a solution of 10 mL 40% KOH, 5 mL H_2O_2 (30%), and 20 mL water (1 min at 75°C) stained some of the acicular alpha, producing greater contrast. Heat tinting (704°C for 2 min) after a light preetch with Kroll's reagent produced vivid coloration of the alpha platelets while the retained beta trapped between the platelets remained light. Several tint etchants were tried, but none produced useful coloration, although some were satisfactory as etchants.

Zirconium and hafnium Zirconium and hafnium are both quite inert, being attacked only by HF and aqua regia [10]. Both have hexagonal close-packed crystal structures and respond well to polarized light as a result of their strong anisotropy. Hafnium alloys, however, do not respond well to polarized light, and phase identification is quite difficult, especially since etching is also difficult. Zirconium alloys respond well to polarized light.

These metals are often chemically polished, which produces minor etching, as

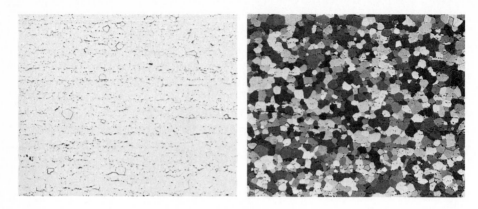

Figure 3-73 Microstructure of chemically polished and etched (45 mL HNO$_3$, 45 mL H$_2$O$_2$, and 10 mL HF) zirconium viewed with bright-field illumination (left) and polarized light (right), 60×.

Figure 3-74 (***inside back cover***) Microstructure of an alloy of Zr and 3% Ag anodized with 5% KOH, 50×. *(Courtesy of R. S. Crouse, Oak Ridge National Laboratory.)*

illustrated in Fig. 3-73. Even after etching, polarized light is usually employed to examine Zr and its alloys [145, 146, 159, 160]. Most of the chemical polishing solutions contain HF, which attacks the surface, and HNO$_3$, which prevents staining. Water, hydrogen peroxide, glycerin, or lactic acid can be used as the solvent. Most are applied vigorously by swabbing, which also facilitates stain removal. Some of the etchants do not produce significant chemical polishing and are essentially etchants, while others produce substantial polishing. All contain HF or a similar fluorine-containing substance.

In general, bright-field examination is reserved for inclusion detection but can be useful for some etched two-phase alloys. Only a portion of the grain boundaries are visible under bright-field illumination. Overetching can bring out details better for bright-field examination, but relief is excessive and fine detail is obscured. Because of these difficulties, polarized light is indispensable for examination of Zr, Hf, and their alloys.

Several electrolytic etching procedures have been developed for these metals. Heat tinting has been used but is not as useful as polarized light. Picklesimer has developed a color anodizing procedure for Zr alloys [145, 146]. The anodic film forms at different oxidation rates that are related to the composition of the phases present. The interference colors produced thus correspond to each phase in a well-defined manner. In addition, anisotropy effects are enhanced with polarized light. Figure 3-74 shows the microstructure of an alloy of Zr and 3% Ag partially transformed from the beta phase and anodically etched with 5% KOH. The red patches and red needles are pearlitic- and bainitic-type transformation products, while the yellow matrix is a martensitic phase.

3-11.2 Borides, Carbides, Nitrides, and Oxides

As with metals, numerous etching techniques and etchants have been used to reveal the structure of borides, carbides, nitrides, and oxides. Procedures for etching these constituents, particularly when they occur within a metal matrix, are listed with the formulations for the particular metal in App. I. Other procedures for carbides, nitrides, and oxides are listed separately in App. I. Many of these materials, particularly the oxide ceramic materials, are extremely inert and, therefore, difficult to etch chemically. Molten salts, thermal etching, and vacuum cathodic etching are commonly used. Thermal etching has the advantage of removing fine polishing scratches and usually develops the structure of the grain boundary of ceramics better than other techniques. Some of the oxides are transparent or translucent and exhibit low reflectivity. Use of oil immersion lenses or a thin layer (20 nm) of vapor-deposited aluminum can enhance the bright-field image. The vapor-deposition technique of Pepperhoff is also quite useful. In the use of this method, etching is not always required before vapor deposition; relief polishing is generally satisfactory.

Etching techniques for ceramic materials have not been developed as extensively as for metals [161, 162]. This is partly due to the greater difficulty in etching

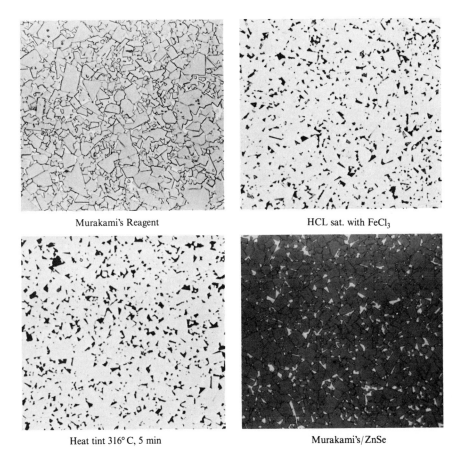

Murakami's Reagent   HCL sat. with FeCl$_3$

Heat tint 316° C, 5 min   Murakami's/ZnSe

Figure 3-75 Microstructure of a sintered carbide cutting tool made from an WC-Co alloy, 640×.

ceramics. Politis and Ohtani have prepared an extensive list of etchants for borides, carbides, nitrides, oxides, and sulfides [162].

Etching techniques for carbides have built upon the selective etching methods for carbides in steels. A number of etchants have been developed for bulk samples. Sintered carbides, particularly those used as cutting tools, have received considerable attention. Heat tinting of sintered carbides as well as the Pepperhoff vapor-deposition method are particularly useful.

Figure 3-75 shows the microstructure of a WC-Co alloy revealed using different etchants and procedures. Murakami's reagent is the most common etchant for revealing the structure of the WC-Co alloy. Murakami's reagent outlines the carbide grains and darkens them slightly, while the Co binder is unaffected. However, the contrast between the Co binder and the WC grains is very low, and the image is not satisfactory for image analysis. To measure the volume fraction of the Co binder, etching in HCl saturated with $FeCl_3$ is useful, since the Co is blackened preferentially without attack on the grain or phase boundaries [31]. Heat tinting in air at 600°F (316°C) colors the Co brown without affecting the WC. The Pepperhoff method reveals only the Co if the sample is not etched. Greater contrast and the location of the WC grains are obtained if the sample is preetched. These methods are illustrated in Fig. 3-75.

Figure 3-76 shows the microstructure of annealed and hardened Ferro TiC C. Nital etching (not shown) did not clearly reveal the structure of either sample because of nital's sensitivity to orientation. Picral plus HCl reveals the structure of the annealed sample very well. Still greater contrast can be obtained if the sample is given a second etch with Murakami's reagent (2 s at 20°C) to darken the TiC. When the hardened sample is etched with either nital or picral plus HCl little detail is revealed in the martensitic matrix. However, by etching lightly with picral plus HCl to outline the carbides followed by etching with 10% aqueous sodium metabisulfite, the structure of the hardened sample is fully revealed.

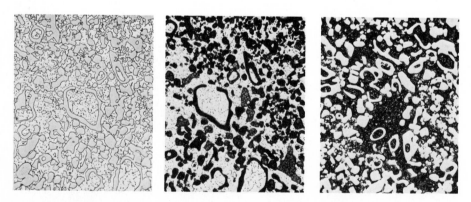

Figure 3-76 Microstructure of annealed Ferro TiC C etched with 4% picral plus HCl (left) and then with Murakami's reagent (center) to darken the carbide. Microstructure of hardened Ferro TiC C etched with 4% picral plus HCl followed by 10% aqueous sodium metabisulfite, 470×.

3-11.3 Polymers

In recent years, considerable attention has been given to the examination of the microstructure of polymers. Examination of thin sections by transmitted light microscopy or electron microscopy is quite common, but some use of reflected light microscopy on bulk samples has occurred. The osmium tetroxide vapor staining method for rubber-reinforced polymers, which is widely used in TEM studies [163], has been used in light microscopy. The OsO_4 vapors degrade, harden, and stain the rubber constituent preferentially. Other staining agents, e.g., ruthenium tetroxide and mercuric trifluoroacetate, have also been applied in TEM studies of polymer blends.

The desire to use optical microscopy for lower-power examination has prompted development of bulk etchants for polymers [163–167] (see App. I). A number of relatively simple etchants have been developed for common polymers. Although some of these solutions are relatively safe to use, others are quite hazardous, and the use of some of these chemicals should be prohibited except in designated locations.

3-11.4 Minerals

Etching and staining procedures have been used by mineralogists as one of several tools for identifying minerals. Etching can be followed by point counting to determine the amount of specific minerals in a sample. Etching and staining have also proved useful for illustration purposes, since the grains of interest are rendered more distinct on a photomicrograph. Etching has also been used to study the structure of minerals.

Two basic approaches to mineral identification using etchants have evolved. The procedure used in the United States, which is described by Davy and Farnham [168] and by Short [169], is based on the reaction of a sample to a standard set of reagents. In this method, a drop of a particular reagent is applied to the sample on the stage of a microscope, and the action of the etchant is viewed optically for 1 min from the time of application. If no reaction occurs during this period, the test is negative. The reaction is termed positive if any of the following effects are observed: effervescence, staining, tarnishing, corrosive attack (darkening, pitting, or structure development), or staining around the edge of the drop. If a reaction begins at the end of the 1-min period, the results are followed. After etching, the surface is washed with a jet of water, and the wet surface is examined to detect any effects obscured by the droplet. This step is necessary with some of the standard etchants in which the color of the drop makes examination difficult. For best results, the drop of etchant should cover only a single grain.

The use of etchants to identify minerals is not simple, and test results from the use of etchants must be viewed with caution. These procedures must be used along with other methods. Because mineral compositions do vary, etch response can also vary. In addition, it has been observed that minerals can produce both positive and negative responses to a given etchant. The method is most useful with coarse-grained minerals, since the droplet cannot be confined to a single grain in fine-grained specimens. The etch test method does not appear to be useful with some types of minerals, e.g., oxide and silicate ores. Thus, for positive identification, etch test results must be combined with other optical and physical tests.

The second etch test approach, which is based on the work of Van der Veen [170], Scheiderhöhn [171], and Ramdohr [172], uses a large number of reagents. Those reagents that give highly specific reactions are employed for identification. However, in this procedure the main purpose of the etch is to reveal the textural details, e.g., twinning, zonal growth, and deformation textures. These features are best revealed by etching in a manner similar to metallographic etching. The cited references should be consulted for additional detail. Sasaki et al. have published etching response procedures for identifying minerals in blast-furnace and basic-oxygen-furnace slags [173].

3-12 SUMMARY

Numerous methods are available for developing the microstructure of materials. While polarized light is highly useful for revealing the microstructure of anisotropic metals, such as beryllium, uranium, and zirconium, most metals and alloys must be treated with an appropriate etching procedure to reveal their microstructure. Chemical etchants are most popular because of their simplicity. However, other procedures, e.g., heat tinting, tint etching, vapor deposition, anodizing, and electrolytic and potentiostatic etching, often produce superior results, particularly if selective phase discrimination is desired.

Several examples in this chapter have demonstrated that some of the common chemical etchants are sensitive to orientation and do not fully delineate all the grain or phase boundaries. It has also been shown that tint etchants can reveal all grains by producing vividly colored contrasts of grains, which are frequently augmented by etching of grain boundaries. These tint etchants often produce striking color contrasts that are both aesthetically pleasing and technically useful. Tint etchants can also be quite selective in their attack or coloration and are quite useful for phase discrimination. Use of tint etchants does require a very high-quality polish for best results.

The Pepperhoff vapor-deposition method has been shown to be a simple, highly versatile procedure which is applicable to any material. For best contrast development, a substance with the proper index of refraction must be chosen for deposition. This becomes more critical as the reflectivity of the matrix increases. With minor experimentation, the optimum contrast condition can be obtained with excellent reproducibility. This technique should be used to a much greater extent.

Electrolytic etching techniques offer controlled etching for obtaining many desired conditions, e.g., grain-boundary development or selective phase delineation. In general, the electrolytes are simple in composition, relatively safe, and easy to use. Further control is possible through the use of a potentiostat, which is used to maintain a constant fixed potential during etching. Potentiostatic etching has had limited application to date but does provide the ultimate in etching control and selectivity and should be further exploited.

Other procedures, such as heat tinting, anodizing, gas contrasting, or vacuum cathodic etching, are highly useful in certain situations. Heat tinting requires only a device to heat the sample to the desired temperature. Best control is achieved using a laboratory furnace. Although heat tinting has frequently been criticized as a difficult technique to control and reproduce, superb results can be obtained, and reproducibility can be good once some experience has been obtained with a given material. Since the oxidation rate of phases varies according to composition and crystal orientation, valuable information, plus vivid coloration, can be obtained. Thermal etching, a variation of heat tinting, produces excellent results on ceramic materials and on some metals. Gas contrasting provides an additional dimension to heat tinting and has been found to be useful for many materials. Anodizing produces excellent grain contrasting and has been applied to several metals, aluminum being the most common. Vacuum cathodic etching is particularly well suited for materials that are difficult to etch chemically and for composite materials in which no one etch or combinations of etchants can reveal the structure of the different materials present. As discussed in this chapter, each method for revealing the structure has certain advantages and disadvantages which must be considered in selecting the most appropriate method.

It must be emphasized that the use of these techniques is both an art and a science, with both aspects blended in the proper proportions for optimum results. Neither aspect can be ignored. Specimen preparation must be carefully performed, otherwise etching will not disclose the true structure, regardless of the technique employed. Many of these techniques require a high-quality polish for good results, and etch response can be altered substantially by the quality of the surface preparation. A properly prepared specimen can be a true creative work of art besides conveying the desired technical information.

REFERENCES

1. Kehl, G. L., and M. Metlay: "The Mechanism of Metallographic Etching," *J. Electrochem. Soc.,* vol. 101, March 1954, pp. 124–127. (See also U.S. Atomic Energy Commission Publ. nos. NYO-830, NYO-831, NYO-832, and NYO-3011.)
2. Lacombe, P.: "Polishing and Etching Methods and Their Applications to Optical Metallography," Iron Steel Inst., London, Spec. Rep. 80, 1964, pp. 50–120.
3. Schatt, W., and H. Worch: "The Development of Metallographic Structures by Solutions," *Neue Huette,* vol. 14, 1969, pp. 685–690.
4. Bloor, D. W.: "Etching with Special Reference to Nickel-Chromium-Cobalt Alloys," *Metallurgia,* vol. 66, no. 395, 1962, pp. 139–142.
5. Bloor, D. W.: "Electrochemical Principles of Etching," *Met. Aust.,* vol. 4, 1972, pp. 279–282.
6. Nelson, J. A.: "The Use of Wetting Agents in Metallographic Etchants," *Prakt. Metallogr.,* vol. 4, 1967, pp. 192–198.

7. Dix, E. H.: "Acceleration of the Rate of Corrosion by High Constant Stresses," *Trans. Am. Inst. Min. Metall. Eng.,* vol. 137, 1940, pp. 11–40.

8. Budd, M. K., and F. F. Booth: "Techniques for Measuring the Solution Potentials of Small Areas of a Metal Surface," *Metallurgia,* vol. 66, no. 397, 1962, pp. 245–252.

9. American Society for Testing and Materials, Standard E407, "Standard Methods for Microetching Metals and Alloys."

10. Anderson, R. L.: "Revealing Microstructures in Metals," Westinghouse Res. Lab. Sci. Paper 425-COOO-P2, Dec. 22, 1961.

11. Smithells, C. J.: "Metallography," *Metals Reference Book,* vol. 1, 4th ed., Plenum Press, Plenum Publishing Corporation, New York, 1967, pp. 315–370.

12. Richardson, J. H.: *Optical Microscopy for the Materials Sciences,* Marcel Dekker, Inc., New York, 1971.

13. Beckert, M., and H. Klemm: *Handbook of Metallographic Etching Methods,* Veb Deutscher Verlag für Grundstoff., Leipzig, 1962.

14. Petzow, G.: *Metallographic Etching,* American Society for Metals, Metals Park, Ohio, 1978.

15. Gifkins, R. C.: "EDTA as an Aid to Metallography," *J. Aust. Inst. Met.,* vol. 21, no. 4, 1976, pp. 175–177.

16. Beraha, E., and B. Shpigler: *Color Metallography,* American Society for Metals, Metals Park, Ohio, 1977.

17. Kilpatrick, J. R., A. O. Benscoter, and A. R. Marder: "Tint Etching Improves Resolution and Contrast of Microstructures," *Met. Prog.,* vol. 100, December 1971, pp. 79–81.

18. Gahm, H., F. Jeglitsch, and E. M. Hörl: "Investigations of the Structure of Chemically Deposited Films Produced by Precipitation Etching," *Prakt. Metallogr.,* vol. 19, 1982, pp. 369–390.

19. Beraha, E.: "Staining Metallographic Reagents for Cast Iron," *Microstructures,* vol. 2, 1971, pp. 23–24, 34.

20. Jacquet, P. A.: "Improvements and New Applications of Non-Destructive Metallography," *Rev. Mét.,* vol. 55, 1958, pp. 531–554.

21. Greene, N. D., P. S. Rudaw, and L. Lee: "Principles of Metallographic Etching," *Corros. Sci.,* vol. 6, 1966, pp. 371–379.

22. Mott, B. W., and H. R. Haines: "The Application of Polarized Light to the Examination of Various Anisotropic Metals and Intermetallic Phases," *J. Inst. Met.,* vol. 80, 1951–1952, pp. 629–636.

23. Mott, B. W., and H. R. Haines: "Examination of Metals under Polarized Light. II. Applications," *Research,* vol. 4, 1951, pp. 63–73.

24. Woodard, D. H.: "Stages in the Deformation of Monel Metal as Shown by Polarized Light," *Trans. Am. Inst. Min. Metall. Eng.,* vol. 185, 1949, pp. 722–726.

25. Perryman, E. C. W., and J. M. Lack: "Examination of Metals by Polarized Light," *Nature,* vol. 167, no. 4247, 1951, p. 479.

26. Gray, R. J., R. S. Crouse, and B. C. Leslie: "Decorative Etching," *Metallographic Specimen Preparation,* Plenum Press, Plenum Publishing Corporation, New York, 1974, pp. 179–206.

27. "Heat Tinting Cast Iron for Microscopic Examination," *Mater. Methods,* vol. 23, 1946, p. 1053 (see also *Met. Treat. Methods,* vol. 12, Winter 1945–1946, p. 236).

28. Emmanuel, G. N.: "Metallographic Identification of Sigma Phase in 25-20 Austenitic Alloy," *Met. Prog.,* vol. 52, July 1947, pp. 78–79 (see also "Sigma Phase and Other Effects of Prolonged Heating at Elevated Temperatures on 25 Per Cent Chromium-20 Per Cent Nickel Steel" *Am. Soc. Test. Mater., Spec. Tech. Publ. 110,* 1951, pp. 82–99).

29. Weeton, J. W., and R. A. Signorelli: "Effect of Heat Treatment upon Microstructures, Microconstituents, and Hardness of a Wrought Cobalt Base Alloy," *Trans. Am. Soc. Met.,* vol. 47, 1955, pp. 815–852.

30. Franssen, H.: "Structure of Cemented Carbide Composites," *Arch. Eisenhuettenwes,* vol. 19, 1948, pp. 79–84 (HB no. 2175).

31. Chaporova, I. N.: "Preparation of Metallographic Sections and Development of Microstructure of Cemented Carbides," *Zavod. Lab.,* vol. 15, 1949, pp. 799–805 (HB no. 3061).

32. Bleecker, W. H.: "A Metallographic Technique for Cemented Carbides," *Iron Age,* vol. 165, May 25, 1950, pp. 71–74.
33. Powers, J. H., and W. J. Loach: "Color Shows up the Unknown in Metallography," *Steel,* vol. 133, 1953, pp. 93–96.
34. Bartz, G.: "Contrasting of Microscopic Objects in a Gas-Ion-Reaction Chamber," *Prakt. Metallogr.,* vol. 10, 1973, pp. 311–323.
35. Exner, H. E., and J. Roth: "Metallographic Contrasting by Reactively Sputtered Interference Layers," *Prakt. Metallogr.,* vol. 17, 1980, pp. 365–389.
36. Kohlhaas, E., and A. Fischer: "Increase of Contrast in the Interference-Layer Technique by the Use of a Continuous Band Interference Filter," *Prakt. Metallogr.,* vol. 6, 1969, pp. 339–345.
37. Bühler, H. E., and D. Kossel: "Guidelines for the Development and Application of Interference Film Metallography," *Prakt. Metallogr.,* vol. 18, 1981, pp. 385–391.
38. Zogg, H., S. Weber, and H. Warlimont: "Optical Contrast Enhancement for Al-Alloys by Vacuum Deposited ZnTe Interference Layers," *Prakt. Metallogr.,* vol. 14, 1977, pp. 553–570.
39. Bühler, H. E., and H. P. Hougardy: *Atlas of Interference Layer Metallography,* Deutsche Gesellschaft für Metallkunde, Oberursel, W. Germany, 1980.
40. Bowman M. J., and A. D. Booth: "A Review of Methods for the Examination of Magnetic Domain Structure," *Metallography,* vol. 4, 1971, pp. 103–131.
41. Shilling, J. W., and G. L. Houze: "Magnetic Properties and Domain Structure in Grain-Oriented 3% Si-Fe," *IEEE Trans. Magn.,* vol. MAG-10, no. 2, 1974, pp. 195–223.
42. Craig, D. J., and P. M. Griffiths: "New Techniques for the Study of Bitter Figures," *Br. J. Appl. Phys.,* vol. 9, 1958, pp. 279–282, 276–277.
43. Tanasoiu, C., D. Feldmann, and I. Schulz: "A Dry Bitter Technique for High Resolution Studies of Magnetic Domains by Optical Microscopy," *Prakt. Metallogr.,* vol. 10, 1978, pp. 210–219.
44. Scortecci, A., and E. Stagno: "New Metallographic Method for Revealing Magnetic Patterns in Ferrite," *Mem. Sci. Rev. Metall.,* vol. 62, 1965, pp. 741–746 (Br. Iron Steel Inst. no. 5569).
45. McCutcheon, D. M., and W. Pahl: "Cathodic Vacuum Etching of Metals," *Met. Prog.,* vol. 56, 1949, pp. 674–679.
46. Padden, T. R., and F. M. Cain: "Cathodic Vacuum Etching," *Met. Prog.,* vol. 66, July 1954, pp. 108–112, 162, 164.
47. Pohl, M., and W. G. Burchard: "Ion Etching in Metallography," *Scanning,* vol. 3, no. 4, 1980, pp. 251–261.
48. Johnston, W. G.: "Dislocation Etch Pits in Non-Metallic Crystals," *Progress in Ceramic Science,* vol. 2, Pergamon Press, Oxford, 1962, pp. 1–75.
49. Gatos, H. C., and M. C. Lavine: "Chemical Behavior of Semiconductors: Etching Characteristics," M.I.T. Lincoln Lab., Tech. Rep. no. 293, Jan. 2, 1963.
50. Amelinckx, S.: *The Direct Observation of Dislocations,* Academic Press, Inc., New York, 1964, pp. 15–53 [*Solid State Phys.,* vol. 6 (suppl.)].
51. Robinson, W. H.: "Dislocation Etch Pit Techniques," *Techniques for the Direct Observation of Structure and Imperfections, Techniques in Metal Research,* vol. II, pt. 1, Interscience Publishers, a division of John Wiley & Sons, Inc., New York, 1968, pp. 291–340.
52. Streicher, M. A.: "Screening Stainless Steels from the 240-hr. Nitric Acid Test by Electrolytic Etching in Oxalic Acid," *Am. Soc. Test. Mater. Bull.,* no. 188, 1953, pp. 35–38; no. 193, 1953, pp. 58–59.
53. Streicher, M. A.: "Results of Cooperative Testing Program for the Evaluation of the Oxalic Acid Etching Test," *Am. Soc. Test. Mater. Bull.,* January 1954, pp. 63–67.
54. Bianchi, G., et al.: "Chemical Etching and Pitting of Stainless Steel," *Corros. Sc.,* vol. 10, January 1970, pp. 19–27.
55. Lacombe, P., and L. Beaujaul: "Metallographic Study of Cold-Working and Recrystallization of Pure Aluminum," *Rev. Mét.,* vol. 44, 1947, pp. 71–76.
56. Hone, A., and E. C. Pearson: "Grain Orientation in Aluminum Revealed by Anodic Film," *Met. Prog.,* vol. 53, 1948, pp. 363–366.
57. Hone, A., and E. C. Pearson: "A New Anodic-Film Method for Studying Orientation in Aluminum," *Met. Prog.,* vol. 58, 1950, pp. 713–715.

58. Barker, L. J.: "Revealing the Grain Structure of Common Aluminum Alloy Metallographic Specimens," *Trans. Am. Soc. Met.,* vol. 42, 1950, pp. 347–356.
59. Cole, H. G., and W. J. D. Brooks: "A Simple Anodizing Process for Revealing the Grain Structure of Aluminum Alloys," *Metallurgia,* vol. 50, no. 298, 1954, pp. 97–100.
60. Graff, W. R., and D. C. Sargent: "A New Grain-Broundary Etchant for Aluminum Alloys," *Metallography,* vol. 14, no. 1, 1981, pp. 69–72.
61. Klemm, H.: "Revealing of Grain Boundaries in Eutectic Aluminum Solid Solutions, Particularly in Alloys Containing Silicon," *Prakt. Metallogr.,* vol. 5, 1968, pp. 662–668.
62. Sperry, P. R., and M. H. Bankard: "Metallographic Techniques for Aluminum Alloys," *ASM Metals Handbook,* vol. 8, 8th ed., 1973, pp. 120–129 (see also: "Metallography of Aluminum and Aluminum Alloys," *Met. Prog.,* vol. 110, December 1976, pp. 61–63).
63. Beraha, E.: "Two New Metallographic Reagents," *Met. Prog.,* vol. 90, September 1966, pp. 135–136, 138, 140.
64. Beraha, E.: "Metallographic Reagents Based on Molybdate Solutions," *Prakt. Metallogr.,* vol. 11, 1974, pp. 271–275.
65. Gerstlauer, W., and M. Franchini: "Colour Etching of Al-Si-Cu-Ni Casting Alloys," *Prakt. Metallogr.,* vol. 6, 1969, pp. 623–626.
66. Mondolfo, L. F.: *Metallography of Aluminum Alloys,* John Wiley & Sons, Inc., New York, 1943.
67. Phragmén, G.: "On the Phases Occurring in Alloys of Aluminum with Copper, Magnesium, Manganese, Iron, and Silicon," *J. Inst. Met.,* vol. 77, 1950, pp. 489–552.
68. Kowatschewa, R., et al.: "Metallographic Determination of Intermetallic Compounds in Aluminum Alloys," *Prakt. Metallogr.,* vol. 10, 1973, pp. 131–143.
69. Price, C. W., and J. L. McCall: "A Review of Metallographic Preparation Procedures for Beryllium and Beryllium Alloys," DMIC Memo. no. 237, Battelle Memorial Institute, Defense Metal Information Center, Columbus, Ohio, June 1, 1968.
70. Slepian, R. M., and G. A. Blann: "Improved Metallographic Preparation of Lead and Lead Alloys," *Metallography,* vol. 12, no. 3, 1979, pp. 195–214.
71. Anderson, E. A.: "Physical Metallurgy of Zinc," *Zinc,* Reinhold Publ. Corporation, New York, 1959, pp. 400–405.
72. Gennone, R. J., and E. C. Kersey: "A New Etchant for Zinc Alloys," *Trans. Am. Inst. Min. Metall. Eng.,* vol. 215, 1959, pp. 307–308.
73. Wolff, U. E.: "Anodic Oxidation to Reveal Inhomogeneity in Refractory Alloys," *Trans. Am. Soc. Met.,* vol. 55, 1962, pp. 363–365.
74. Buchheit, R. D., C. H. Brady, and G. A. Wheeler: "Procedures for the Metallographic Preparation of Beryllium, Titanium, and the Refractory Metals," DMIC Memo. no. 37, Battelle Memorial Institute, Defense Metal Information Center, Columbus, Ohio, Oct. 26, 1959.
75. Hasson, R.: "Metallography of Molybdenum in Color," *Microscope,* vol. 16, 1968, pp. 329–334.
76. Hasson, R.: "An Improved Orientation-Dependent Chemical Anodizing Color Reagent for Molybdenum," *Microscope,* vol. 22, 1974, pp. 317–322.
77. Lehwald, S., W. Erley, and H. Wagner: "An Orientation-Sensitive Colour-Etching Technique for Polycrystalline Tungsten," *Prakt. Metallogr.,* vol. 9, 1972, pp. 510–515.
78. Morral, F. R.: "Metallography of Cobalt-Base and Cobalt-Containing Alloys," *Prakt. Metallogr.,* vol. 10, 1973, pp. 398–413.
79. Young, R. S.: "Metallographic Differentiation of Cobalt Metal, Oxide and Sulphide," *Metallurgia,* vol. 59, April 1959, p. 210.
80. Beraha, E.: "Two New Metallographic Reagents for Stainless Steel and Heat-Resisting Alloys," *J. Iron Steel Inst.,* vol. 204, 1966, pp. 248–251.
81. Kennon, N. F., D. P. Dunne, and L. A. Middleton: "Metallographic Method for Manganese-Copper Alloys," *Metallography,* vol. 14, 1981, pp. 329–334.
82. Greene, N. D., and G. A. Teterin: "Development of Brass Etchants by Electrochemical Techniques," *Corros. Sci.,* vol. 12, 1972, pp. 57–63.
83. Beraha, E.: "Staining Metallographic Reagent for Copper-Base Alloys," *Prakt. Metallogr.,* vol. 7, 1970, pp. 131–134.

84. Slepian, R. M., and J. P. Prohaska: "An Improved Etchant for Copper and Copper Alloys," *Metallography,* vol. 9, 1976, pp. 51–61.
85. Klemm, H.: "Uses of Sodium Thiosulphate (Klemm's Reagent) as an Etchant," *Prakt. Metallogr.,* vol. 5, 1968, pp. 163–177.
86. Coons, W. C., and D. J. Blickwede: "A New Metallographic Etchant for Aluminum Bronze and Copper-Beryllium Alloys," *Trans. Am. Soc. Met.,* vol. 35, 1945, pp. 284–297.
87. Samuels, L. E.: "The Metallographic Detection of Deformation in Copper and Alpha-Brasses," *J. Inst. Met.,* vol. 83, 1954–1955, pp. 359–368.
88. Vander Voort, G. F.: "Etching Techniques for Image Analysis," *Microstructural Science,* vol. 9, Elsevier Publishing Company, New York, 1981, pp. 137–154.
89. Hawkins, D. N.: An Etchant for Revealing the Substructure in Low-Carbon Steels," *Metallography,* vol. 14, 1981, pp. 61–68.
90. Le Pera, F. S.: "Improved Etching Technique for the Determination of Percent Martensite in High-Strength Dual-Phase Steels," *Metallography,* vol. 12, 1979, pp. 263–268.
91. Marder, A. R.: "Factors Affecting the Ductility of Dual-Phase Alloys," *Formable HSLA and Dual-Phase Steels,* The Metallurgical Society/American Institute of Mining, Metallurgical and Petroleum Engineers, New York, 1979, pp. 87–98.
92. Lawson, R. D., D. K. Matlock, and G. Krauss: "An Etching Technique for Microalloyed Dual-Phase Steels," *Metallography,* vol. 13, 1980, pp. 71–87.
93. Marder, A. R., and A. O. Benscoter: "Quantitative Microanalysis of Dual-Phase Steels," *Metallography,* vol. 15, 1982, pp. 73–85.
94. Cohen, J. B., A. Hurlich, and M. Jacobson: "A Metallographic Etchant to Reveal Temper Brittleness in Steel," *Trans. Am. Soc. Met.,* vol. 39, 1947, pp. 109–138.
95. McLean, D., and L. Northcott: "Micro-Examination and Electrode-Potential Measurements of Temper-Brittle Steels," *J. Iron Steel Inst.,* vol. 158, 1948, pp. 169–177.
96. Rucker, J. P.: "Improved Metallographic Technique for Revealing Temper Brittleness Network in Ordnance Steels," NPG Rep. no. 1555, U.S. Naval Proving Ground, Dahlgren, Va., Aug. 28, 1957.
97. Preece, A., and R. D. Carter: "Temper-Brittleness in High-Purity Iron-Base Alloys," *J. Iron Steel Inst.,* vol. 173, 1953, pp. 387–398.
98. Ücisik, A. H., H. C. Feng, and C. J. McMahon: "The Influence of Intercritical Heat Treatment on the Temper Embrittlement of a P-Doped Ni-Cr Steel," *Metall. Trans.,* vol. 9A, 1978, pp. 321–329.
99. Cianelli, A. K., et al.: "Temper Embrittlement of a Ni-Cr Steel by Sn," *Metall. Trans.,* vol. 8A, 1977, pp. 1059–1061.
100. Ücisik, A. H., C. J. McMahon, and H. C. Feng: "The Influence of Intercritical Heat Treatment on the Temper Embrittlement Susceptibility of an Sb-Doped Ni-Cr Steel," *Metall. Trans.,* vol. 9A, 1978, pp. 604–606.
101. Vilella, J. R.: *Metallographic Technique for Steel,* American Society for Metals, Cleveland, Ohio, 1938.
102. Miller, O. O., and M. J. Day: "Ferric Chloride Etchant for Austenite Grain Size of Low-Carbon Steel," *Met. Prog.,* vol. 56, 1949, pp. 692–695.
103. Bechet, S., and L. Beaujard: "New Reagent for the Micrographical Demonstration of the Austenite Grain of Hardened or Hardened-Tempered Steels," *Rev. Mét.,* vol. 52, 1955, pp. 830–836.
104. Skuin, K.: "On the Determination of the Austenite Grain Size in Heat Treatable Steels," *Neue Huette,* vol. 7, no. 11, 1962, pp. 698–699 (HB no. 5831).
105. Dreyer, G. A., D. E. Austin, and W. D. Smith: "New Etchant Brings Out Grain Boundaries in Martensitic Steels," *Met. Prog.,* vol. 86, July 1964, pp. 116–117.
106. Grange, R. A.: "The Rapid Heat Treatment of Steel," *Metall. Trans.,* vol. 2, 1971, pp. 65–78.
107. Campbell, R. F., et al.: "Constitution of Fe-C-Mo Alloys Containing 0.05–1.3 pct C and 0.03–6.0 pct Mo," *Trans. Am. Inst. Min. Metall. Eng.,* vol. 218, 1960, pp. 723–732.
108. Nishizawa, T.: "Thermodynamic Study of the Fe-Mo-C System at 1000C," *Scand. J. Metall.,* vol. 1, 1972, pp. 41–48.

109. Maratray, F., and R. Usseglio-Nanot: *Factors Affecting the Structure of Chromium and Chromium-Molybdenum White Irons,* Climax Molybdenum SA, Paris, p. 27.

110. Woodyatt, L. R.: "A Study of the Iron-Chromium-Molybdenum-1% Carbon System at 870C (1600F)," Ph.D. thesis, Lehigh University, Bethlehem, Pa., 1975 (see also L. R. Woodyatt and G. Krauss: "Phase Equilibria in the Iron-Molybdenum-1% Carbon System between 1143 and 1253K," *Metall. Trans.,* vol. 10A, 1979, pp. 1893–1900).

111. Fine, L.: "A New Etching Reagent for the Detection of Oxygen Segregation in Steel," *Met. Prog.,* vol. 49, January 1946, pp. 108–112.

112. Hall, A. M.: "Metallographic Etchant to Distinguish Oxidation in Steel," *Met. Prog.,* vol. 50, July 1946, pp. 92–96.

113. Künkele, M.: "A New Etching Reagent for Determining Sulfide Inclusions in Technical Iron," *Werkst. Eisenhuetten. Ber.,* no. 75, 1925.

114. Wallner, J.: "Double Etching for the Detection of Sulfidic Inclusions in Technical Iron Alloys," *Arch. Eisenhuettenwes,* vol. 27, February 1956, pp. 101–102.

115. Whiteley, J. H.: "A Method of Identifying Manganese Sulphide Inclusions in Steel," *J. Iron Steel Inst.,* vol. 160, 1948, pp. 365–366.

116. Raghupathy, V. P., and V. Srinivasan: "Determination of Volume Fraction of Sulfide Inclusions in Steels," *Metallography,* vol. 14, 1981, pp. 87–97.

117. Beraha, E.: "Metallographic Reagent for Identification of Sulphide Inclusions," *J. Iron Steel Inst.,* vol. 202, 1964, pp. 696–698.

118. Vergesack, A. V.: "Method of Etching for Identification of Lead in the Microstructure of Free-Cutting Steels Alloyed with Lead," *Jernkontorets Ann.,* vol. 126, 1942, pp. 559–564.

119. Gerds, A. E., and C. W. Melton: "New Etch Spots Leaded Steels," *Iron Age,* vol. 178, August 30, 1956, pp. 86–87.

120. Hussey, R. J., P. E. Beaubien, and D. Caplan: "The Etching of Oxide Scales on Metals," *Metallography,* vol. 6, 1973, pp. 17–25.

121. Hurdus, M. H., and L. Tomlinson: "Etching of Oxide Scales on Chromium Ferritic Steels," *Br. Corros. J.,* vol. 13, no. 4, 1978, pp. 158–162.

122. Edstrom, J. O.: "The Mechanism of Reduction of Iron Oxides," *J. Iron Steel Inst.,* vol. 175, 1953, pp. 289–304.

123. Kegley, T. M.: "Metallographic Etching of Type 308 Stainless Steel Weld Metal," *Metallogr. Rev.,* vol. 1, no. 1, 1972, pp. 23–26.

124. Ellinger, G. A.: "Oxalic Acid as an Electrolytic Etching Reagent for Stainless Steel," *Trans. Am. Soc. Met.,* vol. 24, 1936, pp. 26–45.

125. Arness, W. B.: "The Sodium Cyanide Metallographic Etch Test for Revealing Precipitated Carbides in the 18-8 Type Stainless Steels," *Trans. Am. Soc. Met.,* vol. 24, 1936, pp. 701–720.

126. Gilman, J. J.: "Electrolytic Etching—The Sigma Phase Steels," *Trans. Am. Soc. Met.,* vol. 44, 1952, pp. 566–600.

127. Dulis, E. J., and G. V. Smith: "Identification and Modes of Formation and Re-Solution of Sigma Phase in Austenitic Chromium-Nickel Steels," *Am. Soc. Test. Mater., Spec. Tech. Publ. 110,* 1951, pp. 3–37.

128. Slattery, G. F., and P. O'Riordan: "Microstructural Transformations in Stress Relieved Type 316 Stainless Steel Weld Metal," *Metallography,* vol. 13, 1980, pp. 59–70 (see also: G. F. Slattery et al.: "An Integrated Electron and Optical Metallographic Procedure for the Identification of Precipitate Phases in Type 316 Stainless Steel," *J. Microsc.,* vol. 122, pt. 2, 1981, pp. 109–130).

129. Hattersley, B., and W. Hume-Rothery: "Constitution of Certain Austenitic Steels," *J. Iron Steel Inst.,* vol. 204, 1966, pp. 683–701.

130. Bell, F. C., and D. E. Sonon: "Improved Metallographic Etching Techniques for Stainless Steel and for Stainless Steel to Carbon Steel Weldments," *Metallography,* vol. 9, 1976, pp. 91–107.

131. Stephenson, J. M., and B. M. Patchett: "Grain-Boundary Etches for Austenitic and Ferritic Ni-Cr-Mo Corrosion-Resistent Alloys," *Sheet Met. Ind.,* vol. 56, 1979, pp. 45–50, 57.

132. Gray, R. J., et al.: "A Metallographic Study of Ferrite-Sigma Transformation Using Ferromag-

netic Colloid, Microprobe Analysis, and Color Etching," *Microstructural Science,* vol. 5, Elsevier Publishing Company, New York, 1977, pp. 65–84.

133. Gray, R. J., V. K. Sikka, and R. T. King: "Detecting Transformation of Delta-Ferrite to Sigma-Phase in Stainless Steels by Advanced Metallographic Techniques," *J. Met.,* vol. 30, 1978, pp. 18–26.

134. Hess, J. B., and P. F. George: "The Metallography of Commercial Magnesium Alloys," *Trans. Am. Soc. Met.,* vol. 31, 1943, pp. 423–457.

135. George, P. F.: "Some Special Metallographic Techniques for Magnesium Alloys," *Trans. Am. Soc. Met.,* vol. 38, 1947, pp. 686–707.

136. George, P. F.: "Metallography of Cast Magnesium Alloys," *Trans. Am. Foundrymen's Soc.,* vol. 57, 1949, pp. 133–149.

137. Oberländer, B., and K. P. Lillerud: "Structural Development of Magnesium Alloys," *Prakt. Metallogr.,* vol. 17, 1980, pp. 473–478.

138. Beland, R. A.: "Metallographic Techniques Used with Pure Nickel," *Met. Mater.,* vol. 2, 1968, pp. 54–57.

139. Kotval, P. S.: "The Microstructure of Superalloys," *Metallography,* vol. 1, 1969, pp. 251–285.

140. Kohlhaas, E., and A. Fischer: "The Metallography of Superalloys," *Prakt. Metallogr.,* vol. 8, 1971, pp. 3–25.

141. Lund, C. H., and H. J. Wagner: "Identification of Microconstituents in Superalloys," DMIC Memo. no. 160, Battelle Memorial Institute, Defense Metal Information Center, Columbus, Ohio, November 15, 1962.

142. Forgeng, W. D.: "Metallography of Columbium and Tantalum," *Columbium and Tantalum,* John Wiley & Sons, Inc., New York 1963, pp. 507–534.

143. Eary, R. S., and R. D. Johnston: "A New Feature in the Metallographic Etching of Niobium," *Metallurgia,* vol. 69, no. 411, 1964, pp. 43–49.

144. Crouse, R. S.: "Identification of Carbides, Nitrides, and Oxides of Niobium and Niobium Alloys by Anodic Staining," ORNL-3821, Oak Ridge National Laboratory, Oak Ridge, Tenn., July 1965.

145. Picklesimer, M. L.: "Anodizing as a Metallographic Technique for Zirconium Base Alloys," ORNL-2296, Oak Ridge National Laboratory, Oak Ridge, Tenn., 1957.

146. Picklesimer, M. L.: "Anodizing for Controlled Microstructural Contrast by Color," *Microscope,* vol. 15, 1967, pp. 427–479.

147. Piotrowski, T., and D. J. Accinno: "Metallography of the Precious Metals," *Metallography,* vol. 10, 1977, pp. 243–289.

148. Dickerson, R. F.: "Metallography of Uranium," *Trans. Am. Soc. Met.,* vol. 52, 1960, pp. 748–762.

149. Wyatt, B. S.: "The Effect of Carbon on the δ-Peritectoid Reaction in Uranium-Silicon Alloys," *J. Nucl. Mater.,* vol. 27, 1968, pp. 201–215.

150. Rencken, D. G.: "A New Procedure for Revealing the Microstructure of α-Plutonium," *Metallography,* vol. 1, 1969, pp. 365–372.

151. Koch, C. C., and M. L. Picklesimer: "A Metallographic Technique for Lanthanum and Cerium," *Trans. Am. Inst. Min. Metall. Eng.,* vol. 239, 1967, pp. 759–761.

152. Dobbins, A. G.: "Metallographic Preparation of Holmium," Report Y-1618, Union Carbide Corp., Oak Ridge Y-12 Plant, Oak Ridge, Tenn., May 28, 1968.

153. Ence, E., and H. Margolin: "Phases in Titanium Alloys Identified by Cumulative Etching," *J. Met.,* vol. 6, 1954, pp. 346–348.

154. Ogden, H. R., and F. C. Holden: "Metallography of Titanium Alloys," Titanium Metallurgical Laboratory Rep. no. 103, Battelle Memorial Institute, Defense Metal Information Center, Columbus, Ohio, May 29, 1958.

155. Hiltz, R. H., and R. W. Douglass: "Orientation Sensitivity of Alpha Titanium to Electrostaining," *Trans. Am. Inst. Min. Metall. Eng.,* vol. 215, 1959, pp. 286–289.

156. Grosso, J., and D. J. Nagel: "Anodizing as a Technique for Studying Diffusion in the TiCb System," *Trans. Am. Inst. Min. Metall. Eng.,* vol. 236, 1966, pp. 1377–1379.

157. Horn, E.: "Investigations of the Etching Behavior of Titanium Alloys," *Prakt. Metallogr.*, vol. 9, 1972, pp. 270–280.
158. Olsen, R. H., and W. D. Smith: "Color Metallography for Texture Analysis of Titanium," *Metallography*, vol. 4, 1971, pp. 515–520.
159. Robinson, A. H.: "Metallography of Zirconium and Zirconium Alloys," *Met. Prog.*, vol. 56, 1949, pp. 667–669.
160. Roth, H. P.: "Metallography of Zirconium," *The Metallurgy of Zirconium*, McGraw-Hill Book Company, New York, 1955, pp. 709–732.
161. Houle, M. C., and R. L. Coble: "Ceramographic Techniques: 1. Single Phase, Polycrystalline, Hard Metals," *Ceram. Bull.*, vol. 41, no. 6, 1962, pp. 378–381.
162. Politis, C., and S. Ohtani: "Methods of Chemical Etching for Ceramic Materials," *Prakt. Metallogr.*, vol. 4, 1967, pp. 401–416.
163. Kato, K.: "Morphological Aspects of ABS Plastics," *Japan Plast.*, vol. 2, 1968, pp. 6–17.
164. Armond, V. J., and J. R. Atkinson: "The Effect of Chromic Acid on Polypropylene," *J. Mater. Sci.*, vol. 3, 1968, pp. 332–335 (see also: "Chronic Acid as an Etchant for Bulk Polypropylene and Its Use to Study (*i*) Nitric Acid Attack on Polypropyline (*ii*) Cracks in Polypropylene Induced by Tensile Stress," *J. Mater. Sci.*, vol. 4, 1969, pp. 509–517).
165. Bucknall, C. B., I. C. Drinkwater, and W. E. Keast: "An Etch Method for Microscopy of Rubber-Toughened Plastics," *Polymer*, vol. 13, 1972, pp. 115–118.
166. Kowatschewa, R., and S. Semerdjiev: "Techniques for Revealing the Supermolecular Structure of Polyethylene and Its Observation under the Optical Microscope," *Prakt. Metallogr.*, vol. 9, 1972, pp. 147–160.
167. Linke, U., and W. U. Kopp: "Preparation of Polished Specimens and Thin Sections of Plastics," *Prakt. Metallogr.*, vol. 17, 1980, pp. 479–488.
168. Davy, W. M., and C. M. Farnham: *Microscopic Examination of the Ore Minerals*, McGraw-Hill Book Company, New York, 1920.
169. Short, M. N.: *Microscopic Determination of the Ore Minerals*, U.S. Geological Survey Bull. no. 914, 1940.
170. Van der Veen, R. W.: *Mineragraphy and Ore-Deposition*, G. Naeff, The Hague, 1925.
171. Schneiderhöhn, H.: *Practical Course in Ore Microscopy*, E. Schwerzerbart'sche Verlagsbuch-handlung, Stuttgart, 1952.
172. Ramdohr, P.: *The Ore Minerals and Their Intergrowths*, 3d ed., Akademie-Verlag GmbH, Berlin, 1960 (English translation of 3d ed. published by Pergamon Press, Oxford, 1969).
173. Sasaki, M., et al.: "Method of Identifying Minerals in Blast-Furnace and BOF Slags by Optical Microscope," *Nippon Steel Tech. Rep.* no. 17, June 1981, pp. 1–8.

FOUR

LIGHT MICROSCOPY

4-1 INTRODUCTION

Although numerous sophisticated electron metallographic tools are now available to an investigator, the light microscope remains the single most important device. While the transmission electron microscope (TEM) and the scanning electron microscope (SEM) overcome two of the most important limitations of the light microscope, namely resolution and depth of field, they have not reduced the importance of the light microscope. Indeed, the limitations of the TEM and the SEM are the strong points of the light microscope and vice versa, so that the light and electron microscopy techniques are complementary rather than competitive.

In any study of materials, the wisest procedure is to start on the macroscopic level before proceeding to microscopic and submicroscopic detail. Simple visual examination, perhaps aided by special print techniques and macroetching, should be the prelude to low-power, medium-power, and finally, high-power observation. In this way, the normal and abnormal characteristics can be discerned and held in proper perspective.

In this chapter we discuss the application of light microscopy, typically at magnifications between about 50 and 2000X, to the study of materials. Although a thorough understanding of optics is not usually necessary for the bulk of metallographic observations, a basic knowledge is required in more fundamental studies or in working with unusual or difficult materials. Although the bulk of metallographic observation is conducted using incident bright-field illumination, application of other illumination techniques is imperative with materials exhibiting low contrast or with optically anisotropic materials, especially those that are difficult to etch.

Light microscopy has numerous applications. The most important application is the determination of the structural phases present and the constitution of the bulk of the metal. (The constitution of the metal is the whole physical makeup of the material, which consists of the inherited qualities of the phases as modified by the processing and environment and the mode and manner of the phase distribution, compositions, and characteristics.) These observations are of practical importance because the structure and constitution have a strong influence on the behavior of the material. In these studies, the surface of a properly prepared material is examined either without etching or after etching, or in both conditions.

In order to obtain optimum resolution of detail, the sample surface being examined must have adequate contrast. There are numerous microscopic techniques [1–7] that can be used to observe the microstructure of materials, and these techniques produce images that have the resolution and contrast needed for observing microscopic structural details. The types of surfaces examined by these techniques include the following:

- As-polished surfaces (inclusions and precipitates)
- As-polished surfaces of optically anisotropic metals
- Relief-polished, unetched surfaces
- Etched surfaces

The technique used depends on the nature of the problem, the expertise of the investigator, and the available equipment. Microscopy methods for enhancing contrast include the following

- Dark-field illumination
- Polarized light
- Phase contrast
- Interference methods
- Filters

4-2 BASIC CONCEPTS IN LIGHT OPTICAL THEORY

Light has characteristics that are sometimes best understood by considering light as a stream of particles, while other characteristics are best understood by considering light to be a wave. This dual nature of light causes some problems to the beginning student, but the concepts are easily applied to optical systems. In understanding lens aberrations it is convenient to consider light as a stream of particles; on the other hand, the wave nature of light is the basis for understanding polarization, interference, and diffraction effects. The latter approach is the basis of geometric optical theory, which is based on several fundamental assumptions and laws:

1. Light travels in a straight line.
2. Portions of light beams can be treated as individual rays.

3. Law of reflection.
4. Law of refraction.

It is convenient to describe light as a wave motion with a certain amplitude (brightness) and wavelength (color). Other aspects of the wave motion of reflected light are not so obvious, such as the phase of the wave and its plane of vibration or degree of polarization. Figure 4-1 from Gifkins [2] shows the significance of these four characteristics of light. The amplitude, or brightness, is the peak height above the mean level (see Fig. 4-1a). The intensity of light increases as the square of the amplitude. Wavelength is a familiar term used in the radio industry and is inversely related to the frequency. The wavelength is the distance between adjacent peaks measured at similar locations on the curve (see Fig. 4-1b). As the frequency increases, the wavelength decreases. The wavelengths of light are much shorter than wavelengths used in the communications industry. Phase refers to the propagation of a light wave in space (see Fig. 4-1c). If we were to somehow observe a wave moving past a particular point, we would see the wave moving up and down as a result of the wave motion. In polarization, the orientation of the vibrating wave with respect to the axis of propagation is studied (see Fig. 4-1d).

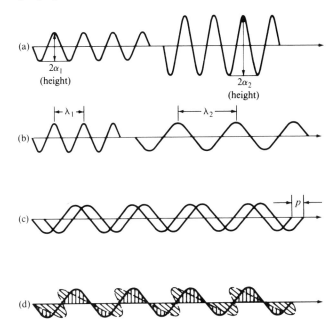

Figure 4-1 Schematic illustrating characteristics of light waves. (a) the amplitude is a measure of light intensity; as the amplitude (α_1, or α_2) increases, brightness increases. (b) color depends on wavelength; the shortest visible wavelength (λ_1) is blue and the longest (λ_2) is red. (c) phase is the displacement p along the time axis. (d) polarization is defined by the plane of the light vibrations. Phase and polarization are not detected by the human eye. *(From Gifkins, Ref. 2, courtesy of Elsevier Science Publishing Co., Inc.)*

Table 4-1 Spectral ranges in microscopy

Radiation	Wavelength, nm
Electrons (electron microscopy)	0.005†
X-rays	0.01–15
Ultraviolet	15–400
Visible spectrum (blue to green to yellow to red)	400–700
Infrared	700–860

† Approximate, varies with accelerating potential.
Source: From Phillips, Ref. 1.

An ideal light source is one which emits light of only one wavelength, i.e., monochromatic radiation. In actual practice, except for the laser, it is impossible to obtain completely pure monochromatic radiation, and, at best, a narrow band of radiation is generated. By contrast, a white light source is one that emits light of many wavelengths, i.e., continuous emission. The light-emitting characteristics of a given light source are best described by developing a plot of light intensity versus wavelength.

Most light microscopy techniques use light in the visible spectrum, while only limited studies have been devoted to developing ultraviolet or infrared microscopy techniques. Although the eye is sensitive to only the visible spectrum, photographic film records radiation outside of this range. Phillips has summarized the types of radiation used in microscopy, and Table 4-1 lists the resulting wavelengths [1].

Light sources have been categorized as being coherent or incoherent. A coherent white light source is one with a constant phase difference between the emitted waves. A laser is a coherent light source. A point white light source can be considered to be coherent; however, it emits both coherent and incoherent waves and is really semicoherent.

The law of refraction, which was developed by Snell, states that a refracted ray will lie in the same plane as the incident ray and the normal to the plane of incidence and is described by the following equation:

$$n \sin \phi = n' \sin \phi' \qquad (4\text{-}1)$$

where ϕ = the angle of incidence in the medium with refractive index n
ϕ' = the angle of refraction in the medium with refractive index n'

Figure 4-2 illustrates both Snell's law of refraction and the law of reflection. A portion of the incident ray is also reflected, and the angle of reflection is equal to the angle of incidence (law of reflection).

4-3 THE LIGHT MICROSCOPE

The light microscope has been designed by combining various lenses to resolve and reveal the fine details of the microstructure of the sample being examined.

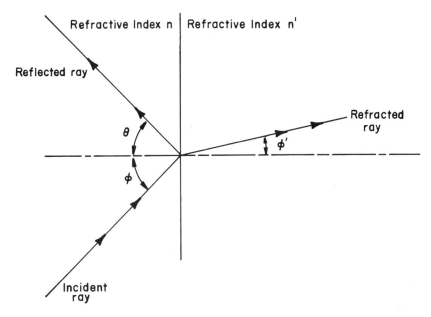

Figure 4-2 Schematic illustrating the laws of refraction and reflection.

The metallurgical microscope illuminates the specimen with incident (reflected) light. Microscopes are also designed for illumination with transmitted light. Since these are usually used in biological or mineralogical studies and rarely with metallurgical samples, only incident light illumination (reflected light microscopy) is discussed here.

There are two basic types of metallurgical microscopes: the upright microscope and the inverted (Le Chatelier) microscope, where the terms upright and inverted refer to the orientation of the face of the polished specimen that is being examined. In each case, the specimen surface must be made parallel to the stage of the microscope to avoid continual refocusing of the image as the stage is moved. Whether upright or inverted, microscopes of each type are available in various price ranges and complexity. Figure 4-3 shows an upright bench microscope, and Fig. 4-4 shows an inverted metallograph. Both are used with reflected light. The various components of these microscopes are described in the sections that follow.

4-3.1 Illumination

Various light sources are available to the metallographer. The most common light sources are described in the sections that follow.

Low-voltage tungsten filament lamp This low-cost source of medium-intensity light is widely used in bench microscopes for bright-field, dark-field, polarized-light, interference- and phase-contrast viewing. This system is ideal for viewing but not for photomicrography, since long exposures are required as a result of its limited intensity.

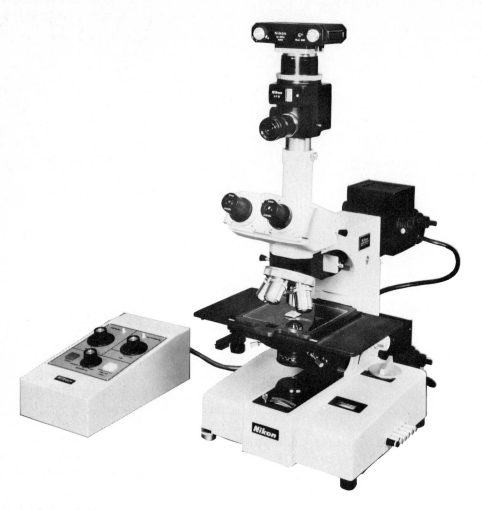

Figure 4-3 Nikon Metaphot metallurgical microscope with large stage and 35-mm camera with automatic exposure control. *(Courtesy of Nikon, Inc., Instrument Division.)*

Carbon arc This system has been widely used because of the extreme intensity of the arc established between vertical and horizontal carbon electrodes. The high light intensity provides good illumination for dark-field, oblique, polarized-light, and phase-contrast examination. The spectrum is very similar to that of sunlight, which is helpful in color photomicrography. However, the limitations of this system and the development of more suitable light sources have made it less desirable in modern metallographs, and it is no longer used. Direct radiation exposure from the arc can cause severe ultraviolet burns to the eye. Replacement of the electrodes must be made with great care because of the danger of electric

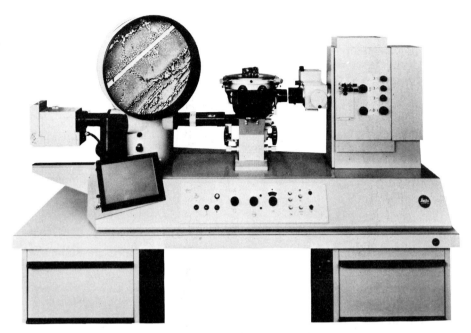

Figure 4-4 Leitz MM6 metallograph. *(Courtesy of E. Leitz, Inc.)*

shock. Uneven electrode movement and alignment can cause problems during a photographic exposure.

Xenon arc This is currently the most popular illumination source for all types of viewing and photomicrography on modern metallographs. The xenon source has a continuous visual spectrum of daylight quality, which is good for color photomicrography. After a short warm-up the light output is sufficiently constant for nearly all work. Extreme care must be taken when replacing a worn-out bulb, as the quartz envelope becomes embrittled during usage. Non-ozone-producing xenon bulbs are now available. Light intensity can be varied only through the use of filters.

Quartz-iodine lamp This system is an improvement over the incandescent lamp and is characterized by a high color temperature, high intensity, and relatively long life. Since it is not an arc type, light intensity can be controlled simply by varying the current.

Zirconium arc lamp This is an excellent light source of high intensity and very steady output. The light spectrum is satisfactory for color photomicrography.

Mercury vapor lamp This is a medium- to high-intensity light source with a line-type spectrum. The most prominent wavelength light is an intense green at 546 nm. Monochromatic radiation is easily obtained.

4-3.2 Condenser System

An adjustable lens placed in front of the illumination source images the light at a desired point in the optical path. This lens should be aplanatic, that is, free of spherical aberration and coma. A field diaphragm is usually placed in front of the lamp or field condenser to minimize internal glare and multiple light reflections within the microscope. The field diaphragm is adjusted for best image contrast. Generally, it is stopped down to the edge of the field of view.

The aperture diaphragm is a second adjustable iris diaphragm in the condenser system and is located between the lamp condenser and the vertical illuminator. Adjustment of the aperture diaphragm varies the intensity of the light and the angle of the cone of light entering the objective lens. The optimum setting of the aperture diaphragm is a compromise and is usually 80 to 90 percent of the aperture of the objective lens. If the aperture diaphragm is too large, poor contrast results; if it is too small, there is a loss of sharpness as a result of diffraction fringe effects. Reducing the aperture diaphragm should not be used to reduce the intensity of the light source. In general, the optimum setting of the aperture diaphragm varies with magnification. As the magnification is raised, the aperture diaphragm is stopped down.

The substage condenser (used with transmitted light illumination) images the light from the source onto the specimen. In incident light microscopes, this function is performed by the objective lens. In the transmitted light microscope, the field and aperture diaphragms are usually located in the substage condenser. Condensers designed to give numerical apertures greater than 1.0 must be used as an immersion system, that is, a drop of oil compatible with the system is placed between the specimen and the objective lens. The degree of optical correction of the condenser is a significant factor in obtaining maximum image definition. Condenser lenses must be corrected for spherical aberration and, if color photography is performed, for chromatic aberration.

For examination of opaque specimens, the light must be directed as nearly vertical as possible along the optic axis of the objective lens to the specimen. This is the function of the vertical illuminator, which is located immediately behind the objective lens.

4-3.3 Light Filters

Filters are often required to modify the light for optimum visual examination or photomicrography [8]. Neutral density filters reduce the intensity of the illumination across the visible spectrum without noticeably changing the spectral distribution. Thus they are useful for safe, comfortable viewing and for reducing the light intensity without reducing the numerical aperture of the system. Filters are available that permit light transmission from 85 to 0.01 percent of the incident light.

Selective filters, either absorption or interference, alter the light to provide wavelengths for which the objective lenses are corrected. Selective filters are often used to match the color temperature of the light source to that required by the film. These filters can also be used to increase contrast between phases of different colors. To improve contrast, the filter selected should have a color complementary to that of the object being viewed, as shown in the following table.

Object color	Filter color	Object color	Filter color
Blue	Red, yellow, or orange	Brown	Blue
Green	Red	Purple	Green
Red	Green	Violet	Yellow
Yellow	Blue		

Polarizing filters transmit only light that vibrates in one direction. Either the prism polarizer or the selective absorption film (Polaroid) type of filter can be used. Prism polarizers transmit 40 to 50 percent of the incident light and produce a very sharply defined polarization direction. However, they are expensive. The selective absorption film type transmits 20 to 35 percent of the incident light. Either type can be used to produce plane-polarized or cross-polarized light for examination of noncubic materials.

A sensitive-tint plate can be used in conjunction with polarizing filters to provide very sensitive detection of birefringence or double refraction.

4-3.4 Objective Lens

The objective lens forms the primary image of the specimen and, thus, is the most critical item of the microscope [9]. The objective collects as much light as possible coming from any point on the specimen and combines this light to form the image. The numerical aperture (NA) is a measure of the light collection capability of the objective and is defined as:

$$NA = n \sin \alpha \qquad (4\text{-}2)$$

where n is the minimum refraction index of the various materials between the specimen and the objective lens and α is the half-angle of the most oblique rays entering the front lens of the objective (see Fig. 4-5). The larger the angle of the oblique rays, the greater is the light-collecting ability of the objective lens. The NA of the substage condenser lens system also influences the "effective" $NA^{\dagger}$ of the objective lens:

$$NA_{eff} = \frac{NA_{obj} + NA_{cond}}{2} \qquad (4\text{-}3)$$

†In the reflected light microscope the objective lens performs the functions of the substage condenser, thus $NA_{obj} = NA_{cond}$. Equation 4-3 is applicable to the transmitted light microscope, although some have criticized its accuracy (discussed later). In transmitted light work the numerical aperture of the substage condenser should be greater than that of the objective for best results.

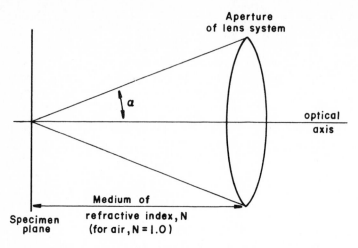

Figure 4-5 The numerical aperture (NA) of the objective is equal to product of the minimum refractive index of the lens and any material between the lens and specimen and the sine of the half-angle of the most oblique light rays entering the front lens of the objective.

The aperture diaphragm setting can be used to adjust the NA of the condenser and, therefore, will alter the effective NA of the system.

The tube length, that is, the length of the body tube from the eye line of the ocular to the objective thread, is not standardized. Objectives, except those corrected for infinity, are designed to be used with a certain fixed tube length (normally 160 to 250 mm). Since the tube length is not a standardized unit, use of objectives on a microscope of different tube length will result in several problems:

1. Loss of parfocality
2. Variation from rated objective magnification
3. Reduction of image quality, especially for the higher-power, higher-NA lenses
4. Variation in working distance (distance between objective and sample)

The achromatic or "achromat," the most common type of objective, is corrected spherically for one color (yellow-green normally) and corrected for longitudinal chromatical aberration for two colors (red and green normally). These objectives are not very good for color photomicrography. They provide moderate-to-good resolution at low cost. Optimum performance is obtained by using yellow-green light and orthochromatic film. Achromats are useful in fluorescence microscopy, since fluorite components in more highly corrected objectives will autofluoresce. Achromats generally have relatively large working distances (distance from front of lens to sample) and are useful in hot-stage microscopy. Achromats are easy to produce strain-free, a desirable condition for polarized-light microscopy. Since fewer lenses are incorporated in achromats, achromats are useful in interference microscopy, since internal reflection losses are reduced.

Semiapochromatic or fluorite objectives provide better simultaneous correction for both chromatic and spherical aberration and, thus, provide better image quality than the achromat-type objective. Neofluors have synthetic fluorite lenses and can be obtained strain-free.

Apochromatic objectives are the most highly corrected objectives. They are recommended for resolution of fine detail and for highest image quality. The apochromats are corrected spherically for two colors (blue and green normally) and chromatically for three colors (red, green, and blue normally). Lateral chromatic aberration is corrected in the eyepiece.

Plano objectives are characterized by extensive correction for flatness of field. These lenses are good for reducing eyestrain. They can also be extensively corrected spherically and chromatically. Typical plano-type objectives are shown in Fig. 4-6.

The working distance, i.e., the distance between the front surface of the objective lens and the sample, can be an important lens parameter. In general, the working distance is a matter of lens design. Although the working distance has no

Figure 4-6 Cross sections of Leitz plano-type objectives. *(Courtesy of E. Leitz, Inc.)*

direct relationship to the objective lens focal length, it is in general much shorter than the focal length. As a rule, as the magnifying power of the objective increases, the working distance decreases. When switching from a low-power objective to a high-power objective, a parfocal lens system helps to prevent the objective lens from striking the specimen surface. Parfocal lens systems are very helpful in practice, since all the objectives on the turret will be approximately in focus when the objectives are switched. The objectives are usually mounted on a rotating nosepiece turret that can hold from four to six objectives.

Oil immersion objectives are useful in metallography because they provide a simple means for achieving improved resolution. With air objectives, the NA of the objective cannot exceed 0.95. To obtain a higher NA and thus improved resolution, oil immersion objectives must be used. They are available over a wide range of magnification—25 to 160X. Since the air interface is eliminated, image quality is improved. Since bubbles present in the oil block the light path and obscure detail, this problem can be minimized by allowing the oil to drip off the applicator—the oil should never be wiped off the applicator onto the specimen. After use, the lenses should be cleaned with a solvent such as xylene. A solvent that will attack the cement holding the lenses together should never be used.

The oil used must be compatible with the refractive index of the front lens of the objective. Since there are a great many immersion oils available, it is best to consult the microscope manufacturer as to the correct oil for your objectives. Oil immersion objectives are not frequently used in metallography, but they are heavily used by the coal petrographer and mineralogist. Water immersion objectives are frequently used by biologists.

4-3.5 Eyepieces

The major function of the eyepiece (ocular) is to magnify the primary image produced by the objective so that the eye can use the full resolution of the objective. Cross-sectional views of two typical eyepieces are shown in Fig. 4-7.

A virtual image of the specimen is formed at the point of most distinct vision, approximately 250 mm from the eye. The eyepiece enables the user to achieve useful magnification with available objectives. The maximum viewing angle which the average metallographer can observe without moving the eye is 50 to 55°. A viewing angle of 51° corresponds to a 24-mm diameter field of view for a 10X eyepiece. Leitz has developed a 30-mm wide-field eyepiece for use with their plano objectives to increase the usable area of the primary image.

Today's eyepieces are modifications of those developed by Huygens (1629–1695) and Ramsden (1735–1800). The Huygenian is the most common, least expensive eyepiece and is suitable for use with low- and medium-power achromatic objectives (NA less than 0.65). The major use for Ramsden-type eyepieces is in micrometer eyepieces.

The compensating-type eyepiece developed by Zeiss is suitable for use with achromatic objectives with NA of 0.65 and greater. All apochromatic, semiapochromatic and plano objectives, because of their undercorrection for lateral chromatic aberration, require these special eyepieces for best results.

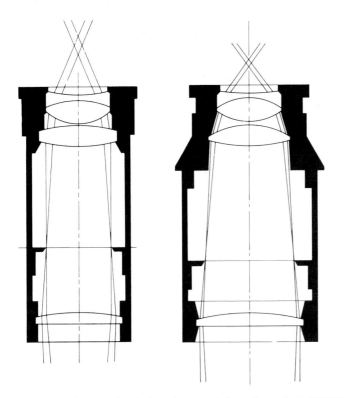

Figure 4-7 Cross-sectional view of two typical eyepieces. Left, GF10X (23.2-mm diameter); right, GW10X (30-mm diameter). *(Courtesy of E. Leitz, Inc.)*

The eye clearance (distance between the ocular eye lens and the eye) is 10 mm or less. This is usually inadequate for viewing with glasses and will severely limit the image size viewed. If the eyeglass wearer is merely nearsighted or farsighted, the required compensation (glasses off) can be made with the fine focus adjustment. If the eyeglass wearer suffers from astigmatism, the image will be affected by the astigmatism if he or she views without wearing glasses. High-eyepoint eyepieces have been developed to provide a full field of view at a clearance distance of about 20 mm, which is sufficient for people who wear glasses.

Eyepieces are often fitted with reticles or graticules. Although these words are often used interchangeably, there is a fine difference in meaning [6]. A reticle is a system of lines, cross hairs, or wires on the focal plane of the eyepiece, while a graticule is a scale that is printed or engraved on a transparent disc and placed in the focal plane of the eyepiece. These devices are used for locating, measuring, counting, or comparing structures. The eyepiece magnifies the reticle or graticule as well as the image from the objective. Both images must be in focus simultaneously.

Special types of eyepieces have been developed to facilitate certain types of measurements. In general, these devices provide more accurate measurements than graticules. The filar micrometer ocular or screw-micrometer ocular provides measurements with an accuracy of about 1 μm. The filar eyepiece is used on only one eyepiece. Measurement is made by locating the object to be sized between two parallel lines, one of which is movable. The goniometer eyepiece has been developed to permit accurate measurement of angles. Image-splitting eyepieces, also referred to as image-shearing eyepieces, are used to measure features even if they are not stationary. Turret eyepieces are fitted with a series of reticle discs that can slide into the field of view sequentially. They are used in measuring grain size, graphite type, or particle size and shape.

Eyepiece type and magnification should be matched to that of the objective. In general, follow the manufacturer's recommendation. The most commonly used eyepiece is of 10X magnification. Eyepiece magnifications less than 6.3X are of little value. Use of high-power eyepieces (15 to 25X) can be helpful in obtaining high magnifications. If greater depth of field is required, improvement can be obtained by using a high-magnification eyepiece with a low-power objective with a high NA.

In the compound microscope, the image produced by the objective lens system is further magnified by the eyepiece. The total magnification is, therefore, the product of the magnification of the objective lens M_o and the eyepiece M_e as shown in Eq. (4-4).

$$\text{Magnification}_{\text{total}} = M_o \times M_e \qquad (4\text{-}4)$$

If a relay or "zoom" system is placed between the objective and eyepiece, this factor should be included in this equation.

In photomicrography, the image is projected from an eyepiece to a ground glass (or film) at a distance of 250 mm to achieve the rated magnification. If the projected distance is greater than 250 mm, the image will be enlarged proportionally. Likewise, if the projected distance is less than 250 mm, the image will be reduced proportionally. The projected magnification is given by the following equation:

$$M_p = M_o M_e M_r \left(\frac{D}{250}\right) \qquad (4\text{-}5)$$

where M_p = total projected magnification
M_r = relay or zoom factor (if one is used)
D = distance of projection (eyepiece to film), mm

4-3.6 Stage

The mechanical stage used to hold the specimen is an important part of the microscope because it is generally involved in focusing the specimen; once focused, the specimen should stay focused as different areas are examined. Stage design varies depending on whether the microscope is upright or inverted (i.e., sample plane of polish is upright or inverted). The stage must be sturdy so that vibrations are not encountered. Stage movement should be smooth and precise. Rack-and-pinion gearing is generally employed. Recently, motorized stages have become popular, with movement controlled through a joystick.

The stage surface is usually fitted with an X and Y graduated scale for making measurements or locating features. In some cases, a vernier is also attached for more exact measurements. Special stages are available with a micrometer screw control for precise measurement.

In mineralogy and petrography, circular stages are generally used. In this case, the stage is graduated to permit measurement of the angle of rotation. This is especially important in polarized-light work. Two verniers can be used to permit angular measurements to 0.1°. In some cases, a rectilinear stage is placed on top of the circular stage.

Special stages are also available to facilitate holding of small parts. Most manufacturers provide an autoleveling stage on upright microscopes which permits rapid leveling of mounted specimens without the need for mounting the sample on clay.

4-3.7 Control of Microscope Variables

A microscope or metallograph is a complex instrument that must be kept in fine tune if best results are to be obtained. The best instrument can be rendered ineffective if it is not properly adjusted. Each laboratory should have a maintenance program adequate to ensure consistent top performance [10]. Simple problems such as dirt or dust on the lenses can severely degrade optical quality.

To achieve optimum resolution, the following steps should be followed:

- Use objectives with highest NA and suitable corrections.
- Use high magnifications, including those above 1000 NA.
- Use eyepieces compatible with the chosen objective.
- Use yellow-green monochromatic light with achromat objectives.
- Use the shortest possible wavelength light practical with objectives used.
- Keep the light system properly centered and lenses clean.
- Use oil immersion lenses if available.
- Adjust field diaphragm for maximum contrast and aperture diaphragm for maximum resolution and contrast.
- Use dark-field, phase-contrast or interference-contrast illumination if additional contrast is required.
- Adjust brightness for best resolution.
- Use best photographic practices for maximum contrast.

When depth of field must be improved, some loss of resolution will result, since conditions that maximize resolution reduce depth of field and vice versa. Depth of field is improved by the following:

- Reduce the NA of the system by closing down the aperture diaphragm and/or use a lower NA objective.
- Lower the magnification for a given NA.
- Use a high-power eyepiece with a low-magnification, high-NA objective to obtain the desired magnification.

- Reduce the bellows extension or zoom factor.
- Use the longest possible wavelength light possible with the objective.

In many cases, the microscopist must compromise between resolution and depth of field to achieve the necessary results.

4-3.8 Lens Defects

Many types of lens defects affect the sharpness of the image obtained. These problems are as follows: longitudinal chromatic aberration, lateral chromatic aberration, spherical aberration, coma, astigmatism, and distortion. It is theoretically impossible to eliminate all these defects.

Aberrations should not be considered as defects due to sloppy workmanship, since they are a consequence of the basic laws of reflection and refraction at a spherical surface. Since the refractive index of a lens varies with the wavelength of light used and the focal length of the lens varies with refractive index, the focal length will be different for different color light. Thus, an image viewed under white light consists of a separate image for each wavelength present, and each image is focused at different distances from the lens. This problem is known as longitudinal chromatic aberration. In addition, as the focal length changes, the magnification changes, producing a variation in image size, or lateral chromatic aberration.

If the light rays from a point object on the lens axis are more strongly refracted at either the center or the periphery of the lens, there will be a series of focal positions with the image point appearing as a circle of finite area. This problem, known as spherical aberration, can be minimized by using an aperture which restricts the use of the objective to the central portion of the lens. Alternatively, the problem can be minimized by the design of the compound lens.

Coma affects light rays off the optical axis and is due to refraction differences between rays from a point object passing through the inner and outer lens zones. The point object will be imaged as a comet-shaped object. Astigmatism is caused by the same circumstances.

The image surface of best focus is curved, not planar. Thus, curvature of field results unless compensating eyepieces with equal but opposite curvature are employed.

4-3.9 Resolution and Depth of Field

The subject of resolution, or resolving power, is of great practical significance to the microscopist. A complete and comprehensive presentation of this subject would require that the reader have extensive knowledge of mathematics and optical principles. Since the vast majority of practicing metallographers do not have the required background to use such information, an approach of this type does not seem useful to the readers of this book. On the other hand, many texts on microscopy treat this subject in a very simple, brief manner, which, unfortunately, creates misconceptions about factors influencing resolution and limits the microscopist's ability to control and enhance resolution. In this book we present a descriptive view of the subject which we believe will be of value to the practicing metallographer.

Usually, most general books on metallography state that the resolving power of an objective is a function of the wavelength of the light used and the NA of the objective. The subject is confused by the quoting of a number of formulas that relate resolution and the above two parameters [11]:

$$d = \frac{0.5\lambda}{NA} \tag{4-6}$$

$$d = \frac{0.61\lambda}{NA} \tag{4-7}$$

$$\frac{\lambda}{NA} \geq d \geq \frac{0.5\lambda}{NA} \tag{4-8}$$

$$d = \frac{1.22\ C\lambda}{NA} \tag{4-9}$$

where d = the minimum distance between two points that are just resolved
C = a factor varying between 0.4 and 1.0
λ = the wavelength[†] of the light used
NA = the numerical aperture of the objective

In most books, either the first or the second formula is frequently given along with plots such as Fig. 4-8. Such relationships should not be taken at face value without proper explanation.

These first two equations, Eqs. (4-6) and (4-7), state that the resolving power of a given objective with a certain NA and a given light source is constant. Most microscopists will realize that this is not the case because other factors are involved. The two equations produce similar results except that the second produces more conservative estimates of resolution by about 20 percent. Equation (4-8) states that the resolution is not constant for a given value of NA and λ but varies from the value given in Equation (4-6) to a value twice as large. The variation is due to a third factor, the NA of the illumination. In such cases, the resolving power is often described by the following formula rather than Eq. (4-8):

$$d = \frac{\lambda}{NA_{ill} + NA_{obj}} \tag{4-10}$$

where NA_{ill} is the numerical aperture of the illumination system and NA_{obj} is the

---

[†] The wavelength of light has historically been given in angstrom units (Å), but in the modern SI system it is listed in units of nanometers (nm). For conversion purposes, 1 nm = 10 Å. For example, the wavelength of a sodium light source is 589 nm or 5890 Å.

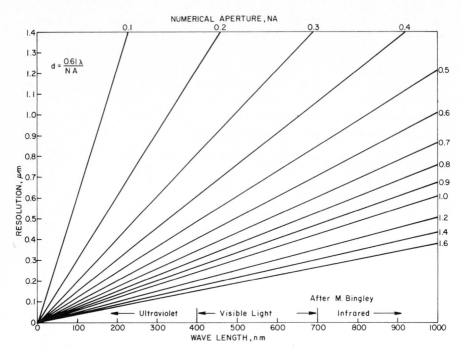

Figure 4-8 Relationship between numerical aperture, wavelength, and resolution.

numerical aperture of the objective. The fourth resolving power equation also says that resolving power is not simply a factor of NA and λ but is variable. The factor C, as described by McLaughlin [7], varies between 0.4 and 1.0, depending on factors such as the corrections given to the objective in the manufacturing process and on the visual acuity of the particular microscopist. It is important to mention that these equations, which are based on the original theories of Abbe, are for resolution of self-luminous points, a condition rarely obtained in metallography.

A discussion of the resolving power of the optical microscope must consider the important role of the human eye and the observation conditions. Of historical interest is the technique of ultramicroscopy, which is a technique that was used previously to study liquids containing very small particles, such as blood. The technique is based on the concept that particles will become self-luminous as a result of light scattering if they are illuminated by a very intense light beam. In the ultramicroscope, particles can be visibly detected that are well below the size limits calculated using the formulas just presented. With this instrument, particle observation has been shown to be independent of the NA of the objective and the wavelength of the light. Instead, it depends only on the intensity of the incident light beam and the image contrast. However, although the particles can be observed, no conclusions can be drawn as to the color or size of the particles.

Van Duijn's study on resolution of microscopic detail is undoubtedly the most comprehensive work on the subject [12]. Since this work is infrequently cited and the reference is not readily available, his conclusions are discussed here in detail. Van Duijn emphasized that the theory of resolution is only part of a more general theory of visibility. Visibility covers any phenomenon which permits the observer to distinguish detail irrespective of whether the real shape or dimensions can be properly delineated.

Resolving power is the ability to produce separated images of multiple structures under the best conditions and is usually expressed as the number of uniformly spaced similar parallel black lines per unit length on a white background that can be separated in the image. In microscopy, it is more common to determine the minimum distance d between two parallel lines or adjacent points that can be separated. These two measures are inversely proportional to each other. As the number of lines per unit length increases, the minimum separation decreases. For example, if we have a resolving power of 1000 (black) lines per millimeter where the thickness of the black lines and the white space between lines are equal, the minimum spacing between adjacent black lines is 0.0005 mm or 0.5 μm. The minimum separation d is referred to as the resolution of the lens.

An important aspect of image visibility is contrast, i.e., the ratio of the brightness of some specific detail to that of an adjacent structure or to that of the background. Contrast sensitivity refers to the ability of the observer's eye to detect small differences in brightness, which is a function of the amount of illumination and the color of the feature of interest and its surroundings.

Magnification also plays an important role in image visibility, since the degree of visual perception of the human eye varies from person to person. Thus, we can define a lowest useful magnification which just permits a given observer to observe all the detail that is resolved by the objective. Obviously, this quantity varies among microscopists.

Theories of resolving power stem from the pioneering work of Abbe. His test subject consisted of a flat periodic grating with black-and-white contrast, where the black was opaque and the white transparent. The grating had no thickness and an ideal point light source was used to produce coherent light waves. Lens defects were not considered. Under these conditions, Abbe stated that the resolution is $d = \lambda/\text{NA}$ for parallel illumination and $d = \lambda/2\text{NA}$ for completely incoherent illumination. Thus, the limit of resolution using these formula for an objective with NA of 1.4 and visible light is about 0.2 μm.

Next, it is necessary to determine how much magnification is required in order to see lines with a minimum separation of 0.2 μm. The minimum required magnification can be determined by dividing the resolving power of the objective by the resolving power of the observer's eye. However, the resolving power of a particular observer's eye under the conditions of observation is difficult to determine and varies considerably from person to person. Abbe assumed that the limit of resolving power of the human eye is about 1 minute of arc, or a separation of 0.07 mm at a distance of 250 mm (the distance away from the normal eye for best visibility). Since this limit is rather challenging to meet in practice, Abbe used a more realistic estimate of 4 minutes of arc, or 0.3 mm, for his calculations. For conditions of white light with a mean wavelength of 550 nm, the required magnification is 1100 times the NA of the objective. This is the origin of the often quoted rule of the useful magnification being 1000 NA.

Most books on microscopy state that the upper limit of useful magnification is 1000 NA and any higher magnification is "empty." It must be emphasized that Abbe's theory was developed for a subject that is certainly far different from those observed by metallographers. In addition, the limit of resolution for structures that are not self-luminous is poorer than for self-luminous structures. It should also be mentioned that the resolution varies with the type of illumination, i.e., the resolution is different under dark-field illumination and interference-contrast or phase-contrast illumination. Furthermore, Abbe's work did not consider the influence of lens defects.

Although the limit of resolving power is 0.2 μm with white light, this does not indicate how small an isolated particle can be and still remain visible in the light microscope. As previously mentioned, by maximizing image contrast with the ultramicroscope, particles much smaller than 0.2 μm can be observed. According to Van Duijn, particles as small as 0.005 μm are detectable with the ultramicroscope. This is possible because the particles are rendered self-luminous. Using dark-field illumination, it is claimed that particles as small as 0.006 μm can be detected. For phase-contrast and interference-contrast illumination, the limit of visibility is a function of the smallest phase change produced. Thus, the smallest size detectable depends on the refractive index difference between the feature and its surroundings and on its thickness. For phase-contrast illumination, Van Duijn states that the smallest phase difference that can be rendered visible varies from $\lambda/30$ to $\lambda/100$, while for an interference microscope it varies from $\lambda/100$ to $\lambda/300$. Hence the smallest size spherical particles that can be observed by these methods varies from 0.05 to 0.02 μm. A prime factor in detectability is image contrast.

The human eye distinguishes features through light intensity differences (amplitude) and by color. Thus, the microscopic image must exhibit sufficient contrast to render structures visible. Since contrast is required for detectability, resolution depends on both resolving power and contrast. In the manufacture of optical components, flare must be minimized. Flare is light produced by internal reflections within the lens system. Flare is controlled through the use of antireflection lens coatings and by painting all internal metal surfaces black. Glare also reduces image contrast. Glare is similar to flare but occurs in the object space rather than in the image space.

Van Duijn also discusses Abbe's choice of 4 minutes of arc, or 0.3 mm at 250 mm, as the resolving power of the human eye [12]. The optometrist measures vision by use of a chart with black letters on a white background, a condition of high contrast. The rows of letters are of different size to test vision. According to Van Duijn, normal 20/20 vision corresponds to a minimum separable distance d of 150 μm at a distance of 250 mm. Only about 1 percent of the population has better vision that is comparable to a separation of 70 μm at 250 mm. Visual acuity is not constant over the entire area of the retina. Optimum vision is obtained only for the portion of the retina known as the fovea, and, therefore, the eye must scan the image so that the finest detail falls on the fovea.

If an object with features similar to the eye chart is viewed through the microscope, one can make an estimate of the lowest useful magnification. For normal 20/20 vision and optimum conditions with white light of a mean wavelength of 550 nm, the lowest useful magnification is 550 NA. Van Duijn states that for the average individual the useful magnification should be 4 × 550 NA or 2200 NA.

Another factor influencing visual acuity is the pupil diameter, which is 3 to 4 mm in daylight. At smaller or greater diameters the resolving power of the eye decreases by as much as 25 to 30 percent at the extremes. Pupil diameter is a function of image brightness but also varies with a person's age. The subject-to-eye distance also influences pupil diameter, as can other factors such as stress or illness.

For detail to be detected by the human eye, the contrast between features in the image must be equal to or greater than the contrast sensitivity of the eye. According to Van Duijn, detail can be detected by the eye under optimum conditions if the difference in brightness between the feature and its surroundings is at least 1.7 percent [12]. However, if the size of the features being studied is very small, it is very likely that a much greater brightness difference is required. Van Duijn suggests that the practical limit of brightness difference for objects viewed through a microscope is about 3 to 7 percent.

The resolving power of the eye has been shown to depend on image contrast. Near the limit of contrast sensitivity, the resolving power of the eye decreases to about 25 percent of that obtained under optimum conditions. Thus, the lowest useful magnification for maximum resolution is four times greater than under optimum conditions, i.e., 2200 NA. The relationship between the resolving power of the eye and that of the objective and the lowest useful magnification as a function of image contrast is given in the nomogram (see Fig. 4-9) from the work of Van Duijn [12]. In using the nomogram, one must allow for the variability of the resolving power of the optics and the eye according to the nature of the subject and the observation conditions. As magnification increases, image brightness decreases. A photomicrograph can actually improve the contrast seen in the viewed image and, thus, can improve the resolution. According to Van Duijn, use of photographs with magnifications up to 4000X or more is fully justified. It is this writer's experience that this statement is indeed correct.

The comments made thus far are based on black-and-white images; the influence of color complicates the analysis, since one must be able to identify colors and distinguish one from another. Color perception depends on the quality of the eye, the brightness level, and the size of the colored features. Hartridge has reviewed the problems of color perception in microscopy [13]. According to Hartridge, very small colorless objects frequently appear colored, usually crimson or blue-green. The true color of small features can usually be determined if they are blue-green or red. However, if they are orange, yellow, yellow-green, or violet, they generally appear to be red, blue-green, or colorless. Larger particles

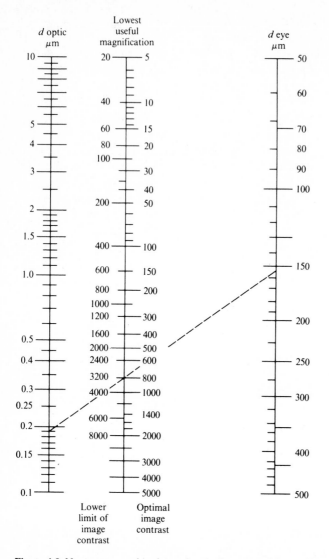

Figure 4-9 Nomogram used to determine the lowest useful magnification for a given combination of optical resolution and visual acuitity. *(From Van Duijn, Ref. 12, courtesy of Microscope Publications.)*

can be correctly assessed for color hue if the illumination is satisfactory. Low brightness levels make yellow and blue colors difficult to discern, while excessive brightness impairs the detection of red and green details. Thus, in the study of small particles, one cannot assume that the color is being correctly identified. These problems are particularly important in biological studies, where it has been shown that staining objects red produces better detectability of small features than staining with blue or green.

In color microscopy, one must pay strict attention to the spectral composition of the illumination source. Light sources are rated in terms of the color temperature of the source as compared to that of sunlight (5200–5800 K). Most artificial light sources have substantially lower color temperatures. The xenon arc has a color temperature of 5200 K, which makes it ideal for color microscopy. A low color temperature makes the blue and violet colors dark, while the yellow-to-red region is lightened. A color-conversion filter can be used to correct this problem.

The preceding discussion has dealt with lateral resolving power and resolution, i.e., the ability to discern adjacent structural details. In Abbe's analysis, the subject matter had no thickness; thus, the problem of axial resolution was not considered. However, in microscopy the detail being observed has height differences, and the microscopist must determine whether features are on the same plane or above or below it. Photomicrography deals with this problem constantly. All the subject, regardless of its elevation differences, must be in focus in order to obtain a crisp image.

The depth of field is the distance along the optical axis over which details of the object can be observed with adequate sharpness. Factors that affect resolving power influence depth of field as well but in the opposite direction, i.e., increasing the resolving power decreases the depth of field. Thus, once more the microscopist is faced with a compromise. The depth of field T_f is approximated using the following equation [7]:

$$T_f = \frac{\lambda\sqrt{n^2 - NA^2}}{2NA^2} \tag{4-11}$$

where n is the refractive index of the medium between the sample and the objective ($n \approx 1.0$ for air). Since the object plane can be moved both above and below the plane of focus, the actual depth of field is $2T_f$. Figure 4-10 shows a plot of the visual depth of field as a function of NA for red, green, and blue light. As expected, the depth of field drops as NA increases and resolution increases. Longer wavelength light sources provide slightly greater depth of field.

Axial resolving power is not a direct function of the lateral resolution. The axial resolving power is the smallest axial height difference that is detectable. Eye accommodation is an important factor in axial resolution. In practice, the eye distinguishes height differences through differences in the crispness of detail lying on different planes. Again, magnification is important, since image crispness is dependent on magnification. Figure 4-11, which is from the work of Van Duijn [12], shows the relationship between the axial resolution and magnification for objectives with different NAs. The figure is based on light with a mean wavelength of 550 nm and a refractive index of 1.45. To convert to other values of n, such as air, the axial resolving power is multiplied by $n/1.45$. Eye accommodation is not considered in the chart, as would be the case in photomicrography. One can conclude that in order to determine whether two features are on the same or different planes, the NA and magnification must be as high as feasible.

The term "empty magnification" has been used in the microscopy literature to describe any magnification in excess of the 1100-NA limit (usually quoted as 1000

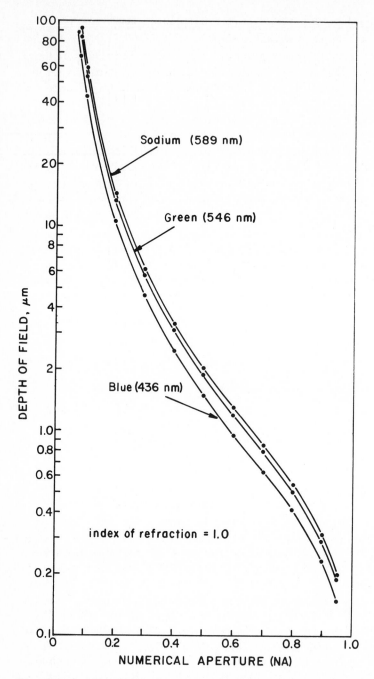

Figure 4-10 Relationship between numerical aperature, wavelength, and depth of field.

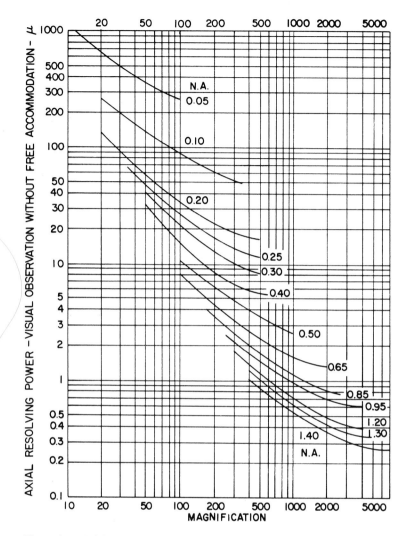

Figure 4-11 Axial resolving power for an average eye as a function of magnification and numerical aperture based upon a refractive index of 1.45 and light with a wavelength of 550 nm. To obtain the axial resolving power for a different refractive index *n* multiply the value obtained above by *n*/1.45. *(From Van Duijn, Ref. 12, courtesy of Microscope Publications.)*

NA to simplify calculations) derived by Abbe using an ideal contrasting image with an ideal eye. In this chapter we have described at length the objections raised by Van Duijn to the dogmatic use of this rule. Microscopists have faithfully adhered to this limit in the belief that nothing is gained by exceeding this limit and that detail can also be lost and spurious effects produced from the use of excess magnification. However, high magnifications can be useful in recognizing optical artifacts in the microscopic image. Extreme magnifications do lead to blurred images.

Van Duijn defined empty magnification as "every magnification value that does not increase the amount of information already contained in an image obtained at some lower magnification, regardless of the amount of trouble that has to be expended in the act of perceiving." One should consider the magnification to be empty only if information is not obtained by raising the magnification. In photomicrography one can further enhance both contrast and magnification. However, much of this ability is forfeited when instant photography processes are used.

To summarize, strict adherence to the 1000-NA rule clearly imposes an undesirable limitation to obtaining all possible information. For maximum resolution, one must pay strict attention to the choice of illumination, magnification, lens quality, image contrast, and observation conditions. Resolution using illumination processes other than bright-field illumination can be considerably better as the result of improved contrast. In viewing an object, the magnification should be raised continuously until the detail is adequate for the purpose of the investigation. It should be kept in mind that the resolving power of the human eye varies considerably. Careful use of photography can enhance contrast and improve the resolution of detail. For critical work, control of the photographic process is a must.

4-4 EXAMINATION MODES IN LIGHT MICROSCOPY

High resolution can be achieved only if there is adequate contrast between detail so that varying amounts of light reach the observer's eye. There are two types of features that can be discerned on metal surfaces—amplitude features and optical phase features. Amplitude features occur as a result of reflectivity differences. Figure 4-12 illustrates the difference in reflectivity of constituents in several materials. Samples with the same reflectivity but with differences in surface height can be detected by the differences in optical phase, since there is a phase-path reflectivity difference. The human eye can detect amplitude differences but not optical phase differences. Such phase differences are translated into amplitude differences through phase-contrast and interference-contrast procedures.

4-4.1 Methods of Examination

Bright-field illumination The predominant method of examination of metallurgical specimens is by incident bright-field illumination. Figure 4-13 shows the light path in the vertical illuminator for bright-field illumination. Most of the micrographs in this book were taken using bright-field vertical illumination.

Oblique illumination Oblique illumination is obtained by decentering the condenser assembly or the mirror. Oblique illumination casts shadows as a result of any relief or differences in height, which provides a three-dimensional appear-

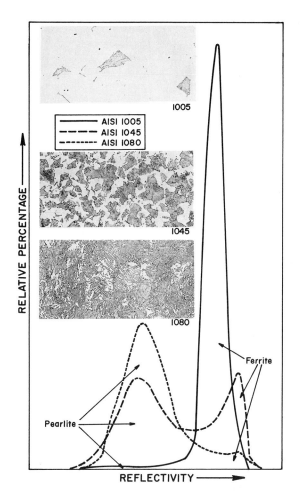

Figure 4-12 Relative reflectivity of polished and etched (4% picral) carbon steel as influenced by the amount of ferrite and pearlite.

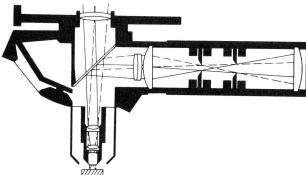

Figure 4-13 Optical path in the vertical illuminator of the metallurgical microscope in the bright-field illumination mode. *(Courtesy of E. Leitz, Inc.)*

ance. Only a certain amount of "obliqueness" can be used because decentering the condenser reduces the NA (and thus resolution) of the lens.

Dark-field illumination Dark-field illumination produces an intensity contrast image from effects which do not usually contribute significant intensity contrast to the image in bright-field illumination. Dark-field illumination is useful for observing the colors of structures, for improving contrast in colorless structures, and for viewing very small particles (ultramicroscopy). In this mode, objects appear self-luminous, a condition that improves resolution. Because of the low illumination levels an intense light source must be used. Even when this is done, exposures can be rather long. Dark-field incident light microscopy accentuates surface irregularities such as grain boundaries, cracks, and pits. Figure 4-14 shows the optical path in the vertical illuminator for dark-field illumination. Examples of the use of dark-field illumination are given in Fig. 4-15.

Polarized light While the use of polarized light in the identification of minerals is a long-established important practice, its use in metallography has, in general, been limited to the study of only certain metals [14–16]. Mineralogical methods have been used for many years for inclusion identification. Application of polarized light in metallography has increased since the introduction of the Foster prism by Bausch and Lomb and since the increase in interest in beryllium, titanium, uranium, and zirconium. Beryllium, uranium, and zirconium are rather difficult to etch; thus, polarized light is nearly always used to examine these metals.

Early microscopes used the Nicol prism invented by William Nicol in 1828. Today, most microscopes use synthetic "Polaroid" material for the polarizer and analyzer. The "polarizer" is placed in the light path ahead of the vertical illuminator, while the "analyzer" is located after the objective, usually in the microscope tube just below the eyepieces. Polaroid-type filters are widely used because of their lower cost. They are adequate for all but the most critical work. Polaroid sheet was invented by Edmund Land in 1934. This material exhibits dichroism; that is, the material will preferentially absorb one component, em-

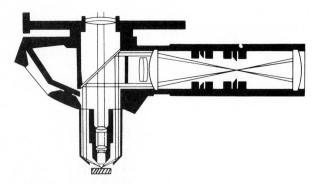

Figure 4-14 Optical path in the vertical illuminator of the metallurgical microscope in the dark-field illumination mode. *(Courtesy of E. Leitz, Inc.)*

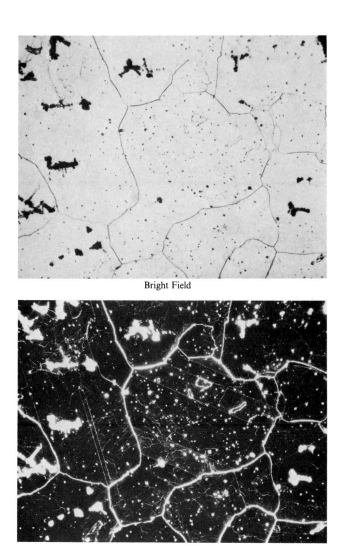

Bright Field

Dark Field

Figure 4-15 Use of dark-field illumination to reveal annealing twins and substructure in an AISI 1080 sample thermally etched at 2000°F. Austenite grain boundaries and oxide particles are visible using both modes (75×).

phasizing the other component. A number of crystals, such as tourmaline, are doubly refracting and exhibit dichroism. The Polaroid sheet is made of submicroscopic dichroic crystals aligned parallel to each other on one sheet.

Calcite is used for prism polarizers. If an object is viewed through a piece of calcite several millimeters thick, two images are observed. If the calcite is rotated, one image remains stationary while the second image rotates around the stationary image. This phenomenon is called birefringence. When a normal incident light ray strikes the calcite crystal, one of the two rays passes directly through the crystal along the optic axis while the second ray is displaced laterally. These two rays are referred to as the ordinary and extraordinary ray, respectively. These rays have different velocities, i.e., different refractive indexes. The difference in refractive indexes is a characteristic of the particular substance and can be determined with the polarizing microscope. This measured difference is the birefringenece. Birefringent substances can exhibit either positive or negative birefringence. The two rays produced in a birefringent material differ in their polarization directions and are at right angles to each other.

Light consists of electromagnetic waves vibrating in all directions perpendicular to the direction of propagation. If light is passed through a polarizing filter, the transmitted light will vibrate in a single plane. Such light is referred to as "plane-polarized" light. If two linearly polarized-light vibrations of the same frequency (i.e., monochromatic) but perpendicular to each other with a phase difference of exactly $\lambda/4$ are combined, a circularly polarized vibration is produced. Phase differences of $\lambda/2$ produce a linearly polarized vibration. Other phase differences produce elliptically polarized vibrations.

An isotropic metal (cubic or amorphous crystal structures) transmits or reflects light of the same velocity in all directions. If a plane-polarized light beam strikes normal to the surface of an isotropic metal, it will be reflected as a plane-polarized beam with the same azimuth of polarization. The amplitude of the beam, of course, will be reduced by an amount that varies with the reflectivity of the particular metal.

If a plane-polarized light beam strikes normal to the surface of an isotropic metal surface and the reflected light is passed through a second polarizing filter (the analyzer) placed 90° to the polarizer, the light will be extinguished. This position of the polarizer and analyzer is referred to as "crossed." If an anisotropic metal is substituted for an isotropic metal in the previous experiment, an image of the microstructure will be observed. Thus, the microstructure of anisotropic metals can be observed without recourse to etching. This is extremely fortuitous in the case of anisotropic metals such as beryllium, uranium, and zirconium that are difficult to etch (see Figs. 4-16 to 4-18 and Fig. 3-73 in Chap. 3). Other anisotropic metals include antimony, bismuth, cadmium, cobalt, magnesium, scandium, tellurium, tin, titanium, and zinc.

In the study of anisotropic metals with the polarizer and analyzer in the crossed position, rotation of the sample under the beam through 360° produces four positions of maximum and minimum light intensity in each grain. This is a straightforward procedure with monochromatic light but more complex for white light, since the birefringence varies with wavelength. Use of white light produces color contrast effects which can be useful as well as aesthetically pleasing. Color contrast can be further enhanced by adding a sensitive-tint plate to the light path. The relative darkness or brightness of a polycrystalline anisotropic metal varies depending on the degree of ellipticity created by reflection from the grains of different orientation.

The degree of image contrast produced is a function of the inherent aniso-

As–Polished

Bright Field

Polarized Light
(crossed polars)

Figure 4-16 Example of the value of polarized light in the examination of an optically anisotropic material (beryllium) that is difficult to etch (65×). *(Courtesy of A. E. Calabra.)*

Figure 4-17 Cross-polarized light used to reveal the microstructure of uranium (electropolished with phosphoric acid, alcohol, and ethylene glycol), 75×. *(Courtesy of B. C. Leslie, Oak Ridge National Laboratory.)*

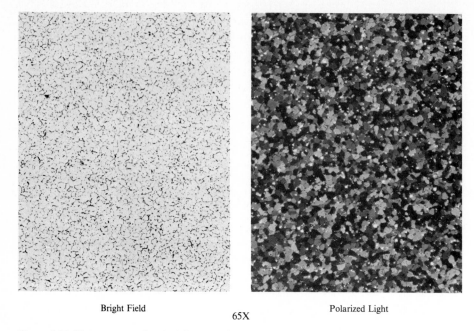

Bright Field   Polarized Light

65X

Figure 4-18 The structure of etched (0.5% HF) commercially pure titanium is more clearly revealed by the use of polarized light. *(Courtesy of N. Gendron, General Electric Co.)*

Figure 4-19 (*inside front cover*) Example of the use of crossed-polarized light on etched low-carbon steel containing lath martensite. Sample etched with 2% nital and viewed with (*a*) bright-field illumination and (*b*) polarized-light illumination, 100 ×. *(Courtesy of A. O. Benscoter, Bethlehem Steel Corp.)*

Figure 4-20 (*inside back cover*) Example of color contrast developed by the use of a sensitive-tint plate and crossed-polarized light. The specimen is a Monel tube weld. The controlled rotation of the sensitive-tint plate is obtained by a "degree wing" modification to the Bausch and Lomb metallograph. *(Courtesy of A. E. Calabra.)*

tropy of the metal being examined and the quality of the sample preparation. Electropolishing is generally the preferred preparation technique, although several investigators have shown that properly prepared mechanically polished samples can also be used effectively. A strain-free, clean, scratch-free, and pit-free surface is required for best results. Many of the anisotropic metals twin readily during mechanical polishing. Formation of these deformation twins can lead to erroneous interpretations of the true microstructure. As the quality of the mechanical polish improves, the polarized-light image contrast improves. Attack-polishing procedures, where applicable, are highly useful; however, they do not always remove all deformation twins produced in the previous steps. Electropolishing has the decided advantage of producing a deformation-free surface. However, not all metals and alloys can be electropolished effectively, and when used, conditions must be controlled to minimize or prevent etching or roughening of the surface. Chemical polishing procedures have also been effectively used with certain metals.

Isotropic metals can be examined in polarized light if the surface can be rendered optically active by etching (see Fig. 4-19), staining, or anodizing (see Figs. 3-16, 3-17, and 3-74 in Chap. 3). Successful procedures have been developed for many cubic metals and are reviewed in the chapter on etching. Not all etched surfaces respond to polarized light. The etch must produce well-defined etch pits or facets in each grain. Plane-polarized light becomes elliptically polarized by double reflection off the pit walls. Since the angle of incidence influences the degree of ellipticity, grains with different crystallographic orientation and, therefore, differently oriented etch pits, produce different amounts of ellipticity. Thus the light intensity varies from grain to grain with similar intensities in grains with similar orientation. The surfaces of the etch pits are low-index crystal faces and vary with the grain orientation. On rotation of the specimen, the contrast in each grain changes.

Anodizing, a process frequently used with aluminum, produces a thick oxide film on the metal surface electrolytically. The polarizing effect observed is due to double reflection from the surface irregularities in the film. Thin sulfide films can be deposited on many cubic metals. Interference colors are observed under bright-field illumination, and polarized light enhances these colors.

An interesting experiment on the nature of polarized-light grain contrast was conducted by Perryman and Lack [17]. In this study, electropolished zinc and cadmium, electropolished and anodized aluminum, and etched Monel were examined before and after vapor deposition of a silver film (about 80 nm thick) on the prepared surfaces. If the grain contrast was due to optical anisotropy, no effect should be observed after silver coating, since silver is isotropic. If the grain contrast was due to surface roughness effects, the silver layer should not alter the polarization effect, since the silver layer would preserve the surface roughness. Prior to silver coating, all the samples exhibited polarization effects. After silver coating, grain contrast was not observed for the electropolished (unetched) zinc and cadmium samples. However, both the etched Monel and the anodized aluminum exhibited grain contrast after silver coating. Therefore, the grain contrast revealed with polarized light in etched or anodized specimens is due to the surface irregularities and not to the optical anisotropy that produces grain contrast under polarized light in as-polished anisotropic metals.

The image produced using polarized light can be enhanced using a sensitive-tint plate placed between the polarizer and analyzer. The sensitive-tint plate greatly increases the ability to detect double reflection and birefringence. This device produces a one-wavelength path difference between the ordinary and extraordinary rays. The sensitive-tint plate is used to produce color contrast in polarized-light images (see Fig. 4-20). The wavelength selected is near the middle of the visible spectrum and a slight change in birefringence produces different colors as illustrated. Grains with different crystallographic orientation exhibit different colors. Rotation of the specimen causes the colors to change in each grain. Quartz or gypsum is generally used to make the plate.

Besides the obvious aesthetic benefits of the sensitive-tint plate, there are technical merits as well. It is possible to assess the degree of preferred orientation. Grain size measurements are more readily made when color differences are present on each side of a grain boundary. In such measurements, annealing twins are more easily detected when the sensitive-tint plate is employed.

Polarized light can be used qualitatively or quantitatively. Metallographers in general use qualitative methods, while mineralogists and biologists make both qualitative and quantitative measurements. For qualitative studies, a polarizer and analyzer are adequate. However, other accessories are required for quantitative measurements. In general, these devices are present only on microscopes specifically designed for such studies, while a polarizer and analyzer can be fitted to nearly any microscope regardless of price or sophistication.

The complex polarizing microscope is usually fitted with cross hairs in the eyepiece. Below the eyepiece a Bertrand lens is fitted in the body tube. This device can be swung or slid in and out of the tube axis. An adjustable iris diaphragm can be placed just above the Bertrand lens. The Bertrand lens is used to examine the backfocal plane of the objective. The analyzer is rotatable through 90°. An accessory slot is located between the objective and the analyzer for use of a quartz wedge. The objectives must be centerable. Strain-free objectives must be employed. The microscope stage is circular and rotatable through 360° and is graduated in 1° increments for angular measurements. The stage of a research-quality polarizing microscope is also fitted with verniers for more precise angular measurements. An engaging click stop is used to permit rotation in exact steps of 45°. For transmitted light studies, a substage condenser is employed which has a carrier for the polarizer and perhaps also one for the sensitive-tint plate.

The light source must be carefully aligned, uniform, and centered for precise polarization work. Use of tungsten filament light produces a spectrum different from that of daylight. The blues are diminished, while the red end of the spectrum is enhanced. Thus, the colors produced with a tungsten lamp differ from those produced with a xenon lamp, which more closely resembles sunlight. Xenon lamps are preferred when the image is to be projected. Mercury and halogen arc lamps are used only with interference filters.

Characteristics that can be measured using polarized light include the following [7]:

- Birefringence or amount of double refraction
- Thickness of thin sections
- Extinction angle or direction in a double refracting material
- Optical axis determination
- Right- and/or left-handedness of crystalline structures
- Dichroism, pleochroism
- Crystal system determination
- Dispersion
- Refractive index

While some of these characteristics are directly indicated, others must be calculated from the measurements or deduced from the observations. Details concerning such measurements can be found in the references.

Prior to the development of the electron microprobe, polarized light was frequently used in the identification of inclusions [18]. Such examinations were based on knowledge developed in mineralogy. Under polarized light, inclusions respond differently depending on their crystal structure and on whether they are opaque or transparent. An opaque inclusion appears dark under crossed polars if it has a cubic structure and bright if it is noncubic. In the case of anisotropic opaque inclusions, four intensity minima and maxima are observed on rotation of the specimen stage through 360°, while isotropic opaque inclusions remain dark.

The polarized-light behavior of transparent inclusions, such as glassy silicates, is more complex. A portion of the light striking the inclusion is transmitted through the inclusion and is reflected from the lower surface at the inclusion-metal interface. Since the reflection is oblique, elliptical polarization results. Preferential absorption of certain colors can occur in the transmitted light and results in a specific transmission color which can be helpful in identifying the particular inclusion.

Isotropic spherical inclusions frequently exhibit a dark "optical cross" which is stationary when the sample is rotated through 360°. In this case, light transmitted and then reflected at the inclusion-metal interface will be extinguished by a crossed analyzer in two directions at right angles to the vibration direction of the polarizer and analyzer. The optical cross is observed only if the inclusion shape is spherical, since irregular shapes produce reflections at varying angles of incidence. Pleochroism is observed in certain inclusions. In these specimens, the inclusion color varies as the stage is rotated because of preferred absorption of certain colors.

Polarized light has been used to examine oxide coatings, particularly on aluminum alloys. Since these coatings are quite thin, they are difficult to see on mounted cross sections using regular bright-field illumination. However, with polarized light they are observed as light colored bands, thus facilitating thickness measurements. In addition, if more than one coating is present or if the anodized surface is painted, the individual layers can be separated under polarized light. The polarization color differences can be used to identify the layers. Metal coatings have been examined also but less commonly. Galvanized coatings can be examined effectively using polarized light. In these samples, the zinc layer is bright and the alloy layer appears dark under crossed polars.

Polarized light has also been shown to be useful in studying metal deformation. When an isotropic transparent material is stressed, it becomes anisotropic and responds to polarized light. This effect is widely used in photoelasticity studies. When anisotropic metals are plastically deformed, intensity variations within individual grains are observed, whereas in annealed samples, the intensity within individual grains is uniform. Woodard has employed polarized light in the study of deformed Monel [19]. After suitable etching, examination under crossed polars reveals nonuniformity within the grains. Such procedures have been used to study deformed phosphor bronze, beryllium, and aluminum.

Polarized light has also been used to identify phases or constituents in many alloys. First, the phases are examined under crossed-polarized light to determine which are cubic and which are noncubic by noting their response while rotating the stage. It is possible, however, for an anisotropic phase to be oriented so that its axis of symmetry is perpendicular to the polished surface, which makes it appear to be isotropic. The examination of phases in iron-based alloys under polarized light shows that many constituents can be identified or examined more successfully than under bright-field illumination. For example, the structure of graphite nodules is vividly revealed under crossed polars (see Fig. 4-21). Surface relief effects can also produce response to polarized light, and this can be confused with effects due to anisotropy. Nonferrous alloys have been widely studied with polarized light. As an example, one can differentiate between the α and β phases in two-phase titanium alloys.

A number of investigators have used polarized light to obtain information about the crystallographic orientation of specific grains in anisotropic metals. Couling and Pearsall have described a simple method for studying grain orientations in magnesium that can be applied to other anisotropic metals [20]. Polished samples were etched and studied using an adjustable full-wave retardation plate placed between the specimen and the polarizer. The retardation plate causes selective wavelength extinction to occur, resulting in sharp color changes as the specimen is rotated in 90° increments. They observed that the trace of the basal plane in each grain was exactly parallel to a vertical cross hair in the eyepiece when the grain color changed abruptly from blue to orange upon stage rotation. The degree of basal-plane tilt was estimated from the magnitude of the intensity change. This change is highest when the basal plane is perpendicular to the surface, while no change results if it is parallel to the surface. Reed-Hill and Baldwin [21] have applied this method to the study of zirconium, and Larson and Picklesimer [22] have shown that the precision of such measurements can be improved by using a Nakamura plate to determine the exact extinction position after a sensitive-tint plate is used to approximately locate the basal-plane trace.

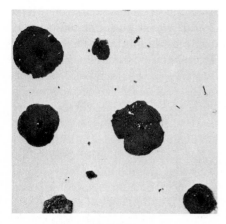

Bright Field

Crossed Polars

Figure 4-21 Cross-polarized light reveals the fine structure within graphite nodules (320 ×).

In summary, the use of polarized light in metallographic studies can be of considerable value. While its value is paramount in the study of noncubic metals, it has substantial merit in the study of cubic materials as well. The technique is reasonably easy to apply, at least for qualitative studies. The more advanced techniques require considerable effort to master but are worth the effort where justified.

Phase-contrast illumination Phase-contrast illumination [23] was developed by Zernike. This technique permits study of subtle phase variations in microstructures which have little or no intensity contrast from differences in the optical path at the surface (reflected light) or from differences in the optical path through the sample (transmitted light). Height differences of as little as 5 nm can be differentiated. Phase contrast has been applied chiefly in transmission microscopy of biological specimens, and its application to opaque samples has been rather limited. Phase contrast is especially useful in the examination of living substance in which contrast cannot be improved by staining methods. Phase contrast is useful in distinguishing between elevations and depressions or between any height difference where color contrast and reflectivity are similar.

Interference techniques Interference techniques, either interference fringe mode [24, 25] or interference contrast mode [26–29] are useful for studying microstructures with phases which exhibit little or no intensity contrast.

Use of the interference fringe mode for observing an absolutely flat specimen produces straight fringes of equal width and spacing. Any surface irregularity produces a fringe displacement and variation in fringe width or spacing. Numerous types of interference fringe illumination systems are available.

The interference-contrast mode produces an optical view of the specimen that is somewhat similar to that produced by bright-field illumination but with improved definition of low-contrast features. Examples of the application of interference contrast are given in Fig. 4-22.

If two light rays from the same point source are superimposed, interference can be obtained (this does not work if the two rays come from separate sources). The interferometer divides the incident light ray from the single point source into two or more waves which are superimposed after traveling different paths; this procedure results in interference. There are two basic types of interferometers—the two-beam instrument and the multiple-beam interferometer. The two-beam interferometer is capable of detecting height differences as small as $\lambda/20$, while the multiple-beam interferometer can detect height differences as small as $\lambda/200$. The application of special procedures, as suggested by Tolansky, can improve the resolution of each instrument. A number of interferometers are available that produce either interference fringes or interference contrast. Some typical units are described in the section that follows.

The Linnik-type interferometer is a two-beam reflection microscope employing nonpolarized light (see Fig. 4-23). Monochromatic light is split into two beams with the beam-splitting prism. One of the beams passes through the test piece objective to the test piece surface and is reflected back through the objective

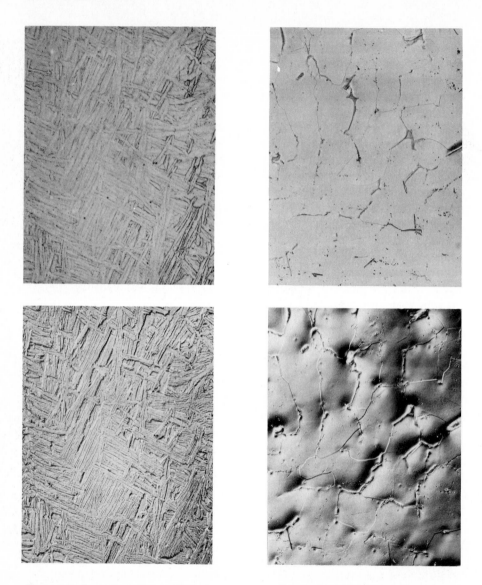

Figure 4-22 Examples of the use of interference-contrast illumination (DIC) for revealing microstructure. Top, bright-field illumination, bottom, interference-contrast illumination. On the left is a sample of alloy of Ti, 6% Al, and 4% V etched in 0.5% HF at 120× magnification. On the right is an unetched specimen of δ-plutonium at 240×. Note the improvement of detail using interference-contrast illumination. *(Courtesy of A. E. Calabra.)*

1. 6V 15W lamp
2. lamp-condenser lenses
3. adjustable aperture diaphragm
4. illuminating condenser
5. swing-out green filter
6. condenser system
7. beam-splitting prism
8. stop for blocking the reference beam
9. reference objective
10. reference (comparison) mirror
11. testpiece objective
12. testpiece
13. beam-splitting prism
14. film plane
15. image plane
16. eyepiece
17. fine adjustment
18. coarse adjustment
19. tube clamping lever
20. switch for magnet
21. lever for adjusting the aperture diaphragm 3
22. knurled ring for adjusting the green filter
23. knurled knob for focusing the mirror 10
24. lever for rotating the mirror 10 (different reflactance)
25. knurled screw for setting the inter-ference bands
26. knurled ring for setting the refer-ence part
27. lever for diaphragm 8

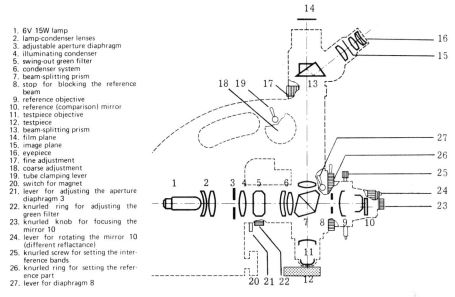

Figure 4-23 Schematic of Linnik system reflected light two-beam interference microscope. *(Courtesy of E. Leitz, Inc.)*

into the eyepiece. The second beam passes through the reference objective (identical to the test piece objective), strikes an optically flat reference mirror, and goes back to the beam splitter and to the eyepiece. If the optical path difference is equal, or is an exact multiple of $\lambda/2$, the beams reinforce each other. If the path difference is not equal, or a multiple of $\lambda/2$, interference results. Contour lines are formed that indicate the location of constant elevation. The height distance between fringes is $\lambda/2$.

The Tolansky multiple-beam interferometer produces interference between many light beams by placing a reference mirror (partially transmitting, partially reflecting) near the specimen surface, slightly out of parallel. The reference mirror has a known reflectivity which must be chosen to approximately match that of the specimen surface. Light entering the reference mirror that strikes the sample surface and is reflected by the sample surface can interfere with the rays reflected by the reference mirror. The sample and reference mirror must be close together. If the reflectance of the sample and reference mirror are very low, broad fringes result. As the reflectivity improves, the fringes become sharper and narrower. The fringe intensity produced by multiple-beam interferometers is much sharper than that from a two-beam interferometer, which accounts for the greater measurement accuracy of the multiple-beam instruments.

Interpretation of two-beam interferometer fringe patterns is rather straightforward, since the fringes are contour lines as on a map. The height between contours is $\lambda/2$. Smaller heights distorting a fringe can be estimated as a percentage of $\lambda/2$. Distinguishing elevations from depressions can be difficult without other aids such as subsequent examination with oblique light or interference-contrast illumination. If white light is used with the two-beam interferometer, colored fringes result, which replace the dark bands created by monochromatic light.

The equipment for multiple-beam interferometry is rather simple compared to that for a two-beam interferometer and also permits more accurate, higher-resolution height measurements. The distance between fringes is λ/2 (monochromatic light source), and elevations or depressions are detected as deviations from straight parallel lines. The distance between fringes can be adjusted by changing the angular relationship between the reference mirror and sample surface.

If polarized light is employed with the reflection microscope, interference-contrast illumination can be obtained, as in the Nomarski interference microscope. The principle of the interference-contrast microscope is illustrated in Fig. 4-24. A double quartz prism (Wollaston prism) is placed between one objective and the vertical illuminator, and the polarizer and analyzer are crossed. A high-intensity light source is required. The two beams created by the prism interfere coherently in the image plane and produce two slightly displaced (laterally) images differing in phase (λ/2), thus producing height contrast. Examples of the value of interference-contrast illumination were given previously in Fig. 4-22.

Ultraviolet microscopy As shown by Eqs. (4-6) to (4-9) and Fig. 4-8, the limit of resolution can be improved by increasing the NA or by decreasing the wavelength of the incident light. In the early days of optical microscopy, emphasis was placed on raising the magnification range of the optical microscope [30]. This was

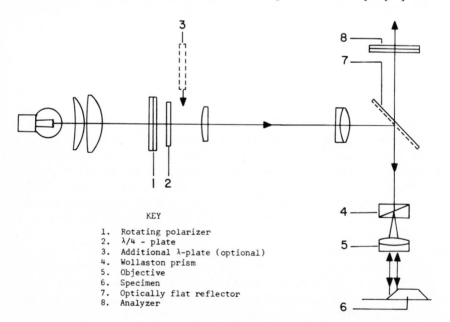

KEY

1. Rotating polarizer
2. λ/4 – plate
3. Additional λ-plate (optional)
4. Wollaston prism
5. Objective
6. Specimen
7. Optically flat reflector
8. Analyzer

Figure 4-24 Schematic diagram illustrating the light path in the Leitz interference contrast device R.

obtained primarily by improving the quality of the optics. Next, effort was placed on improving resolution through use of shorter-wavelength light. Prior to the development of the electron microscope, considerable attention was given to improving the resolution of the light microscope by the use of ultraviolet light (365 nm) [31, 32]. The extra cost of these microscopes for the small gain in resolution, the difficulty of using them, and the development of electron microscopes with vastly better resolution inhibited the development of ultraviolet microscopy. Recently, a scanning optical microscope employing a helium-neon laser has been developed [33]. This instrument, which can operate in several illumination modes, provides resolution superior to the optical microscope.

Light-section microscopy The light-section microscope, which was developed by Schmaltz and improved by Tolansky, is used for measuring surface topography, a technique which complements interferometry. In light-section microscopy, a slit is placed near the field iris in the illumination system and is imaged by objective O_1 as a light line on the surface to be examined (see Fig. 4-25). Oblique illumination is used, and the background is dark. The light band is observed through the microscope with objective O_2, which is identical to objective O_1. The illumination and observation objectives are at right angles to each other and are at an angle of 45° to the specimen surface. Reticle M is visible in eyepiece Ok and can be shifted within the field of view to facilitate measurements. Magnifications as high as 400X are employed, permitting roughness measurements from about 1 to 400 μm. In certain cases higher magnifications have been used, permitting measurements down to about 0.25 μm. Although the vertical resolution is not as good as can be achieved with interferometers, lateral resolution is better, and the technique is quite useful with rough surfaces. The light-section microscope is widely used in the study of machined surfaces and has been employed to measure the thickness of various types of surface layers or films [34, 35].

Fluorescence microscopy Certain materials emit radiation of their own when illuminated by ultraviolet, violet, blue, or green light. The emitted light has a longer wavelength than that of the incident stimulus. The emission phenomenon is termed luminescence of which there are two forms—phosphorescence and fluorescence. The difference between these two relates to the presence or absence of the emission after the stimulating light is removed. Phosphorescent materials exhibit some level of emission for a while after the light stimulus is removed, while fluorescent materials only emit excited radiation when the stimulus is present.

Two types of fluorescence occur. Certain unstained materials emit fluorescent light of short wavelength. Other materials must be stained with certain dyes (fluorchromes) to produce fluorescence. The former condition is referred to as primary fluorescence or autofluorescence, while the latter is secondary fluorescence. Staining techniques are widely used to identify certain tissues.

Reflection and transmission fluorescence microscopes are available from a variety of manufacturers. The technique is not used in metallography but has been widely applied in medicine and biology and has been used to study wood and coal.

Camera attachment,
consisting of a film casing,
shutter and photo tube

Eyepiece micrometer
with a measuring drum
and zeroing device

Knurled screw for focusing
the light on the test-piece
surface, and knob for
centering the light band
on the reticle

Combined coarse and
fine focusing adjustment

Switch for

    ◇ ocular viewing
    ▽ photographing

Revolving nosepiece for
pairs of objectives
of 200× and 400×
magnification

Mechanical stage
25×25 mm (1 × 1 in.)

On — off switch
with brightness adjuster

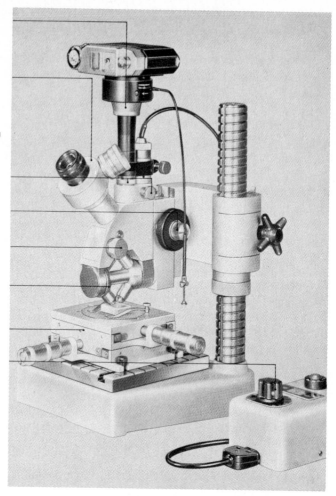

Q   light source
Ok   ocular (or eyepiece)
M   reticle
O₁ ⎫
O₂ ⎭ pairs of objectives
O₃   optical parts in photo tube

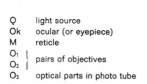
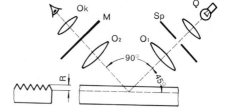

Figure 4-25 Light-section microscope and schematic of the light path. *(Courtesy of C. Zeiss, Inc.)*

Fluorescence microscopy is generally performed using reflected light, since much of the excited light is lost during transmission. Leitz has developed a special opaque illuminator which overcomes the low image brightness produced using normal illuminators. Besides increasing the amount of reflected light, this illuminator also blocks the invisible portion of the excited light in the ultraviolet region that would damage the eye. Zeiss has also developed a very suitable opaque illuminator for fluorescence studies.

Fluorescence studies have been done on low-rank coals. Since the illumination level is low, all diaphragms are open. In general, rather high-magnification objectives, either dry or oil immersion, are used. Only certain macerals in coal, such as exinite, exhibit fluorescent characteristics. Use of fluorescence microscopy is helpful in the study of these macerals, since additional information that would not be provided using bright-field illumination can be obtained.

Infrared microscopy The use in microscopy of infrared or near-infrared light has been quite limited. Early work used photographic techniques to record the infrared image produced with the polarized-light microscope. The little work that has been done has been mainly in mineralogy. Recently an infrared image tube assembly that replaces the microscope eyepiece has been developed and provides a direct view of the infrared image. Harris has shown that certain optical measurements done with ordinary light can also be performed with infrared light [36].

4-5 LIGHT PHENOMENA

Observation of specimens with the light microscope enables the microscopist to learn a great deal about the nature of the specimen and to draw conclusions about the processing steps used in manufacturing the material and about the properties of the material. As such it is an invaluable tool in materials science. Characteristics of materials can be determined by observation of the type, shape, size, and nature of the phases, features, or constituents present. For certain measurements, special equipment is required, as in the case of the study of polarized-light phenomena or reflectance measurements. The behavior of light results in a number of phenomena: reflection, refraction, dispersion, diffraction, interference, absorption, polarization and fluorescence.

Reflection has been discussed previously in the section on polarized light. Reflection from a smooth surface is referred to as specular or regular, while reflection from a rough surface is called diffuse or scattered. Refraction occurs when monochromatic light is bent as it passes obliquely from one medium to another. Dispersion is the spreading out of light into its component colors. Although we generally assume that light travels in a straight line, light bends slightly around the edge of objects in its path and spreads out behind the obstacle. This phenomenon is called diffraction. Interference occurs when two or more light waves are out of phase with each other, resulting in decreased intensity or in extinction if they are of opposite phase. When incident light strikes an object, part of the light is reflected while the balance is absorbed. The amount of absorbed light varies with the material and its thickness. Polarization occurs when the light waves are restricted to a single plane, as has been discussed previously. Fluorescence occurs when certain materials are excited by light.

The refractive index n of minerals is frequently measured as an aid to qualitative analysis. The refractive index of an unknown mineral can be determined by immersing it in liquids of known refractive index [37, 38]. If the mineral grains are in sharp focus under oblique illumination, those grains appearing in positive relief have an index of refraction that is greater than the index of refraction of the immersion fluid. If the grains are lowered slightly from sharp focus, those appearing brighter are of higher refractive index than the immersion fluid while those appearing darker are lower in refractive index. If a colorless isotropic substance is immersed in a liquid with the same refractive index as the substance, the substance will be invisible. Since the refractive index of an immersion liquid varies slightly with temperature, measurements should be made at a standard temperature.

The differentiation of phases or constituents is a basic objective in microscopy. In making such discriminations in bright-field illumination, the observer depends primarily on the reflectivity differences between the phases. For bright-field illumination and air objectives with small apertures, the reflectance is described by the following equation:

$$R = \frac{I_r}{I_i} = \frac{(n_1 - n_0)^2 + k^2}{(n_1 + n_0)^2 + k^2} \tag{4-12}$$

where I_r, I_i = the intensities of the reflected and incident light

n_1, n_0 = the refractive indexes of the material and immersion medium

k = absorption coefficient

Reflectivity differences can be detected by the human eye, but greater sensitivity is obtained with a photometer. Photometry is widely applied in coal petrography and mineralogy but infrequently in metallography [39–42].

The photometer consists of a microscope with a photomultiplier and a device to measure the amplified current—a potentiometer, galvanometer, or cathode-ray oscilloscope is employed (see Fig. 4-26). The mechanical stage is usually equipped to move in fixed increments. Monochromatic light is employed. Generally, a double wave-band filter (546 nm for coal) is used to create monochromatic light. The measurement area is stopped down to less than 10 μm , frequently 1-μm diameter is employed, through the use of a special aperture. Measurements are usually made at high magnifications employing either air or oil immersion objectives. In coal petrography, oil immersion objectives are employed along with plane-polarized light.

The rank of a given coal is directly related to its coking power and is determined by measuring the reflectivity of the vitrinite maceral. As the reflect-

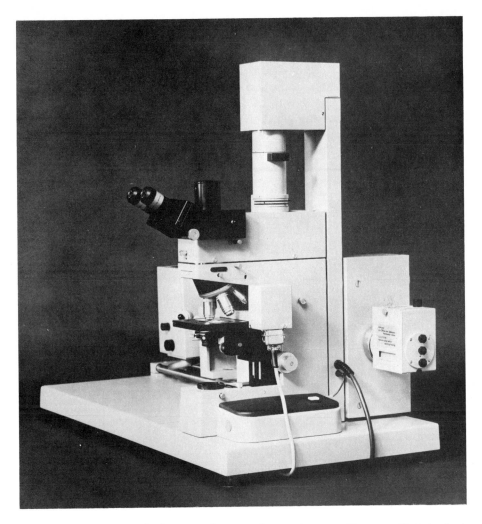

Figure 4-26 The Leitz MPV2 microscope photometer/spectrophometer. *(Courtesy of E. Leitz, Inc.)*

ance of vitrinite increases, the coal rank as well as its value in coke making increases. The measurement is conducted by determining the maximum reflectance of 100 vitrinite grains. In each measurement, the stage is rotated to find the maximum reflectance. If the anisotropy is weak ($R_{max} - R_{min} < 0.2$ percent), mean reflectance is generally recorded. The average maximum reflectance of the 100 measurements (mean maximum reflectance) is used to rank the coal. In such measurements, glass standards of known reflectance are used to determine the absolute reflectance. The reflectance of the other macerals in coal can also be measured, but this measurement is somewhat more difficult, since the other macerals are generally smaller in size. In recent years a considerable effort has been made to automate reflectance measurements. Except for the iron pyrite in coal, the light reflectance of the macerals in coal is less than 5 percent with oil immersion objectives. In such work, an intense, stable light source must be employed. Quartz-iodide and tungsten-halogen lamps are widely used.

A wide variety of techniques are used to identify minerals. One popular method combines microhardness and reflectance measurements. In contrast to work with coal, reflectance measurements on minerals have involved numerous monochromatic light wavelengths between blue and red. Again, plane-polarized light is employed, and standards must be used to obtain absolute values of reflectance. Several different standards are employed in order to determine the spectral characteristics of the measuring system and the linearity of the detector. Tabulations of the reflectance characteristics of many minerals can be found in the references.

4-6 PHOTOMICROGRAPHY

In the early days of metallography the observer had to record information through drawings because photography was also in its infancy. Furthermore, printing processes could handle line drawings much more easily than photographic half-tones. For example, Sorby's pioneering work in the metallography of iron and steel was published initially without inclusion of the micrographs. Fortunately, this situation was corrected by the end of the nineteenth century. However, the practice of sketching microstructures is an excellent teaching tool which, unfortunately, is rarely used.

It is quite obvious that metallography is highly dependent on photography. By the 1920s, the art of photomicroscopy had reached a highly respectable level. A study of publications by the eminent American metallographer Francis F. Lucas in that period reveals work that even today would be considered exceptional. However, with the equipment and photographic advances made since the 1920s, it is reasonably easy for the average metallographer to produce high-quality photomicrographs. But to achieve the best possible results, a thorough knowledge of the operation of the microscope and a mastering of photographic principles are imperative. In the past, nearly all photomicrographs were taken on the metallograph. In recent years bench microscopes have been used with increasing frequency. Good results can be obtained with a bench microscope provided vibrations can be eliminated.

Since the introduction of "instant" photographic materials (Polaroid), photomicroscopy has been considerably simplified. Traditional darkroom photographic techniques do involve considerable time and expense. For the small laboratory or occasional microscopist, instant photography is of great value. With the instant process, however, the metallographer does sacrifice some quality for the gain in speed and convenience. For the larger laboratory, considerable automation of printing techniques is available, but the cost of such equipment cannot be justified by the occasional user. Although a complete review of photographic principles is not provided here, references are given covering photomicroscopy in general [43–

48], color photomicroscopy [49, 50], special photographic methods [51–53], stereomicroscopy [54–56], and macrophotography [57–63]. Besides taking photomicrographs, the metallographer frequently takes macrophotographs and, in many cases, acts as the company's industrial photographer. In recent years, the use of color photography both in microscopy and macrophotography has gained considerable popularity. Because of its greater reproduction costs, however, color photography is much less common than black-and-white photography. Thus, color photography is usually limited to those instances, such as in failure analysis, where its use is justified.

The value of photomicroscopy in illustrating important points or documenting existing conditions is undeniably great. Since microstructure is an important factor in the establishment and control of the properties and behavior of materials, proper rendition of the microstructure is necessary. Of course, prior to applying photographic methods the specimen must be suitably prepared. Application of the best photographic principles is useless if specimen preparation is poorly performed. Once the specimen has been properly prepared, the metallographer must apply suitable observational procedures to produce an image suitable for photography. The preceding sections have discussed how the metallographer can make best use of the microscope or metallograph. The metallographer is now ready to record the observations on film so that this information can be conveyed to associates. Proper photographic techniques are applied, and these pictures are incorporated in a report or paper, thus completing the task.

4-6.1 Obtaining Good Photomicrographs

In the observation of details through the microscope, three separate effects are used to create the visual impression of good focus over the field of view:

1. The depth of field of the objective (depends on magnification, NA, light wavelength, etc.)
2. The adjustment of the fine-focus control while viewing
3. The slight change in focus due to eye accomodation

In the photographic process, only the first effect can be used. In obtaining sharp photomicrographs, the microscopist must control the following variables:

- Eliminate vibrations
- Align illumination
- Match illumination color to objective corrections
- Maintain cleanliness of optics
- Correct adjustment of field and aperture diaphragms
- Focus precisely, generally with the aid of a focusing telescope

Since focusing on a ground glass is difficult because of the rough texture of the glass, a central, clear area is provided for focusing. When viewing the image at this location through a focusing telescope, one must be sure that the illumination level is reduced to a safe level through the use of neutral density and color correction filters in order to prevent injury to the eye.

A wide range of photographic devices can be employed. Traditionally, a bellows or zoom system is employed on the metallograph to provide greater choice of magnifications. In many cases, 4 by 5 in sheet film is employed, and contact prints are made from the negative. In this case, a simple film holder is placed in front of the ground glass. This device is designed to place the sheet film at the plane of focus. For most work, the magnification can be calculated using either Eqs. (4-4) or (4-5). Alternatively, one can photograph a stage micrometer using the various objectives, eyepieces, and bellows extension or zoom magnification factor and determine the true magnification. The apparent length of the ruling is divided by the true length to obtain the total magnification for the particular combination of optical variables. These data can be summarized in a table available to anyone using the instrument.

4-6.2 Black-and-White Photography

A wide range of black and white photographic films are available using either traditional or instant techniques. Plates, sheet film, or roll film in various formats can be employed depending on the particular equipment available. In recent years, 35-mm film has received increased use, although it is less convenient to use unless a considerable number of photographs are taken. In addition, the negatives must be enlarged in printing and the amount of enlargement must be controlled in order to obtain the desired magnification. Manufacturers of photographic films provide complete information on film characteristics and recommended practices.

Besides the lower reproduction costs, black-and-white films exhibit better contrast control, simpler processing, and quicker results than color processes. In traditional black-and-white photography, a negative image is first produced; this negative image is then used to produce a positive image of the microstructure on suitable paper. Selection of the negative material requires knowledge of the characteristics of available films, such as color sensitivity, contrast, resolving power, graininess, speed, exposure, and development latitude.

Not all black-and-white films are sensitive to the entire visible spectrum. Panchromatic films are sensitive to the entire visible spectrum, while orthochromatic films are sensitive to all colors (particularly green) except orange and red. Infrared-sensitive films provide sensitivity to red and the infrared spectrum. Film is also available that is sensitive to the ultraviolet region, violet, and blue.

The gray-level scale of color rendition of panchromatic film does not exactly reproduce the visual color spectrum. Violet and blue colors are brighter, while yellows are darker than they should be. Thus, use of a yellow filter with daylight illumination (xenon) is useful. Panchromatic films must be developed in complete darkness.

Orthochromatic films are widely used in microscopy, since achromats are used with green or yellow-green light to minimize lens abberations. Since they are not sensitive to red light, safelights can be used in handling these films. If the microscopic image contains red colors, panchromatic films should be used.

Films with low, medium, or high contrast are available. In addition, for a given film, contrast can be altered somewhat in development and in printing. Development contrast can be adjusted by altering the development time or by the choice of developing solution. As a rule, the use of such techniques is beyond the ability of many metallographers. It is best to rigorously follow the manufacturer's recommendations regarding development practice. For low-contrast images, it is helpful to use a high-contrast film. For high-contrast images, a low- or medium-contrast film is best.

The resolving power of a film is its ability to record fine details present in the image. The "graininess" of a film depends on the size of the silver grains in the film emulsion, and it will vary with the developer used and development time. As the speed of the film increases, its graininess increases. Graininess is important if the negative is to be enlarged substantially. For high resolution, one should choose a fine-grained film. If the image resolution obtained with the microscope objectives is to be faithfully reproduced on the film, a fine-grained film with high resolving power is necessary to provide a high probability of obtaining a good image.

The speed of films is described by the ASA (American Standards Association) number [or the German DIN (Deutche Industrie Norm)]. The American ASA system is arithmetic, while the German system is logarithmic. Thus, a film with 400 ASA speed is twice as fast as one at 200 ASA and four times as fast as one at 100 ASA. For the DIN system, an increase of three units indicates a doubling of the speed. With modern metallographs, the film speed is not a critical parameter. Film speed can be altered during development.

In exposing a negative there is a range of allowable exposures over which a useful negative can be produced. Thus, the range of exposure latitude is important to the metallographer, especially if an automatic exposure device is unavailable. Each film has a characteristic curve of exposure versus density. Figure 4-27 illustrates the typical shape of such a curve. The exposure should be controlled so that it lies on the linear portion of the curve. The tangent of the slope of the linear region is a measure of the contrast of the film and is referred to as the gamma (λ) value of the film. For a gamma of 1, the image contrast and negative contrast are equal. In practice a gamma slightly greater than 1 is best for photomicroscopy. Development time and temperature influence the gamma value. These variables must be carefully controlled.

Processing of the photographic negative involves the following steps: developing, fixing, washing, and drying. The developer recommended by the manufacturer should be used.

The correct exposure is most easily determined through use of an exposure meter. If one is not available, a test exposure series can be made. This is done by pulling out the film-holder slide completely and exposing the entire film for a time judged to be shorter than required. Then, the slide is inserted so that it covers about 1/2 to 1 in (12 to 25 mm) of the film, and the film is exposed again for the same length of time. This process is repeated until the slide is fully closed. After

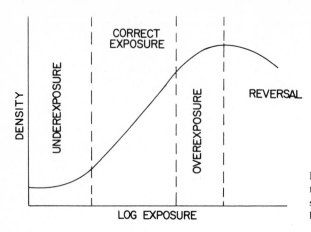

Figure 4-27 Schematic illustrating the relationship between exposure time and film density for a black-and-white film.

development of the negative, the proper exposure time can be determined. Instant photography is particularly helpful for such purposes. However, differences in film speed must be accounted for if the speed of the instant film and the negative film are different. Once a correct exposure time has been determined for a certain objective and magnification, the correct exposure time for different conditions can be calculated using the following relationship [46]:

$$\text{New exposure time} = (\text{standard time}) \ \frac{\text{standard NA} \times \text{new magnification}}{\text{new NA} \times \text{standard magnification}}$$

$$(4\text{-}13)$$

Since the exposure time is altered by the use of filters and the aperture settings, these factors will vary the results calculated with Eq. (4-13) if they are altered.

Contact printing of black-and-white negatives (such as 4 by 5, 5 by 7, 8 by 10 in) is widely employed in metallography. The use of 35-mm negatives requires enlargement. It is best to utilize glossy-surface papers in printing in order to obtain maximum brilliance and detail. Most publications request glossy prints for reproduction. Either chloride-type or bromide-type papers can be used for printing. Bromide types are best for enlarging and are usually preferred for contact printing. Printing papers usually have higher contrast (gamma) than negatives but exhibit less exposure latitude. Contrast in contact printing is controlled by the choice of paper and by development time. The contrast or exposure scale of contact-printing paper varies from extra soft to extra contrasty (grade numbers 0 to 5). In practice, no. 3 paper is preferred for normal negatives, with no. 4 paper used to increase the contrast or no. 2 paper used to decrease it if needed.

4-6.3 Color Photography

Two types of color films are available: reversal color film and negative color films. A positive color transparency is produced by color reversal films after processing. With these films, the colors are substantially the same as in the image. Since color negative films produce a negative with complimentary colors, printing is required to obtain the true colors.

While reversal film is less expensive to process, color negative films offer greater versatility. It is also possible to make black-and-white prints from a color negative. To keep film and processing costs down, use of an automatic exposure device is recommended. Good results can be obtained by exposing a roll of color negative film and having it processed by a commercial laboratory. However, in printing, the true colors are sometimes shifted somewhat, since the laboratory technicians are not familiar with the subject matter. Best results are obtained if metallographers process and print their own work. Certain color films can be processed with relatively simple equipment, while others require elaborate, expensive equipment. The choice of approach depends on the volume of photographs required, the available funds, and the need for such work. Larger companies frequently have color laboratories used primarily for advertisements. In such cases, the metallographer can provide the necessary instructions to the personnel running the color laboratory and obtain excellent color renditions.

In selecting the proper color film, the metallographer must pay particular attention to the type of light source used, since films are balanced for either artificial light or daylight. The xenon light source is particularly useful in color photomicroscopy, since it provides a very useful daylight spectrum. For other light sources, it may be necessary to use color-balancing filters to balance the color temperature of the light to that of the film. Crouse et al. have compared a number of color films and have shown that differences in contrast and color rendition occur with different films [49]. Their work should be consulted by anyone interested in using color in photomicrography.

Color films are characterized by the same factors as black-and-white films plus color balance. However, contrast and granularity of color films are not as varied as with black-and-white films. Thus, the key factors in selecting a color film are the type of image (print or transparency), the format (size), type of processing, and color balance. When using color reversal films, the illumination should be adjusted to provide a relatively short exposure, generally faster than about 1/4 s. Longer exposure will produce a color shift (reciprocity effect).

4-6.4 Film Handling

As a final note on photography, some comments on film handling are given. When handling films and papers, one should always hold them by the edge, since fingerprints will show up in the final product. Good darkroom techniques are required. Thorough washing of negatives and prints before drying is an absolute necessity. During negative development, the negative should be immersed rapidly into the developer to prevent uneven development. Since air bubbles can adhere to the negative surface, periodic agitation of the negative or developer is suggested. After immersing the negatives, one should shake them to dislodge air bubbles, and this process should be repeated at least once a minute thereafter. Spent developer or fixers should be replenished. Agitation of the negatives is also required during fixing. It is important that the negatives be rinsed thoroughly before fixing in order to prevent carryover of the developer into the fixer, which will degrade the negative. After thorough washing, the negatives should be dried in a dust-free environment. Negatives should be stored in envelopes to prevent them from being scratched and to keep them dust-free.

Photographic films are damaged by high temperature and high humidity. Color films are more sensitive to these factors than black-and-white films. Photographic products have a certain shelf life as indicated by the expiration date on the wrapper. The useful life of films can be extended if they are stored in a freezer or refrigerator. Film stored in this manner should be allowed to warm up to room temperature before being opened to prevent condensation.

4-7 PHOTOMACROGRAPHY

Microscopic examination may not be representative of the gross condition of the specimen being studied if only a few areas are examined, especially if the component is heterogeneous. It is usually best to perform a macroscopic examination prior to sample preparation for microscopic examination in order to determine the significant areas of interest. This is especially critical when performing a failure analysis. A hand lens or low-power stereomicroscope (see Fig. 4-28) are very helpful tools for macroscopic examination [54–56].

Macroexamination is often performed to study the following:

- General distribution of nonmetallic inclusions (sulfur print, oxide print, or lead print)
- Location and extent of chemical segregation
- Location and extent of mechanically induced heterogeneity
- Presence of defects resulting from manufacture, fabrication, or service
- Nature of solidification pattern and soundness
- Flow lines induced by forging
- Examination of fracture features

For optimum results fracture surfaces should be carefully preserved, especially if fractography is contemplated. Sectioning and grinding must be carefully performed so that artifacts are not induced.

Photomacrography can easily be accomplished with amateur or professional cameras, with a simple microscope, or with a magnifier using a magnification up to about 50X. Some metallographs can be equipped with low-magnification objectives which permit performance of photomacrography. Likewise, photomacrography can also be performed with a camera attached to a compound stereoviewer-type microscope. The use of 35-mm cameras with a macro lens, close-up lens, or bellows extension is very popular in photomacrography.

Photomacrography in most laboratories requires very flexible equipment because of the great variety of specimen sizes and magnifications or reductions required (see Fig. 4-29). The simple microscope for photomacrography consists of

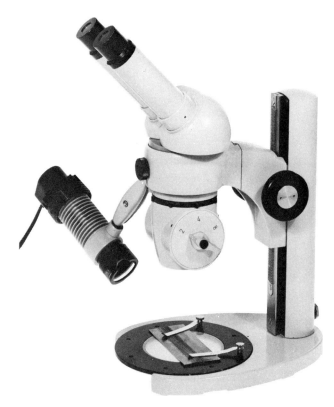

Figure 4-28 Zeiss high-resolution stereomicroscope with three objective pairs on a quick-change turret. *(Courtesy of C. Zeiss, Inc.)*

a macrocamera lens, diaphragm, and shutter assembly coupled to a bellows and film holder. Focusing can be accomplished either with a reflex mirror or by viewing the image on a ground glass in the film holder. Lenses normally have a focal length of 19 to 150 mm.

Magnification with the simple microscope is a function of the focal length of the macrocamera lens (FL) and the lens-to-film distance (D):

$$M = \frac{D - \text{FL}}{\text{FL}} \tag{4-14}$$

In practice, the magnification can easily be determined by placing a measuring scale on the object to be photographed and then ratioing the change in scale length to the original length.

The depth of field depends upon the aperture diaphragm setting of the macrocamera lens, the magnification, and the focal length of the lens. The depth of field increases as the aperture is stopped down; however, the image brightness and sharpness decrease. Depth of field increases with decreasing magnification and increasing focal length.

Figure 4-29 Polaroid MP4 macrocamera, light box, and fiber-optic light source.

In photomacrography, the most important elements are adequate lighting, depth of field, and resolution. Since most objects being photographed are three-dimensional, the lighting must reveal the shape and texture of the object. In some instances, available natural light proves adequate, perhaps aided by an auxiliary light to remove undesired shadows. It is often helpful to rest the specimen on a piece of translucent plastic which is illuminated from below. This produces a pleasant background for dark objects and helps remove shadows. For light objects, it is useful to place them on a black background. In color photography, colored objects can be photographed while resting on a cloth or paper of a complementary color.

A wide variety of illumination techniques can be applied. Indeed, photomacrography generally taxes the creative ability of the microscopist in producing good, aesthetically pleasing macrographs. For example, for specimens with holes or cavities, it is useful to place a light close to the lens axis. For polished specimens, it is useful to tilt the specimen slightly and reflect light onto the specimen surface. In such work, the light beam should be as broad as possible in order to eliminate hot spots. For irregularly shaped rough surfaces, it is useful to permit some shadows in order to emphasize the texture. This is best accomplished using a focused beam striking the sample at an angle. Highly reflective objects can be photographed by surrounding the object with a cylinder or cone of tissue paper and then surrounding the paper with illumination. Ring lights are available that fit around the camera lens and are useful in illuminating small objects. The light box, which is shown in Figure 4-29, is also useful for photographing small objects. A fluorescent tube lamp is located at the top of the box just under the lip. The bottom side of the box is equipped with a translucent sheet of plastic. The box can be turned upside down, and objects are placed on the sheet. In this way, bottom lighting is provided. The top surface of the subject is illuminated by a ring lamp or by oblique lighting. It is also possible to provide axial lighting using a thin sheet of half-reflecting glass placed between the lens and the object. Light is directed horizontally at the half-reflecting mirror to light the subject.

Control of depth of field is important in obtaining good photomacrographs. The depth of field that can be obtained depends on the f-number of the lens and the desired magnification, as given by the following equation [58]:

$$\text{Depth of field} = 2(\text{f-number})(C)\left(1 + \frac{1}{M}\right) \qquad (4\text{-}15)$$

where depth of field is in millimeters, C is the circle of confusion of the subject which is equal to $0.33/M$, and M is the desired magnification. For example, if a 2X magnification is desired and the lens is stopped down to f/22, the depth of field is 11 mm. As the lens is opened (lower f-stop numbers), the depth of field decreases.

It is commonly believed that short focal length lenses provide greater depth than longer focal length lenses, but the difference is minor. However, long focal length lenses provide a greater working distance between lens and subject and are therefore preferred.

Another important factor is the depth of detail, i.e., the ability to separate detail throughout the depth of focus. Although the depth of focus increases as the f-number increases, the depth of detail increases as the f-number increases and then drops rapidly with further increases in f-number. Thus, there is an optimum f-stop for depth of detail which lies between f/10 and f/16. Since the depth of detail drops as the magnification increases, there is an optimum f-setting for any given magnification.

In photomacrography the metallographer should start by examining the subject's texture and shape. One must then determine which features are of greatest importance and adjust the lighting to bring out the required detail. This usually involves considerable trial and error, but experience will shorten the required effort. Next, the optical parameters such as the f-stop and desired magnification are selected. The type of film is selected based on color requirements, speed, contrast, format, etc. The exposure is determined through the use of a light meter or a stepwise series of exposures or guessed through experience with the particular setup. In arranging the subject, it is best to minimize the depth of detail as far as possible. If a high magnification is required, one should try to obtain as much as possible on the film. As wide a lens opening as possible should be used for the depth of detail and resolution required. It is wise to take several photographs using slightly different conditions and choose the best for the report. This is easy to do once the lighting is arranged rather than having to setup again later. A word of advice is that a good print describes details more easily and simpler than words and is clear proof of your observations. In illustrating conditions, an overall view along with needed close-up enlargements is a good technique for clearly illustrating important points.

4-8 AUXILIARY TECHNIQUES

4-8.1 Microhardness

Microhardness testing, or the technique of making hardness measurements of phases observable only with the aid of the light microscope, is a very useful tool. Most microscope manufacturers supply accessory equipment for microhardness determinations with bench microscopes or metallographs. Single-purpose units are also available which cover a variety of loads from as low as 1 to 1000 g and, thus, can be used for measuring the hardness of a wide range of materials (soft to hard) or sizes.

Microhardness testing is useful for determining the depth of decarburization, carburization, nitriding, etc. Microhardness testing is also useful in phase identification and is ideal for evaluating weldments. This subject is described in greater detail in Chap. 5.

4-8.2 Hot-Stage Microscopy

Hot-stage microscopy can be used to study microstructure changes occurring on heating or cooling or at a constant temperature [64–68]. Hot-stage accessories are available for many bench microscopes or metallographs or as single-purpose units. Long working-distance objectives are used, since there is usually a minimum required clearance between the specimen and the objective lens because of the presence of the quartz window above the specimen. Usually, objectives of about 20X or higher magnifications must be quartz-corrected. Hot-stage techniques have also been developed for the electron microscope.

Transformations involving considerable surface relief, such as the austenite-to-martensite or austenite-to-lower bainite reactions, can be examined under bright-field illumination. Transformations involving a very limited amount of surface relief, such as the austenite-to-pearlite reaction, are best examined using phase-contrast, interference-contrast, or polarized-light illumination. For kinetic studies, it is usually best to record the sequence of events with a motion picture camera. The samples are heated under vacuum or under an inert-gas atmosphere. The heating rate is controlled by varying the current applied to the stage. For isothermal conditions the temperature must be maintained constant throughout the desired time period. The cooling rate is controlled by gradually decreasing the current or by introducing a blast of an inert gas, such as helium, at a certain pressure. Chilling the inert gas can also be used to increase the cooling rate.

The following are some of the topics that can be studied using hot-stage microscopy:

- Melting and solidification
- Surface reactions
- Grain growth
- Transformations
- Welding

- Sintering
- Graphitization
- Gaseous reactions

Figure 4-30 shows a hot-stage microscope which is capable of performing controlled heating and quenching experiments [67, 68]. Figure 4-31 shows austenite grains in AISI 1080 steel at 2000°F. Note that the grains are growing at the expense of smaller grains (faint lines). Figure 4-32 shows a sample of AISI 1080 quenched at a rate that produces considerable martensite (areas of high surface relief). Figure 4-33 shows the same specimen after polishing and etching. Note that the areas showing little or no surface relief coincide with pearlite and upper bainite. The kinetics of phase transformations can be studied by equipping the microscope with a 16-mm movie camera (see Fig. 4-30). An example of the use of this technique is given in Fig. 4-34.

4-8.3 Special Stages for *In Situ* Experiments

Special stages have been designed to enable the metallographer to accomplish a wide variety of tasks or to simplify operating procedures. For example, autoleveling stages are available that facilitate rapid leveling of mounted samples in the upright microscope without the need for clay. For the examination of fractures,

Figure 4-30 Hot-stage microscope system with a specially designed temperature control system *(From Benscoter et al., Ref. 67, 68, courtesy of A. Z. Publishing Corp.)*

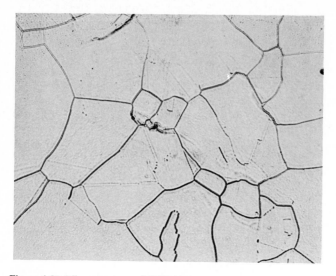

Figure 4-31 Microstructure of AISI 1080 steel heated to 2000°F in the hot-stage microscope using a nitrogen atmosphere. Thermal etching shows the location of the austenite grain boundaries. The faint boundaries are remnants of thermally etched grains produced at a lower temperature (240×). *(Courtesy of J. R. Kilpatrick, Bethlehem Steel Corp.)*

Figure 4-32 Microstructure of AISI 1080 steel quenched in the hot-stage microscope to produce mostly plate martensite (high relief areas) and some upper transformation products (low relief areas) at 240×, unetched. *(Courtesy of J. R. Kilpatrick, Bethlehem Steel Corp.)*

Figure 4-33 Microstructure of the sample shown in Fig. 4-32 after light repolishing and etching with 2% nital. The light etching structure is plate martensite (plus some retained austenite). Some lower bainite is observed near the center (medium gray), while the dark constituent is pearlite (240×). *(Courtesy of J. R. Kilpatrick, Bethlehem Steel Corp.)*

universal tilting stages have been developed for rapid manipulation of rough, irregular samples [69]. A variety of stages have been designed to facilitate handling of small objects during examination.

Metallurgists seem to have a natural urge to observe processes or behavior while it is occurring. These *in situ* experiments require the adaptation of metallographic equipment to permit such observations. Hot-stage microscopy is the major technique used for observing *in situ* experiments. While some of the commercial hot-stage microscopes can be operated at ambient or subambient temperatures, a number of special "cold-stage" microscopes have been developed [70, 71]. However, cold-stage microscopes have less applicability to metallographic studies, since only a few important transformations occur at low temperatures compared to the wide variety of phenomena that can be observed at high temperature. In solidification studies, considerable work has been done by *in situ* observation of the solidification of low-melting-point organic materials, such as camphene (melting point of 46°C), which solidify like metals [72]. Likewise, the recrystallization of low-melting-point metals and alloys has been observed with such equipment [73].

Metallographers have made particular use of electrolytic polishing and etching cells and similar devices to examine metals as they are electrolytically polished and etched [74]. Similar types of devices have been used to study corrosion [75–77] and the growth of electrodeposits [78].

Likewise, many *in situ* experiments have been performed to study the behavior of materials under load. For example, numerous studies have been made using special stressing stages and direct microscopic examination [79–84]. *In situ*

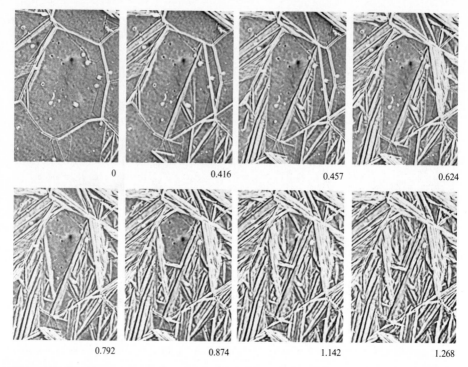

0   0.416   0.457   0.624

0.792   0.874   1.142   1.268

Figure 4-34 Cinephotomicrographic sequence illustrating the formation of plate martensite in an alloy of Fe and 0.8% carbon. The sample was quenched in the hot-stage microscope at 17°C per second. The numbers under the photomicrographs are the time in seconds after the beginning of transformation (180×). *(From Bramfitt et al., Ref. 68; copyright, American Society for Testing and Materials, reprinted with permission.)*

experiments have been conducted in the study of fretting [85], creep [86], wear [87], fatigue [88], and thermal fatigue [89]. Special microscope stages have also been constructed for the physical extraction of specific inclusions [90, 91]. Reactive metals have also been studied using special microscope stages [92].

4-8.4 Hot-Cell Microscopy

Special metallographic facilities have been constructed for the remote preparation and examination of radioactive materials [93–96]. Considerable ingenuity is required to perform normal metallographic specimen preparation in these hot cells without the ability to physically handle the specimens. The High Radiation Level Examination Laboratory (HRLEL) at Oak Ridge National Laboratory consists of three straightline banks arranged in a U shape that are constructed from 3-ft thick high-density concrete lined with stainless steel [95]. Thick oil-filled, lead-glass shielded windows permit visual examination of operations within the hot cell. Periscopes are also used to permit viewing anywhere within the cell. Figure 4-35 shows the interior of a metallographic hot cell at Oak Ridge.

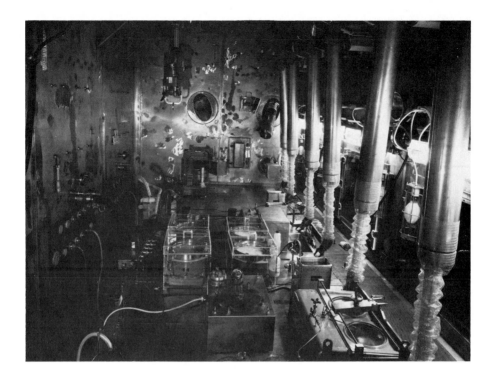

Figure 4-35 Interior of metallographic hot cells. Note sample grinding device in the foreground, ultrasonic cleaner and vibratory polishers in the center, and a hardness tester in the rear. Transfer openings to the metallographs and electron microprobe are on the rear wall. *(Courtesy of R. S. Crouse, Oak Ridge National laboratory.)*

4-8.5 Field Microscopy

The metallographer is occasionally faced with the need to examine the microstructure of a structure or a large object that cannot be cut or physically brought into the laboratory. In such cases, the laboratory must be moved to the test piece. Several equipment manufacturers make portable polishing equipment (mechanical or electrolytic) and portable microscopes.

There are samples in which the polished section is difficult to examine with a portable microscope. In such cases, it is possible to replicate the surface and examine the replicas using a light microscope or a transmission electron microscope. Replication methods have been in use for many years since being first suggested by Haycraft in 1891. Although the method is common in electron microscopy, it is infrequently used in optical metallography. However, the technique is a highly useful addition to the metallographers' "bag of tricks" [97, 98]. Acetate sheet, as used in electron microscopy, is cut to an appropriate size to cover the polished and etched area. Generally, a small piece about 1-in square is adequate. If larger areas are to be covered, thicker acetate tape can be employed. The tape is moistened with acetone and pressed onto the etched area. A moderate pressure should be maintained for a few minutes, taking care not to move the tape. After the tape has thoroughly dried, one corner is lifted and the tape is peeled off. Contrast can be increased by shadowing the replica with a heavy-weight metal, such as chromium, by vacuum deposition. It is helpful to coat the back side of the replica with a thin layer of aluminum before fixing the tape to a glass slide. Alternatively, the tape can be placed impression side up on a mirror. The edges of the tape are held down with Scotch tape to keep it flat. The replica can then be examined with a reflected light microscope. Struers makes a very convenient kit (Transcopy) for optical replicas that has a green-colored tape and an aluminum-coated back side. Results obtained with optical replicas are quite adequate for microstructural examination. An example is shown in Fig. 4-36 of a replicated ferrite-pearlite structure photographed at 150X.

4-8.6 Comparison Microscopes

The comparison of two microsamples for similarities or differences is a commonly encountered task [99]. This problem is most easily attacked if both microstructures can be viewed simultaneously. This can be accomplished through the use of a microscope bridge comparator which combines images from two different microscopes. A specially constructed comparison microscope is widely used in forensic science to compare bullets.

4-8.7 Television Monitors

For group viewing, it is possible to project the microscope image directly on a screen. Use of television cameras and monitors for group viewing has become

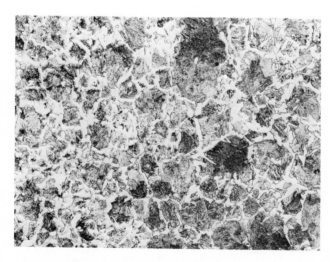

Figure 4-36 Example of an optical replica of ferrite and pearlite in AISI 1040 using the Struers Transcopy replication tape. The sample was etched in 4% picral, 150×.

quite popular, especially for educational purposes. It is now possible to purchase high-resolution television monitors that use a denser raster than used by commercial television in the United States. The images displayed on these new monitors are quite good.

4-8.8 Clean-room Microscopy

The study of certain subjects, such as small particles, is influenced by dust contamination during examination. McCrone and Hertrich estimate that a clean microscope slide collects about 5000 visible dust particles per square inch of surface area per hour in the average laboratory [100]. Thus, in the study of small particles it becomes difficult to distinguish the particles unless special steps are taken. In the preparation of the specimen, the particles can be shielded from contamination by the use of a cover slip. In general, it is necessary to provide a clean room atmosphere for such studies. McCrone and Hertrich have described the construction of the clean benches used in their laboratory [100]. The clean bench is a good alternative to the clean room, since less time is required for changing clothes, washing, etc. Clean boxes (glove box) provide a simple solution to the problem, but they are rather awkward to use.

4-9 SUMMARY

The value of microscopic examination in the study of materials has been firmly established. Optical microscopy remains the single most important tool of the metallurgist even though it lacks the resolution of electron microscopy. While examination of opaque specimens with incident bright-field vertical illumination is the most widely used technique, application of other illumination procedures is often advantageous in the study of certain materials. The metallographer should be aware of the options available and their advantages and disadvantages to obtain the maximum amount of information. Correct sample preparation is obviously highly important in the application of these techniques. The best equipment is rendered useless if sample preparation is inadequate.

In any study, one should always begin the examination by visual observation followed by application of progressively higher magnification and resolution and more sophisticated electron metallographic procedures if required. It is often beneficial to examine specimens in the as-polished condition before etching. Use of different etching solutions or stains can prove useful in identifying constituents. Phase identification is often aided by observing height differences through use of interference-contrast or oblique illumination and by microhardness testing. In solving problems, the metallographer should apply every procedure available to reach sound conclusions.

In many studies the end result is a written report describing the results of the study. In many cases, only a qualitative description of the microstructure is given. Incorporation of quantitative information can be much more convincing proof of the nature of the problem. Likewise, technically accurate photographs illustrating the problem and solution are most important. Frequently, the entire value judgment of the use of metallography within a given organization is based on these reports. Presentation of technical data in a clear, logical manner is imperative if the desired message is to be comprehended and used.

REFERENCES

1. Phillips, V. A.: *Modern Metallographic Techniques and Their Applications,* Interscience Publishers, a division of John Wiley & Sons, Inc., New York, 1971.
2. Gifkins, R. C.: *Optical Microscopy of Metals,* American Elsevier Publishing Company, New York, 1970.
3. Richardson, J. H.: *Optical Microscopy for the Materials Sciences,* Marcel Dekker, Inc., New York, 1971.
4. Zieler, H. W.: *The Optical Performance of the Light Microscope,* pt. 1, Microscope Publications Ltd., London, 1972.
5. Zieler, H. W.: *The Optical Performance of the Light Microscope,* pt. 2, Microscope Publications Ltd., London, 1974.
6. McLaughlin, R. B.: *Accessories for The Light Microscope,* Microscope Publications Ltd., London, 1975.
7. McLaughlin, R. B.: *Special Methods in Light Microscopy,* Microscope Publications Ltd., London, 1977.
8. Delly, J. G.: "Light Filters in Visual Microscopy," *Microscope,* vol. 17, 1969, pp. 193–200.
9. Benford, J. R., and H. E. Rosenberger: "Microscope Objectives and Eyepieces," *Handbook of Optics,* McGraw-Hill Book Company, New York, 1978, pp. 6-1 to 6-41.
10. Woodbury, J. L.: "Achieving Optimum Optical Performance Through a Customized Maintenance Program," *Interpretive Techniques for Microstructural Analysis,* Plenum Press, Plenum Publishing Corporation, New York, 1977, pp. 183–193.
11. Zieler, H. W.: "What Resolving Power Formula Do You Use?," *Microscope,* vol. 17, 1969, pp. 249–270.
12. Van Duijn, Jr., C.: "Visibility and Resolution of Microscopic Detail," *Microscope,* vol. 11, 1957, pp. 196–208; ibid, "Part 2," vol. 11, 1957, pp. 222–230, vol. 11, 1958, pp. 254–258; ibid, "Part 3," vol. 11, 1958, pp. 273–281; ibid, "Part 4," vol. 11, 1958, pp. 301–309; ibid, "Part 5," vol. 12, 1958, pp. 16–24, vol. 12, 1958, pp. 38–43; ibid, "Part 6," vol. 12, 1959, pp. 92–101; ibid, "Part 7," vol. 12, 1959, pp. 131–138, vol. 12, 1960, pp. 185–195, vol. 12, 1960, pp. 201–211; ibid, "Part 8," vol. 12, 1960, pp. 269–278, vol. 12, 1960, pp. 298–303.
13. Hartridge, H.: "The Visual Perception of the Colours of Microscopic Subjects," *J. Quekett Microsc. Club,* ser. 4, vol. 3, 1950, pp. 163–170.
14. Conn, G. K., and F. J. Bradshaw (eds.): *Polarized Light in Metallography,* Butterworth & Co. (Publishers), Ltd., London, 1952.
15. McCrone, W. C., L. B. McCrone, and J. G. Delly: *Polarized Light Microscopy,* Ann Arbor Science Publishers, Inc., Ann Arbor, Mich., 1978.
16. Hallimond, A. F.: *The Polarizing Microscope,* 3d ed., Vickers Instruments, New York, 1970.
17. Perryman, E. C. W., and J. M. Lack: "Examination of Metals by Polarized Light," *Nature,* vol. 167, no. 4247, 1951, p. 479.
18. Morrough, H.: "The Examination and Identification of Inclusions in Metals and Alloys," *Polarized Light in Metallography,* Butterworth & Co. (Publishers), Ltd., London, 1952, pp. 88–104.
19. Woodard, D. H.: "Stages in The Deformation of Monel Metal as Shown by Polarized Light," *Trans. Am. Inst. Min. Metall. Eng.,* vol. 185, 1949, pp. 722–726.

20. Couling, S. L., and G. W. Pearsall: "Determination of Orientation in Magnesium by Polarized Light Examination," *Trans. Am. Inst. Min. Metall. Eng.*, vol. 209, 1957, pp. 939–940.
21. Reed-Hill, R. E., and D. H. Baldwin: "A Technique for Orienting Grains in a Fine-Grained Polycrystalline Hexagonal Close-Packed Metal Using the Polarized Light Microscope," *Trans. Am. Inst. Min. Metall. Eng.*, vol. 233, 1965, pp. 842–844.
22. Larson, L. T., and M. L. Picklesimer: "Determination of the Basal-Pole Orientation in Zirconium by Polarized-Light Microscopy," *Trans. Am. Inst. Min. Metall. Eng.*, vol. 236, 1966, pp. 1104–1106.
23. Bennett, A. H., et al.: *Phase Microscopy*, John Wiley & Sons, Inc., New York, 1951.
24. Tolansky, S.: *Multiple-Beam Interferometry of Surface and Films*, Clarendon Press, Oxford, 1948.
25. Tolansky, S.: *Surface Microtopography*, Interscience Publishers, Inc., New York, 1960.
26. Padawer, J.: "The Nomarski Interference-Contrast Microscope. An Experimental Basis for Image Interpretation," *J. R. Microsc. Soc.*, vol. 88, pt. 3, 1968, pp. 305–349.
27. Hoffman, R., and L. Gross: "Reflected-Light Differential-Interference Microscopy: Principles, Use and Image Interpretation," *J. Microsc.*, vol. 91, pt. 3, 1970, pp. 149–172.
28. Holik, A. S.: "Surface Characterization by Interference Microscopy," *Microstructural Science*, vol. 3, pt. B, Elsevier Publishing Company, New York, 1975, pp. 991–1010.
29. Calabra, A. E., W. L. Johns, and D. L. Marts: "Interference Contrast for Examination and Photomicrography in Metallography," *Microstructural Science*, vol. 2, Elsevier Publishing Company, New York, 1974, pp. 1–11.
30. Lucas, F. F.: "High-Power Photomicrography of Metallurgical Specimens," *Am. Soc. Steel Treat.*, vol. 4, 1923, pp. 611–634.
31. Lucas, F. F.: "An Introduction to Ultra-Violet Metallography," *Trans. Am. Inst. Min. Metall. Eng.*, vol. 73, 1926, pp. 909–925.
32. Trivelli, A. P. H., and L. V. Foster: "Photomicrography with The 365-Millimicron Mercury Arc Line," *J. Opt. Soc. Am.*, vol. 21, 1931, pp. 124–131.
33. Wilson, T., et al.: "Scanning Optical Microscope as New Metallographic Tool," *Met. Sc.* vol. 14, 1980, pp. 144–146.
34. Mansour, T. M.: "A Nondestructive Method of Measuring Thickness of Transparent Coatings," *Mater. Res. Stand.*, vol. 3, no. 1, 1963, pp. 29–32.
35. Illig, W.: "Measurement of Anodically Formed Layers on Aluminum," *Metalloberflaeche*, vol. 13, no. 2, 1959, pp. 32–36.
36. Harris, L. A.: "The Application of Near-Infrared Microscopy to Materials Science," *Microstructural Science*, vol. 6, Elsevier Publishing Company, New York, 1978, pp. 119–129.
37. Frechette, V. D.: "Petrographic Analysis," *Characterization of Ceramics*, Marcel Dekker, Inc., New York, 1971, pp. 257–271.
38. Wylie, A. G., and P. J. M. Ypma: "Determination of Optical Parameters—n and k—of Absorbing Minerals with the Microscope: I. Isotropic Minerals," *Econ. Geol.*, vol. 69, 1974, pp. 1300–1327.
39. Knosp, H.: "Microphotometry—Uses in Metallography," *Prakt. Metallogr.*, vol. 7, no. 9, 1970, pp. 494–509.
40. Piller, H.: "Domains of Microscope Photometry in Materials Science," *J. Microsc.*, vol. 116, pt. 3, 1979, pp. 295–310.
41. Ting, F. T. C.: "Petrographic Techniques in Coal Analysis," *Analytical Methods for Coal and Coal Products*, vol. 1, Academic Press, Inc., New York, 1978, pp. 3–26.
42. Davis, A.: "The Reflectance of Coal," *Analytical Methods for Coal and Coal Products*, vol. 1, Academic Press, Inc., New York, 1978, pp. 27–81.
43. *Photomicrography of Metals*, Kodak Scientific Publication P-39, 1971.
44. Allen, R. M.: *Photomicrography*, 2d ed., D. Van Nostrand, Company, Inc., New York, 1958.
45. Loveland, R. P.: *Photomicrography, A Comprehensive Treatise*, vols. 1 and 2, John Wiley & Sons, Inc., New York, 1970.
46. *Photography Through the Microscope*, Kodak Scientific Publication P-2, 1970.
47. Samuels, L. E.: "Photographic Methods," *Interpretative Techniques for Microstructural Analysis*, Plenum Press, Plenum Publishing Corporation, New York, 1977, pp. 17–42.

48. Carroll, B. H., G. C. Higgins, and T. H. James: *Introduction to Photographic Theory*, John Wiley & Sons, Inc., New York, 1980.
49. Crouse, R. S., R. J. Gray, and B. C. Leslie: "Applications of Color in Metallography and Photography," *Interpretive Techniques for Microstructural Analysis*, Plenum Press, Plenum Publishing Corporation, New York, 1977, pp. 43–64.
50. Exner, H. E., H. Back, and J. Roth: "Some Experiences in the Documentation of Colour Micrographs," *Prakt. Metallogr.*, vol. 17, 1980, pp. 344–351.
51. Hyzer, W. G.: "Time-Lapse Photography in the Laboratory," *Res. Dev.*, vol. 24, no. 10, 1973, pp. 74–75.
52. Hyzer, W. G.: "Optimum Technique of High-Speed Cinematography," *Res. Dev.*, vol. 26, no. 2, 1975, pp. 64–66, 68.
53. Hyzer, W. G.: "Instant Analysis of High-Speed Events with Color Camera," *Ind. Res. Dev.*, vol. 22, no. 5, 1980, pp. 118–121.
54. Schlueter, G. E., and W. E. Gumpertz: "The Stereomicroscope—Instrumentation and Techniques," *Am. Lab.*, vol. 8, April 1976, pp. 61–71.
55. Hyzer, W. G.: "Taking Stereo Photos in the Laboratory," *Res. Dev.*, vol. 23, no. 12, 1972, pp. 51, 52, 54, 56.
56. Seidenberg, R. L.: "Stereomicroscopy: a Review," *Am. Lab.*, vol. 13, April 1981, pp. 114, 119, 120, 122–125.
57. *Simplified Photomacrography*, Kodak Scientific Publication P-53, 1970.
58. *Photomacrography*, Kodak Technical Publication N-12B, 1972.
59. Dvorak, J. R.: "Photomacrography in Metallography," *Microstructural Science*, vol. 3, pt. B. Elsevier Publishing Company, New York, 1975, pp. 1011–1025.
60. Hyzer, W. G.: "How to Use Ringlights," *Res. Dev.*, Vol. 22, no. 6, 1971, pp. 65, 66, 69.
61. Noritake, C. S., F. D. Walsh, and E. C. Roberts: "Polarized Light Brings Out Details of Fracture Zones," *Met. Prog.*, vol. 99, February 1971, pp. 95–98.
62. Gumpertz, W. E.: "High Resolution Photomacrography. Closing the Gap Between the Macro and Micro Range," *Microscope*, vol. 27, nos. 3 and 4, 1979, pp. 107-112.
63. *Photomacrography and Photomicrography*, Wild Heerbrugg Ltd., Switzerland, 1979.
64. Lozinskii, M. G.: *High Temperature Metallography*, Pergamon Press, Oxford, 1961.
65. Kulmburg, A., and K. Swoboda: "Experiences with the Vacutherm Hot Stage," *Prakt. Metallogr.*, vol. 3, no. 5, 1966, pp. 193–200.
66. Okamoto, M., O. Miyagawa, and T. Saga: "High Temperature Microscope Observation of the Austenite Grain Size of Steels," *Trans. Jpn. Inst. Met.* vol. 7, no. 4, 1966, pp. 217–223.
67. Benscoter, A. O., et al.: "A Hot-Stage Microscope for Rapid-Quenching Studies," *Microstructures*, vol. 1, no. 1, 1979, pp. 21–23, 40.
68. Bramfitt, B. L., et al.: "The Use of Hot-Stage Microscopy in the Study of Phase Transformation," *Am. Soc. Test. Mater. Spec. Tech. Publ.* 557, 1974, pp. 43–70.
69. McNeil, J. F.: "A Precision Universal Stage for the Microscopical Examination of Fracture Surfaces," *Metallurgia*, vol. 54, December 1956, pp. 207–210.
70. Bouttier, L.: "A New Polarizing Microscope Operating With Convergent Light at Temperatures as Low as −150C," *Comptes Rendus*, vol. 227, 1948, pp. 1084–1086.
71. Kessler, G., and M. R. Rudman: "A Convenient Technique for Low Temperature Optical Microscopy," *Prakt. Metallogr.*, vol. 8, no. 1, 1971, pp. 40–43.
72. Jackson, K. A., and J. D. Hunt: "Transparent Compounds that Freeze Like Metals," *Acta Metall.*, vol. 13, 1965, pp. 1212–1215.
73. Tardy, P.: "New Methods for Direct Observation of the Recrystallization of Low Melting Metals," *Prakt. Metallogr.*, vol. 9, 1968, pp. 485–593.
74. Markworth, M.: "Preparation of Metallographic Specimens of Ferrous Materials by Electrolytic Polish Attack under Direct Microscope Observation," *Neue Huette*, vol. 13, no. 11, 1968, pp. 684–689.
75. Wall, R., and D. I. Roberts: "A Cell Technique for Miscroscopic Observation of Selective Corrosion," *Metallurgia*, vol. 68, no. 410, 1963, pp. 291–294.
76. Edeleanu, C.: "A Mechanism of Stress-Corrosion in Aluminum-Magnesium Alloys," *J. Inst. Met.* vol. 80, 1951-1952, pp. 187–191.

77. Edeleanu, C.: "Crack Propagation During Stress Corrosion," *Physical Metallurgy of Stress Corrosion Fracture,* AIME Met. Soc. Conf., vol. 4, Interscience Publishers Inc., New York, 1959, pp. 79–98.
78. Damjanovic, A., M. M. Paunovic, and J. O'M. Bockris: "A Cell for the Continuous Observation of a Growing Electrodeposit," *Plating,* vol. 50, no. 8, 1963, pp. 735–736.
79. Gindin, E. A., and Y. D. Starodubov: "Direct Observation of the Beginning and Development of Mechanical Twins in Pure Iron Extended at Low Temperatures," *Phys. Met. Metallogr.,* vol. 18, no. 4, 1964, pp. 120–126.
80. Pond, R. B., and N. K. Chen: "Develop New Technique for Metal Structure Study," *Iron Age,* vol. 170, no. 6, 1952, pp. 122–126.
81. Flinn, R. A., and P. K. Trojan: "Examination of Microstructures under Varying Stress," *Met. Prog.,* vol. 68, July 1955, pp. 88–89.
82. Brobery, E., and R. Attermo: "A Miniature Tensile-Testing Machine for Deformation During Microscopic Observation," *Jernkontorets Ann.,* vol. 152, no. 10, 1968, pp. 525–526.
83. Jacobson, J. W.: "Metallurgical Yield-Stress Observation," *Mech. Eng.,* vol. 79, January 1957, pp. 13–15.
84. Rhines, F. N., and R. Ward: "Observing Plastic Deformation with the Microgrid," *Met. Alloys,* vol. 10, April 1939, pp. 129–132.
85. Godfrey, D.: "Investigation of Fretting by Microscopic Observation," National Advisory Committee for Aeronautics, Report 1009, 1951.
86. Walter, J. L., and H. E. Cline: "Grain Boundary Sliding, Migration, and Deformation in High-Purity Aluminum," *Trans. Am. Inst. Min. Metall. Eng.,* vol. 242, 1968, pp. 1823–1830.
87. Sliney, H. E.: "Dynamics of Solid Lubrication as Observed by Optical Microscopy," *ASLE Trans.,* vol. 21, no. 2, 1978, pp. 109–117.
88. Nishijima, S.: "An Experimental Study of the Deformation Process of Fatigue Crack Tip by a Special Fatigue Tester Having Micrographic Apparatus," *Trans. Natl. Res. Inst. Met.* vol. 11, no. 1, 1969, pp. 59–66.
89. Takeuchi, S., and T. Homma: "Direct Observation for High Temperature Fatigue in Pure Metals by Means of Microscopic Cine-Camera," *Proc. First Intern. Conf. on Fracture,* Sendai, Japan, vol. 2, 1966, pp. 1071–1086.
90. Kehl, G. L., H. Steinmetz, and W. J. McGonnagle: "The Removal of Inclusions for Analysis by an Ultrasonic 'Jack Hammer,'" *Metallurgia,* vol. 55, March 1957, pp. 151–154.
91. Uchiyama, I., M. Nomura, and M. Ueno: "Extraction of Nonmetallic Inclusions from Steel by Using an Ultrasonic Drill," *Tetsu-to-Hagane* vol. 47, no. 3, 1961, pp. 519–521 (HB 6063).
92. Hume-Rothery, W.: "Methods for the Thermal and Microscopic Investigation of Alloys of Reactive Metals," *J. Inst. Met.* vol. 40, no. 2, 1928, pp. 65–83.
93. Evans, J. H.: "Remote Metallography," *Interpretive Techniques for Microstructural Analysis,* Plenum Press, Plenum Publishing Corporation, New York, 1977, pp. 145–168.
94. Krautwedel, H. L.: "A Review of Remote Optical Metallography," *Metallography,* vol. 2, no. 2 and 3, 1969, pp. 191–208.
95. Gray, R. J., E. L. Long, and A. E. Richt: "Metallography of Radioactive Materials at Oak Ridge National Laboratory," *Am. Soc. Test. Mater. Spec. Tech. Publ. 480,* 1970, pp. 67–96.
96. Evans, J. H.: "Remote Control Microscopy," *Advances in Optical and Election Microscopy,* vol. 5, Academic Press, Inc., New York, 1973, pp. 1–42.
97. Kosec, L. and F. Vodopivec.: "Examples of the Replica Technique in Optical Microscopy," *Prakt. Metallogr.,* vol. 6, 1969, pp. 118–121.
98. Neri, J.: "Optical Replicas—A Nondestructive Metallographic Evaluation Technique," *Failure Analysis,* American Society for Metals, Metals Park, Ohio, 1969, pp. 241–268.
99. Palenik, S.: "Comparison Microscopy in the Industrial Laboratory," *Am. Lab.,* vol. 12, December 1980, pp. 49–51.
100. McCrone, W. C., and J. A. Hertrich: "Clean Room Microscopy," *Microscope,* vol. 17, no. 1, 1969, pp. 77–81.

HARDNESS

5-1 INTRODUCTION

O'Neill in his classic book on hardness states that "the hardness of metals, like the storminess of seas, is easily appreciated but not readily measured for one would hope to express it in terms of fundamental units" [1]. This statement accurately reflects the fundamental foible of hardness; i.e., although it is an intuitively simple concept and hardness tests are widely used in the metals industry because of their low cost and straightforward manner of implementation, it cannot be defined rigorously nor be measured absolutely. The test procedures do not bear a direct relationship to service conditions, a problem shared by many metallurgical tests. However, hardness data do provide important information about material quality that is of indispensable value in quality control, design, alloy development, and materials selection. The science of physical metallurgy has relied heavily on hardness tests.

Many claim that hardness is a vague concept. Tuckerman states that hardness is "a hazily conceived conglomeration of properties of a material more or less related to each other." His conclusion was founded on the fact that hardness manifests itself in many different ways and has different meanings to different people. In its most general sense, hardness implies resistance to deformation. As applied to metals, hardness is a measure of resistance to plastic, i.e., permanent, deformation as would be determined in a uniaxial tensile test. It is not surprising, therefore, that hardness can be correlated with both yield strength and tensile strength. Hard materials exhibit high strengths, while soft materials have low strengths.

Hardness also has other connotations—resistance to scratching, resistance to cutting, ability to cut softer materials, brittleness, lack of elastic damping, wear resistance, lack of malleability, magnetic retention, and so forth. Because of these different attributes, the myriad of materials tested, and the multitude of tests available, hardness has not been defined in the neat, concise, universal manner normally desired in science.

Although the subject of hardness testing is quite diverse, most engineers need only a few of the many different tests that are commercially available. This is especially true in quality control, a field in which hardness tests are used extensively. Those involved in research generally use a wider range of test procedures, especially if a wide range of materials are being investigated. Fortunately, many of these tests have been thoroughly evaluated and standardized by organizations such as the American Society for Testing and Materials (ASTM). A number of excellent reviews have been published covering the science of hardness testing [1–8]. In this chapter, we concentrate on the physical meaning of hardness, test procedures, factors affecting their accuracy, hardness conversions, relationships to other properties, and hardness applications.

5-2 INDENTATION HARDNESS

Hardness testing using indentations can be accomplished in several ways. If a hard object is pressed into the surface of a softer material with enough force to produce an indentation, the indentation size will depend on the magnitude of the applied force and the hardness of the indented material. For a fixed set of test conditions, if two different materials are indented, the one with the smaller indentation is harder. If these test conditions can be accurately controlled and reproduced, a hardness number can easily be calculated from the applied load and the projected area of the impression in terms of a pressure in units such as kilograms per square millimeter.

5-2.1 Relationship to Stress-Strain Curve

Examination of the indentation hardness test reveals some close parallels to the uniaxial tension test [5]. When a cylindrically shaped specimen is loaded uniaxially in tension, there is an initial linear relationship between stress and strain prior to the onset of plastic deformation. The slope of the linear portion of the stress-strain curve is the modulus of elasticity (Young's modulus). In the elastic region Hooke's law is obeyed. If a sample is loaded in this elastic region and the load is then removed, the sample returns to its original length. Higher loads produce plastic deformation and deviation from linear behavior. If a sample is loaded to produce plastic deformation but not enough to cause separation into two pieces and the load is removed, the specimen length will be increased. The plastic deformation has produced a certain amount of permanent elongation. As the stress producing plastic deformation is increased, the strain increases and the specimen elongates. Such deformation increases the strength and hardness of the material in the deformed region.

The true stress-strain curve can be approximately fitted to a simple power curve of the following form:

$$\sigma = K\epsilon^n \tag{5-1}$$

where σ = true stress
$\quad \epsilon$ = true strain
$\quad K$ = true stress at $\epsilon = 1.0$
$\quad n$ = slope of a log-log plot of σ versus ϵ

The slope value n is called the strain-hardening coefficient and has values from 0 (no strain hardening) to about 0.7.

Tabor has applied the tensile test–indentation hardness analogy to the indentation of ideal plastic materials. An ideal plastic material is one with constant yield stress. A material that can be plastically deformed in the uniaxial tension test will not deform plastically under a hydrostatic pressure, even if the applied load significantly exceeds the material's yield strength. Plastic deformation requires either shear-stress or shear-strain conditions. This has important consequences in indentation hardness because about two-thirds of the mean contact pressure is hydrostatic pressure. Only about one-third of the applied pressure produces plastic flow. Thus, the mean pressure P between the metal and the indenter is three times the yield stress σ_{ys}:

$$\tfrac{1}{3} P \approx \sigma_{ys} \qquad \text{or} \qquad P \approx 3\sigma_{ys} \tag{5-2}$$

In the case of hardness testing with the square-based pyramidal-shaped Vickers indenter, the mean yield pressure is influenced by the indenter's apex angle, but the ratio of P to σ_{ys} is close to 3. Tabor illustrated this point by work hardening several different materials to such a degree that the yield strength was relatively constant. Then, Tabor made Vickers indentations in these materials and calculated the mean pressure of each (load/projected area). In each case, $P = 3.2\sigma_{ys}$.

The Vickers hardness number (HV) is calculated by dividing the load by the surface area of the pyramidal impression rather than by the projected area. Thus, the value of the Vickers hardness number is less than P by about 7 percent. If this correction is made, we obtain the following:

$$HV = (0.9272)(3.2)\sigma_{ys} \approx 3\sigma_{ys} \tag{5-3}$$

For the case of an ideal plastic material, the Vickers hardness number is about three times its yield strength in kilograms per square millimeter. The ultimate tensile strength of an ideal plastic material is essentially the same as the yield strength.

If different loads are used to make two geometrically similar impressions, the stress and strain distribution around the indentations are geometrically similar, even if the material work-hardens. In such cases, a large impression is basically a magnified version of a smaller one. Thus, the mean pressure on the indenter is the same regardless of the size of the impression. The value of geometrically similar impressions, as made by pyramidal and conical indenters (but not ball indenters), centers on the desirable condition that the hardness values are not altered as the applied load is changed. This, of course, is a major advantage of the Vickers test, and a major disadvantage of the Brinell test. As is shown in the section on microindentation hardness testing, at very low loads the Vickers hardness number does deviate from constancy. This problem arises from a number of factors that are chiefly experimental in nature.

When a Vickers impression is made in a material that work-hardens, the metal is plastically deformed and strengthened. The stress and strain around the impression vary, as do the mechanical properties. Tabor has determined experimentally that the Vickers indentation produces an average strain equal to 8 percent strain in the uniaxial tensile test. If the tensile load-elongation curve is used to define the yield strength at 8 percent strain, the Vickers hardness number will be about three times this value (in the same units, kilograms per square millimeter). Tabor has shown that this relationship holds irrespective of the initial degree of specimen work hardening.

The indentation pressure of the spherical Brinell indenter is also about three times the yield strength of the test metal. Consequently, Brinell hardness numbers and Vickers hardness numbers are approximately equal over the range of the Brinell test. However, Brinell impressions are not geometrically similar, i.e., the larger the impression, the greater the strains around the impression. This produces a higher effective yield strength and an increased hardness. Spherical indenters can be used to measure a material's ability to work-harden, as is discussed in the section on the Meyer analysis.

5-2.2 Effects of Time, Velocity, and Size

The load duration time during the indentation process can be an important factor, since creep can occur. Indentation creep is observed during testing of low-melting-point metals at room temperature and is also observed in many metals tested at elevated temperatures. In the testing of "hard" metals at ambient temperatures, creep is negligible. Even so, load duration times should be standardized. When creep does occur during indentation, the operator should permit the indenter to reach equilibrium before removing the load. The time of loading should be recorded.

Loading speed can also influence the hardness number. Neville states that in the Vickers test the hardness increases as the speed of loading decreases, with the rise being very steep when the velocity is extremely low [9]. In the calibration of test blocks, a velocity of 3 to 12 μm/s was chosen based on hardness-velocity plots. In commercial test machines the velocity changes during the indentation cycle. As the indenter approaches the surface and begins penetration, the velocity is high. As penetration progresses, the velocity decreases. Neville also observed the same velocity effects in the Rockwell test.

Mass effects may also be present in hardness tests, but they are primarily controlled by the homogeneity of the material and the size of the impression. In the testing of bulk hardness of heterogeneous materials, the largest possible impression should be used so as to even out the variations. For example, in the case of ferrite-pearlite gray iron four constituents (graphite, ferrite, pearlite, and iron phosphide) with vastly different hardnesses contribute to the bulk hardness. To obtain valid bulk hardnesses, a large indentation, such as a Brinell impression, should be employed. The hardness of each of these constituents can be assessed by small, low-load impressions placed in each constituent, i.e., by microindentation hardness.

5-2.3 Effects of Lubrication and Adhesion

During the indentation process, the indenter faces slide against the metal being indented. High frictional forces between these surfaces increases the pressure required to form the impression. Lubrication reduces the friction and decreases the required pressure. In tests of machined surfaces, a thin lubricant film is often present which can reduce the hardness slightly, since a larger impression will result for a given fixed test load.

According to Tabor, the coefficient of friction for a polished diamond indenter sliding on most unlubricated metals is 0.1 to 0.15 [5]. If the unlubricated metal surface is polished, the coefficient of friction is about 0.2. Lubrication reduces the measured hardness and the degree of strain hardening around the impression.

During indentation, adhesion and pressure welding may be encountered along the contact points. For a hard specimen, these areas are broken by the elastic recovery stresses. However, for soft metals, adhesion can occur and a pressure must be exerted to free the indenter. Adhesion problems have been encountered in hot hardness testing.

5-2.4 Indentation Size and Shape Changes

It is well recognized that on removal of the indenter, size and shape changes of the impression can occur in varying amounts as a result of elastic recovery. Recovered cone impressions exhibit larger included angles than the unloaded impression, while recovered ball impressions exhibit an increased radius of curvature. This phenomenon is referred to as "shallowing" in the literature. The chordal diameter of the recovered impression also changes but to a much lesser extent, generally less than a few percent. Changes in the radius of curvature can be substantial for hard metals and are usually negligible for soft metals. Elastic depth recovery for steels can be as much as 10 to 30 percent [2].

The indentation process also produces changes in the surface level around the impression, resulting in "ridging" or "sinking." Ridging is observed in highly worked (ideal plastic materials) metals when the metal being displaced by the indenter flows upward around the edge of the indenter. Annealed metals behave differently. The initial contact with the indenter produces work hardening under the indenter. Subsequent flow is easier in the region below the work-hardened zone. As indentation proceeds, the flow occurs at still greater depths. Consequently, the material at the edge of the impression is at a lower level than the material further away from the impression, which results in sinking.

With a pyramidal indenter, the effects of ridging and sinking are more complex, especially if the specimen is anisotropic. When ridging occurs, the impression corners are relatively unaffected but the sides are extruded upward, producing a "barrel-shaped" (convex) appearance.

Ridging and sinking around Brinell impressions constitutes a major source of error in the reproducibility of measurements between operators. Anisotropy produces distorted impressions. When this problem is encountered, the mean of four measurements of the diameter should be used. Ridging and sinking are not a problem in the Rockwell test, since the hardness is determined with the minor load still applied. In the Vickers test, ridging and sinking influence the diagonal measurement and can produce errors of up to 10 percent. Ridging produces higher values, while sinking produces lower values. In the microindentation test, the erratic hardness values obtained at very low loads have been attributed by Bückle to these effects.

5-2.5 Surface Roughness

In bulk-hardness testing the roughness of the test sample surface has little influence on indentation size and shape so long as the impression is relatively large compared to the size of the surface asperities. Thus, in routine bulk testing a machine-ground surface is adequate. Only in microindentation hardness testing because of the small size of the impression is a finely polished surface required. As is shown in a later section, the quality of the polished surface affects the microhardness values substantially as the test load decreases.

5-3 STATIC HARDNESS TESTS

Many different hardness tests and evaluation procedures have been developed, a factor that can introduce considerable confusion to the novice metallurgist or technician. However, these techniques can be grouped together on the basis of the particular concepts employed, as described in Table 5-1. Of the methods described in this chapter, the static indentation tests are the ones most commonly employed to evaluated hardness.

5-3.1 Brinell Hardness

Development of ball bearings at the end of the nineteenth century prompted Brinell to use them as indenters [10]. His procedure, which was based on the earlier work by Auerback, lead to the introduction of the Brinell test in 1900. It is the oldest of the modern indentation tests and gained immediate popularity.

Table 5-1 Types of hardness tests

Scratch tests	A series of minerals, as in the Mohs test, or files of graded hardness are run across a sample of unknown hardness until one determines that a certain standard will not scratch the sample but the next harder standard will. Scratch tests can also be performed with an indenter that is run across a sample, producing a plowing action. The scratch width is the measure of hardness.
Static indentation tests	A ball, cone, or pyramid significantly harder than the specimen is pressed into the surface under a known load. The load per unit of contact surface area or projected area is a measure of the hardness, as in the Brinell, Vickers, Knoop, or Meyer tests. Alternatively, the depth of the partly recovered impression can be measured, as in the Rockwell test. Mutual indentation of two samples with the same or different geometry under a known load can also be used to measure hardness.
Dynamic tests	A rounded diamond-tipped hammer, or similar device, is dropped from a known height onto the specimen surface. The height of the rebound is a measure of the hardness, as in the Shore test.
Abrasion tests	A number of wear tests have been developed in which the sample is pressed against a rotating disc in the presence of an abrasive and the wear rate determined as a measure of hardness.
Erosion tests	Sand, an abrasive, or steel shot is impinged onto the surface of the sample at a known velocity, and the loss of weight due to erosion is a measure of hardness. The hardness uniformity can be assessed from the erosion pattern.

Brinell tests have been widely used by the metals industry ever since, particularly in the United States.

Brinell used a 10-mm diameter ball pressed into the flat, smooth specimen surface for 30 s. After the load was removed, the impression diameter was measured. His initial experiments on annealed material revealed that the hardness varied with the load. Consequently, Brinell decided to divide the load by the surface area of the impression rather than by the projected area. While this did not correct the problem, the practice has been retained, and hardness is still calculated in this way. Although Meyer in 1908 recommended that the projected area be used, the test was too well established, even after only 8 years, to permit the change [11].

Brinell decided to adopt standard loads L of 500 kgf (kilograms-force) for soft metals and 3000 kgf for harder metals such as steel. The Brinell hardness number (HB) is calculated on the basis of the average of two measurements of the impression diameter d made at right angles to each other using the following formula in which D is the ball diameter:

$$HB = \frac{2L}{\pi D^2 \{1 - [1 - (d/D)^2]^{1/2}\}} \tag{5-4}$$

Several other variations of this equation have been suggested. The following is one popular arrangement:

$$HB = \frac{L}{\frac{\pi D}{2}[D - (D^2 - d^2)^{1/2}]} \tag{5-5}$$

In practice, the HB value is determined by consulting tables supplied with the machine that give the HB for various diameters for each possible load.

Meyer proposed calculation of the hardness using the projected area [11]. This hardness value is called the Meyer hardness (HM) and is calculated from Eq. (5-6).

$$HM = \frac{4L}{\pi d^2} \tag{5-6}$$

This formula is considerably simpler to apply and yields values slightly higher than the corresponding HB.

Rasor has developed a simplified formula for calculating Brinell numbers which results in an error of less than 0.2 percent over the usual HB range [12]. This formula is as follows:

$$HB = \frac{4L}{\pi d^2} - \frac{L}{\pi D^2} \tag{5-7}$$

This format is instructive because the first term is the Meyer hardness and the second term is a correction factor for the difference between the contact area and the projected area. This equation can be further simplified for the two standard test conditions:

1. For a 10-mm ball and 3000-kgf load

$$HB = \frac{3820}{d^2} - 9.6 \tag{5-8}$$

2. For a 10-mm ball and 500-kgf load

$$HB = \frac{637}{d^2} - 1.6 \tag{5-9}$$

Because HBs vary noticeably as the load is changed, ASTM Specification E10 recommends use of standard loads for a given ball diameter for metals of different hardnesses. The most common test procedure uses a 10-mm diameter hardened steel ball with a load of 3000 kgf applied for 10 to 15 s. Loads of 1500 and 500 kgf are also employed but less frequently. The test load is chosen so that the impression diameter is in the range of 2.50 to 6.0 mm, i.e., 25 to 60 percent of the diameter of the 10-mm ball. The standard ball should be 10.000 mm in diameter with a tolerance of ± 0.005 mm. Steel balls with a Vickers hardness of 850 or greater can be used on material with a hardness of less than 450 HB. Carbide balls are recommended for testing harder materials but not for those over 630 HB. Since use of the tungsten carbide ball gives a slightly different hardness than the steel ball, when this type indenter is used, this fact should be mentioned in the test report. The Brinell test is not recommended for materials above 630 HB. The ball indenter will deform if its yield strength is less than 2.5 times that of the specimen. If a steel ball is used on material harder than 450 HB, the ball will be permanently deformed. Since a permanent diameter change of more than 0.005 mm destroys the value of the ball, it is recommended that the ball shape be checked regularly, especially if a test is accidentally made on material above the critical hardness.

The recommended standard loads, according to ASTM Specification E10, for use with the 10-mm diameter ball, are listed in Table 5-2. The relationships between impression diameter and HB using a 10-mm diameter steel ball and loads of 500, 1500, and 3000 kgf are listed in ASTM Specification E10. If the same sample is tested using the three standard loads, one observes that the HB value increases as the applied load increases.

To circumvent this problem, it is recommended that the L/D^2 ratio be held constant for a given material. Recommended L/D^2 ratios for different materials are also given in ASTM E10. For steels, the combination of 3000 kgf and a 10-mm diameter ball yields a ratio of 30 while the 1500-kgf load and 10-mm diameter ball yield a ratio of 15 and the 500-kgf load and 10-mm ball yield a ratio of 5. Therefore, equivalent HB results should not be expected for these combinations. An L/D^2 ratio of 30 can also be obtained with a load of 750 kgf and a 5-mm diameter ball. These L/D^2 ratios have been chosen to provide values of d/D that are easiest to read, i.e., between 0.25 and 0.50, with 0.375 as optimum.

Because of the variations in HB that can occur under nonstandard test conditions, it is recommended that the nature of these conditions be stated when reporting such data. For example, if a hardness of 70 HB was obtained using a 10-mm ball, a load of 1500 kgf, and a load duration of 60 s, the hardness results would be expressed as 70 HB 10/1500/60.

Brinell testers are made by many manufacturers. Units vary in complexity and sophistication, ranging from deadweight loading to hydraulic loading. Efforts are being made to introduce automation into various phases of the test cycle. Figure 5-1 shows a typical commercially available Brinell tester. While some machines are

Table 5-2 Standard test loads for the Brinell test†

Ball diameter, mm	Load, kgf	Recommended range, HB
10	3000	96–600
10	1500	48–300
10	500	16–100

†Based on ASTM Specification E10.

Figure 5-1 Model KDR-10 hydraulic Brinell hardness tester with direct readout comparator dial. *(Courtesy of Page-Wilson Corp., Measurement Systems Div.)*

designed to operate under fixed operating conditions, others provide loads that can be stepped up in 500-kgf increments or can be varied continuously over the whole range. The machine type to choose depends chiefly upon the variety of materials to be tested, the number of samples to be tested, and the funds available. Some machines operate with a fixed contact time, while in others the load duration is variable. In the testing of many nonferrous metals, a loading time of 30 s or more is recommended. In the case of magnesium and its alloys, a 2-min load time is preferred. Very soft metals that creep during indentation at room temperature require still longer times for equilibrium.

The thickness of Brinell test specimens should be great enough that the supporting anvil does not affect the reading. The usual rule of thumb states that the thickness should be at least 10 times the indentation depth. This is merely a guide, as exceptions have been reported. For example, Hankins and Aldous found that 6 times the impression depth was adequate for mild steel but 20 times the depth was required for a hardened spring steel [13]. Impression depth is calculated with the following formula:

$$\text{Impression depth} = \frac{L}{\pi D \, \text{HB}} \qquad (5\text{-}10)$$

where impression depth is in millimeters and L, D, and HB are as previously defined. ASTM E10 also provides recommendations regarding test sample thickness. If these values are not followed, the supporting anvil will resist the deformation and bulging will be observed on the back side of the sample. If this occurs, the test results will be inaccurate.

Test samples should be cleaned, and any scale or rust present should be removed. This applies to the surface against the anvil as well. If the surface of the sample is decarburized, the true bulk hardness will not be obtained. Thus, the surfaces of as-rolled or as-heat-treated samples should be ground before testing. Surface preparation steps should be done carefully so that they do not cold-work the surface layer or introduce excessive heat which could alter the structure. In addition, the test surface must be flat and parallel to the surface that will be placed on the anvil. The test surface must also be perpendicular to the indenter axis. The angle between the indenter axis and the sample surface should be within 2° of perpendicular, otherwise errors will occur. A smooth surface is best for precise diameter measurements. Grinding is the preferred procedure. The test surface should not be lubricated. If a curved surface is to be tested using the 10-mm ball, the radius of curvature should not be less than 1 in (2.54 cm). The two principle axes of the impression should be measured and averaged.

Impressions should be spaced apart so that the work hardening around the impression does not alter the hardness of subsequent impressions. The usual rule of thumb states that the spacing between adjacent impressions should be 2.5 times the impression diameter. Impressions should not be placed near enough to the edge of a specimen that the edge becomes distorted. It is recommended that the distance from the edge of the sample to the center of the impression should be 2.5 times the impression diameter.

The Brinell test produces the largest impression size of all the standard hardness tests. A large impression size is an advantage in certain situations and a disadvantage in others. In tests of materials with heterogeneous microstructures or segregation, a large impression is helpful because it averages out much of the variations. However, in instances where there is a hardness gradient, large impressions are not sensitive enough to define the gradient accurately. The Brinell test is not suitable for testing small parts or thin sections.

The Brinell test can be performed with a number of portable units, as

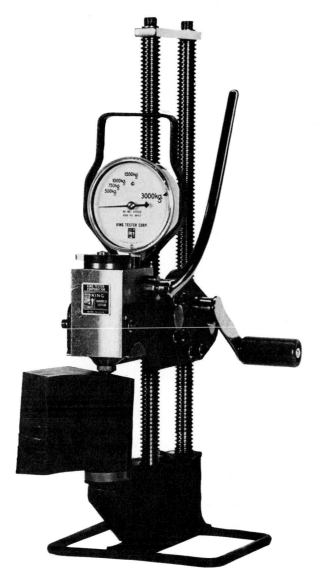

Figure 5-2 Model 134 portable Brinell tester. *(Courtesy of King Tester Corp.)*

illustrated in Fig. 5-2. These devices are used in those situations where the test piece cannot be brought into the laboratory, a commonly encountered situation. The principles used can be quite similar to that of laboratory testers or quite different as in the case of impact-type devices. In either case, the tester must be carefully and frequently checked using load cells and standard test blocks to ensure accuracy.

The precision and accuracy of the Brinell test is controlled by the accuracy and repeatability of the loading, the quality of the indenter, and the measurement of the impression. As discussed previously, sinking and ridging produce measurement problems. The nature of the illumination used during measurement can influence the ability to size the impression. The light should be adjusted to produce maximum contrast at first one edge and then the other edge. Distortion of the impression due to anisotropy also presents measurement difficulty. One solution is to measure the area of the irregular impression and calculate a diameter. Effort is currently underway to develop automated devices for this purpose.

The measuring microscope should be checked occasionally with a stage micrometer to verify its calibration. The precision of the measuring microscope is generally on the order of 0.1 mm, but estimates to as little as 0.02 mm are possible. In routine testing, the impression diameter is usually estimated to the nearest 0.05 mm. However, for calibration or referee purposes, the impression diameter should be estimated to the nearest 0.02 mm.

The applied load can be verified using several procedures such as proving rings, deadweights, and proving levers or using elastic calibration devices. The loads for a laboratory or referee tester should not deviate more than $\pm$ 1 percent from the specified load. A tester used for routine work should be within $\pm$ 2 percent of the required load. Every laboratory using Brinell testers, or any other type, should have an established verification and cleaning program for their testers. The accuracy of the machines should be certified by an independent agency. This is especially important if data are to be provided to customers.

Although the accuracy of the loading device and the measuring microscope need only be checked at regular intervals of, for example, 6 months, the machine should be checked more frequently through the use of test blocks. Use of test blocks at weekly intervals, or more frequently depending on the testing frequency, will spot any unexpected machine problems. Test blocks covering a wide range of hardnesses can be purchased from equipment manufacturers. The mean diameter of a test impression on these blocks should differ by no more than 3 percent from the certified values for the test block.

5-3.2 Meyer Hardness

As mentioned, the use of the spherical contact area rather than the projected area in calculating Brinell hardness was a poor choice. Use of the Meyer equation [(Eq. (5-6)] yields a hardness number that accurately reflects the applied pressure. Neither the Brinell number nor the Meyer number are constant when the load is changed because the ball indentation does not produce geometrically similar impressions.

Meyer's work showed that the resistance to penetration with a ball indenter is a function of the depth of penetration [11]. He showed that the ball impression test followed the relationship:

$$L = ad^n \tag{5-11}$$

where L = load, kgf

d = indentation diameter, mm

a, n = constants for the material tested

Hoyt stated that the constant a is a measure of the material's resistance to the initial penetration, while the constant n measures the effect of deformation on the hardness of the metal[14]. The metal's hardness is altered during the test, with the amount of change depending on the metal and its initial condition.

The Meyer constants a and n can be determined graphically or mathematically using two data points and two simultaneous equations of the following form:

$$\log L = \log a + n \log d \qquad (5\text{-}12)$$

One can plot the load in kilograms-force and the diameter in millimeters on log-log paper, yielding a linear relationship, and the Meyer constants a and n can be obtained graphically. The constant a is the load in kilograms-force required to produce a 1-mm diameter impression, while n is the slope of the line.

For fully annealed materials, n usually has a value close to 2.5, while for fully work-hardened metals, n is about 2. If different ball diameters are used, the values of a and n change. Meyer found that n varied very little as the ball diameter changed, but the value of a decreased as the ball diameter increased. This relationship has been expressed as follows:

$$C = a_1 D_1{}^{n-2} = a_2 D_2{}^{n-2} = a_3 D_3{}^{n-2} = \cdots = a_n D_n{}^{n-2} \qquad (5\text{-}13)$$

where C is a constant. The relationship between ball diameter D and impression diameter d has been expressed as follows:

$$L = \frac{C d_1{}^n}{D_1{}^{n-2}} = \frac{C d_2{}^n}{D_2{}^{n-2}} = \frac{C d_3{}^n}{D_3{}^{n-2}} = \cdots = \frac{C d_n{}^n}{D_n{}^{n-3}} \qquad (5\text{-}14)$$

This expression can be rewritten in the following form:

$$\frac{L}{d^2} = C\left(\frac{d}{D}\right)^{n-2} \qquad (5\text{-}15)$$

For the case of geometrically similar impressions, d/D is constant and L/d^2 is constant. For spherical indenters, L/d^2 is proportional to the Meyer hardness; the Brinell hardness is a geometric factor equal to d/D times the Meyer hardness.

Equation (5-14) can be rewritten in the form:

$$\frac{L}{D^2} = C\left(\frac{d}{D}\right)^n \qquad (5\text{-}16)$$

Again d/D and L/D^2 are constant. This equation indicates that geometrically similar impressions will be formed using a 10-mm ball and a load of 3000 kgf, a 5-mm ball and a load of 750 kgf, or a 1-mm ball and a load of 30 kgf because the L/D^2

[†] Strain-hardening capacity, as determined by tensile testing, is given by $n - 2$.

ratio in each instance is 30. This is the origin of the use of a constant L/D^2 ratio in the standardization of the Brinell test.

For fully cold-worked metals the Meyer hardness is nearly constant as the load is varied while the Brinell hardness is relatively constant at low loads and decreases at high loads. For fully annealed metals that work-harden appreciably, the Meyer hardness rises as the load is raised because of strain hardening during loading. The Brinell hardness rises with increasing load and then falls at still higher loads. The Meyer hardness more clearly reflects the material's response to loading than does the Brinell hardness.

In performing the Meyer test, the relationship given in Eq. (5-11) is followed for impression diameters approaching the ball diameter; however, for small loads and small impressions, erroneously high n values can be obtained. According to Meyer, the lower limit of applicability occurs when the impression diameter is 10 percent of the ball diameter. This lower limit is influenced by the hardness of the metal being tested.

A plot of Meyer hardness versus applied load exhibits a characteristic shape, as shown in Fig. 5-3. Low applied loads that produce visible impressions yield low values of applied pressure. Minor increases of the applied load produce substantial pressure increases and then a leveling off of the pressure as the load is increased further. The strength of the material and its ability to work-harden determine the shape of the curve (see Fig. 5-4). The onset of plastic deformation occurs at a mean pressure of 1.1 times the yield strength Y and is determined graphically as the highest load in the initial linear portion of the curve shown in

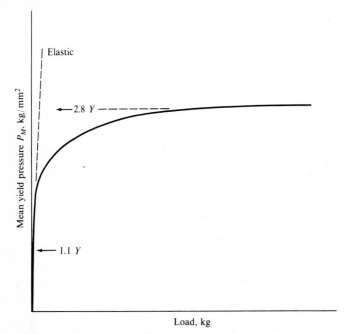

Figure 5-3 Plot of mean yield pressure, i.e., Meyer hardness, as a function of applied load.

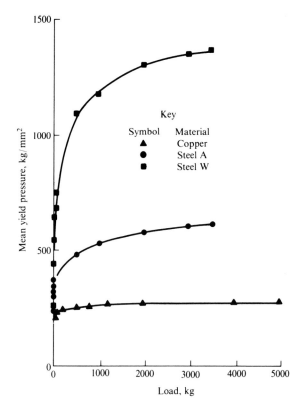

Figure 5-4 Relationship between load and mean yield pressure, i.e., Meyer hardness, as a function of load.

Fig. 5-3. The onset of plastic deformation at $1.1Y$ can be difficult to detect by this method because a very careful experimental technique is required at the very low test loads used. With higher loads, plastic deformation increases until a load is obtained with which the mean pressure is essentially constant. Full plasticity occurs at a mean pressure of approximately $3Y$. Tabor has tested this analysis by indenting a variety of fully work-hardened metals with a spherical indenter [15]. Because these metals do not exhibit significant work hardening during testing, their yield strength is essentially constant. For a fully work-hardened metal, a Meyer plot on log-log paper gave a bowed line where only the high-load region was linear. In this region the slope n exhibited a value of 2. If the slope was determined in the lower region, values approaching 3 were obtained. Hence, only in the high-load region is Meyer's law valid for highly worked metals. As the material's yield strength is increased, the minimum loads for valid Meyer analyses are raised.

Mackenzie and Newcomb have described how the Rockwell tester can be used to measure Meyer hardness [16]. In this study, indentations were made using loads from 20 to 100 kgf with ball indenters of ¼- and ½-in diameter. In the Rockwell test, the hardness is based on the difference in penetration depth h_2 between application of a minor and a major load. If corrections are made for machine distortion and bulk specimen deformation, the actual depth of the impression h_1 before elastic recovery occurs can be determined. The impression diameter d is relatively unchanged after removal of the major load and is given by Eq. (5-17):

$$d^2 = 8r_1h_1 = 8r_2h_2 \qquad (5\text{-}17)$$

where r_1 is the ball radius and r_2 is the radius of curvature of the recovered impression. The Meyer hardness (HM) is calculated using Eq. (5-18):

$$\text{HM} = \frac{L}{2\pi r_1 h_1} \qquad (5\text{-}18)$$

This work showed that the Meyer hardness calculated from Rockwell test data does not agree well with traditionally determined Meyer hardnesses if elastic recovery occurs. However, with a smaller ball and a greater load, conditions that produce a fully worked state, good agreement is obtained.

5-3.3 Vickers Hardness

In 1925, Smith and Sandland introduced the use of a pyramidal-shaped indenter (Fig. 5-5) made from diamond in order to test metals too hard for the Brinell test

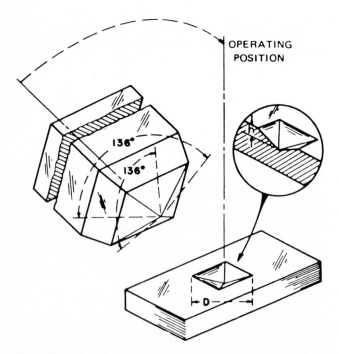

Figure 5-5 Schematic illustrating the Vickers diamond pyramid indenter and the indentation produced. *(From Lysaght and DeBellis, Ref. 8, courtesy of Page-Wilson Corp., Measurement Systems Div.)*

[17]. A square-based pyramid was chosen with an angle of 136° between opposite faces in order to obtain hardness numbers similar in magnitude to Brinell numbers. The ideal d/D ratio for a spherical indenter is 0.375. Tangents drawn to the ball at the impression edges meet below the center of the impression at an angle of 136°. Thus, a square-based pyramidal indenter with a 136° angle between opposite faces will produce Vickers hardness (HV) values approximately equal to HB values over the range of the Brinell test. This was a smart choice, since it permitted easy acceptance of the test.

An outstanding advantage of the Vickers diamond pyramid hardness test is that one continuous scale is used to test all materials regardless of their hardness. Because a geometrically similar impression is made, irrespective of the applied load, the HV value is reasonably constant over the load range normally applied (except for very low loads in microhardness testing), provided the material is homogeneous. The ability to use a wide variety of loads and still obtain the same hardness number makes the test useful on materials of different thickness. In the standard Vickers test, loads from 1 to 120 kgf have been employed. Loads above 30 kgf are infrequently used, and the most common load is 10 kgf. Figure 5-6 shows typical Vickers hardness testers.

In performing the test, the load must be applied smoothly without impact and held in contact for 10 to 15 s. The load should be correct to better than 1 percent. After removal of the load, both impression diagonals are measured, and the average value is used to calculate HV by the following equation:

$$HV = \frac{2L \sin (\alpha/2)}{d^2} = \frac{1.8544L}{d^2} \qquad (5\text{-}19)$$

where d = mean diagonal, mm
 L = load, kgf
 α = face angle (136°)

In nearly all cases, HV is determined by referring to tables of HV for each possible load and diagonal measurement. There are samples in which the measured diagonal is smaller than the data in the tables, and a calculation must be employed. Most equipment manufacturers supply a set of tables with the instrument; these tables are also found in ASTM Specification E92.

The pyramidal-surface area is greater than the projected area of the impression. Therefore, if the projected area is measured, for example, by image analysis, HV can be calculated with the following formula [5]:

$$HV = \frac{0.9272L}{\text{projected area}} \qquad (5\text{-}20)$$

where the projected area is in square millimeters. Thus, the relationship between HV and the mean yield pressure over the indentation P_M is given by the following equation:

$$P_M = \frac{HV}{0.9272} \qquad (5\text{-}21)$$

(a)

(b)

(c)

HV values are expressed in the same manner as HB values. For example, 350 HV 30 means that the measured Vickers hardness is 350 and a load of 30 kgf was applied. If the load duration was greater than the usual 15 s, for example 60 s, the hardness would be written as 350 HV 30/60. Longer holding times are commonly employed when testing low-melting-point alloys that creep during indentation.

In performing the test, the sample surface should be perpendicular to the indenter axis within ±1° otherwise errors will be introduced. Mulhearn and Samuels have shown that tilt angles less than 2° from perpendicular introduce alignment errors of 1 percent or less [18]. Tilting greater amounts produces nonsymmetrical impressions and lateral movement between the specimen and the indenter. Figure 5-7 from Ref. 18 shows the percentage of error introduced for tilt angles up to 8° from perpendicular. The curves show the mean theoretical error M for a large number of tests, for one test, and for the average of three or five impressions. The errors are larger than one would normally expect from simple geometric considerations. The lateral movement between sample and indenter due to tilting produces greater enlargement than expected.

In the ideal situation, the impression is square, but distortion can arise from several factors. In a heavily cold-worked metal, ridging can occur, which results in a bowing out of the edges. Because the diagonals are used to calculate the pyramidal-surface area, the area of a convex impression will be underestimated, and the hardness will appear to be greater than it is. An annealed material will exhibit a pincushion-shaped concave impression. In this case the diagonal measurement will overestimate the indentation surface area and produce a lower hardness. The errors introduced by these problems can be as great as 10 percent. Crow and Hinsley have developed procedures for measuring the change in pyramidal-surface area for convex Vickers impressions and for calculating the true hardness [19]. Equipment manufacturers are developing machines to read the projected area of the impression regardless of its shape. Anisotropy due to rolling or annealing textures can also produce severe distortion of the impression shape. Some investigators have used automatic image analyzers to measure the projected area.

The indenter quality can affect measurements. The 136° face angle must be accurate within 0.5°, the surfaces should be highly polished, and the apex should be pointed. It is a good practice to periodically inspect the indenter and determine the quality of the mounting and check for any cracking or chipping of the diamond.

When measuring the impression, one should place it in the center of the microscope field to minimize possible lens distortions. The light source should provide even illumination and maximum contrast between the impression and its surroundings. The graduations in the microscope should be ruled in 0.001-mm increments. In practice it should be possible to estimate the diagonal length to the

Figure 5-6 (*a*) Vickers diamond pyramid hardness tester. (*Courtesy of Vickers Limited.*) (*b*) Vickers, Brinell, and Rockwell tests can be performed on the Dia-Testor 2Rc hardness tester. (*Courtesy of Otto Wolpert-Werke GmbH.*) (*c*) Vickers, Brinell, and Rockwell tests can be performed on the Briviskop BVR 250H hardness tester (*Courtesy of George Reicherter GmbH and Co. KG*)

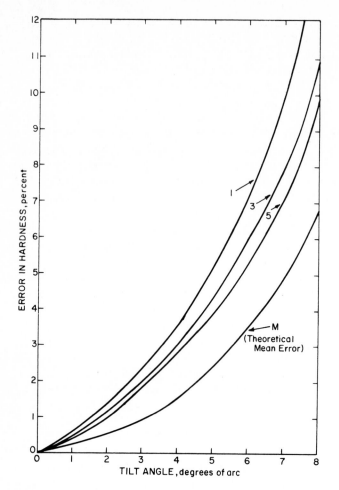

Figure 5-7 Percentage decrease in Vickers hardness due to specimen tilting for 1, 3, or 5 or a large number (*M*) of indentations. *(From Mulhearn and Samuels, Ref. 18, courtesy of the Metals Society.)*

nearest 0.0002 mm. The accuracy of the measuring microscope can be tested using a stage micrometer.

The surface finish of the test sample becomes more critical as the applied load is decreased. Either smooth-ground or polished samples are required. During smooth grinding, both sides can be made flat and parallel, thus eliminating tilting problems. Sample preparation must not alter the hardness of the surface.

The sample should be thick enough so that the applied load does not produce a mark or bulge on the back side of the sample. The wide range of test loads permits testing of much thinner stock than can be done with the Brinell test. ASTM E92 recommends that the sample thickness be at least 1.5 times the diagonal length. Samuels and Mulhearn recommend that the minimum thickness should be 2.5 times the diagonal length, based on their measurements of the deformation around Vickers impressions in alpha brass [20].

The minimum impression spacing (center to edge of adjacent impression) is generally recommended to be 2.5 times the diagonal. Samuels and Mulhearn recommended 2.7 times d [20]. The minimum distance between the center of an impression and the sample edge is usually given as 2.5 times d; however, Samuels and Mulhearn found that 1.8 times d was adequate.

Hardness testing on a curved surface always presents problems, and the Vickers test is no exception. In ASTM E92 correction procedures have been adopted based on the shape of the curved surface, i.e., spherical or cylindrical, and on the diagonal orientation on the cylindrical surface. After determining the apparent HV, the ratio of the impression diagonal to the diameter of the sphere or cylinder is calculated. The correction factor for this ratio is read from the table in ASTM E92 and is multiplied by the apparent HV value to obtain the corrected HV.

ASTM E92 also provides guidelines on the repeatability of HV measurements. If 10 measurements are made on a homogeneous material at the same load by the same operator, the range of the diagonal measurements provides an indicator of the repeatability of the test machine. The range of the diagonal measurements $(d_{max} - d_{min})$ should be less than the percentages given in ASTM E92 based on the average of the diagonal measurements.

The precision of the Vickers measurement depends on the accuracy of the loading, the quality of the diamond indenter, and the accuracy of the diagonal measurement. Tests of homogeneous materials with different machines and operators should produce hardness differences of not more than ± 2 percent.

The Meyer analysis can also be applied to Vickers hardness impressions. A log-log plot of impression diameter and load produces a linear relationship. However, because geometrically similar impressions are made, the deformations are similar (Kick's law) and the slope n is constant at 2. Tabor has shown that in the Vickers test the mean yield pressure P_M is $3.2Y$ [5]. Since HV equals $0.9272P_M$, HV is approximately three times the yield strength. Tabor claims that the best correlation between HV and Y for copper and steel occurs at 8 percent tensile strain. Dugdale obtained good correlations at any value of strain up to 15 percent in his tests of 20 different materials [21].

As an example of the constancy of HV as a function of test load, five steel test blocks (see Table 5-3) were tested at loads of 1, 5, 10, 20, 30, and 50 kgf. The data are given in Fig. 5-8 and listed in Table 5-4. The test results are uniform for loads of 10 to 50 kgf. Lower hardnesses were obtained at loads of 1 and 5 kgf. Table 5-4 shows that the 95 percent confidence limits increase as the test load decreases and as the hardness of the test block increases, i.e., as the diagonal decreases. These results are expected because there is a steep rise in HV with decreasing diagonal length (figure not shown). As the diagonal length decreases, small variations in measurement accuracy produce larger variations in hardness.

5-3.4 Rockwell Hardness

The Brinell test quickly became an important industrial tool after its introduction in 1900. However, the disadvantages of the test, such as the large amount of time

Table 5-3 Hardness measurements of test blocks evaluated by Vickers test at various loads (see Table 5-4)

Test Block	Measured hardness†				
	HRC‡	HRA§	HR 30N¶	Knoop (500 gf)	Equotip L value
A	22.9 ± 0.14	61.9 ± 0.17	43.5 ± 0.96	267.4 ± 0.8	519.6 ± 5.2
B	35.0 ± 0.10	67.9 ± 0.11	54.8 ± 0.31	359.8 ± 4.8	596.6 ± 5.6
C	46.8 ± 0.12	74.0 ± 0.05	65.9 ± 0.34	482.1 ± 4.0	684.8 ± 5.0
D	54.9 ± 0.23	78.5 ± 0.18	73.9 ± 0.41	635.6 ± 6.8	761.5 ± 2.4
E	63.2 ± 0.17	82.8 ± 0.12	79.9 ± 0.38	761.1 ± 7.0	825.1 ± 3.3

†Hardness value ± 95% confidence limit. Average and confidence limits based on 6 readings each test, except for Equotip in which 10 readings were averaged.
‡Rockwell hardness on C scale.
§Rockwell hardness on A scale.
¶Rockwell superficial hardness, N-Brale indenter, 30 kgf major load.

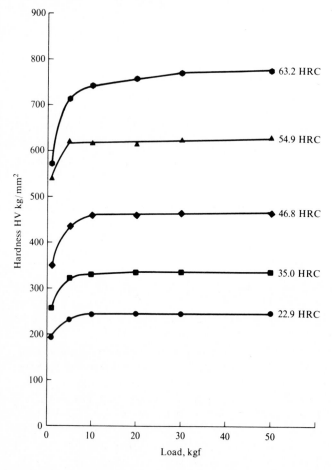

Figure 5-8 Vickers hardness as a function of applied load (1 to 50 kgf) for five steel test blocks.

Table 5-4 Vickers hardness data for five test blocks (see Table 5-3)

Test block† hardness, HRC	Load, kgf	Vickers hardness, HV‡	Mean diagonal, μm‡
22.9	1	192.0 ± 2.4	98.25 ± 0.6
	5	235.3 ± 2.4	198.38 ± 0.99
	10	244.3 ± 0.9	275.33 ± 0.47
	20	245.2 ± 0.8	388.83 ± 0.8
	30	248.3 ± 0.5	473.75 ± 0.5
	50	247.4 ± 0.8	612.25 ± 1.19
35.0	1	259.5 ± 5.1	84.58 ± 0.85
	5	322.0 ± 3.8	169.75 ± 0.94
	10	330.0 ± 2.2	236.75 ± 1.0
	20	334.3 ± 2.5	333.3 ± 1.24
	30	337.3 ± 1.5	406.0 ± 0.96
	50	337.8 ± 2.3	523.9 ± 1.76
46.8	1	348.3 ± 3.0	73.0 ± 0.3
	5	434.7 ± 4.1	146.0 ± 0.7
	10	456.7 ± 1.7	201.6 ± 0.4
	20	458.7 ± 1.7	284.3 ± 0.6
	30	465.3 ± 2.0	345.7 ± 0.9
	50	466.3 ± 1.2	445.8 ± 0.6
54.9	1	540.7 ± 14.3	58.5 ± 0.8
	5	620.8 ± 4.6	122.2 ± 0.5
	10	616.7 ± 7.9	173.5 ± 1.2
	20	615.7 ± 3.9	245.4 ± 0.7
	30	627.6 ± 5.6	297.7 ± 1.3
	50	631.2 ± 2.6	383.3 ± 0.8
63.2	1	572.7 ± 11.3	56.9 ± 0.6
	5	715.3 ± 7.6	113.8 ± 0.6
	10	743.2 ± 5.5	158.0 ± 0.6
	20	758.5 ± 4.0	221.1 ± 0.7
	30	770.0 ± 4.7	268.8 ± 0.8
	50	776.2 ± 5.9	345.7 ± 1.4

†Measured as Rockwell hardness on the C scale.

‡Average, plus and minus the 95% confidence limit, was calculated based on six impressions at each load on each test block.

required to perform the test, the large impression size required, and the fact that high-hardness steels could not be tested, prompted development of other tests such as the Vickers test just described and the Rockwell test. In 1919, Stanley P. Rockwell, a metallurgist in a ball-bearing factory, invented the tester known today by his name [22]. In 1920, Charles H. Wilson became the manufacturer and seller of the Rockwell tester. Wilson, an instrument manufacturer, made many contributions of his own to the unit. In the original tester, the hardness scale was 0 to 100, with low hardness numbers for hard materials and high numbers for soft materials. Wilson reversed this pattern to conform with the other hardness scales.

Wilson also standardized the minor load at 10 kgf. Application of the minor load provided a starting point for the test and eliminated the effects of sinking and ridging. Because the minor load is still applied when the hardness is determined, elastic recovery effects are reduced and the deflection of tester components is eliminated from affecting test results. Rockwell initially used a hardened $\frac{1}{16}$-in diameter steel ball which flattened during testing. Rockwell tried working with a 100-kgf load and a flattened ball but found that small hardness differences could not be discerned. Wilson developed a diamond indenter referred to as a "Brale" penetrator and increased the major load to 150 kgf for testing hard steels. After some trials, Wilson adopted a cone angle of 120° and a true tangent nose radius of 0.2 mm for the diamond Brale (see Fig. 5-9). Diamond, of course, does not deform during testing of steel because of its great hardness. The nose radius, as opposed to a sharp point, minimizes penetration under the minor load and improves indenter life. The broad cone angle and the nose radius, plus the relatively low applied load, produce a small test impression.

The use of the $\frac{1}{16}$-in diameter hardened steel ball and 100-kgf major load was retained for testing of soft steels and many nonferrous alloys. However, the upper limit of the scale was raised from 100 to 130 so that tests on soft copper and brass alloys would not produce negative numbers.

In the Rockwell test, a 10-kgf minor load is used to press the indenter into the sample and establish a zero point for the test. Then the major load, 60, 100, or 150 kgf, is applied and removed. The hardness is indicated on the dial gauge with the minor load still applied. The hardness is an inverse function of the penetration depth due to the major load. Table 5-5 lists the various combinations of loads and

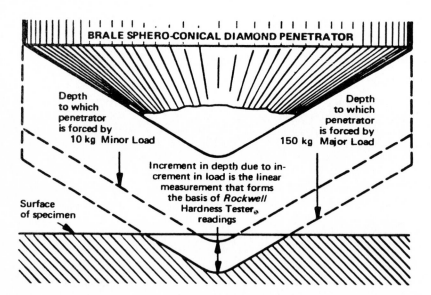

Figure 5-9 Schematic illustrating the Rockwell Brale indenter and the test method. *(From Lysaght and DeBellis, Ref. 8, courtesy of Page-Wilson Corp., Measurement Systems Div.)*

Table 5-5 Rockwell test scales—standard tester

Scale symbol	Penetrator	Load kgf	Dial gauge scale
A	Brale	60	Black
B	$\frac{1}{16}$-in ball	100	Red
C	Brale	150	Black
D	Brale	100	Black
E	$\frac{1}{8}$-in ball	100	Red
F	$\frac{1}{16}$-in ball	60	Red
G	$\frac{1}{16}$-in ball	150	Red
H	$\frac{1}{8}$-in ball	60	Red
K	$\frac{1}{8}$-in ball	150	Red
L	$\frac{1}{4}$-in ball	60	Red
M	$\frac{1}{4}$-in ball	100	Red
P	$\frac{1}{4}$-in ball	150	Red
R	$\frac{1}{2}$-in ball	60	Red
S	$\frac{1}{2}$-in ball	100	Red
V	$\frac{1}{2}$-in ball	150	Red

Source: From Lysaght and DeBellis, Ref. 8.

Table 5-6 Typical applications of Rockwell test scales

Scale	Applications
A	Cemented carbides, thin steels, shallow case-hardened steels. Only scale that is continuous over a wide range of material hardnesses.
B	Aluminum, copper, soft steels, and malleable iron.
C	Steels with hardnesses above 100 HRB, hard irons, deep-case hardened steels, titanium, etc.
D	Thin steels, medium case-hardened steels, and pearlitic malleable iron.
E	Cast iron, aluminum, magnesium, and bearing metals.
F	Annealed coppers and thin, soft sheet metal.
G	Phosphor bronze, beryllium copper, and malleable irons (materials less than 92 HRG to prevent flattening of the ball).
H	Aluminum, zinc, and lead.
K, L, M, P, R, S, V	Bearing metals and other very soft or thin materials. Use smallest ball and heaviest load that does not produce anvil effects.
N	Used for same materials as for HRA, HRC, and HRD but for thinner gauge or case depths.
T	Used for same materials as for HRB, HRF, and HRG but for thinner gauge.
W, X, Y	Used for very soft materials.

Source: From Lysaght and DeBellis, Ref. 8.

indenters that comprise the 15 different standard Rockwell test scales. Table 5-6 lists typical applications for these scales. Figure 5-10 illustrates a typical Rockwell-type laboratory hardness tester. Portable Rockwell testers are also available (see Fig. 5-11).

The Rockwell test is based on measurement of an incremental change in penetration depth under an incremental change in load. The depth measurement is automatically indicated on a calibrated dial that has units of hardness rather than depth. Thus, the test is quite rapid, and the impression measurement errors

Figure 5-10 Model 3-DT Rockwell standard and superficial hardness tester with digital readout. *(Courtesy of Page-Wilson Corp., Measurement Systems Div.)*

Figure 5-11 Model MR-DI multirange portable tester for HRA, HRB, and HB tests. *(Courtesy of Newage Industries, Inc.)*

and tedium are eliminated. However, the hardness scales are completely arbitrary and do not have the physical meaning of the hardness values from the Brinell and Vickers tests. Because the depth of a partially recovered impression is measured, the hardness scales are unique to the test, and correlations with tests involving the measurement of completely recovered impressions are difficult.

In the Rockwell test, one point of hardness corresponds to a depth of only 0.002 mm (0.00008 in). Making such small measurements accurately and repeatably requires an accurate, sensitive depth measurement system as well as a highly accurate loading system.

The dial gauge has two sets of scales—black numbers on the outside and red numbers on the inside. The black scale is used with tests requiring the Brale indenters, while the red scale is used for all tests requiring ball indenters. The set point, that is, the indicator for the minor-load application, is at 0 on the black scale and 30 on the red scale. The dial gauge is a 1-mm gauge; that is, the gauge makes one revolution for 1 mm of travel. Because the dial is divided into 100 divisions and a lever ratio of 5:1 is employed, each division represents a depth of 0.002 mm. Thus, with the red or black scales, the impression depth Δh (depth difference between application of minor and major loads) is as follows:

$$
\begin{array}{ll}
\text{Black scale:} & \Delta h = 0.002\,(100 - \text{dial reading}) \\
\text{Red scale:} & \Delta h = 0.002\,(130 - \text{dial reading})
\end{array}
\qquad (5\text{-}22)
$$

In performing the Rockwell test, the operator must first decide which test scale is most appropriate for the material to be tested. Table 5-6 provides guidelines that should prove useful when an unfamiliar material is encountered. Frequently a particular material specification is encountered which dictates the scale to be used and the hardness range to be expected. The appropriate indenter is inserted, and the weight is adjusted to the prescribed level. Next, a suitable anvil is chosen to support the sample firmly. The specimen is placed on the anvil, and the minor load is applied by zeroing the set point. The major load is applied fully and then removed. The increase in depth due to the major load is displayed on the dial gauge as a hardness number. The hardness is read from either the red or the black scale depending on the test scale selected, as listed in Table 5-5. The minor load is then removed before taking another reading in another area. Historically, the Rockwell B and C scales are the most commonly employed. The C Brale is not used for materials softer than 20 HRC and the B ball is not used for materials harder than 100 HRB. The resulting hardness is expressed as the dial reading followed by HR and the scale designation. For example, 60 HRC means that the Rockwell hardness was 60 on the C scale.

As with the other tests, the quality of the Rockwell indenters should be determined by periodic inspection. A chipped diamond or a flattened ball produces incorrect results. In addition, indenters and anvils should be kept clean, since dust, dirt, or grease on these surfaces affects test results. Marking of the anvil by the indenter or by the sample produces erroneous results. Vibrations also cause problems and must be eliminated or isolated. If a sample cannot be rigidly fixed on the anvil, inaccuracies result. Samples that hang over the edge of the anvil must be supported properly.

The minimum sample thickness that can be tested depends on the hardness of the material and the test parameters chosen. Guidelines are given in ASTM E18. The thickness should be adequate so that the hardness test is not influenced by the anvil support ("anvil effect").

A smooth surface is desirable. Again, the surface preparation procedure should not affect the hardness of the sample. The test surface must be oriented perpendicular to the indenter axis. Bastin and Mulhearn have studied the influence of tilt angle on HRC measurements and found that the indenter must be within 1° of perpendicular if the error in hardness is to be less than 5 percent [23]. Soft materials are more strongly influenced by tilting than hard materials. Figure 5-12 shows the influence of tilt angle on the change in HRC for materials from 30 to 60 HRC.

As with other hardness tests, the impressions must be separated by a specific minimum distance so that the second impression is not influenced by the strain field associated with the first impression. In general, it is recommended that the center-to-center distance between two adjacent impressions be not less than three impression diameters. The distance between the center of an impression and the edge of the sample should be not less than 2.5 times the impression diameter.

Test readings made on curved surfaces must be corrected to produce valid results. Correction factors for different hardness materials tested with different scales are given in ASTM Specification E18 as a function of the diameter of cylindrical samples.

The repeatability of hardnesses measured on different machines and by different operators or the repeatability of hardness on the same machine can be determined by comparing the range ($HR_{max} - HR_{min}$) of five test values with the guidelines given in ASTM E18.

Peek and Ingerson have examined the Rockwell test using $\frac{1}{16}$-, $\frac{1}{8}$- and $\frac{1}{4}$-in diameter balls and loads of 60, 100, and 150 kgf and have developed an analysis based on the depth increment between minor- and major-load application that is similar to the Meyer analysis [24]. They concluded that if the ratio of $\Delta h/D$ is less than 0.1, the relationship between the incremental depth increase and the applied load can be expressed as follows:

$$\frac{\Delta h}{D} = \frac{C\,(L - L_o)^{1/m}}{SD^2} \tag{5-23}$$

where Δh = the incremental depth, cm
D = the ball diameter, cm
L = the major load, kgf
L_o = the minor load, kgf
S = material constant, stress units
C, m = dimensionless constants

A log-log plot of $(L - L_o)/D^2$ versus $\Delta h/D$ produces a linear relationship. The

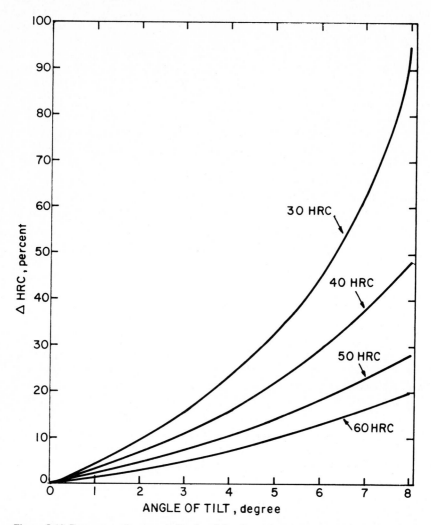

Figure 5-12 Percentage decrease in Rockwell hardness due to specimen tilting as a function of tilt angle and hardness. *(From Bastin and Mulhearn, Ref. 23, courtesy of The Metals Society.)*

values of L, L_o, and D are known, and Δh can be calculated from the dial reading and Eq. (5-22). To obtain Δh in centimeters, one should multiply by 0.0002 rather than by 0.002. Peek and Ingerson found that this relationship was followed by a number of soft materials. The value of m is a measure of strain hardening similar to n in the Meyer analysis. For hardened samples, m has a value of 1. The value of C depends on the work-hardening characteristics of the material. If S is assumed to be equal to the tensile strength of the test sample, C and m can be calculated.

Meyer made a detailed study of the Rockwell ball tests and developed conversions from Rockwell hardness to Meyer and Brinell hardnesses [25]. His relationship between Rockwell ball hardness and Meyer hardness (HM) is as follows:

$$HR = 130 - \frac{250L}{\pi r \, HM} \left[1 - \left(\frac{L_o}{L} \right)^{2/n} \right] \qquad (5\text{-}24)$$

where r is the radius of the Rockwell ball used. The quantity inside the square brackets, called η by Meyer, varies about 6% when n varies from 2 to 2.5 for a particular minor/major load (L_o/L) ratio. Meyer simplified the above relation as follows:

$$HR = 130 - \frac{79.6L}{r \, HM} \, \eta = 130 - \frac{\mu}{HM} \qquad (5\text{-}25)$$

This equation can be rewritten as follows:

$$HM = \frac{\mu}{130 - HR} \qquad (5\text{-}26)$$

Values of μ and η were given for different values of n as a function of the particular Rockwell ball test (D and L_o/L).

In 1932, the Rockwell superficial tester was developed, principally to determine the hardness of thin nitrided cases on steels [26]. Initial attempts involved lowering the major load to 30 kgf. This effort was not successful because Δh was only slightly larger than the depth due to the minor load. The final solution used a minor load of 3 kgf; a major load of 15, 30, or 45 kgf; and different loading and depth-measuring procedures. Outwardly, the superficial and standard testers appear to be quite similar. However, the depth measurement system is twice as sensitive as in the standard tester. A ½-mm dial gauge is used so that one revolution equals ½ mm of travel. There are 100 divisions on the scale, and with the 5:1 lever ratio, 1 division equals a depth of 0.001 mm (0.00004 in). Table 5-7 lists the 15 possible superficial test scales and the test conditions for each. The N Brale indenter is identical to the C Brale but is made to closer tolerances. The test is performed in the same manner as described for the standard tester. Hardness readings are given as the dial reading followed by HR and the test symbol as listed in Table 5-7. For example, if the N Brale is used with a major load of 30 kgf and produces a dial reading of 75, the hardness is expressed as 75 HR 30N. Table 5-6 lists typical applications for the superficial test scales. The 30N scale covers the full range of the HRC scale and is commonly used on hardened steels.

The superficial test is used to determine surface hardnesses of materials with shallow cases, to test very small areas, to measure hardness gradients (as in the Shepherd P-F or P-V tests of the hardenability of carbon tool steels), or to test thin metals. Very thin materials that are subject to anvil effect can be tested by placing the material on an anvil which has a polished diamond at its center. This permits comparative tests on thin samples. The diamond spot anvil should not be used to test hard materials with the N Brale because if the piece cracks, the Brale or the

Table 5-7 Rockwell test scales—superficial tester

Scale symbol	Penetrator	Load, kgf
15N	N Brale	15
30N	N Brale	30
45N	N Brale	45
15T	$\frac{1}{16}$-in ball	15
30T	$\frac{1}{16}$-in ball	30
45T	$\frac{1}{16}$-in ball	45
15W	$\frac{1}{8}$-in ball	15
30W	$\frac{1}{8}$-in ball	30
45W	$\frac{1}{8}$-in ball	45
15X	$\frac{1}{4}$-in ball	15
30X	$\frac{1}{4}$-in ball	30
45X	$\frac{1}{4}$-in ball	45
15Y	$\frac{1}{2}$-in ball	15
30Y	$\frac{1}{2}$-in ball	30
45Y	$\frac{1}{2}$-in ball	45

Source: From Lysaght and DeBellis, Ref. 8.

anvil can be damaged. One should never use the diamond spot anvil with the standard tester because the heavier loads can break the diamond.

All the previously mentioned precautions pertain to the superficial test. However, because of the lighter loads, the surface finish must be smoother than with the standard tester. The repeatability of superficial hardness measurements using different machines and operators can be evaluated in the same way as shown for the standard tester. Guidelines on performance are given in ASTM E18.

5-3.5 Other Static Hardness Tests

Over the years many other static hardness tests have been proposed. Some of these have enjoyed limited application and are no longer or infrequently used today. Others are still used but only in very specific areas. In this section, a few of these tests are briefly reviewed.

Ludwik conical indentation test Ludwik developed a test in 1908 that employed a conical indenter with a 90° angle to overcome the disadvantage of the Brinell test, i.e., the changing hardness with changing load. Although the conical indenter produces geometrically similar impressions, the intense ridging around the indentation made the impression difficult to measure. This problem often resulted in decreasing cone hardness numbers with increasing load.

The selection of a 90° apex angle for the cone produces an impression depth equal to the impression diameter. The Ludwik cone hardness (CHN) was determined by dividing the load by the surface contact area of the recovered impression:

$$CHN = \frac{load}{conical\ contact\ area}$$

$$CHN = \frac{4L\ \sin\ (\alpha/2)}{\pi d^2} = \frac{2.828L}{\pi d^2} \qquad (5\text{-}27)$$

where L = load, kgf
α = cone angle (90°)
d = imprint diameter, mm

The Ludwik cone hardness number has no direct physical significance. The true pressure between the indenter and the test sample is determined by dividing the load by the projected area of the impression, assuming frictionless conditions. Studies have shown that the yield pressure increases as the sharpness of the cone increases.

Mutual indentation tests Mutual indentation as a measure of hardness was first suggested by Reaumur in 1722. He struck two crossed 90° triangular prisms with a hammer and used the relative impression depths as a measure of hardness. Haigh used crossed bars with a square cross section and defined the hardness as the load divided by the projected area of the impression, following Meyer's suggestion. Föppl used crossed round bars, Cowdrey employed two round bars aligned parallel to each other, and Auerback pressed a sphere or a round bar with a spherical end into the surface of a flat plate.

Crossed cylindrical specimens produce an impression shape similar to that obtained in the Brinell test, while crossed wedges produce an impression shape similar to that of the Vickers test. Atkins and Tabor found that for crossed cylinders of highly work-hardened metals, the mutual hardness was approximately equal to 2.3 times the uniaxial yield strength of the test material [27]. They found that the wedge angle of the crossed wedges influenced the mutual hardness. With square or rectangular crossed wedges, the hardness of fully work-hardened metals was approximately equal to 3.3 times the yield strength of the metal.

Although mutual hardness tests lack the convenience of conventional tests, they have been used to advantage in measuring the hot hardness of extremely hard materials. For the failure analyst, Atkins and Felbeck have developed a useful method for interpreting and analyzing indentations made during service failures [28].

Mallock cone test In 1926, Mallock introduced a hardness test procedure in which a very small pointed conical specimen was slowly pressed against a sapphire plate and the diameter of the flattened tip was measured. The Mallock hardness was calculated by dividing the load (usually between 0.5 and 5 kgf) by the area of the flattened tip. Because the impressions were geometrically similar, the Mallock hardness was approximately constant with the load.

Kenneford and O'Neill [29] performed Mallock tests on lead, tin, and bearing metals, and Williams and O'Neill [30] studied a wide range of materials using large cones with included angles from 30 to 150° and loads up to 6000 kgf. Aside from these studies, little use has been made of the test because of the need to prepare polished conical specimens.

Scratch hardness Scratch tests were the earliest procedure developed for the evaluation of hardness. In 1637, Barba described the use of a file to determine the hardness of tools. In 1722, Reaumur developed a set of seven standard materials for scratch grading the hardness of materials. This was followed by the development of similar scales by Werner in 1774 and Hauy in 1801, but the most popular scratch series was that of Friedrich Mohs in 1822. This scale [7, 31] is described in Table 5-8. Many developments in scratch testing were made in the nineteenth century. Following this, O'Neill devised an instrument for studying directional hardness in single crystals [1, 2]. The load was varied to produce a scratch with a standard width. The hardness was expressed as follows:

$$H = \frac{8L}{\pi d^2} \qquad (5\text{-}28)$$

where d was the width of the scratch.

Table 5-8 Mohs hardness scale

Mohs standard	Other materials	Hardness number	
		Mohs scale	Knoop (equiv.)
Talc		1	2
	Pb	1–2	5
Gypsum		2	32
	Cu	2–3	40
Calcite		3	120
	Mild steel	3–4	100
Fluorite		4	150
Apatite		5	400
Feldspar		6	560
	W	7	
Quartz		7	700
	Martensitic steel	7–8	700
Topaz		8	1300
	Hard Cr Plating	8	1800
Corundum		9	1800
	WC	9–10	1800
Diamond		10	6000

Source: From Petty, Ref. 7.

Other instruments used for this purpose were the Graton sclerometer developed in 1925 and the Bierbaum Microcharacter tester patented in 1926 [32, 33]. The Bierbaum tester is a sclerometer attached to the stage of a bench microscope. A diamond, in the form of the corner of a cube, is held in an elastic support and is run across the sample surface to produce a scratch. A 3-gf load is used, and the scratch width is measured with the microscope. The scratch microhardness is calculated with the following formula:

$$H = \frac{10^4}{d^2} \qquad (5\text{-}29)$$

where d is the scratch width in micrometers. If a 9-gf load is employed to scratch harder materials, one-half the scratch width is used in the calculation. The scarf along the edge of the scratch furrow reduces the accuracy of the measurement. Bierbaum microcharacter hardness values have no physical significance, being an arbitrary definition of hardness.

Scratch hardness is generally employed today using special pointed indenters which are available with several modern microhardness testers. The test has value in that a single trace can be made through a microstructure and the relative hardness of the different phases and constituents can be assessed. Strengthening effects due to embrittlement can be detected at grain boundaries.

Hardness tests for nonmetallic materials Hardness tests have been applied to a wide range of nonmetallic materials including wax, wood, rubber, paint, and polymers and even to foods such as ice cream. To accommodate these materials, a variety of special tests have been proposed, such as the Barber Colman Impressor. Standard testers can also be used to evaluate the hardness of many nonmetallic materials.

5-4 DYNAMIC HARDNESS TESTS

If hardness can be defined as resistance to permanent deformation, it follows that there is a definite relationship between hardness and the elastic characteristics of materials. Elasticity implies that a material will return to its original length if it is compressed, stretched, or distorted without causing permanent deformation when the load is removed. Hooke's law states that the ratio of stress to strain is constant within the elastic limit of the material. This ratio, the modulus of elasticity, is constant for a given material and is a measure of the rigidity of a material. Dynamic, or rebound, hardness test methods measure hardness as related to the elastic behavior of materials, while the indentation methods determine hardness as related to the plastic behavior of materials. A number of rebound tests have been developed, but only a few are currently employed to any extent.

5-4.1 Shore Scleroscope

The Shore scleroscope, invented by A. F. Shore in 1907, is the most commonly used rebound-type tester. It is best known for its use in determining the surface hardness of chilled iron or hardened steel rolls where a large, permanent indentation on the surface cannot be tolerated. Hardness is measured as the degree of rebound of a diamond-tipped hammer dropped onto the surface of the component from a known height. The operator reads the rebound height by watching the rebound within a graduated tube or by direct reading of a dial. The device is lightweight and completely portable.

The two types of scleroscopes made are the Model C and the Model D. The Model C scleroscope consists of a vertically oriented tube containing a glass inner tube with a carefully controlled bore surface. A graduated scale, from 0 to 140, is visible through the glass. At the top of the tube is a pneumatically actuated head operated by a rubber bulb and connected to a rubber tube. The bulb is used to drop the hammer from the top of the tube onto the surface of the test sample. The hammer rebounds from the sample back up the tube to a height that depends on the material's hardness. The measured height is the Shore hardness.

The Model D scleroscope uses a dial gauge to record the rebound height, i.e., the Shore hardness. A clutch is employed to stop the hammer at the peak of the rebound. Because the hammer is longer and heavier than in the Model C scleroscope, the drop distance is shortened so that the same striking energy is developed.

The diamond tip will penetrate a mild steel sample to a depth of about 0.025 mm and a hardened tool steel to about 0.013 mm. The diamond tip is convex in shape with a flat striking surface which is approximately circular with a diameter of 0.1 to 0.4 mm depending on the instrument.

Several scales are employed depending on the tester model and test material. The standard models have a scale divided into 100 units, and the hardness is reported as HSc or HSd units depending on the tester model. For testing hardened steel rolls, a slightly larger striking surface is used. The hardness scales are HFRSc or HFRSd, again depending on the tester model. The forged roll scleroscope produces higher hardness numbers than the smaller-tipped hammer models.

A wide variety of sample sizes can be tested using the attachments provided with the instrument. Surface finish is important if good test results are to be obtained. Misalignment will affect the test results. The scleroscope must be held vertically, which is most easily accomplished with the clamping stand. Vibrations must be avoided. Even though the test produces very small impressions, errors will result if the impressions are not spaced apart properly. ASTM Specification E448 recommends spacing indentations at least 0.020 in (0.51 mm) apart. A test can be made within 0.25 inch (6 mm) of an edge. If the sample is magnetized, erroneous results will be obtained.

Calibrated test blocks can be obtained to test the accuracy of the machine. ASTM E448 recommends making five tests on each of the four sides of the block. The tests should not be made within ½ in (13 mm) of the ends of the block or within

¼ in (6 mm) of the sides. The scleroscope is considered to be accurate if 90 percent of the readings are within ± 3 scleroscope units of the mean of the readings.

5-4.2 Pendulum Hardness

One of the more ingenious methods for measuring hardness was developed by Herbert. In this method, an inverted compound pendulum is supported on the horizontal specimen surface by a 1-mm diameter steel or diamond ball. The center of gravity is controlled with an adjustable weight and is usually set to be 0.1 mm below the center of the ball. The pendulum is tilted until a bubble level is zeroed. The hardness is determined by releasing the arm and noting the scale number in the bubble level at the end of one swing of the arm. Herbert obtained a value of 100 for glass and 0 for lead. An alternative procedure for determining hardness is to note the time in seconds for 10 swings of the arm. With this procedure, Herbert obtained a value of 100 for glass, 85 for hardened steel, and 3 for lead. Indentation tests of glass produce lower hardness than tests of hardened steel. Herbert also performed pendulum hardness tests above and below ambient temperature. This test never became popular, and the tester has not been manufactured for some time. Another type of pendulum hardness tester was developed by Kusnezow.

5-4.3 Cloudburst Test

Surface hardness can be evaluated by sandblasting or shotblasting a surface and observing the surface indentations. These processes are well known to work-harden the surface and produce a favorable residual stress pattern for improving fatigue life. Herbert referred to the method as the "cloudburst" process and used hardened steel balls that were dropped onto the specimen surface from a known height. The impact produces many small imprints on the surface which reveal nonuniform hardness patterns. Chalmers used sand dropped from a height of 1 m. He determined the weight of sand required to reduce the optical reflectivity of the surface by 50 percent.

5-4.4 Equotip Hardness

The Equotip portable hardness tester, which was introduced in 1977, determines hardness on the basis of the difference between impact and rebound velocities of a 3-mm diameter spherical tungsten carbide ball indenter propelled against the specimen surface. The velocities are measured electronically without contact when the indenter is 1 mm from the test surface. Hardness is expressed as an L value, or "Leeb value," after the inventor, Dietmar Leeb. This value is obtained by dividing the rebound velocity by the impact velocity and then multiplying by 1000. For a given orientation of the test probe, the impact velocity is constant. The rebound velocity increases as the test sample hardness increases. Thus, L increases with increasing hardness. Materials harder than 940 HV or 68 HRC should not be tested because the WC-Co ball will be deformed.

The instrument is battery-operated, and tests can be made at any angle. Simple corrections are made for nonvertical tests. A small indent is made on the test surface. The average spacing between impacts or between a surface edge and an indent should be greater than 3 mm. The hardness value is displayed digitally on the indicator device. The average deviation of measurements should be within ± 0.8 percent at an L value of 800, i.e., ± 6 L units.

Because of the influence of the impacting force, sample size can influence test results. Samples heavier than 5 kg (11 lb) with a compact shape present no measurement problems. Smaller test samples are sometimes moved by the impact force, which alters the rebound velocity. Samples weighing between 2 and 5 kg (4.4 to 11 lb) or thin samples of greater total weight can be placed on a solid support to prevent movement. Samples lighter than 2 kg can be tested by applying a thin layer of coupling paste to the bottom of the test sample and placing it on a thick, heavy, flat plate. The sample is pressed against the plate surface and moved with a circular motion to obtain good coupling. The test blocks listed in Table 5-3 were tested in this manner.

Conversion of L values to other test scales has been accomplished by the manufacturer. Efforts to correlate L values to Shore hardness are described in Ref. 34. Conversions must be based on specific material types, since the L value is influenced by the material's modulus of elasticity.

5-5 NONDESTRUCTIVE HARDNESS TESTS

A number of nondestructive techniques have been developed to determine hardness. These methods are based on magnetic characteristics [4, 35], eddy currents [36], ultrasonic properties [37], acoustic properties [38], electrical characteristics such as thermoelectric power and resistance [39], and x-ray diffraction patterns [40]. The observation that the magnetic characteristics of ferromagnetic materials are strongly influenced by hardness has led to the extensive use of magnetic methods. Also, automated eddy current devices have become quite popular in recent years.

Williams has used magnetic methods to test the hardness of steel balls, samples in which the presence of an indentation would be quite harmful [4]. Since magnetic procedures measure the hardness of the entire ball, that is, the interior as well as the exterior, nonuniformity of ball hardness will affect any correlations attempted with indentation or rebound tests.

A number of devices that use the magnetic characteristics of the material have been developed to measure hardness. The Ferrograph, which was developed by Förster, plots the hysteresis loop of the material on a cathode-ray tube, and the area within the loop and its shape are used to sort steel bars according to composition and hardness. The Cyclograph, which was developed by the Du Mont Company, has been used in nondestructive testing of both ferromagnetic and nonferromagnetic materials. Case depth, plating thickness, surface stresses, and hardness have been measured with this device. For steels above 55 HRC, the

Cyclograph reportedly can determine hardness differences of 2 HRC units. At lower hardnesses, differences of 5 HRC units can be discerned.

5-6 MICROINDENTATION HARDNESS

Scratch tests at low loads, such as the Bierbaum Microcharacter test performed with either 3- or 9-g loads, preceded the development of microhardness testers using traditional indenters. The first reference to the use of the Vickers indenter with low loads was made in the annual report of the National Physical Laboratory in 1932. Lips and Sack described the first Vickers tester using low loads in 1936. In America, Knoop and his associates [41, 42] at the National Bureau of Standards developed a low-load tester employing a rhombohedral-shaped diamond indenter in which the long diagonal is seven times as long as the short diagonal (see Fig. 5-13).

The term microhardness has been widely employed in the literature to describe the hardness testing of materials with low applied loads; however, microhardness implies that the hardness is very small rather than the load. A more precise term is microindentation hardness testing. However, the term microhardness is well established and properly interpreted by those employing the test methods and usually presents no confusion. Two excellent reviews on microhardness testing are the book by Mott [43] and the paper by Bückle [44].

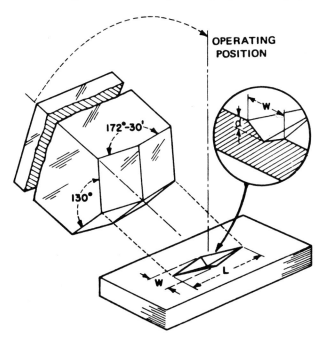

Figure 5-13 Schematic showing the configuration of the Knoop indenter and resulting impression. *(From Lysaght and DeBellis, Ref. 8, courtesy of Page-Wilson Corp., Measurement Systems Div.)*

There is some disagreement in the literature regarding the load range applicable to microhardness testing. ASTM Specification E384, for example, states that the load range for microhardness testing is 1 to 1000 gf. Because of the deviation of n from 2 for Vickers impressions smaller than about 30 μm, Bückle confines microhardness testing to loads of up to 200 gf or indentations of up to 30 to 50 μm [44]. He uses the term "low-load" hardness for indentations made with loads of 200 gf to 3 kgf, i.e., indentations of up to about 300 μm. Loads above 3 kgf are reserved for standard "macrohardness" tests. Bückle considers the low-load hardness test region as basically a refined version of the standard hardness test regime that can be conducted without much risk of abnormal errors. Bückle's classification scheme is a useful guideline for those interested in low-load hardness testing.

For loads of 1 kgf and below, the Vickers hardness is calculated with an equation similar to Eq. (5-19) except that the load L is in grams-force and the diagonal d is in micrometers:

$$HV = \frac{1854.4L}{d^2} \tag{5-30}$$

The Knoop hardness is calculated in similar fashion from the following relationship:

$$HK = \frac{14{,}229L}{d^2} \tag{5-31}$$

where d is the length of the long diagonal in micrometers, sometimes represented by l. In routine use, however, the Vickers or Knoop hardnesses are determined by referring to tables provided with the instrument or from ASTM E384. These tables list hardnesses as a function of the test load and diagonal. For any given load, the hardness increases rapidly at low diagonal lengths, with the effect becoming more pronounced as the load decreases. Thus, in the vertical portion of these curves, small measurement errors will produce large hardness deviations. Consequently, one should always use the highest possible load in any test. Examples of commercially available microhardness testers are shown in Fig. 5-14.

In the discussion of the standard Vickers test, it was shown that Meyer's law relating the load and impression diameter yields a constant value for n of 2 because of the geometric similarity (Kick's law) of the impressions. A constant value of 2 indicates that the hardness will be constant irrespective of the load. Unfortunately, at very low loads n does not equal 2 with Vickers impressions, a fact that seriously reduces the value of the test. If n is less than 2, the hardness rises as the test load decreases, while if n is greater than 2, the hardness drops as the load decreases. Both types of behavior have been observed, as well as little or no change in n. When this problem was first recognized, efforts were made to define a standard microhardness value as the hardness corresponding to some fixed diagonal measurement, e.g., 10 μm. A series of impressions were made with a number of loads, and a log-log plot of L versus d was made to determine the microhardness for the desired indent size chosen. It was hoped that this procedure would permit determination of reproducible hardness values at low loads, but instead large variations still resulted. The study by Brown and Ineson of eight samples tested with 10 different microhardness testers in 13 different laboratories clearly showed the variability of test results [45]. Although such results paint a bleak picture for microhardness testing, the test does provide useful information. However, one must be aware of the difficulties inherent in the test and the care required in order to obtain optimum results.

Alternate formulas to equate L and d have been proposed because of the variability of n at very low loads from the ideal value of 2—values from 1.3 to 3.0 have been reported [46]. None of these equations has proved to be universally applicable. Some experimenters believed that elastic recovery of the diagonals, which would shorten the diagonals and increase the hardness, was responsible for the deviation of n from 2—at least for the cases where n was lower than 2. Bückle has shown that the elastic recovery of the diagonals does not exceed about 0.1 μm, an amount that cannot account for the degree of observed deviation [46]. Deformation of the surface due to poor mechanical polishing procedures has also been suggested as a cause of the deviation of n from 2 at very low loads. This problem produces higher hardness values at low loads, but, of course, cannot explain the lower hardnesses at low loads observed by some experimenters. Bückle has carefully examined the problem and claims that it is due to the influence of the ridge that forms around the impressions [44, 46, 47]. The height of this ridge is on the order of 0.5 to 0.8 percent of the diagonal. Ridging produces measurement difficulties. The geometric shape of the ridge and the impression sides are influenced by elastic depth recovery, which produces focusing problems when one attempts to define the impression edges and diagonals.

There are many sources of error in microhardness testing. These can be broadly categorized as instrument errors, measurement errors, and material errors, as summarized in Table 5-9. Some of these factors produce systematic errors, while others influence low-load hardness values by either increasing or decreasing the observed hardness.

Instrument errors can be controlled through proper choice of the instrument and careful testing procedures. As shown previously for other tests, the angle of the indenter axis to the test sample cannot deviate by more than about 2° from perpendicular. Vibrations can be a prime source of error, resulting in enlarged impressions and lower hardnesses. Campbell et al. have shown that vibrations producing accelerations of up to 12 in/s^2 had no appreciable influence on impressions made at loads of 500 or 1000 gf [48]. At lower loads, the hardness increased as the intensity of the shock accelerations increased. As the test sample hardness decreased, the influence of vibrations on the measured hardness increased. The speed of loading can influence the measured hardness, particularly at low loads.

It is this author's experience that some experienced operators consistently read the diagonal size on either the low or the high side while others consistently obtain very accurate readings. This occurs because of the manner in which the operators align the micrometer lines on the diagonals. As the diagonal length decreases, substantial differences can be obtained by different operators measuring the same impression. The deviation in diagonal length measurement can be

(a)

Figure 5-14 (a) Model 300 Tukon microhardness tester with digital readout. *(Courtesy of Page-Wilson Corp., Measurement Systems Div.)* (b) Leitz Miniload 2 microhardness tester with digital eyepiece and display. *(Courtesy of E. Leitz, Inc.)*

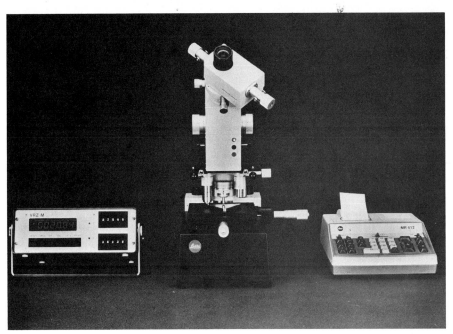

(*b*)

Table 5-9 Sources of errors in microindentation hardness testing

Instrument errors

Accuracy of the load
Inertia effects, speed of loading
Vibrations
Angle of indentation
Lateral movement of the indenter or sample
Indentation time
Indenter shape deviations

Measurement errors

Calibration of measuring device
Resolving power of objective
Magnification
Operator bias
Inadequate image quality, nonuniform lighting

Material errors

Nonuniformity of microstructure and chemistry
Orientation effects
Quality of polish
Low reflectivity, transparency

about 0.5 μm for an individual remeasuring the same impression and up to 1 μm for various operators measuring the same impression. These errors alone can account for the deviation of the log L versus log d curve from the ideal value. Deviations in both directions can be obtained. These deviations arise from the difficulty of focusing the impression, which is influenced by the surface upheaval around the impression, as well as from impression shape distortion.

Brown and Ineson have shown that the numerical aperture of the objective influences the measurement of diagonal length [45]. Figure 5-15 shows their data illustrating the theoretical decrease in diagonal length of Vickers and Knoop impressions as a function of decreasing numerical aperture (NA). According to these data, for a typical objective with NA of 0.6, as might be found in many commercial testers, measurement length decreases of up to 0.5 and 1.5 μm for Vickers and Knoop impressions, respectively, can be expected.

Most commercial microhardness testers are equipped with objectives and eyepieces that produce a maximum magnification of 400 to 600X. For impressions smaller than about 20 μm, higher magnifications are required to permit accurate measurement. Image quality, which depends on the sample as well as the optics, can play an important role in measurement accuracy. Tests of transparent or translucent minerals and ceramics are complicated by the difficulties encountered in observing the impressions. Low-reflectivity materials, such as coal or coke, also present observational challenges for the experimenter.

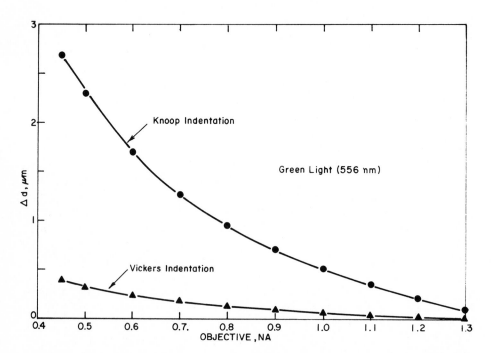

Figure 5-15 Influence of objective numerical aperture on the decrease in measured diagonal length for Vickers and Knoop impressions. *(From Brown and Ineson, Ref. 45, courtesy of The Metals Society.)*

Sample heterogeneity also affects measurement results. The operator must determine if the hardness variations are due to the material or to the measurement technique. Test blocks must be homogeneous—deviations must be due only to the experimental procedure and equipment. In tests of high-alloy material, one can expect segregation and hardness fluctuations. In such instances, microhardness testing can be used to evaluate etched samples. Campbell et al. made the interesting observation that tests performed with loads of 50 gf or less on unetched surfaces yielded lower hardnesses than tests on the same sample after etching [48]. This effect was attributed to the presence of a deformed layer at the surface of the metal; however, a deformed surface layer would produce higher hardnesses on the unetched surface rather than lower hardness values. The observed effect might be explained better on the basis of frictional differences between etched and unetched surfaces.

Numerous studies have clearly shown that improper mechanical polishing will produce higher hardnesses at low test loads. Electropolishing is cited as the preferred preparation technique. However, not all materials can be electropolished successfully. Mechanical polishing, when skillfully employed, is a suitable technique. It is usually best to alternately etch and polish in the last few polishing steps or to apply attack-polishing procedures where possible. Vibratory polishing is another useful procedure. Chemical polishing after 600-grit grinding and before diamond polishing is also quite helpful for those materials that can be chemically polished. Electropolishing is particularly well suited for the softer metals. It is primarily a technique for single-phase metals, since preferential attack and relief frequently occurs with multiphase metals.

The variation in HV as the test load is altered was determined using the five steel test blocks (Table 5-3) mechanically polished and tested using loads from 5 to 500 gf. Six impressions were made for each test condition, and the averages and 95 percent confidence limits were calculated. The results are listed in Table 5-10. In general, the test data show that the accuracy improves as the test load increases and the sample hardness decreases, i.e., as the diagonal length increases. The strain-hardening coefficient n is close to 2 for the data at 25 to 500 gf but greater than 2 at lighter loads. Comparison of the microhardness data with the previously listed Vickers macrohardness data (see Table 5-4) reveals similar test results at the higher loads for both machines. Comparison of the plotted data, Fig. 5-16 for the microhardness values and Fig. 5-8 for the macrohardness values, shows similar trends of decreasing hardness at light loads. At the lowest test loads both the bulk hardness tester and the microhardness tester gave lower hardnesses with the same specimens. The magnifications used for the measurements were 100X for the bulk tester and 500X for the microhardness tester. This author suggests that the low hardnesses obtained with each machine at the lightest loads and smallest diagonals are due mostly to the inadequate resolution of the optics and the difficulty in detecting the diagonals. The microhardness measurements for the 46.8 HRC test block are slightly higher than the macrohardness data, while the reverse trend is observed for the 63.2 HRC test block.

There is no universally acceptable method for converting microhardness data

Table 5-10 Vickers microindentation hardness for five test blocks

Test block hardness, HRC	Load, gf	Hardness, HV†	Mean diagonal, μm†
22.9	5	199.0 ± 22.7	6.87 ± 0.42
	10	223.8 ± 24.3	9.13 ± 0.49
	15	247.0 ± 11.9	10.62 ± 0.26
	25	247.0 ± 20.4	13.73 ± 0.55
	50	249.4 ± 32.3	19.40 ± 1.45
	100	257.8 ± 5.8	26.82 ± 0.31
	200	250.6 ± 2.0	38.48 ± 0.14
	300	249.8 ± 3.6	47.23 ± 0.37
	500	241.5 ± 6.9	61.96 ± 0.89
35.0	5	295.9 ± 42.5	5.65 ± 0.39
	10	314.5 ± 51.3	7.73 ± 0.68
	15	326.2 ± 41.9	9.28 ± 0.64
	25	346.8 ± 40.4	11.60 ± 0.72
	50	358.4 ± 9.3	16.10 ± 0.19
	100	348.1 ± 10.0	23.12 ± 0.36
	200	353.6 ± 5.2	32.38 ± 0.25
	300	340.7 ± 25.4	39.75 ± 0.41
	500	337.3 ± 2.1	52.38 ± 0.19
46.8	5	329.5 ± 31.3	5.33 ± 0.26
	10	420.6 ± 55.1	6.67 ± 0.43
	15	464.0 ± 24.0	7.76 ± 0.24
	25	476.7 ± 18.6	9.87 ± 0.19
	50	487.2 ± 12.2	13.79 ± 0.16
	100	480.0 ± 9.3	19.66 ± 0.19
	200	486.3 ± 6.0	27.61 ± 0.17
	300	480.4 ± 5.5	34.03 ± 0.20
	500	477.5 ± 5.6	44.04 ± 0.26
54.9	5	513.3 ± 63.0	4.27 ± 0.27
	10	620.7 ± 27.8	5.47 ± 0.12
	15	669.2 ± 37.3	6.45 ± 0.18
	25	665.0 ± 8.2	8.37 ± 0.09
	50	661.2 ± 11.3	11.84 ± 0.11
	100	653.8 ± 10.4	16.82 ± 0.12
	200	627.3 ± 10.2	24.32 ± 0.20
	300	631.7 ± 6.1	29.66 ± 0.15
	500	631.2 ± 11.8	38.29 ± 0.31
63.2	5	633.3 ± 101.9	3.85 ± 0.31
	10	665.2 ± 37.8	5.28 ± 0.15
	15	750.2 ± 25.5	6.09 ± 0.11
	25	740.3 ± 31.9	7.92 ± 0.17
	50	754.8 ± 22.8	11.08 ± 0.17
	100	729.5 ± 13.2	15.95 ± 0.15
	200	734.5 ± 11.1	22.48 ± 0.17
	300	727.3 ± 6.7	27.66 ± 0.13
	500	729.7 ± 8.6	35.65 ± 0.20

†Average, plus and minus the 95% confidence limit, was calculated based on six impressions at each load on each test block.

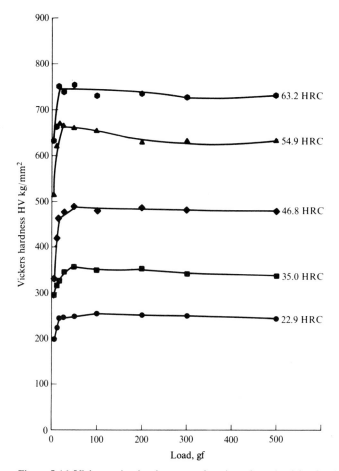

Figure 5-16 Vickers microhardness as a function of test load for five hardened steel test blocks.

to macrohardness values. The best procedure is for each operator to develop data similar to that given in Tables 5-3, 5-4, and 5-10, for use with commonly tested materials. This will reveal features of the test machine, the material, and the operator that contribute to the measurement accuracy and the load-diagonal relationship. With such data, one can predict macrohardness from microhardness data with a high degree of confidence.

Numerous investigators have shown that Knoop hardness increases with decreasing applied load. This effect becomes stronger as the sample hardness increases. This effect was originally attributed to surface work hardening due to improper polishing and to elastic recovery of the long diagonal. Tate made direct observations of elastic recovery in Knoop tests of glass and found a long-diagonal recovery of about 5 μm [49]. This observation was applied to metals to explain the increased hardness at low loads; however, it is now recognized that elastic recovery in metals is extremely small.

Experiments have shown that the true length of the long diagonal is difficult to measure and substantial errors are encountered [45, 50, 51]. This problem becomes more acute as the diagonal length decreases. In the case of Knoop indents, it is expected that measurement errors will always underestimate diagonal length and produce higher hardness. This agrees with the fact that Knoop hardness always rises with decreasing load. In contrast, tests with the symmetrical Vickers indenter have produced both increasing and decreasing hardness with decreasing load, since there is about equal probability that the diagonal lengths will be either overestimated or underestimated by a given operator.

Tarasov and Thibault have shown that the visibility error for Knoop indents increases as the objective NA decreases [51]. Their experimental measurements are similar to the theoretical estimates of Brown and Ineson [45] shown in Fig. 5-15. However, because Tarasov and Thibault considered the visual acuity of the operator and also specimen contrast problems, their results reveal a larger error.

Some correction factors have been used empirically to develop load-independent Knoop hardnesses. Young and Rhee have reviewed the various approaches and found that they can be successfully used [52]. The magnitude of the correction factors was found to be different for different testers.

Accuracy of Knoop indentation measurements can be enhanced through measurement of both diagonals in certain cases, or by measurement of the projected area [53]. Since only a very small fraction of the projected area is in the tip area of the indent, errors in measurements of projected areas will be virtually unaffected by errors in defining the precise ends of the indents. Projected-area measurements are the only practical method for measuring distorted Vickers impressions. Equation (5-20) is used to compute Vickers hardnesses in such cases. For calculation of Knoop hardness, the load is simply divided by the projected area.

5-7 HARDNESS CONVERSIONS

Although each of the hardness test methods described has its own particular range of applications, which commonly overlap, many instances arise in which tests made with one particular scale must be converted to another test scale. To obtain the other hardness value, reference is usually made to conversion charts. Many studies have been conducted to develop such relationships, but it is prudent to use only the conversions in ASTM Specification E140 wherever possible. This specification covers many standard materials.

Since conversion charts are based on empirical data and are not precise, the converted hardness is typified by a certain degree of uncertainty that is based on the quality of the effort expended in developing the chart. In making such correlations, it is best to consult the tables in ASTM E140. It is often useful to fit equations to some of these conversions. These equations can then be stored in small programmable calculators. This author has derived the following equations:

$$HB = 169.46 + 0.582 \ HRC + 0.111 \ (HRC)^2 \qquad (5\text{-}32)$$

$$HV = 109.3 + 8.19 \ HRC - 0.145 \ (HRC)^2 + 0.0029 \ (HRC)^3 \quad (5\text{-}33)$$

In presenting converted hardnesses, the measured value should be listed first followed by the converted value in parenthesis indicating that it is a conversion. Published equations showing the relationship between different scales are listed in Table 5-11 [54–61]. Conversions of Vickers to Knoop hardnesses have been published by Emond [62]. Five steels that were heat-treated to provide a range of microstructures and hardnesses and Monel metal were tested with loads of 10, 25, 50, 100, 200, and 500 gf for the Knoop test and a 10-kgf load for the Vickers test. Emond's data are shown in Fig. 5-17. Batchelder measured the Knoop hardness of five steel test blocks at loads of 15 to 1000 gf in order to show the load versus hardness relationship and derive relationships between HRC and HK at each load [58]. His correlation between HRC and HK is shown in Fig. 5-18, and his equations are listed in Table 5-11.

Hardness tests have proved to be an indispensable tool for both research and quality control. Despite the myriad of tests and scales available, one can reduce the list to a few standard tests. The other tests have very narrow applicability but are of great value in these particular instances. The operator decides which test and test load to employ on the basis of the material to be tested, its thickness, its anticipated hardness, specification requirements, and so forth. Sometimes, one observes conflicts between the specified hardness test method and the variables of the material. In such cases, permission to test by alternate procedures and conversion to the desired scale can usually be obtained.

5-8 APPLICATIONS

The primary application of hardness testing is simply to determine the hardness of a given material. Almost every known material has been tested. The literature in this area is so vast that space does not permit a summary. The reader is directed to the general references, in which much of this information can be found.

5-8.1 Anisotropy

The hardness of crystalline surfaces varies depending on the surface tested and the crystallographic direction [63–65]. The Knoop indenter is ideal for such measurements. Hardness variations in single crystals are larger than those in polycrystalline samples, and the degree of anisotropy varies with crystal symmetry. Cold working also produces hardness anisotropy. Figure 5-19 shows 200-gf Knoop indentations made on cobalt at different directions within the grains. Note the wide range of hardnesses obtained.

Table 5-11 Published hardness conversion equations

Equation		Reference
	For steels:	

$$HB = \frac{7300}{130 - HRB} \qquad (40\text{--}100\ HRB) \qquad 54, 55$$

$$HB = \frac{3710}{130 - HRE} \qquad (30\text{--}100\ HRE) \qquad 54, 55$$

$$HB = \frac{1,520,000 - 4500\ HRC}{(100 - HRC)^2} \qquad (< 40\ HRC) \qquad 54, 55$$

$$HB = \frac{25,000 - 10(57 - HRC)^2}{100 - HRC} \qquad (40\text{--}70\ HRC) \qquad 54, 55$$

$$HRB = 134 - \frac{6700}{HB} \qquad (\pm 7\ HRB,\ 95\%\ CL) \qquad 56$$

$$HRC = 119.0 - \left(\frac{2.43 \times 10^6}{HV}\right)^{1/2} \qquad (240\text{--}1040\ HV) \qquad 57$$

$$HRA = 112.3 - \left(\frac{6.85 \times 10^5}{HV}\right)^{1/2} \qquad (240\text{--}1040\ HV) \qquad 57$$

$$HR15N = 117.94 - \left(\frac{5.53 \times 10^5}{HV}\right)^{1/2} \qquad (240\text{--}1040\ HV) \qquad 57$$

$$HR30N = 129.52 - \left(\frac{1.88 \times 10^6}{HV}\right)^{1/2} \qquad (240\text{--}1040\ HV) \qquad 57$$

$$HR45N = 133.51 - \left(\frac{3.132 \times 10^6}{HV}\right)^{1/2} \qquad (240\text{--}1040\ HV) \qquad 57$$

$HB = 0.951\ HV$	(steel ball, 200–400 HV)	57
$HB = 0.941\ HV$	(WC ball, 200–700 HV)	57
	For WC:	

$$HRC = 117.35 - \left(\frac{2.43 \times 10^6}{HV}\right)^{1/2} \qquad (900\text{--}1800\ HV) \qquad 57$$

$$HRA = \frac{211 - \left(\frac{2.43 - 10^6}{HV}\right)^{1/2}}{1.885} \qquad (900\text{--}1800\ HV) \qquad 57$$

Table 5-11 (*continued*)

Equation		Reference
	For steels:	
HRC = 64.934 log HK − 140.38	(15 gf)	58
HRC = 67.353 log HK − 144.32	(25 gf)	58
HRC = 71.983 log HK − 154.28	(50 gf)	58
HRC = 76.572 log HK − 163.89	(100 gf)	58
HRC = 79.758 log HK − 170.92	(200 gf)	58
HRC = 82.283 log HK − 176.92	(300 gf)	58
HRC = 83.58 log HK − 179.30	(500 gf)	58
HRC = 85.848 log HK − 184.55	(1000 gf)	58
	For white cast irons:	
HB = 0.363 (HRC)^2 − 22.515 (HRC) + 717.8		59
HV = 0.343 (HRC)^2 − 18.132 (HRC) + 595.3		59
HV = 1.136 (HB)^2 − 26.0		59
	For austenitic stainless steel:	
$\dfrac{1}{HB} = 0.0001304(130 - HRB)$	(60–90 HRB, 110–192 HB)	60
	For stable alpha-beta titanium alloys:	
HRC = 0.078 HV + 8.1		61

5-8.2 Indentation Fracture

Numerous researchers have observed cracking around hardness indentations made in brittle materials. While some have performed tests over a range of loads in order to determine a threshold load above which cracking occurs and below which it does not, most have employed the procedure developed by Palmqvist [66]. In this method, Vickers hardness impressions are made on a carefully polished sample using a range of loads. While cracking is observed with other impression types, the cracking associated with the Vickers indentation is most suitable for such work (see Fig. 5-20). The lengths of the cracks emanating from the impression are measured. A plot is constructed of the applied load and the crack length, and a linear relationship is produced. Figure 5-21 shows typical data for two different TiC-Al$_2$O$_3$ cermets. When plotted in this manner, the inverse of the slope in kilograms per millimeter is a measure of the fracture toughness. Several studies have shown that the quality of the polishing operation is critical

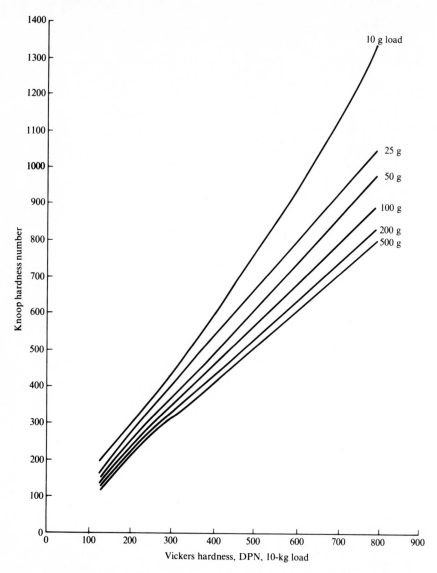

Figure 5-17 Correlation of Vickers hardness with a 10-kgf load with Knoop hardness for Knoop test loads of 10 to 500 gf. *(From Emond, Ref. 62, courtesy of the American Society for Metals.)*

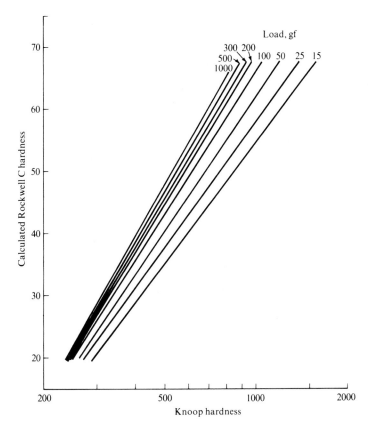

Figure 5-18 Correlation between Knoop hardness at loads from 15 to 1000 gf with Rockwell C hardness. *(From Batchelder, Ref. 58; copyright, American Society for Testing and Materials, reprinted with permission.)*

[67, 68]. The deformation produced by sectioning, grinding, and polishing must be removed.

The Palmqvist method has traditionally been performed at room temperature; however, Vander Voort and Hinton have conducted the test at elevated temperatures [69]. Tests performed on TiC-Al$_2$O$_3$ cermets revealed that the Palmqvist toughness decreased in the temperature range of 400 to 1400° F and increased in the range of 1200 to 1600° F, depending on the material tested. The loss of toughness and the degree of recovery at higher temperatures varied depending on the amount of entrapped grinding media in the samples.

Most tests have been performed on WC-Co sintered materials. Viswanadham and Venables have shown that the fracture toughness increases as the cobalt binder content increases and the hardness decreases [70]. Exner et al. have also demonstrated this relationship and obtained a correlation between Palmqvist toughness and the plain-strain energy release rate G_{IC} [71]. These conclusions have also been verified by Peters [72].

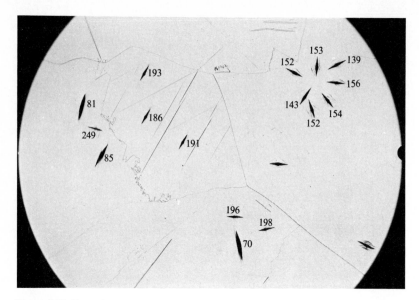

Figure 5-19 Example of hardness anisotropy in zone-melted cobalt using 200-gf Knoop impressions, 42×. *(Courtesy of R. D. Buchheit, Battelle Memorial Laboratories.)*

Figure 5-20 Example of indentation fracture in an alloy of 70% Al_2O_3 and 30% TiC made with Vickers indenter (75×).

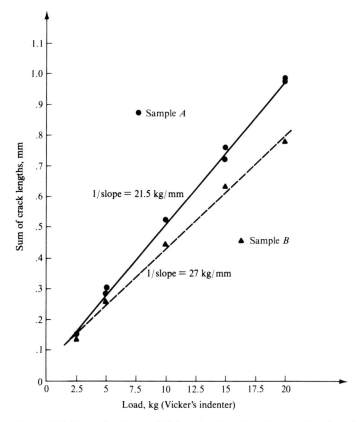

Figure 5-21 Example of typical Palmqvist identation fracture data for alumina–titanium carbide cermets. The inverse of the slope is the Palmqvist fracture toughness in kilograms per millimeter.

5-8.3 Machinability

Hardness exerts a strong influence on machinability [73]. In general, 300 to 350 HB is considered to be the maximum tolerable hardness for production machining of steels. The rate of work hardening, which can be measured by the Meyer analysis, also influences machinability. The relationship between hardness and machinability, however, is not linear. For steels with hardnesses of about 250 HB and greater, there is a fairly good linear inverse relationship between hardness and machinability. Steels softer than 250 HB do not follow a simple trend. For these steels, the composition, microstructure, and ductility exert strong influences on machinability. For the majority of machining operations, hardnesses of about 180 to 200 HB are optimum. If the hardness is appreciably below this level, that is, about 160 HB and below, poor chip formation results and a built-up edge forms on the tool because of the high material ductility. Machining of such soft steels requires more power, and substantial heat is generated. Poor surface finishes are obtained.

Several equations relating tool life as a machinability index and material properties have been proposed. The following is the simplest equation relating tool life and hardness:

$$V_T = \frac{C}{HB^X} \qquad (5\text{-}34)$$

where V_T is the cutting speed for a tool life T, the constant C depends on the material being machined and the tool being used, and the exponent X depends on the tool material. For the full range of steel workpiece hardnesses, this relationship is subject to considerable scatter.

Janitzky [73] proposed the following formula relating cutting speed in feet per minute for a 60-min tool life to Brinell hardness (HB) and the tensile reduction of area (RA):

$$V_{60} = \frac{C}{HB^{1.63} \, RA^{1.01}} \qquad (5\text{-}35)$$

where C is a constant pertaining to the type and size of tool used. The formula is useful for quenched and tempered steels with hardnesses of 200 to 400 HB. It is not applicable to annealed steels, cold-worked steels, or free-machining steels.

Henkin and Datsko [74] also developed an equation relating V_{60} tool life to Brinell hardness and tensile reduction of area:

$$V_{60} = \frac{1150k}{HB} \left(1 - \frac{RA}{100} \right)^{1/2} \qquad (5\text{-}36)$$

where k is the thermal conductivity of the workpiece.

Gulbransen studied the influence of microstructure on the drillability of a steel (0.50% C, 1.25% Mn, 0.65% Cr, 0.18% Mo, and 0.08% S) heat-treated to form a variety of microstructures with hardnesses between 175 and 388 HB [75]. He related the Brinell hardness to the mean free path, i.e., the average edge-to-edge distance between carbides, by the following:

$$HB = C_1 \, (\log \lambda - C_2) \qquad (5\text{-}37)$$

where λ is the mean free path and C_1 and C_2 are constants. For standard drills, equations reportedly developed by Shaw and Oxford permit determination of torque M and thrust T as a function of the feed t, drill diameter D, and Brinell hardness of the workpiece:

$$M = 0.087 \, HB \, t^{0.8} D^{1.8} \qquad (5\text{-}38)$$

$$T = 0.195 \, HB \, t^{0.8} D^{1.8} + 0.0022 \, HB \, D^2 \qquad (5\text{-}39)$$

Gulbransen assumed that if the feed and drill size are held constant, the three equations could be combined and the torque and thrust could be correlated to the mean free path as follows:

$$M = C_3 \, (\log \lambda - C_4) \qquad (5\text{-}40)$$

$$T = C_5 (\log \lambda - C_6) \tag{5-41}$$

where C_3 to C_6 are constants. Test results showed that there was a linear relationship between torque or thrust and the logarithm of the mean free path.

5-8.4 Phase Identification

In the early days of the development of microhardness testing, it was believed that microhardness results would be an excellent means for identifying phases, compounds, or inclusions in metals. By itself, microhardness values can only identify phases in the simplest of cases; for example, they can be used to determine whether a light, unetched feature in steel is carbide or ferrite. As a diagnostic tool, microhardness can help to narrow down the possibilities, but it must be coupled with other tests.

5-8.5 Prediction of Other Properties

For many metals and alloys there has been found to be a reasonably accurate correlation between hardness and tensile strength—a fact of great significance. The recognition and development of such correlations began after the introduction of the Brinell test. Greaves and Jones reviewed most of the early work and conducted an extensive statistical study of their own. They recommended the relationships, which are converted to tensile strength in pounds per square inch, shown in Table 5-12 [76].

Taylor conducted a detailed study of the relationship between hardness and tensile strength [77]. His results are summarized in Table 5-13. Magnesium alloy castings did not exhibit a hardness-strength correlation.

Tabor developed an equation to calculate tensile strength (TS) in kilograms per square millimeter using Vickers hardness and the Meyer strain-hardening coefficient n [78]:

$$\text{TS} = \frac{\text{HV}}{2.9} \left[1 - (n - 2) \right] \left[\frac{12.5(n - 2)}{1 - (n - 2)} \right]^{n - 2} \tag{5-42}$$

Table 5-12 Hardness–tensile strength conversions

Material	Multiplying factor†
Heat-treated alloy steel (250–400 HB)	470 HB
Heat-treated carbon and alloy steel (<250 HB)	482 HB
Medium carbon steel (as-rolled, normalized, or annealed)	493 HB

†Tensile strength (lb/in²) = Multiplying factor × HB.
Source: From Greaves and Jones, Ref. 76.

Table 5-13 Multiplying factors for obtaining tensile strength from hardness

Material	Multiplying factor range†
Heat-treated carbon and alloy steel	470–515 HB
Annealed carbon steel	515–560 HB
All steels	448–515 HV
Ni-Cr austenitic steels	448–482 HV
Steel; sheet, strip, and tube	414–538 HV
Aluminum alloys; bar and extrusions	426–650 HB
Aluminum alloys; bar and extrusions	414–605 HV
Aluminum alloys; sheet, strip, and tube	470–582 HV
Al-Cu castings	246–426 HB
Al-Si-Ni castings	336–426 HB
Al-Si castings	381–538 HB
Phosphor bronze castings	336–470 HB
Brass castings	470–672 HB

†Tensile strength (1b/in^2) = multiplying factor × hardness.
Source: From Taylor, Ref. 77.

Tabor suggested using HV/2.9 in the above equation for steels and HV/3.0 for copper. Cahoon et al. found that HV/3.0 was satisfactory for steel, brass, and aluminum [79].

Petty examined the relationship between Vickers hardness and tensile strength for aluminum alloys [80]. The following equations were proposed:

$$TS = 0.189 \ HV - 1.38 \tag{5-43}$$

$$0.2\% \ YS = 0.148 \ HV - 1.59 \tag{5-44}$$

where tensile strength (TS) and yield strength (YS) are in tons per square inch. To convert to pounds per square inch, the tensile strength or yield strength are multiplied by 2240.

Hickey studied the hardness–tensile strength correlation of various titanium alloys [61]. His results are listed in Table 5-14.

MacKenzie developed the following formula relating Brinell hardness to tensile strength for gray cast irons with hardnesses between 111 and 363 HB [81]:

$$TS = 1.82 \ HB^{1.85} \tag{5-45}$$

where TS is in pounds per square inch. The degree of test scatter increases with increasing strength and hardness.

Hardness tests have also been used to predict other mechanical properties, such as compressive strength [21], strain or strain rate by methods other than the Meyer analysis [82], and yield strength [79, 83, 84]. The estimation of yield strength from hardness data is of significant value to the metallurgist.

Cahoon et al. used an aluminum alloy and AISI 1040 carbon steel, each in a range of conditions and hardnesses, to develop correlations between yield

Table 5-14 Tensile strength–hardness relationships for titanium alloys

Grade	Tensile strength, lb/in^2†	Sigma, lb/in^2
Ti-7% Al-4% Mo		
Ti-7% Al-3% Mo	435 HV + 9200	8300
Ti-6% Al-4% V	5200 HRC − 24,000	8600
Ti-4% Al-3% Mo-1% V		
Ti-6.5% Al-3% Mo-1% V		
Ti-6% Al-4% V	5170 HRC − 38,600	8150
Ti-6% Mo-3% Al		
Ti-4% Al-3% Mo-1% V		
Ti-6% Al-4% V	225 HV + 73,000	4500
All above, plus others	5050 HRC − 27,000	8250
	395 HV + 14,000	Not given

†10-kgf load used for Vickers tests.
Source: From Hickey, Ref. 61.

strength and hardness [79]. With aluminum alloys, the yield strength–hardness correlation depended on the particular strengthening mechanism. For example, at the same hardness, aged alloys exhibited lower yield strengths and higher strain-hardening coefficients than cold-worked alloys. The yield strength–hardness correlation is more straightforward for the carbon steels where the strain-hardening coefficient varied directly with hardness. The following equation was developed to determine the yield strength (in kilograms per square millimeter) from Vickers hardness data and Meyer's strain-hardening coefficient n:

$$YS = \frac{HV}{3}(0.1)^{n-2} \tag{5-46}$$

To convert kilograms per square millimeter to pounds per square inch, yield strength is multiplied by 1422.2.

George et al. prepared two nomograms for determining the yield strength of sheet steels based on measurements with three different Rockwell scales (HRF, HRB, and HRG or HR 15T, HR 30T, and HR 45T) [84]. The correlation is based on equating the constant C in Eq. 5-16, which is determined by the Meyer analysis, with the measured yield strength. George et al. found that there was a linear relationship between C in kilograms per square millimeter and the yield strength in ksi. Once this relationship is established, the three hardness values are obtained and the appropriate nomogram is employed to determine the yield strength.

5-8.6 Quality Control

There are many applications for hardness tests in manufacturing operations. Many of these applications use hardness tests as a quick and simple check of the success of a given process step. Such processes include annealing, hardenability, heat treatments, cold working, recrystallization, surface treatments and tempering.

Annealed hardness is a good indicator of material performance in forming or machining. Materials are usually annealed to produce a specific microstructure and hardness level. Hardness tests are performed as a check of the success of the operation and conformance to applicable specifications.

The prediction and control of steel hardenability has been an important accomplishment. A steel bar is considered to be just through-hardened if the center contains 50% martensite. Hardenability analyses can be used to relate steel composition and grain size to the hardening response of different size bars subjected to a variety of quench rates. This knowledge is critical in obtaining martensitic structures in alloy steel components so that the best properties can be developed. Steel hardenability [85] can be calculated or determined experimentally with the Jominy test. In this method, a bar 1-in in diameter and 4-in in length of the desired composition is austenitized at the recommended temperature and end-quenched with water. This produces a wide range of cooling rates along the bar length. Flats are ground on two opposite sides of the bar for hardness testing. A plot is constructed of the hardness as a function of the distance from the water-quenched end face. The hardness at the water-quenched end face is a function of the carbon content. Numerous studies have shown that there is a linear increase in the hardness of fully martensitic steels as the carbon content is raised from 0.10 to about 0.55 percent. The shape of the Jominy curve depends on the steel alloy content for a given carbon content and the grain size. As the alloy content increases, martensite can be formed at slower cooling rates. Coarsening of the austenite grain size also increases hardenability, but this is seldom done because of the detrimental influence on toughness.

The response of metals to heat treatments, such as precipitation hardening, normalizing, or quenching and tempering, is generally evaluated by hardness testing. Hardness tests are an inexpensive substitute for tensile tests.

Recrystallization of cold-worked metals has been studied with a number of techniques including hardness tests [86, 87]. The microhardness population count method developed by Wallbaum and Mischer has been used by a number of researchers to study recrystallization [86]. In this procedure, 100-gf load impressions are made at 1-mm intervals in a square grid pattern on the surface of a properly prepared sample until 100 indents have been made. The hardness of each impression is determined, and the data are summarized in a frequency histogram. Mould and Cotterill compared this technique to metallography and x-ray methods [87]. The microhardness histogram method revealed two distinct peaks after about 10 percent recrystallization. At lower annealing temperatures or shorter holding times, only a single peak was observed. The average hardness of this peak, which represented the cold-worked condition, decreased slightly before two peaks could be discerned. As annealing progressed, the height of the lower hardness peak, which represented the recrystallized grains, increased and its average hardness decreased slightly. Recrystallization was complete when the higher hardness peak disappeared. This method is rather time-consuming but does provide detailed information.

Microhardness testing has been widely used to determine the thickness of surface layers due to decarburization, carburization, nitriding, plating, surface hardening, and work hardening [88–91]. Hardness testing is usually performed on a plane that is perpendicular to the surface of the component. The polished and etched section is tested at regular intervals, starting as close to the edge as possible and going toward the center. The depth below the surface for each impression must be measured. Knoop indentations are especially useful for such measurements, especially if the long diagonal is oriented parallel to the surface. After measuring the hardness impressions, a plot is constructed of the hardness as a function of the depth below the surface. For the case of a decarburized steel, the hardness is low at the surface and increases with depth until it becomes relatively constant. The total depth of decarburization is determined by noting the depth where the hardness becomes constant and equivalent to that of the interior. For carburized samples, two measurements of case depth are possible. The "effective" case depth is that depth at which the equivalent of 50 HRC is obtained. Total case depth, however, is that depth where the hardness becomes constant and typical of the interior hardness. Dawes has shown that measurement of carburized case depth by the appearance of etching does not correlate with either the effective case depth or the total case depth [88]. The line of etch contrast between case and core corresponded to a hardness about 200 HV above the core hardness in his study.

Enberg has described a method for measuring the thickness of thin platings on metals [89]. First, a standard curve of hardness (HV or HK) versus load is made on a bulk sample of the coating or plating. The coating or plating must be thick enough that the depth of the highest load impression is less than 10 percent of the thickness. A plated part is then tested, again with a range of test loads. As the load increases, the hardness of the substrate will influence the measured hardness, which can be detected by comparing the test data for the plated part to that of the standard and noting the test load where deviation begins. Since the impression diagonal is known, the depth can be calculated by dividing the diagonal length by 7 for the Vickers test or by 30 for the Knoop test. To obtain an accurate depth measurement, one must section a few parts with different plating thicknesses and divide the true coating thickness by the impression depth at which the substrate begins to influence the hardness-load curve. Once this number is known for a particular plating, thicknesses can be judged by surface hardness tests alone. Murly developed an alternate method for measuring the thickness of anodized layers and electrodeposits using Vickers indentations [91].

The tempered hardness of martensitic steels has been studied as a function of temperature, time, and chemical composition. Hollomon and Jaffe showed that a plot of hardness versus $T (c + \log t)$ produces a linear relationship [92]. In this equation, T is the absolute temperature, t is the time in seconds, and c is a constant, determined experimentally, that varies depending on the steel tested. Secondary hardening reactions produce nonlinearity in the part of the curve in which they occur. Once such a curve is developed, the hardness for any tempering cycle can be predicted for the particular steel.

5-8.7 Residual Stress

Many procedures have been developed to measure residual stresses. The most important methods are destructive and require removal of the stressed material incrementally as the stresses in the portion that is being removed are determined by changes in shape or strain. Another popular relaxation method involves the drilling of a small hole in the stressed surface. The most popular nondestructive method uses x-ray diffraction to measure lattice distortion due to the residual stresses. Less well known is that residual stresses alter hardness, and hardness tests can be used to measure residual stresses. Bareiss has shown how the surface strain in a material indented with a 10-mm diameter carbide ball indicates the magnitude and direction of the residual stresses in the surface [93]. Strain gauges are employed to measure the strains in three directions around the indentation during and after indentation. These strains can be related to the residual stresses by the use of calibration test data.

5-8.8 Temperature Effects

While the majority of hardness tests are conducted at ambient temperature, tests at low temperatures [94, 95] and elevated temperatures [96–99] are quite common. Testing at nonambient temperatures greatly expands the usefulness of hardness testing. In the earliest procedures, a heated sample was removed from a furnace, placed on the anvil of an ordinary Brinell machine, and tested. Although a rather crude procedure, it showed the potential value of hot-hardness testing. Modern testers employ their own furnaces with a preheated indenter and either a vacuum or an inert atmosphere, or both, to protect the sample surface from oxidation and other surface chemistry changes. Low-temperature testing is much simpler with the specimen placed in an open cryostat and the indenter mounted on a long rod so that it can reach into the vessel and indent the sample. Many of the previously described hardness tests have been performed at high and low temperatures, including Rockwell (HRC and HRA), Vickers, dynamic, and mutual indentation tests. The latter technique has been employed in tests of ceramics. For hot-hardness tests, diamond indenters are commonly employed, but their use is restricted to temperatures below about 900°C because of interactions with the test sample at higher temperatures. Sapphire indenters have been used at test temperatures up to about 1700°C, although they are rather soft at these temperatures. Boron carbide has been used as an indenter material at temperatures up to 2000°C. In many instances the impressions are measured at room temperature after testing and no correction is made for thermal contraction, although some prefer to measure the indent at the test temperature. Figure 5-22 shows the Akashi AVK-HF Vickers hot-hardness tester.

For some metals, there is a linear relationship between hardness and tempera-

Figure 5-22 Akashi Model AVK-HF Vickers hot-hardness tester.

ture over a broad, but limited, temperature range. For other metals, most of the measurements follow a linear trend except at high temperatures, where the hardness change is less rapid. Metals such as molybdenum and aluminum show a smooth, curved relationship between temperature and hardness. Certain metals, such as nickel and vanadium, exhibit a rapid change in hardness at intermediate temperatures. Hardness-temperature relationships are also influenced by phase changes. Thus, one cannot make universally applicable generalizations about the relationship between hardness and temperature. Several equations have been suggested to relate hardness and temperature, but each has only a limited degree of usefulness.

As with hardness data from room temperature tests, hardness data from high- and low-temperature hardness tests can be used to correlate hardness with various mechanical properties. Hot hardness has been employed to determine high-

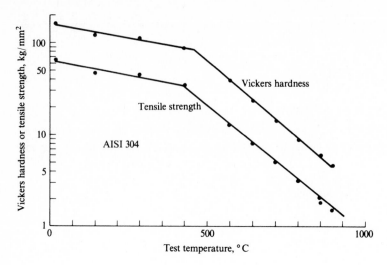

Figure 5-23 Vickers hardness and tensile strength of AISI 304 stainless steel as a function of test temperature. *(From Moteff et al., Ref. 100, courtesy of the American Society for Metals.)*

temperature strength and creep resistance. An example of the type of information that can be obtained is shown in Fig. 5-23 which is a plot developed by Moteff et al. of Vickers hardness and tensile strength as a function of test temperature for AISI 304 stainless steel [100]. Figure 5-24 shows the correlation between hot Vickers hardness and hot tensile strength from the data shown in Fig. 5-23. The use of hot-hardness data to predict high-temperature properties and behavior significantly reduces testing costs.

5-8.9 Wear

Wear is a mechanical process involving fracture which, in some instances, is modified by the environment. Wear resistance is often considered to be a mechanical property. The wear rate of a component is influenced by the specific aspects of the operating conditions and by the choice of materials, their compositions, mechanical properties, and microstructure. The behavior of materials in wear situations also depends on the nature of contact, the stresses encountered, the temperature and the environmental conditions. Thus, wear is a very complex phenomenon.

The most common forms of wear are adhesive wear and abrasive wear. Adhesive wear is associated with the break-in period of equipment and involves the rubbing of two mating surfaces, which results in bonding of the two surfaces followed by tearing to produce loose wear debris. The adhesive wear rate increases significantly if the applied load produces compressive stresses greater than one-third of the hardness, i.e., high enough for bulk yielding.

Abrasive wear occurs as a result of penetration of a soft surface by a harder, rough surface. The harder rough surface slides over the soft surface and produces

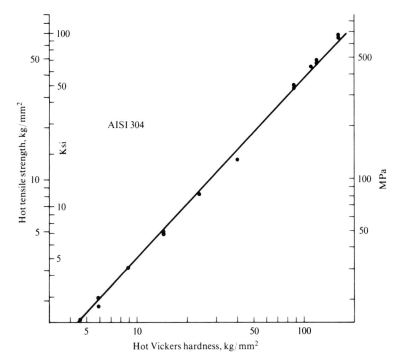

Figure 5-24 Correlation between hot hardness (HV) and hot tensile strength for AISI 304 stainless steel. *(From Moteff et al., Ref. 100, courtesy of the American Society for Metals.)*

a plowing action. The result is a grooved surface and free fragments of wear debris. Two basic forms of abrasive wear occur. One type, referred to as two-body abrasion, occurs when a hard, rough surface slides over a softer surface. Wear does not occur if the hard surface is smooth. Two-body abrasion is a very common problem. If an abrasive particle or grain is free to move between the two surfaces, three-body abrasion results. Abrasion does not occur if these particles are softer than the two contacting surfaces. Two-body abrasion occurs during filing and during abrasive grinding with stones or fixed grit paper, while three-body abrasion occurs during lapping and polishing.

During equipment break-in, the wear rate can be quite high. It is advantageous to obtain mechanical oxidation of the surface as soon as possible, since the oxide film prevents metal-to-metal contact and thus reduces the wear rate. The wear rate of carbon steels is controlled substantially by the hardness and oxidation of the rubbing surfaces. According to Hurricks, a bulk hardness of 350 to 450 HV is required in hypoeutectoid carbon steels to support the oxide film and produce mild wear in air [101]. The carbon content influences the critical hardness level. For medium carbon steels, about 350 HV is required, while for eutectoid and hypereutectoid carbon steels, only 250 HV is needed. If the surface hardness is increased to 340 to 425 HV as a result of the rubbing action, the oxide will be supported regardless of the carbon content as long as this level of surface hardness is maintained. At very high hardnesses, i.e., above 700 HV, severe adhesive wear does not occur during break-in, even in the absence of air.

In abrasive wear situations, hardness is widely employed to compare material properties and wear rates, although it is well recognized that other factors are important and this relationship does not always hold for dissimilar metals in contact. When the abrasive material is much harder than the material being abraded, "hard" abrasion occurs; however, if the abrasive's hardness is approximately equal to or less than the hardness of the strained surface, "soft" abrasion results.

A number of investigators have suggested relationships between wear resistance and mechanical properties such as hardness. Several have also incorporated parameters relating to the wear situation. One of the earliest equations was suggested by Oberle [102]:

$$\text{Modell} = \frac{10^6 \text{ HB}}{E} \tag{5-47}$$

where HB is the Brinell hardness and E is Young's modulus. The Modell number indicates the depth of penetration a metal can tolerate without exceeding its elastic limit. Materials with high Modell numbers should exhibit good wear characteristics.

Archard suggested the following relationship [103]:

$$\frac{V}{L} = \frac{kW}{3H} \tag{5-48}$$

where V = wear volume
L = sliding distance
W = applied load
H = hardness
k = a nondimensional wear coefficient

The value of k is not fixed but varies for each material.

Khruschov performed pin-on-disc wear tests of pure metals, heat-treated steels, and cold-worked metals and observed various relationships between wear resistance and hardness [104]. A load of 0.3 kgf was used, resulting in a pressure of 9.55 kg/cm^2 (135 lb/in^2). The abrasive used was corundum with a grain size of about 80 μm and a hardness of about 2290 HV. The relative wear resistance ϵ of each metal was determined compared to that of a standard tin-lead alloy. For the pure metals the hardness was directly proportional to the relative wear resistance, i.e.,

$$\epsilon = b \text{ HV} \tag{5-49}$$

where b is the coefficient of proportionality. If the hardness is in Vickers units of kilograms per square millimeter, b is 0.1374.

For annealed and heat-treated (tempered martensite) steels, Khruschov observed a linear relationship which began at the value for the annealed sample. The slopes of the curves were different than the slopes for the pure metals and became steeper with rising carbon content. For each steel, the relationship between wear resistance and hardness was given by the following equation:

$$\epsilon = \epsilon_0 + b_1 \, (\text{HV} - \text{HV}_0) \qquad (5\text{-}50)$$

where ϵ_0 is the relative wear resistance of the annealed steel of hardness HV_0 and b_1 is the constant of proportionality for each steel.

For cold-worked steels and copper-based alloys, Khruschov observed that work hardening did not increase the abrasive resistance of the metals even though the hardness was increased. In some cases, the wear resistance decreased slightly. The explanation for the fact that mechanical deformation did not improve wear resistance was that the maximum work-hardened condition was achieved during the test itself; thus, preliminary work hardening had no influence on wear resistance.

Richardson performed tests similar to those of Khruschov with 60- and 180-grit SiC and 180-grit corundum [105]. He observed that in general the relative wear resistance of annealed commercially pure metals and some annealed alloys increased with hardness. Cold rolling of annealed metals had little influence on wear resistance, and in some cases, wear resistance decreased. The wear resistance of steels increased with hardness and carbon content. For steels at the same hardness, higher carbon content gave better wear resistance. Bainitic steels at the same hardness as tempered martensitic steels gave slightly better (7 percent) wear resistance. The relative wear resistance depended on the specific abrasive used.

Several studies have been made to determine the relationship between hardness and abrasive wear resistance for steels containing ferrite and/or pearlite or martensite. Moore found that the wear resistance of pearlitic steels depended on the bulk hardness, which depended on the volume fraction of pearlite (balance ferrite), while the wear resistance of martensitic steels varied with the square root of the carbon content [106]. In each case there was a linear relationship between wear resistance and bulk hardness. Moore's tests were conducted on a rotating disc abrasion tester at a speed of 0.56 r/s, with a load of 500 gf, and with both 60- and 180-grit SiC.

Avient et al. found an approximately linear relationship between the abrasive wear resistance of commercially pure metals and the hardness of the abraded surface [107]. For a given similar group of metals with similar work-hardening characteristics, the hardness of the abraded surface is related to the bulk hardness. Thus the abrasion resistance is proportional to the bulk hardness and to the abraded surface hardness.

Larsen-Badse tested a low-carbon steel and five heat-treated (tempered martensite) carbon steels using the pin-abrasive disc procedure with 400-grit SiC paper (about 37-μm particle size) and a 1-kgf load [108]. He compared the wear resistance with both the bulk hardness and the abraded surface hardness. A simple linear relationship was observed between the wear resistance and the abraded surface hardness. The bulk hardness–wear resistance relationship was more complex. Steels tempered at low temperatures and having bulk hardnesses of 650 HV or greater showed a steeper slope, i.e., the wear resistance increased substantially with increasing hardness. For steels tempered between 300 and 600°C, the wear resistance increased very little with increasing hardness between 200 and 650 HV. The annealed and pure metals tested that had bulk hardnesses below 200 HV showed a rapid increase in wear rate with increasing hardness. This work also revealed that the microhardness of the abraded surface increased more for the high-bulk-hardness steels than for the low-bulk-hardness tempered martensite steels. The annealed and pure metals also showed high work-hardening capacity. Larsen-Badse concluded that the wear resistance R could be expressed as a function of the surface hardness H_s and the strain-hardening exponent n as follows:

$$R = CH_s e^n \tag{5-51}$$

where C is a constant.

Clayton investigated the relationship between chemical composition, microstructure, and various mechanical properties and the abrasive wear rate of pearlitic steels [109]. A pin-ring wear testing machine was employed with a load range of 75 to 200 kgf and 400-grit SiC paper. Clayton showed that many of the above listed parameters were related to the wear rate. Linear regression revealed the following relationship between wear rate (WR) and hardness (HV):

$$WR = 0.00047 \text{ HV} + 0.1610 \tag{5-52}$$

The severe wear rate of these steels did not correlate with uniaxial fatigue or with fracture properties.

In tests of the wear of high-hardness steels, Kasak and Neumeyer observed that the wear rates of tool steels varied with bulk hardness and were influenced by the types of carbides present [110]. For high-speed steels, the wear rate decreased as the amount of MC-type vanadium carbide increased. An experimental Fe-Mo-Cr-Co alloy containing a fine dispersion of Fe_2Mo-type Laves phase and a bulk hardness of 64 HRC (no carbides) exhibited a higher wear rate than a simple W1 type of carbon tool steel at 62 HRC. Thus, bulk hardness alone does not explain wear rate differences in high-hardness steels. These authors also showed that reducing the size of the carbides improved wear resistance.

Many wear studies of components under sliding conditions have revealed a surface layer condition described frequently as "white" or "nonetching." These layers are produced by friction and have been observed in a wide variety of ferrous alloys. Grozin and Iankevich have identified seven different microstructural forms of white layers on worn components that result from the materials employed and the specific operating conditions [111]. The hardness of these nonetching layers is very high, with values between 700 and 1200 HV being reported [112]. These hardnesses are greater than can be obtained through normal heat treatment of the particular specimen. Eyre and Baxter, for example, observed a surface hardness of 1100 HV in a white layer on the surface of a 0.24% carbon steel [112]. They point out that the appearance of white layers on steel is different than on cast iron. For steels, the white layer usually does not exhibit a sharp interface with the matrix and a heat-affected transition zone is usually present. In contrast, the white layer on cast iron usually exhibits a sharp boundary with the matrix. Tempering softens the white layer more slowly than in normal martensitic structures. Electron microscopy has shown that these layers exhibit very fine structures with high dislocation densities.

Adhesive and abrasive wear conditions produce considerable surface hardening as shown, for example, by the work of Eyre and Baxter [112] and by Hogmark and Vingsbo [113]. These high-hardness, nonetching surface layers generally extend to a depth of about 50 μm.

Several researchers have placed Knoop microhardness impressions on the surface of parts to monitor the wear rate by the change in indent size. Blau has measured both the long diagonal D and the short diagonal d of Knoop indentations made in the work-hardened area of worn components on the cross section in order to evaluate the surface texture alteration [114]. In the ideal case, D/d should be 7.114 for the Knoop indent. This ratio is influenced by textural and crystallographic anisotropy. Because of the variation of D/d, Blau calculated a projected-area hardness (PAH) using the following formula:

$$\text{PAH} = \frac{2L}{Dd} \tag{5-53}$$

In the highly deformed surface layer produced by wear, texturing is extensive. In this region, the D/d ratio is greater than 7.114, indicating greater elastic recovery in the direction perpendicular to the surface (unidirectional wear). His work showed that work hardening extended to a greater depth than texturing.

The results discussed in this section clearly show that hardness is an important property in controlling wear. It is not, however, the only property to control. Wear is a complex phenomenon, and many factors must be considered to optimize wear resistance. Composition and microstructure, hardness, and operating and environmental conditions must all be optimized for best results.

5-8.10 Miscellaneous Applications

The diffusion of atoms in commercial alloys is important in obtaining homogeneous structures after forming and heat treatment. Diffusion rates are frequently determined by placing two pure metals or alloys of specific composition in contact, subjecting them to specific thermal treatments, and measuring the subsequent diffusion. Several techniques, mostly chemical, have been used for this purpose. Bückle and Blin have shown that microhardness surveys of the diffusion couples can be employed to measure the extent of diffusion if the influence of the chemistry on hardness is known [115]. Greater sensitivity can be obtained by taper sectioning at the couple interface.

Embrittlement phenomena have been studied by hardness testing. Westbrook and Wood have examined grain-boundary embrittlement by microhardness testing [116]. Their work showed that for many cases where grain-boundary segregation was suspected, significant hardening was detected at the grain boundary. Ghosh et al. used microhardness testing to determine the amount of hardening induced by alpha-particle bombardment of copper [117].

Microhardness testing has been used to evaluate microsegregation in alloys. For example, Brenner and Kostron evaluated microsegregation in two aluminum alloys [118]. The first step in their procedure was to establish a relationship between chemical composition and hardness. High-purity alloys of known copper and aluminum concentration were made, homogenized, and tested with 20 to 30 microhardness tests to determine the average hardness as a function of composition. The resulting calibration curve was used to relate hardness contour plots to composition contours in the segregated alloy samples.

Belk has employed hardness tests to evaluate superplasticity [119]. The Rockwell F test can be used to define a superplasticity index I as the difference in dial readings after 30 and 60 s of major-load application:

$$I = 500 \ (h_{60} - h_{30}) \tag{5-54}$$

where h_{60} and h_{30} are the impression depths after 60 and 30 s of major-load application, respectively. The superplasticity index depends principally on the strain-rate sensitivity of the material.

Stout has reviewed the use of hardness measurements as an index of weldability and service performance [120]. Vickers tests with loads of 1 to 10 kgf are recommended. Hydrogen-induced heat-affected zone cracking is unlikely if the hardness is below 300 HV. This limit is conservative for many low-hardenability steels and does not hold for high-strength low-alloy steels. Hardness is a good indicator of undermatching or overmatching of the weld metal and base metal. Sulfide-cracking tendency can be gauged by hardness tests. Under the most severe conditions, sulfide cracking can be prevented if the heat-affected zone hardness is less than 200 HV. As the concentration of hydrogen sulfide decreases, or the pH increases above 7, hardnesses of up to 300 HV can be tolerated.

5-9 SUMMARY

Hardness tests are a very valuable test technique because of their simplicity, low test cost, and wide range of correlation to properties and behavior. A large number of tests and testers are available. The choice of the correct test depends on the hardness of the material being tested, its thickness, the size of the indentation made, and the ease or difficulty of bringing the test sample into the laboratory. Most test applications can be handled by the common tests—Vickers, Rockwell, and Brinell. In this chapter, we have outlined the procedures used to obtain accurate hardness measurements. These procedures are simple in nature, relying primarily on good, commonsense engineering judgment. The reasons for performing hardness tests are many and varied. Frequently, inexpensive hardness tests can be substituted for more expensive mechanical tests. Many material or product specifications incorporate hardness requirements in the quality evaluation as a simple but effective means of ensuring conformance to desired conditions. Full utilization of hardness test capabilities can greatly expand and amplify the quality of laboratory studies.

REFERENCES

1. O'Neill, H.: *The Hardness of Metals and Its Measurement,* Chapman & Hall, Ltd., London, 1934.
2. O'Neill, H.: *Hardness Measurement of Metals and Alloys,* 2d ed., Chapman & Hall, Ltd., London, 1967.
3. Lysaght, V. E.: *Indentation Hardness Testing,* Reinhold Publishing Corporation, New York, 1949.
4. Williams, S. R.: *Hardness and Hardness Measurements,* American Society for Metals, Cleveland, Ohio, 1942.
5. Tabor, D.: *The Hardness of Metals,* Oxford University Press, London, 1951.
6. Westbrook, J. H., and H. Conrad (eds.): *The Science of Hardness Testing and Its Research Applications,* American Society for Metals, Metals Park, Ohio, 1973.
7. Petty, E. R.: "Hardness Testing," *Techniques of Metals Research,* vol. V, pt 2, Interscience Publishers, a division of John Wiley & Sons, Inc., New York, 1971, pp. 157–221.
8. Lysaght, V. E., and A. DeBellis: *Hardness Testing Handbook,* American Chain and Cable Co., Page-Wilson Corporation, Bridgeport, Conn., 1969.
9. Neville, N. G.: "Indentation Hardness Testing," *J. Aust. Inst. Met.,* vol. 12, no. 4, 1967, pp. 292–298.
10. Wahlberg, A.: "Brinell's Method of Determining Hardness and Other Properties of Iron and Steel," *J. Iron Steel Inst.,* vol. 59, no. I, 1901, pp. 243–298; vol. 60, no. II, 1901, pp. 234–271.
11. Meyer, E.: "Contribution to the Knowledge of Hardness and Hardness Testing," *Z. Ver. Dtsch. Ing.,* vol. 52, 1908, pp. 645–654; vol 52, 1908, pp. 740–748; vol. 52, 1908, pp. 835–844.
12. Rasor, J. M.: "A New Formula for Determining Brinell Hardness," *Met. Prog.,* vol. 99, April 1971, p. 15.
13. Hankins, G. A., and C. W. Aldous: "Minimum Dimensions of Test-Samples for Brinell and Diamond Pyramid Hardness Tests," *J. Inst. Met.,* vol. 54, no. 1, 1934, pp. 59–88.
14. Hoyt, S. L.: "The Ball Indentation Hardness Test," *Trans. Am. Soc. Steel Treat.,* vol. 6, 1924, pp. 396–420.
15. Tabor, D.: "A Simple Theory of Static and Dynamic Hardness," *Proc. R. Soc., London,* ser. A, vol. 192, no. A-1029, 1948, pp. 247–274.
16. Mackenzie, D. K., and T. P. Newcomb: "The Measurement of Meyer Hardness and Young's Modulus on the Rockwell Test Machine," *Br. J. Appl. Phys.,* vol. 8, 1957, pp. 398–399.
17. Smith, R. L., and G. E. Sandland: "Some Notes on the Use of a Diamond Pyramid for Hardness Testing," *J. Iron Steel Inst.,* vol. 111, no. 1, 1925, pp. 285–304 (U.S. Patent 1,478,621, issued December 25, 1923).
18. Mulhearn, T. O., and L. E. Samuels: "The Errors Introduced into Diamond Pyramid Hardness Testing by Tilting the Specimen," *J. Iron Steel Inst.,* vol. 180, 1955, pp. 354–358.
19. Crow, T. B., and J. F. Hinsley: "Some Anomalies and Some Refinements in the Diamond Pyramid Hardness Testing of Heavily Cold-Rolled Strip," *J. Inst. Met.,* vol. 72, 1946, pp. 461–485.
20. Samuels, L. E., and T. O. Mulhearn: "An Experimental Investigation of the Deformed Zone Associated with Indentation Hardness Impressions," *J. Mech. Phys. Solids,* vol. 5, 1957, pp. 125–134.
21. Dugdale, D. S.: "Vickers Hardness and Compressive Strength," *J. Mech. Phys. Solids,* vol. 6, no. 2, 1958, pp. 85–91.
22. Rockwell, S. P.: "The Testing of Metals for Hardness," *Trans. Am. Soc. Steel Treat.,* vol. 11, 1922, pp. 1013–1033.

23. Bastin, D., and T. O. Mulhearn: "Rockwell Hardness Testing: The Effect of Tilting the Specimen," *J. Iron Steel Inst.*, vol. 207, 1969, pp. 1491–1493.
24. Peek, R. L., and W. E. Ingerson: "Analysis of Rockwell Hardness Data," *Proc. Am. Soc. Test. Mater.*, vol. 39, 1939, pp. 1270–1280.
25. Meyer, M. A. Du Toit: "A Theory of Rockwell Ball Hardness," *Appl. Sci. Res.*, vol. A3, 1951, pp. 11–26.
26. Lysaght, V. E.: "The Rockwell Superficial Hardness Tester," *Met. Alloys*, vol. 3, August 1932, pp. 185–188.
27. Atkins, A. G., and D. Tabor: "The Plastic Deformation of Crossed Cylinders and Wedges," *J. Inst. Met.*, vol. 94, 1966, pp. 107–115.
28. Atkins, A. G., and D. K. Felbeck: "Applying Mutual Indentation Hardness Phenomena to Service Failures," *Am. Soc. Met. Eng. Q.*, vol. 14, no. 2, 1974, pp. 55–61.
29. Kenneford, A., and H. O'Neill: "The Behaviour of White Bearing Metals When Subjected to Various Deformation Tests. Part I—Indentation Tests," *J. Inst. Met.*, vol. 55, no. 2, 1934, pp. 49–70.
30. Williams, G., and H. O'Neill: "The Mallock Cone Hardness Test and Its Relation to Indentation Methods," *J. Iron Steel Inst.*, vol. 189, 1958, pp. 29–37.
31. Tabor, D.: "Mohs's Hardness Scale—A Physical Interpretation," *Proc. R. Soc.*, London, vol. 67, sect. B, 1954, pp. 249–257.
32. Bierbaum, C. H.: "The Microcharacter; Its Application in the Study of the Hardness of Case-Hardened, Nitrided and Chrome-Plated Surfaces," *Trans. Am. Soc. Steel Treat.*, vol. 13, 1930, pp. 1009–1025 (U.S. Patent 1,585,278, issued May 18, 1926).
33. Conley, W. J., et al.: "The Microcharacter as a Research Tool," *Trans. Am. Soc. Met.*, vol. 24, 1936, pp. 721–734.
34. Corbett, R. B., T. H. Caddy, and J. A. McKinnon: "Comparison of Dynamic Hardness Testers," *Mechanical Working & Steel Processing*, vol. XVIII, American Institute of Mining, Metallurgical and Petroleum Engineering, 1980, pp. 183–203.
35. Hadfield, D.: "Magnetic Measurement of the Hardness of Metals," *Met. Treat. Drop Forging*, vol. 22, 1955, pp. 91–96; vol. 22, 1955, pp. 153–159; vol. 22, 1955, pp. 219–224; vol. 22, 1955, pp. 239–244.
36. Wright, L. G.: "Eddy Current Testing of Pearlitic Malleable (Iron)," *Foundry*, vol. 94, October 1966, pp. 116–123.
37. "Ultrasonic Hardness Testing—Quick and Non-Destructive," *Ultrasonics*, vol. 4, April 1966, pp. 88–91.
38. Lebedev, A. A., et al.: "Acoustic Hardness Testing of Steel," *Sov. J. Nondestr. Test.*, vol. 14, 1978, pp. 300–305.
39. Barus, C.: "On the Probability of an Inherent Relation of the Electrical Resistance and Hardness of Steel," *Phys. Rev.*, vol. 30, 1910, pp. 347–349.
40. Marburger, R. E., and D. P. Koistinen: "The Determination of Hardness in Steels from the Breadth of X-Ray Diffraction Lines," *Trans. Am. Soc. Met.*, vol. 53, 1961, pp. 743–752.
41. Knoop, F., C. G. Peters, and W. B. Emerson: "A Sensitive Pyramidal-Diamond Tool for Indentation Measurements," *J. Res. Natl. Bur. Stand.*, vol. 23, July 1939, pp. 39–61 (U.S. Patent 2,091,995, issued September 7, 1937).
42. "National Bureau of Standards Specifications for Knoop Indenters," Letter Circular LC819, Apr. 1, 1946.
43. Mott, B. W.: *Micro-Indentation Hardness Testing*, Butterworth Scientific Publications, London, 1956.
44. Bückle, H.: "Progress in Micro-Indentation Hardness Testing," *Met. Rev.*, vol. 4, no. 13, 1959, pp. 49–100.
45. Brown, A. R. G., and E. Ineson: "Experimental Survey of Low-Load Hardness Testing Instruments," *J. Iron Steel Inst.*, vol. 169, 1951, pp. 376–388.
46. Bückle, H.: "Investigations of the Effect of Load on the Vickers Microhardness," *Z. Metallkund.*, vol. 45, no. 11, 1954, pp. 623–632 (ATS no. 37G5G).

47. Bückle, H.: "Investigations of the Effect of Load on the Vickers Microhardness," *Z. Metallkund.,* vol. 45, no. 12, 1954, pp. 694–701 (summarized in *Eng. Dig.,* vol. 16, 1955, pp. 189–191).

48. Campbell, R. F., Q. Henderson, and M. R. Donleavy: "A New Design of Microhardness Tester and Some Factors Affecting the Diamond Pyramid Hardness Number at Light Loads," *Trans. Am. Soc. Met.,* vol. 40, 1948, pp. 954–982.

49. Tate, D. R.: "A Comparison of Microhardness Indentation Tests," *Trans. Am. Soc. Met.,* vol. 35, 1945, pp. 374–389.

50. Thibault, N. W., and H. L. Nyquist: "The Measured Knoop Hardness of Hard Substances and Factors Affecting Its Determination," *Trans. Am. Soc. Met.,* vol. 38, 1947, pp. 271–330.

51. Tarasov, L. P., and N. W. Thibault: "Determination of Knoop Hardness Numbers Independent of Load," *Trans. Am. Soc. Met.,* vol. 38, 1947, pp. 331–353.

52. Young, C. T., and S. K. Rhee: "Evaluation of Correction Methods for Determining Load-Independent Knoop Microhardness," *J. Test. Eval.,* vol. 6, no. 3, 1978, pp. 221–230.

53. Blau, P. J.: "Use of a Two-Diagonal Measurement Method for Reducing Scatter in Knoop Microhardness Testing," *Scr. Metall.,* vol. 14, no. 7, 1980, pp. 719–724.

54. Petrenko, S. N.: "Relationship Between Rockwell and Brinell Numbers," *Tech. Pap. Natl. Bur. Stand.,* vol. 21, no. 334, 1927, pp. 195–222.

55. Petrenko, S. N.: "Relationship Between Rockwell and Brinell Numbers, *J. Res. Natl. Bur. Stand.,* vol. 5, July 1930, pp. 19–50.

56. Shaw, M. C.: "Hardness," *Mechanical Behavior of Materials,* F. A. McClintock and A. S. Argon (eds.), Addison-Wesley Publishing Company, Inc., Reading, Mass. 1966, pp. 443–470.

57. Gray, T. H., and H. Scott: "Hardness Conversion for Hard Metals," *Iron Age,* vol. 145, June 6, 1940, pp. 39–41.

58. Batchelder, G. M.: "The Nonlinear Disparity in Converting Knoop to Rockwell C Hardness," *Mater. Res. Stand.,* vol. 9, November 1969, pp. 27–30.

59. Parks, J. L.: "Relationships Between Brinell, Rockwell C and Vickers Hardness Values for Alloyed White Irons," *Trans. Am. Foundrymen's Soc.,* vol. 87, 1979, pp. 195–202.

60. Ludwigson, D. C., D. B. Roach, and A. M. Hall: "Rockwell B—Brinell Hardness Conversions for Annealed Austenitic Stainless Steel Plate," *Mater. Res. Stand.,* vol. 2, 1962, pp. 651–654.

61. Hickey, C. F.: "Tensile Strength—Hardness Correlations for Titanium Alloys," *Proc. Am. Soc. Test. Mater.,* vol. 61, 1961, pp. 857–865.

62. Emond, L.: "Vickers-Knoop Hardness Conversion," *Met. Prog.,* vol. 74, September 1958, pp. 97, 96B; vol. 76, August 1959, pp. 114, 116, 118.

63. Daniels, F. W., and C. G. Dunn: "The Effect of Orientation on Knoop Hardness of Single Crystals of Zinc and Silicon Ferrite," *Trans. Am. Soc. Met.,* vol. 41, 1949, pp. 419–442.

64. Rittenhouse, P. L., and M. L. Picklesimer: "Comparison of Pole-Figure Data Obtained by X-Ray Diffraction and Microhardness Measurements in Zircaloy-2," *Trans. Am. Inst. Min. Metall. Eng.,* vol. 236, 1966, pp. 496–501.

65. Garfinkle, M., and R. G. Garlick: "A Stereographic Representation of Knoop Hardness Anisotropy," *Trans. Am. Inst. Min. Metall. Eng.,* vol. 242, 1968, pp. 809–814.

66. Palmqvist, S.: "Method of Determining the Toughness of Brittle Materials, Particularly Sintered Carbides," *Jernkontorets Ann.,* vol. 141, 1957, pp. 300–307 (BISI no. 1865).

67. Exner, H. E.: "The Influence of Sample Preparation on Palmqvist's Method for Toughness Testing of Cemented Carbides," *Trans. Am. Inst. Min. Metall. Eng.,* vol. 245, 1969, pp. 677–683.

68. Snell, P. O. and E. Pärnama: "The Influence of Abrasive Polishing on the Stress State and Toughness Properties of Cemented Carbides," *Planseeber. Pulvermetall.,* vol. 21, 1973, pp. 271–280.

69. Vander Voort, G. F., and R. W. Hinton: "Metallographic Study of Factors Influencing the Toughness of 70% Al_2O_3/30% TiC Cermet Inserts," *International Conference on Productivity Improvement Through New Tools and Applications,* Society of Carbide and Tool Engineers, June 1979, pp. 153–188.

70. Viswanadham, R. K., and J. D. Venables: "A Simple Method for Evaluating Cemented Carbides," *Metall. Trans.,* vol. 8A, 1977, pp. 187–191.

71. Exner, E. L., J. R. Pickens, and J. Gurland: "A Comparison of Indentation Crack Resistance and Fracture Toughness of Five WC-Co Alloys," *Metall. Trans.*, vol. 9A, 1978, pp. 736–738.
72. Peters, C. T.: "The Relationship Between Palmqvist Indentation Toughness and Bulk Fracture Toughness for Some WC-Co Cemented Carbides," *J. Mater. Sci.*, vol. 14, 1979, pp. 1619–1623.
73. Janitzky, E. J.: "Taylor Speed and Its Relation to Reduction of Area and Brinell Hardness," *Trans. Am. Soc. Met.*, vol. 26, 1938, pp. 1122–1131.
74. Henkin, A., and J. Datsko: "The Influence of Physical Properties on Machinability," *Trans. ASME, J. Eng. Ind.*, vol. 85, ser. B, no. 4, 1963, pp. 321–328.
75. Gulbransen, L. B.: "Drilling Forces and the Effect of Microstructure," *Trans. Am. Soc. Met.*, vol. 56, 1963, pp. 880–885.
76. Greaves, R. H., and J. A. Jones: "The Ratio of the Tensile Strength of Steel to the Brinell Hardness Number," *J. Iron Steel Inst.*, vol. 113, no. 1, 1926, pp. 335–353.
77. Taylor, W. J.: "The Hardness Test as a Means of Estimating the Tensile Strength of Metals," *J. R. Aeronaut. Soc.*, vol. 46, no. 380, 1942, pp. 198–209.
78. Tabor, D.: "The Hardness and Strength of Metals," *J. Inst. Met.*, vol. 79, 1951, pp. 1–18, 465–474.
79. Cahoon, J. R., W. H. Broughton, and A. R. Kutzak: "The Determination of Yield Strength from Hardness Measurements," *Metall. Trans.*, vol. 2, 1971, pp. 1979–1983.
80. Petty, E. R.: "Relationship between Hardness and Tensile Properties over a Wide Range of Temperature for Aluminum Alloys," *Metallurgia*, vol. 65, January 1962, pp. 25–26.
81. MacKenzie, J. T.: "The Brinell Hardness of Gray Cast Iron and Its Relation to Some Other Properties," *Proc. Am. Soc. Test. Mater.*, vol. 46, 1946, pp. 1025–1038.
82. Robinson, J. N., and A. H. Shabaik: "The Determination of the Relationship between Strain and Microhardness by Means of Visioplasticity," *Metall. Trans.*, vol. 4, 1973, pp. 2091–2095.
83. Oliver, B. R., and J. E. Bowers: "The Determination of Yield Stress from Hardness Measurements," *J. Inst. Met.*, vol. 94, 1966, pp. 223–225.
84. George, R. A., S. Dinda, and A. S. Kasper: "Estimating Yield Strength from Hardness Data," *Met. Prog.*, vol. 109, May 1976, pp. 30–35.
85. Siebert, C. A., D. V. Doane, and D. H. Breen: *The Hardenability of Steels*, American Society for Metals, Metals Park, Ohio, 1977.
86. Wallbaum, H. J., and R. Mischer: "The Microhardness of Recrystallizing Aluminium Sheet," *Z. Metallkund.*, vol. 40, 1949, pp. 179–182.
87. Mould, P. R., and P. Cotterill: "A Comparison of the Use of the Micro-Hardness Survey Method with Other Techniques for the Investigation of the Recrystallization Process in Aluminium," *Metallurgia*, vol. 71, no. 425, 1965, pp. 149–154.
88. Dawes, C.: "The Measurement of the Depth of a Carburized Case," *Metallurgia*, vol. 64, November 1961, pp. 217–219.
89. Enberg, E. H.: "Testing Plating Hardness and Thickness Using a Microhardness Tester," *Met. Finish.*, vol. 66, March 1968, pp. 48–52.
90. Braunovic, M., and C. W. Haworth: "The Use of Microhardness Testing to Measure the Thickness of Work-Hardened Surface Layers," *Prakt. Metallogr.*, vol. 7, 1970, pp. 183–187.
91. Murly, N.: "Thickness Determination of Anodized Deposits and Electrodeposits by Vickers Indentation Techniques," *Met. Technol.* vol. 1, 1974, pp. 155–156.
92. Hollomon, J. H., and L. D. Jaffe: "Time-Temperature Relations in Tempering Steel," *Trans. Am. Inst. Min. Metall. Eng.*, vol. 162, 1945, pp. 223–249.
93. Bareiss, R. A.: "Determination of Residual Stresses by Indentation Methods," WADC (Wright Air Development Center, Wright-Patterson Air Force Base, Ohio) Tech. Rep. 54–615, December 1954.
94. Nunes, J., and F. R. Larson: "Low-Temperature Tensile-Hardness Correlations for SAE 4340 Steel," *Am. Soc. Test. Mater., Bull.* 1960, pp. 25–29 (see also *Mater. Res. Stand.*, vol. 1, 1961, pp. 286–289).
95. Nunes, J., and F. R. Larson: "Low-Temperature Hardness and Flow-Stress Relationships of Metals," *J. Inst. Met.*, vol. 91, 1962–1963, pp. 114–117.

96. Westbrook, J. H.: "Temperature Dependence of the Hardness of Pure Metals," *Trans. Am. Soc. Met.,* vol. 45, 1953, pp. 221–248.
97. Westbrook, J. H.: "Microhardness Testing at High Temperatures," *Proc. Am. Soc. Test. Mater.,* vol. 57, 1957, pp. 873–897.
98. Petty, E. R.: "Hardness and Other Physical Properties of Metals in Relation to Temperature," *Metallurgia,* vol. 56, November 1957, pp. 231–236.
99. Geach, G. A.: "Hardness and Temperature," *Int. Metall. Rev.,* vol. 19, 1974, pp. 255–267.
100. Moteff, J., R. K. Bhargava, and W. L. McCullough: "Correlation of the Hot-Hardness with the Tensile Strength of 304 Stainless Steel to Temperatures of 1200C," *Metall. Trans.,* vol. 6A, 1975, pp. 1101–1104.
101. Hurricks, P. L.: "Some Metallurgical Factors Controlling the Adhesive and Abrasive Wear Resistance of Steels. A Review," *Wear,* vol. 26, 1973, pp. 285–304.
102. Oberle, T. L.: "Hardness, Elastic Modulus, Wear of Metals," *SAE Q. Trans.,* vol. 6, no. 3, 1952, pp. 511–517.
103. Ludema, K. C.: "A Perspective on Wear Models," *ASTM Standardization News,* Sept. 1974, pp. 13–17, 56.
104. Khruschov, M. M.: "Resistance of Metals to Wear by Abrasion, as Related to Hardness," *Proc. Conf. on Lubrication and Wear,* Institute of Mechanical Engineers, 1957, pp. 655–659.
105. Richardson, R. C. D.: "The Wear of Metals by Hard Abrasives," *Wear,* vol. 10, 1967, pp. 291–309.
106. Moore, M. A.: "The Relationship between the Abrasive Wear Resistance, Hardness and Microstructure of Ferritic Materials," *Wear,* vol. 28, 1974, pp. 59–68.
107. Avient, B. W. E., J. Goddard, and H. Wilman: "An Experimental Study of Friction and Wear during Abrasion of Metals," *Proc. R. Soc.,* ser. A, vol. 258, October 18, 1960, pp. 159–180.
108. Larsen-Badse, J.: "The Abrasion Resistance of Some Hardened and Tempered Carbon Steels," *Trans. Am. Inst. Min. Metall. Eng.,* vol. 236, 1966, pp. 1461–1466.
109. Clayton, P.: "The Relations between Wear Behaviour and Basic Material Properties for Pearlitic Steels," *Wear,* vol. 60, 1980, pp. 75–93.
110. Kasak, A., and T. A. Neumeyer: "Observations on the Wear of High-Hardness Steels," *Wear,* vol. 14, 1969, pp. 445–454.
111. Grozin, B. D., and V. F. Iankevich: "The Structure of White Layers," *Friction and Wear in Machinery,* American Society of Mechanical Engineers, vol. 15, 1962, pp. 143–152.
112. Eyre, T. S., and A. Baxter: "The Formation of White Layers at Rubbing Surfaces," *Met. Mater.,* vol. 6, 1972, pp. 435–439.
113. Hogmark, S., and O. Vingsbo: "Adhesive Mechanisms in the Wear of Some Tool Steels," *Wear,* vol. 38, 1976, pp. 341–359.
114. Blau, P. J.: "The Use of Knoop Indentations for Measuring Microhardness near Worn Metal Surfaces," *Scr. Metall.,* vol. 13, 1979, pp. 95–98.
115. Bückle, H., and J. Blin: "Micrographic Aspects of the Diffusion of Zinc and Aluminium in Copper," *J. Inst. Met.,* vol. 80, 1951–1952, pp. 385–389.
116. Westbrook, J. H., and D. L. Wood: "Embrittlement of Grain Boundaries by Equilibrium Segregation," *Nature,* vol. 192, no. 4809, 1961, pp. 1280–1281.
117. Ghosh, T. K., C. J. Beevers, and R. S. Barnes: "The Microhardness of Copper Bombarded with Alpha-Particles," *J. Inst. Met.,* vol. 89, 1960–1961, pp. 125–127.
118. Brenner, P. and H. Kostron: "Macro- and Micro-Segregation in Ingots of Two Aluminium Alloys," *Metallurgia,* vol. 41, February 1950, pp. 209–218.
119. Belk, J. A.: "Indentation Tests for Superplasticity," *Met. Mater.,* vol. 8, 1974, pp. 414–416.
120. Stout, R. D.: "Hardness as an Index of the Weldability and Service Performance of Steel Weldments," *Weld. Res. Counc. Bull.,* no. 189, November 1973, pp. 1–13.

QUANTITATIVE MICROSCOPY

6-1 INTRODUCTION

Metallurgists have relied, in general, on qualitative descriptions of microstructures. Structural features are rated by comparison to charts describing many types of structural features. For some samples, the accuracy of such ratings, although limited, is adequate for the intended purpose. For example, a chart-comparison grain-size rating is sufficiently accurate for the steelmaker to determine if a given heat of steel is "inherently" fine-grained. This is true as long as the grain size of the material is substantially finer than the dividing line between fine and coarse. Chart comparison methods work best when only one feature of the structure changes. Grain size is the most amenable structural feature to evaluate by chart ratings. When more than one aspect of the structure changes, chart methods cannot cover all degrees and combinations of change. Since the method depends heavily on the grading of the pictures, errors in the grading influence rating accuracy and the ratings become highly dependent on subjective opinion. The result is that reproducibility suffers.

For research and quality control studies, chart comparison ratings are generally unsatisfactory. It is a basic precept of physical metallurgy that microstructure exerts considerable influence on properties and behavior. These trends can best be identified and evaluated through the application of quantitative microscopy methods. Historically, quantitative metallography is a relatively new field. Except for the general concept of grain size, most metallurgists have had no technical training in quantitative metallography. While there are several excellent reviews [1–6] available on the subject, these references tend to concentrate on the development and proof of the various relationships rather than on the practical use of them. In this chapter, we concentrate on the factors influencing the practical employment of the more common methods, giving examples whenever possible. No effort will be made to show the validity of the basic relationships; this information can be found in the references cited.

Metallurgists have used the terms "quantitative metallography" or "quantitative microscopy" in reference to the measurement of microstructural parameters. Researchers in other fields have used terms such as "modal analysis," "morphometry," or "micrometrics." Saltykov, the Russian metallurgist whose epic book has contributed much to this field, uses the term "stereometric metallography" [1]. The preferred terminology today is "quantitative stereology," which was coined by Hans Elias in 1961 and defined as ". . . a body of methods for the exploration of three-dimensional space, when only two-dimensional sections through solid bodies or their projections on a surface are available" [3]. This is the essence of stereology—translation of measurements made on a sectioning plane to conclusions about the volumetric characteristics of the microstructure. While certain stereological relationships depend on the shape or the size and shape of the features, many of the most important relationships are independent of the size and shape as long as the sectioning plane intersects the structure at random.

As with any new body of knowledge, there has been a natural reluctance by metallurgists to employ stereological methods. One often hears statements about the effort required being excessive. Obviously, a certain amount of effort is required to learn these new methods, and their implementation does require some labor. However, the basic measurements are quite straightforward and readily performed without excessive exertion. The recent developments in image analysis make the use of these methods quite routine, removing much of the tedium associated with manual measurements. The value of these methods in quality studies and in structure-property-behavior correlations is substantial.

In the application of stereological principles, it is first necessary to determine what parameters should be measured. The nature of the study influences the selection of these parameters. In routine quality control studies, the manufacturing process is usually well established and fixed. Thus, simple measurements are made to detect deviations from the norm. Typically, these measurements include grain size, volume fraction of phases or constituents, interlamellar spacing, degree of spheroidization, and depth of decarburization. In research studies, the manufacturing process is often varied extensively, and a more thorough description of the structure is generally required.

In applying these methods, the metallographer generally must consider the following:

- What microstructural features are related to the expected service conditions or property requirements?
- How can these features be revealed and measured?
- What is the most accurate and efficient measurement method?
- What manual or automated techniques can be applied to facilitate the analysis?
- How many samples should be measured, where should the samples come from within the product, and what orientation should be examined?

- How should the samples be prepared?
- What magnification should be used?
- How many fields should be measured?
- How should the data be analyzed and expressed?
- What conclusions can be drawn?

These questions, which are not trivial, and their answers enable the metallographer to define the problem, obtain meaningful data, and reach significant conclusions.

6-2 BASIC MEASUREMENT VARIABLES

6-2.1 Sampling

To obtain meaningful stereological data, representative samples must be selected and prepared properly. This implies that the samples chosen must faithfully depict the structure of the tested component. This will be complicated if the microstructure varies through the cross section. Random sampling is frequently employed to obtain statistically significant data. Random sampling implies that all regions and orientations of the structure have an equal opportunity to be cut and tested. Obviously, if the structure is constantly varying across the section, random sampling will not produce meaningful data. In this case, the testing must define the variation with respect to some fixed direction. In practice, truly random sampling is difficult to perform. Section size and shape as well as economic considerations can prohibit such sampling. In such cases, sampling is often based on convenience and ease of specimen cutting. This will not invalidate the results if the samples prepared are representative of the areas that are not easily sampled.

For tests of large components or multiple components from the same ingot or heat, it is usually necessary to specify the location and orientation of the components and sampled areas with respect to their original ingot locations. It is well recognized that the composition varies within an ingot; thus, the microstructure can vary as well. Components processed from different ingot locations can exhibit differences in microstructure and properties as a result of their response to processing. The sampling scheme should be able to detect such variations. It is difficult to establish rigid rules concerning the number and location of test samples. Good engineering judgment must be exercised to ensure adequate testing without incurring excessive sampling.

6-2.2 Sample Preparation

After the desired samples are cut and identified, they must be prepared for inspection. Polishing and etching must faithfully reveal the true microstructure without distortion, smearing, gouging, etc. Shortcuts in the polishing procedure do not save time because the balance of the investigative work can be rendered useless. Indeed, erroneous conclusions can result with dramatic economic consequences. The true structure must be revealed clearly to achieve meaningful results.

Polishing and etching should not produce excessive relief which will alter the apparent size and spacing of constituents. Preparation is even more critical if automated devices are employed to measure the structure. Automatic polishing equipment is recommended to obtain maximum flatness, control of relief, and reproducibility of polishing quality.

6-2.3 Field Selection

After sample preparation, measurement can commence. For manual measurement, a wide variety of test grids can be employed either as eyepiece graticules or as projection overlays. Some degree of automation is possible with manual methods, as is described later in this chapter. If image analysis is employed, the operator selects a predeveloped program stored in the computer memory to perform the required measurements, to accumulate and analyze the data, and to output it in a convenient form.

The operator must decide, in either case, how many fields are to be measured and how to space the fields; The operator must also select the best magnification. As the magnification is raised, the field area is decreased. Sampling statistics depend on the measurement area. If the magnification is raised from 100X to 200X, four times as many fields must be measured to cover the same area. The magnification chosen is a compromise between resolution of the structure and field area. The measurement area needed to obtain a certain measurement accuracy depends on the homogeneity of the structure. This can be assessed from the field-to-field variation of the measurements. In most work, it is advisable to measure a certain number of fields and calculate the relative accuracy of the measurement to determine how many fields are required to obtain a specific relative accuracy, e.g., 10 percent relative accuracy with a 95 percent confidence level. In general, to reduce the observed relative accuracy to one-half the value obtained after x measurements, four times x measurements must be performed in addition. The statistical analysis procedure is given in the section on volume fraction measurements.

In nearly all work, field selection should be performed randomly, i.e., without operator bias of grid placement. It is best to space the measurement fields around the sample surface in a systematic pattern rather than confine them to a small portion of the surface. Placement is easily performed with an upright microscope but is more difficult with an inverted microscope. For example, if the operator decides to measure 25 fields, the operator ignores the image on the projection screen and moves the stage controls to place the objective over the front right corner of the specimen. The image is focused and the measurement is made. The operator looks down at the sample surface and moves the sample parallel to the front edge of the sample a distance of about one-fifth this length. The sample is focused and measured. This procedure is repeated until five rows of five evenly spaced measurements are made. The 25 areas could be selected totally at random, but the operator must employ some sort of random location generator with respect to the stage vernier, which unnecessarily complicates the analysis method. By not looking at the projected image during systematic spacing of the fields, random field selection is ensured. In no case should the observer adjust the sample location with respect to the grid placement, since this introduces bias.

Selective field placement is required in certain instances. For example, if a sample exhibits a duplex grain size with well-defined regions of fine and coarse grains, it is common practice to *randomly* determine the volume fraction of fine- and coarse-grained regions and then to *selectively* measure the grain size in each region.

6-3 STANDARD CHART METHODS

Characterization of microstructure using standard charts was introduced in the mid 1920s. This method has been commonly used to rate grain size [7–10], inclusions [11–14], and graphite [15, 16]. In recent years, standard charts have been prepared as a guide for volume fraction estimation [17–19]. Chart methods have been used extensively by manufacturers because of their simplicity. Many of these chart methods have been adopted in national and international standards, while others are used within a given industry or company.

In using comparison charts, the operator scans the sample at the magnification recommended by the chart, usually 100X, while glancing occasionally at the chart. This process is continued until a decision is made about which picture or pictures are most representative of the structure. In some cases, eyepiece reticles can be obtained with the chart pictures so that the standard and the structure can be viewed simultaneously. Better accuracy should be obtained in this manner. Hull developed a comparison method for viewing the structure and the standard simultaneously on the ground-glass projection screen [20].

6-4 MEASUREMENT OF STRUCTURAL GRADIENTS

The measurement of gradients of composition and/or microstructure at the surface of bulk samples is a commonly encountered metallographic problem, although not a stereological measurement per se. The surface conditions in this category include the following:

- Depth of decarburization
- Case depth after carburizing, nitriding, cyaniding, etc.
- Depth of hardening after heat treatment, flame or induction hardening, etc.
- Coating thickness

There are many similarities in the measurement techniques used to evaluate these surface conditions. In all cases, care must be exercised so that representative samples are obtained and samples are properly prepared (for example, edges are preserved) and measured. In general, a number of measurements should be made at properly spaced intervals in order to obtain a valid statistical estimate of the particular depth. Although a variety of techniques can be employed, only those involving microscopy are discussed here.

6-4.1 Decarburization

Many industrial hot-working and heat-treating processes involve heating procedures in an atmosphere which produces oxidation and/or decarburization. The amount and appearance of the surface decarburization varies depending on the steel grade and processing variables. With some samples, the carbon content at the extreme surface is depleted sufficiently to produce a layer of free ferrite. One can also observe negligible loss of carbon or substantial depletion without free-ferrite formation. The ability to measure the depth of decarburization with a microscope or by microhardness traverses is influenced by the nature of the core microstructure.

In routine work, the depth of decarburization is measured by optical microscopy [21]. Greater accuracy can sometimes be obtained with microhardness traverses or by incremental carbon analysis. These two methods are more time-consuming and are generally reserved for failure analysis or research studies.

In the microscopic method, a number of samples are selected from different test locations, e.g., opposite ends of billets or bars in a specific treatment lot. Depending on the size, the entire periphery on the cross section is examined or a portion of the billet surface at randomly chosen locations around the surface is examined. On a large section, it is not advisable to concentrate all of the samples on one surface face. Decarburization patterns are not necessarily uniform. Seams or laps, when present, exhibit local decarburized conditions whose depth depends on the depth of the defect. Corners of rectangular or square sections exhibit greater depth than the faces, and their depth should not be included with face measurements but can be recorded separately.

The sectioning plane should be oriented in the transverse direction perpendicular to the bar surface. This permits the observer to scan the entire bar periphery and detect any nonuniformity. Polishing must be controlled in order to retain the edges, i.e., to avoid rounding. Bulk samples can be successfully polished without mounting or edge protection through the use of automatic polishing devices. Hand polishing of bulk samples that are unprotected invariably produces rounded edges, which will invalidate measurements. For small samples, or if automatic devices are unavailable, edge protection is required followed by mounting. Mounting in Bakelite or similar materials does not ensure freedom from edge rounding, although edge rounding will not be as bad as with unmounted hand-polished samples. Edge protection, which is discussed in Chap. 2, is a very simple technique.

After polishing, the microstructure is revealed by using either nital or picral or other reagents as required. Depth of decarburization is measured either with a micrometer eyepiece or with a scale, using the image that is projected onto a ground-glass screen. Filar micrometer eyepieces are available with digital output, which permits very accurate, fast measurements. The magnification is adjusted in accordance with the structure. The operator should make a number of measurements, at least five, at randomly chosen locations along the surface of each sample and should calculate an average for each sample. The standard deviation of the measurements is a good indicator of the variability of the decarburization depth.

In the determination of the depth of decarburization, several approaches are possible. For example, if a layer of free ferrite is present, it is best to provide a measurement of the free-ferrite depth as well as the total affected depth. Some technicians supplement this by providing both average and maximum depths of both the free ferrite and the affected depths of decarburization, while others list the average, minimum, and maximum depths. If the minimum and maximum depths are of interest, the surface must be scanned to find these particular locations.

Free-ferrite depth is usually quite simple to measure because of the good contrast between this zone and the adjacent partially decarburized layer. The maximum affected depth is more difficult to estimate visually, and the ease of its estimation depends on the nature of the structure present. In a hypoeutectoid ferrite-pearlite steel sample, the operator looks for the depth where the amount of pearlite and ferrite appears to become constant, a subjective estimate. Such estimations are more difficult in heat-treated samples in which the partially decarburized layer consists of martensite and/or bainite. It is more difficult to estimate where these structures are no longer influenced by a lower carbon content. In such instances, microhardness traverses produce a more accurate estimate. The visual estimates of the maximum affected depths are usually lower than the depths determined by microhardness.

Decarburization in high-speed steels has been estimated by colors produced by etching with 4% nital. According to Powell, during the first 30 s of etching, the macroscopic surface color changes from gray to purple-blue. After about 60 s, the color abruptly changes to blue-green, and etching should be halted. Starting at the surface, the microscopically viewed colors change from light tan to brown to purple to blue to blue-green to green-tan. The effective and total depths of decarburization are measured at 100X based on the observed colors. The effective depth occurs at the start of the blue zone and corresponds to a hardness of about 820 HV (Vickers hardness) on a fully hardened sample. The total depth is measured at the change from blue-green to green-tan. Routine use of this method requires careful evaluation and control.

Decarburization produces interesting microstructual effects in Hadfield austenitic manganese steels (alloys of 1.2 to 1.4% C and 12 to 14% Mn). This composition stabilizes austenite at ambient temperatures. In the decarburized surface zone, however, supersaturated BCC alpha phase and HCP epsilon phase are produced in regions below 0.5% carbon during solution annealing, as illustrated in Fig. 6-1. Sedriks recommends a short, 3-s, etch in 3% nital followed by stain etching with aqueous 20% sodium metabisulphite to reveal this structure [22]. To detect the extent of the decarburized zone, the sample is reheated to 575°C for 30 min to precipitate carbide in the region with a carbon content above

 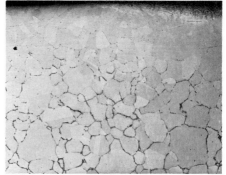

Figure 6-1 Example of decarburized surface of Hadfield manganese steel. Left, martensitic structure in zone with less than 0.48% carbon, solution-annealed condition (50×, nital, then 20% aqueous sodium metabisulphite). Right, aging at 1140°F for 30 min produces carbide precipitation in the grain boundaries where the carbon content is 1.16% or greater (25×, nital).

1.16%. Sedriks recommends etching the polished sample with a 10% solution of equal parts of nitric and acetic acids in glycerin. This solution was tried but found difficult to use. Good results are obtained with either nital or picral, as shown in Fig. 6-1. According to Sedriks, the carbon content at the end of the martensitic alpha and epsilon zone is 0.48 ± 0.03 percent, while at the beginning of the precipitate zone it is 1.16 ± 0.03 percent.

6-4.2 Case Depth

Case depth in samples subjected to carburizing, nitriding, cyaniding, and flame or induction hardening treatments can be measured in much the same way as decarburization. Chemical analysis techniques, of course, are applicable only to those techniques that alter the surface chemistry. If the sample is quite hard, however, incremental machining is not possible without first softening the sample.

Microscopic methods are used widely, but their accuracy depends on the nature of the case and core microstructures. Carburization depth is easier to judge in the unhardened sample than in the heat-treated sample. Case depths of nitrided samples can be difficult to estimate. Case depths in flame- or induction-hardened samples are, in general, easy to measure microscopically because of the good contrast between case and core. In each sample, the sectioning plane must be perpendicular to the sample surface for accurate depth determination. Taper sections can be employed where necessary, but the taper angle must be known.

For routine work, a case-hardened sample can be fractured and the case depth measured with a Brinell scope or with a scale and a stereoviewer. If the core is soft, the fractured surface will exhibit good contrast between case and core. If the core is hard, contrast can be enhanced by blueing the fracture on a hot plate. Macroetching of a ground cut surface or fracture face also reveals the case depth, as is shown in Chap. 1.

Measurement accuracy is improved by using polished and etched sections. Microhardness traverses are frequently employed to determine the total case depth and the effective case depth, i.e., the depth to some specific hardness. From a service standpoint, the total case depth is of little value, since the hardness in part of this region is too low to be useful. Thus, it is preferable to determine the depth to a specific carbon content, generally 0.40 to 0.50%, or to the hardness for 50% martensite.

Dawes compared results of carburization depth measurements made with a microscope and by microhardness traverses. He found that the case depth of slowly cooled samples measured microscopically based on etch appearance bore no relationship to total penetration or to any specific hardness level [23]. It was observed, however, that the etched contrast line between case and core corresponded to a hardness about 200 HV above the core hardness of the particular steel sample.

Polished and etched cross sections can be used to readily detect white-etching surface layers of iron nitride on nitrided samples. Standard nital or picral etches are adequate. Figure 6-2 illustrates the microstructure and hardness profile of a heavily nitrided alloy steel sample. The maximum depth of the iron nitride constituent can be difficult to assess because of the spotty grain-boundary penetration frequently observed. The maximum affected depth of nitriding is more easily measured at low magnifications than at high magnification. Effective case depth can be determined best by hardness testing.

The depth of shallow case-hardened samples produced by standard heat treatments or by flame or induction hardening can be assessed by macroetching, by microscopy, or by hardness traverses. The effective case depth in a high-carbon material can be determined microscopically if the location of 50% martensite can be found. Ability to do this depends largely on the nature of the core microstructure. Figures 6-3 illustrates the microstructure and cross-sectional hardness profile of a brine-quenched sample of a carbon tool steel. The transition from martensite to pearlite is easy to detect in this sample.

Depth of hardening in flame- or induction-hardened samples can be measured using either macroscopic or microscopic procedures. The depth is measured from the surface to the line of demarcation between the hardened and unhardened zones. Effective case depth is best measured by microhardness surveys. The effective case depth hardness varies with the carbon content. The following guidelines from SAE J423a are recommended:

Carbon content, %	Effective case depth hardness, HRC
0.28–0.32	35
0.33–0.42	40
0.43–0.52	45
0.53 and above	50

Figure 6-4 illustrates the measurement of case depth in a flame-hardened sample.

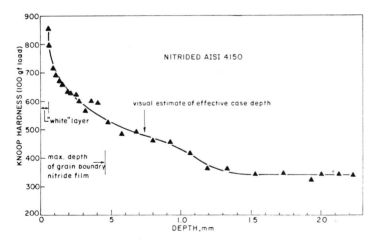

Figure 6-2 Comparison of the effective case depth of a nitrided AISI 4150 alloy steel assessed by visual estimation and by microhardness (100-g) traverses (110×, nital). Note the heavy "white" layer at the surface.

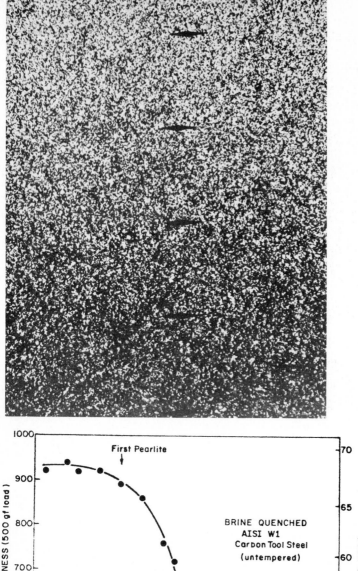

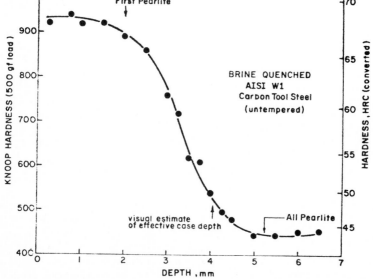

Figure 6-3 Comparison of the effective case depth of a brine-quenched sample of AISI W1 tool steel assessed by visual estimation and by microhardness (500-g) traverses (100×, nital, transition zone shown).

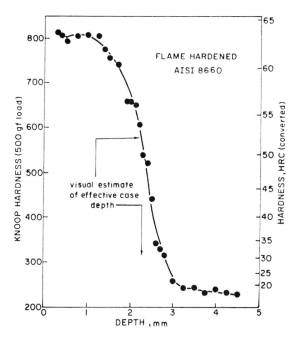

Figure 6-4 Comparison of the effective case depth of flame-hardened AISI 8660 alloy steel assessed by visual estimation and by microhardness (500-g) traverses (100×, nital, transition zone shown).

6-4.3 Coating Thickness

Many destructive and nondestructive techniques have been developed for measuring the thickness of surface coatings. Microscopic methods include nondestructive interferometry [24] or measurements on cross sections [25–30]. ASTM (American Society for Testing and Materials) Specification B487 provides extensive guidelines for the microscopic measurement of coating thickness. The methods described are recommended for coatings thicker than 8 μm (0.3 mil). Coatings other than oxide layers should be protected by overplating to a depth of at least 10 μm (0.4 mil). The plating must be compatible with the coating and should exhibit color contrast. Zinc or cadmium coatings should not be overplated with copper, since etching will produce a copper deposit on the coating which will make measurement difficult.

The coated sample should be mounted so as to produce a plane perpendicular to the coating. If a taper section is used, the taper angle must be measured accurately. Whenever possible, the sample length should be at least 20 mm (0.8 in).

Polishing of coated samples requires considerable attention. If possible, the sample should be oriented so that the harder area leads the softer area during grinding. The grinding direction should be 45° to the coated surface. Each grinding step should be 90° to the prior step. Etching is recommended to produce sharp interfaces and to remove any smeared soft metal. ASTM Specification B487 lists a number of suitable reagents for coatings.

Measurements are made using a micrometer eyepiece or graticule calibrated with a stage micrometer. Digital eyepiece micrometers are very popular. Measurements can also be made on a projection screen with a scale or on a photograph. ASTM B487 recommends that the magnification be chosen so that the field width is 1½ to 3 times the coating thickness. For very thin coatings, the highest available magnification should be used. Coating thickness should be measured at a number of locations along the length of the sample, and the average computed. If the thickness is not particularly uniform, more measurements should be taken. If enough measurements are made, the standard deviation will describe coating uniformity. Gore and Glass have described a statistical procedure for evaluating coating thickness [25]. For rough coatings, the thickness is measured between the interface of the coating and matrix and the midpoint between peaks and valleys. If the minimum and maximum thicknesses are desired, the sample must be scanned to detect these regions. For best accuracy, ASTM B487 recommends duplication of the measurements after regrinding the sample on 600-grit paper, polishing, and etching. The two sets of measurements should agree within 2 percent or 0.5 μm (0.02 mil), whichever is greater.

The accuracy of coating thicknesses measured optically has been studied in great detail [26–29]. These studies have shown that interlaboratory measurements of smooth coatings 8 to 480 μm thick exhibited variations of 7 percent or 1.0 μm (if 1.0 μm is greater than 7 percent). Measurement of rough coatings produced poor agreement and had an uncertainty of 35 percent or 40 μm (if 40 μm is greater than 35 percent). Sample preparation did not contribute significantly to the errors. Most of the error was due to faulty calibration, poor measurement judgment, or equipment problems.

Ogburn performed a detailed analysis of measurement error sources [27]. The magnification provided by the microscope must be determined precisely for each objective-eyepiece combination. The micrometer measuring device or eyepiece reticle must be calibrated at each magnification using a stage micrometer. Ogburn and coworkers showed that 15 operators exhibited a measurement spread of about 0.8 percent in measurements of a fixed interval on a stage micrometer at magnifications of about 175 and 1900X using a filar micrometer eyepiece [30]. The measurement spreads for a single operator were much smaller.

6-5 STEREOLOGY TERMINOLOGY

The stereological literature can be confusing because of the variability of terminology and mathematical symbols used by different authors. To combat this problem, the International Society for Stereology adopted a set of basic symbols and rules for their use. Five basic symbols are employed:

P = point S = surface
L = line V = volume
A = area

These symbols are modified with subscripts or superscripts to describe the various measurements as listed in Table 6-1. In using these symbols, the origin of the parameter must be remembered; i.e., the symbol can refer to features in the sample volume or on the plane of polish or to the intersection of test elements (point, line, or plane) with the feature. Dual usage of the symbols is common. For example, P can represent either a point-count hit, a grid test point, or an intersection count. Test volumes are distinguished by T subscripts, e.g., L_T, A_T, or V_T. The combined symbol, however, does not carry the T subscript because it is defined without it (for example, $V_V = \Sigma V_i / V_T$). Symbols A and S are both used in reference to surfaces. In general, A is used when dealing with flat or planar surfaces, while S is usually reserved for curved surfaces.

Most stereological measurements require only simple counting. The measurements can be combined to produce a variety of useful microstructural parameters. Basic measurements include the following:

P_P = total number of test points in the phase of interest divided by the total number of test points
P_L = number of point intersections of a test line with features divided by the test-line length
N_L = number of interceptions of features by a test line divided by the test-line length
P_A = number of point features divided by the test area
N_A = number of features divided by the test area

Table 6-1 Standard notation recommended by the International Society for Stereology

Symbol	Units	Description	Common name
P		Number of point elements or test points	
P_P		Point fraction, i.e., number of point elements per total number of test points	Point count
L	mm	Length of linear elements or test line length	
P_L	mm^{-1}	Number of point intersections per unit length of test line	
L_L	mm/mm	Sum of linear intercept lengths divided by total test line length	Lineal fraction
A	mm^2	Planar area of intercepted features or test area	
S	mm^2	Surface area or interface area, generally reserved for curved surfaces	
V	mm^3	Volume of three-dimensional structural elements or test volume	
A_A	mm^2/mm^2	Sum of areas of intercepted features divided by total test area	Areal fraction
S_V	mm^2/mm^3	Surface or interface area divided by total test volume, i.e., surface-to-volume ratio	
V_V	mm^3/mm^3	Sum of volumes of structural features divided by total test volume	Volume fraction
N		Number of features	
N_L	mm^{-1}	Number of interceptions of features divided by total test line length	Lineal density
P_A	mm^{-2}	Number of point features divided by total test area	
L_A	mm/mm^2	Sum of lengths of linear features divided by total test area	Perimeter (total)
N_A	mm^{-2}	Number of interceptions of features divided by total test area	Areal density
P_V	mm^{-3}	Number of points per test volume	
L_V	mm/mm^3	Length of features per test volume	
N_V	mm^{-3}	Number of features per test volume	Volumetric density
$\bar{L}$	mm	Mean linear intercept distance, L_L/N_L	
$\bar{A}$	mm^2	Mean areal intercept, A_A/N_A	
$\bar{S}$	mm^2	Mean particle surface area, S_V/N_V	
$\bar{V}$	mm^3	Mean particle volume, V_V/N_V	

Note: Fractional parameters are expressed per unit length, area, or volume.
Source: From Underwood, Ref. 3.

P_L and N_L can cause some confusion. If a test line intersects isolated particles on a surface, there are two point intersections but only one particle interception. For a single-phase continuous structure, such as ferrite grains in a low-carbon steel, the number of grain-boundary intersections P_L will be the same as the number of grains intercepted N_L.

In this chapter, we employ the ISS nomenclature so that the relationships presented are compatible with current usage and our nomenclature is compatible with Underwood's excellent book, where the theoretical background for these relationships can be found [3].

6-6 VOLUME FRACTION

Determination of the volume fraction of a particular phase or constituent in a microstructure is one of the most important and most common stereological measurements. The simplest procedure for estimating the volume fraction of a particular constituent is to survey the microstructure and estimate, or guess, the area fraction. This technique is commonly used but is subject to error. Somewhat better accuracy can be obtained by comparing the microstructure to standard charts illustrating different percentages of an ideal or specific structure [17–19]. The accuracy of the method depends partly on how closely the size and distribution of the constituent agree with those of the chart. Figure 6-5 illustrates a chart that could be employed. Better estimates of V_V can be obtained by the use of stereological measurements as described in the sections that follow. Three basic measurement procedures that employ random two-dimensional section planes have been developed and are referred to as areal analysis, lineal analysis, and point counting.

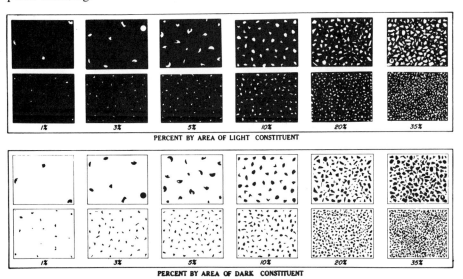

Figure 6-5 Chart for estimating volume fractions developed by Nelson. *(From Nelson, Ref. 17, courtesy of Dr. Riederer-Verlag, GmbH.)*

6-6.1 Areal Analysis

The areal analysis method was introduced by Delesse, a French geologist, in 1848. Delesse showed that the average areal fraction A_A obtained on opaque two-dimensional sections was an estimate of the volume fraction V_V, i.e.,

$$V_V = \frac{\Sigma A_\alpha}{A_T} = A_A \tag{6-1}$$

where ΣA_α is the sum of the areas of the phase of interest α and A_T is the total measurement area. Such measurements have been made either by planimetry or by cutting out the phase of interest on a photograph and dividing the weight of the phase of interest by the original weight of the picture. Naturally, this method is not very satisfactory for very fine structures. Since the method is much slower than the other methods to be described, it is rarely used today.

6-6.2 Lineal Analysis

Although Delesse suggested that V_V could also be determined by lineal ratios, he did not believe that the accuracy of such a technique would be as good as the areal method and, thus, did not follow up the idea and attempt to develop the method. This was accomplished by Rosiwal, a German geologist, in 1898. He demonstrated the equivalence between the lineal fraction L_L and the volume fraction. In lineal analysis, the total length of randomly placed lines within the phase of interest ΣL_α is divided by the total line length L_T to obtain the lineal fraction:

$$L_L = \frac{\Sigma L_\alpha}{L_T} = V_V \tag{6-2}$$

A number of devices have been developed to facilitate the analysis. One of the more popular devices is the Hurlbut counter.

6-6.3 Point Counting

The point-counting method (ASTM Specification E562) for volume fraction estimation is a more recent development and was "independently" proposed by Thomson in 1933, by Glagolev in 1933, and by Chalkley in 1943. The technique has been used with a single test point or with one- or two-dimensional point grids. The test grid can be placed in the eyepiece as a graticule or it can be placed as a plastic overlay on a projection screen or photograph. The magnification should be high enough so that the location of the test points with respect to the structural elements can be clearly discerned. Again, one should always use the lowest possible magnification. Choice of magnification is always a compromise between resolution and field size for best statistical accuracy. As the field size decreases, more fields must be analyzed to obtain a certain degree of statistical accuracy.

The point grid is applied to a field selected at random at the optimum magnification, and the number of points lying in the phase of interest P_α is counted. Points lying on the particle or phase boundary are counted as one-half. Most point-counting grids use crosses rather than points because the latter are often difficult to see. When crosses are employed, the intersection of the two crossed lines is the "point," and the intersection must lie in the phase to be considered a "hit." The arms of the crosses are ignored. Generally, one measures 10 or more fields in this manner and computes the point fraction P_P as follows:

$$P_P = \frac{\Sigma P_\alpha}{P_T} = \frac{\Sigma P_\alpha}{nP_0} \qquad MEAN\ VALUE \qquad (6\text{-}3)$$

where n is the number of fields and P_0 is the number of grid points. Thus, P_T is equal to nP_0, the total number of test points. Alternatively, the value of P_P can be determined for each field, and the measurements for n fields are averaged as an estimate of the volume fraction. Both methods calculate the same value for P_P, but the second procedure produces data ready for further statistical analysis, as described in the next section.

Test grids for eyepiece graticules usually employ low point densities, generally 5, 9, 16, or 25 systematically spaced points. Higher point densities are difficult to count accurately when used in graticules. Graticules have the advantage of sharper structural and grid images, but operator fatigue is greater than with overlays. Grid overlays, which are placed in front of or behind the projection screen, usually employ 16, 25, 49, 64, or 100 points in a systematic pattern. Glagolev used a 289-point grid in the measurement of inclusion content, but grids with more than 100 points are seldom employed. In general, as the volume fraction decreases, the operator should choose a higher point-density grid. The points in constituents with the lowest volume fraction should always be counted in order to minimize effort. The major phase can then be determined by difference. Volume fractions approaching 50 percent are best measured with low-density grids, such as the 25-point grid. This reduces operator fatigue. For very low volume fractions, a high-density grid can be surveyed as rapidly as one with fewer points and provides better precision in the measurement of each field. If the structure is heterogeneous, it is better to make more field measurements with a low-density grid than fewer measurements with a high-point-density grid. Systematic spacing of grid points has been shown to be more effective than random spacing of grid points [31, 32]. The magnification and point density should be chosen so that, in general, no more than one grid point falls on a given particle of interest. If the structure is quite coarse a low-density grid and low magnification should be used to avoid multiple points in the same feature. When this occurs, measurement efficiency and statistical sampling are impaired.

In most work, the volume fraction is expressed as a percentage by multiplying A_A, L_L, or P_P by 100. It has frequently been shown that all three methods yield equivalent test results within limits of statistical accuracy, i.e.,

$$V_V = A_A = L_L = P_P \qquad (6\text{-}4)$$

Figure 6-6 illustrates that the estimation of V_V by the three methods yields approximately the same results. Better equivalence would be obtained by measuring more than one field. In most cases, the sectioning plane must be chosen at random; i.e., the choice of the sectioning plane must not introduce bias into the measurement.

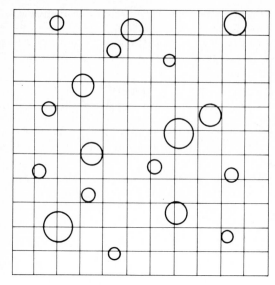

$A_T = 12,100 \text{ mm}^2$
$L_T = 2200 \text{ mm}$
$P_T = 100$

Areal analysis

$$V_{V\alpha} = \frac{\Sigma A_\alpha}{A_T} = \frac{\text{areas of circles}}{\text{frame area}} = \frac{884.75}{12,100} = 0.073$$

Lineal analysis

$$L_{L\alpha} = \frac{\Sigma L_\alpha}{L_T} = \frac{\Sigma \text{ intercept lengths}}{\text{total line length}} = \frac{152.3}{2200} = 0.069$$

Point count

$$P_{P\alpha} = \frac{\Sigma P_\alpha}{P_T} = \frac{\Sigma \text{points in } \alpha}{\text{total points}} = \frac{5 + 2 \left(\frac{1}{2}\right)^+}{100} = 0.06$$

$^+$Tangents to particles counted as $\frac{1}{2}$

Figure 6-6 Example illustrating three methods for estimating V_V using an idealized microstructure of spherical particles intersected by a sectioning plane.

6-6.4 Statistical Analysis

Analysis errors come from a variety of sources. The samples chosen must be representative of the structure. Faulty sample preparation is a major source of error. Operator competence in identifying the structure and performing the test is another source. The sample homogeneity, magnification, and number of measured fields all affect data scatter and reproducibility.

Field-to-field, plane-to-plane, and sample-to-sample microstructural variability is a natural feature of commercial materials. This variability, which is readily measurable, is not a measurement error, but it does influence test results. As the variability increases, the effort required to obtain a reliable statistical estimate of the structural parameters increases. In certain cases, such as inclusion volume fractions in steels with very low inclusion content, the degree of variability can preclude obtainment of a reliable measurement; i.e., the uncertainty of the measurement is as large or larger than the measurement. In such work, the variability itself is an important measurement.

It must be pointed out that all stereological measurements are estimate rather than absolute measurements. If the measurement is repeated several times, the exact same value may not be obtained each time. If the material is relatively uniform and good techniques are employed, the measurement scatter will be quite small.

One cannot approach the estimation of microstructural parameters without an understanding of basic statistical analysis procedures. These techniques are quite simple to perform since the introduction of inexpensive but powerful pocket calculators. The data analysis method described can be used to analyze any type of data, not just V_V estimates.

Let us assume that we have performed a point-counting experiment using 20 applications of a 25-point grid on a sample. The number of hits in the phase of interest P_α are listed in Table 6-2. The total number of grid points P_T is 500 (20×25). Each field measurement is an estimate of $V_{V,\alpha}$. In col. 3 of Table 6-2, we list $V_{V,\alpha}$ in units of percent for each field $P_{P,i}$ calculated as $(P_\alpha/P_0) \times 100$. The mean value of $\overline{P}_{P,\alpha}$ which was calculated using Eq. (6-3), is $(156/500) \times 100$, or 31.2 percent. Note that the individual field measurements vary from 20 to 44 percent and thus have a range of 24 percent, which shows that considerable field-to-field variation exists. The average deviation from the mean is conveniently expressed by calculation of the standard deviation s of the data as follows:

$$s = \left[\frac{\Sigma (X_i - \overline{X})^2}{N - 1} \right]^{1/2} \tag{6-5}$$

where $\overline{X}$ is the mean value of the individual measurements X_i and N is the number of measurements. In this calculation, s is an unbiased estimate of the standard deviation of the population σ from which the sampling data were obtained. When the number of measurements gets quite large, the difference between s and σ becomes negligible. Table 6-2 illustrates the calculation of s. Column 4 lists the value of $(P_{P,i} - \overline{P}_P)^2$ for each field measurement. After each of these 20 values has been calculated, they are summed, yielding 947.2. This value is divided by $N - 1$, i.e., 19, and then the square root is taken to obtain a value of 7.06 for s.

If the test data exhibit a normal distribution about the mean, plus or minus one standard deviation includes 68.26 percent of the test values, plus or minus two standard deviations include 95.46 percent of the values, and plus or minus three standard deviations include 99.73 percent of the test data. These percentages only pertain to a perfect normal distribution.

Although the standard deviation is an absolute measure of data dispersion, it is difficult to compare standard deviations when the mean values differ substantially. Thus, it is useful to normalize the standard deviations by dividing s by the mean and expressing this value as a percentage. This ratio is called the coefficient of variation (CV) and is calculated as follows:

$$\text{CV} = \frac{s}{\overline{X}} \times 100 \tag{6-6}$$

For this example, CV is $(7.06/31.2) \times 100$, or 22.6 percent.

Table 6-2 Example of statistical analysis of point-count data

Field no.	P_α	$P_\alpha/P_0 \times 100$	$(P_{P,i} - \bar{P}_P)^2$
1	5	20	125.44
2	8	32	0.64
3	8	32	0.64
4	8	32	0.64
5	6	24	51.84
6	8	32	0.64
7	5	20	125.44
8	10	40	77.44
9	10	40	77.44
10	8	32	0.64
11	9	36	23.04
12	7	28	10.24
13	9	36	23.04
14	7	28	10.24
15	10	40	77.44
16	8	32	0.64
17	8	32	0.64
18	5	20	125.44
19	11	44	163.84
20	6	24	51.84
	156		947.2

Note: $P_0 = 25$

$\quad\quad P_\alpha/P_0 \times 100 = P_{P,i}$ \quad (in %)

$$\bar{P}_{P,\alpha} = \frac{156}{(20)(25)} \, 100 = 31.2\%$$

$$s(\bar{P}_{P,\alpha}) = \left(\frac{947.2}{19}\right)^{1/2} = 7.0606\%$$

$$CV = \frac{7.0606}{31.2} \, 100 = 22.6\%$$

$$95\% \text{ confidence limit} = \frac{(2.093)\,(7.0606)}{(19)^{1/2}} = 3.39\%$$

$$\% \text{ relative accuracy} = \frac{3.39}{31.2} \, 100 = 10.9\%$$

It is also useful to calculate the 95 percent confidence limit and the percent relative accuracy. The 95 percent confidence limit (CL) is calculated using the following relationship:

$$95\% \text{ CL} = \frac{ts}{(N-1)^{1/2}} \tag{6-7}$$

where the value of t varies with the number of measurements. Table 6-3 lists t values for computing the 95 percent confidence limits. Some users standardize on

Table 6-3 t values for calculating confidence limits

n'	Confidence level 95%	n'	Confidence level 95%
1	12.706	18	2.101
2	4.303	19	2.093
3	3.182	20	2.086
4	2.776	21	2.080
5	2.571	22	2.074
6	2.447	23	2.069
7	2.365	24	2.064
8	2.306	25	2.060
9	2.262	26	2.056
10	2.228	27	2.052
11	2.201	28	2.048
12	2.179	29	2.045
13	2.160	30	2.042
14	2.145	40	2.021
15	2.131	60	2.000
16	2.120	120	1.980
17	2.110	∞	1.960

The degrees of freedom n' is $N-1$.

a single value of t for calculating the 95 percent confidence limit, using either 1.96 or 2 irrespective of the value of N. In this example, the 95 percent confidence limit is $(2.093 \times 7.06)/(19)^{1/2}$, or 3.4 percent. Thus we can state that the volume fraction of the measured phase is 31.2 ± 3.4 percent with a 95 percent confidence. This means that if we were to remeasure the sample repeatedly, 95 times out of a 100 times the mean would be between 27.8 and 34.6 percent.

The percent relative accuracy (% RA) is determined by dividing the 95 percent confidence limit by the mean and expressing it as a percentage, i.e.,

$$\% \ \mathrm{RA} = \frac{95\% \ \mathrm{CL}}{\overline{X}} \times 100 \tag{6-8}$$

In our example, the percent relative accuracy is $(3.4/31.2) \times 100$, or 10.9 percent. Some refer to this determination as the relative confidence limit.

For most measurements, a 10 percent relative accuracy is quite satisfactory. If we had obtained a higher value, or if we desired a lower percent relative accuracy than 10.9 percent, these data could be used to estimate how many fields must be measured. De Hoff [6] has proposed a simple formula for determining how many fields N must be measured to obtain a specific desired degree of relative accuracy at the 95 percent confidence limit:

$$N = \left(\frac{200}{\% \ \mathrm{RA}} \times \frac{s}{\overline{P}_P} \right)^2 \tag{6-9}$$

For the example just presented, if we desired a 5 percent relative accuracy rather than the 10.9 percent value obtained, we would find from this equation that 82 fields must be measured.

6-6.5 Comparison of Methods

A number of studies have evaluated the accuracy and efficiency of areal, lineal, and point-counting methods for estimating A_A. Hilliard and Cahn performed a mathematical comparison of the following methods [32]:

- Areal analysis (planimeter)
- Lineal analysis
- One-dimensional random point count
- One-dimensional systematic point count
- Two-dimensional random point count
- Two-dimensional systematic point count

They concluded that the two-dimensional systematic point count produces the lowest data variance for a given number of measurements and is superior to lineal or areal analysis as long as an excessive point density P_0 is not used; i.e., the average number of points falling in any single particle should not greatly exceed 1. For such conditions, the relative standard deviation $s/\bar{P}_P$ is approximately $1/(\Sigma P_\alpha)^{1/2}$. They concluded that the optimum number of grid points is $3/V_V$, which represents a range of 6 to 300 points for volume fractions from 50 to 1 percent, respectively.

Although these conclusions were developed mathematically, Weibel has provided experimental results using three areal methods, lineal analysis, and two point-counting procedures [5]. An ideal structure with a 20 percent volume fraction was measured independently by seven operators using the same number of measurements. Areal analysis produced the lowest measurement error but required considerable time. Poorest accuracy was produced by lineal analysis. A systematic point count gave an accuracy close to that of the areal analysis but in much less time. It should be mentioned that the synthetic structure measured was quite coarse, a condition favorable for areal analysis.

The study by Abrams is quite informative regarding the reproducibility of point counting [33]. Three microstructures were point-counted using both 25- and 100-point grids by 33 different operators. The results produced by 2 operators were consistently very low, while the results obtained from 4 operators were consistently very high. The largest source of variation was among operators. For the same number of field measurements, the 100-point grid produced better accuracy but required more measurement time.

Mathieu et al. evaluated three sets of synthetic structures, each set consisting of 10 micrographs, using point-counting grids with 4, 25, 64, 100, 196, and 400 test points and a biological sample using grids with 4, 9, 16, 25, 64, 100, 361, and 900 test points [34]. The sets of synthetic microstructures produced a wide range of variability; i.e., the coefficient of variation ranged from 0.1 to 0.66. The synthetic structures were also measured using the semiautomatic MOP tracing device and using automatic image analysis with the Quantimet 720. The efficiency of each method, i.e., the precision obtained per unit measuring time, was determined. For the synthetic structures, the Quantimet and the 100-point grid were the most efficient methods. The tracing device was the slowest procedure. The biological sample could not be analyzed by image analysis because of detection problems.

The following experiment illustrates some of the virtues of specific point-counting grids. Three samples containing relatively homogeneous distributions of ferrite and pearlite in amounts of approximately 3, 30, and 45% (minor phase counted in each case) were point-counted using 9-, 25-, 64-, and 100-point grids. The three counting conditions used were (1) constant number of fields, (2) constant total number of grid points, and (3) constant measuring time. The results are presented in Table 6-4. In each case, the data were tabulated and translated

Table 6-4 Results of point-counting experiment

	Grid density, P_0			
	9	25	64	100
Constant no. of fields (20)				
Sample A				
$\bar{P}_P \pm 95\%$ CL,† %	4.4 ± 2.5	2.4 ± 1.25	2.9 ± 0.7	3.2 ± 0.7
Rel. accuracy, %	57.7	52	23.1	22.9
Time, min	3	7	9	11
Sample B				
$\bar{P}_P \pm 95\%$ CL	25 ± 5.8	31.2 ± 3.2	29.8 ± 2.4	24.8 ± 1.5
Rel. accuracy, %	23	10.4	8.1	6
Time, min	4	7	11	14
Sample C				
$\bar{P}_P \pm 95\%$ CL	47.5 ± 5.3	46.6 ± 4.6	43.5 ± 3	46.3 ± 1.8
Rel. accuracy, %	11.2	9.8	6.9	3.9
Time, min	5	11	17	23
P_T	180	500	1280	2000
Constant total no. of grid points ($P_T = 2000$)				
Sample A				
$\bar{P}_P \pm 95\%$ CL, %	3.7 ± 0.8	3.0 ± 0.7	2.6 ± 0.5	3.2 ± 0.7
Rel. accuracy, %	21.5	24.6	20	22.9
Time, min	34	25	14	11
Sample B				
$\bar{P}_P \pm 95\%$ CL, %	24.7 ± 1.9	28.3 ± 1.6	29.4 ± 1.9	24.8 ± 1.5
Rel. accuracy, %	7.7	5.6	6.5	6
Time, min	41	28	19	14
Sample C				
$\bar{P}_P \pm 95\%$ CL, %	45 ± 2.1	45 ± 2.1	43 ± 2.2	46.3 ± 1.8
Rel. accuracy, %	4.7	4.6	5	3.9
Time, min	52	34	30	23
N	222	80	31	20

Table 6-4 *(continued)*

	Grid density, P_0			
	9	25	64	100
	Constant measurement time			
Sample A				
$P_P \pm 95\%$ CL, %	4.8 ± 1.6	3.1 ± 1.1	3.0 ± 0.6	3.2 ± 0.7
Rel. accuracy, %	32.5	36.4	18.5	22.9
Time, min	11	11	11	11
P_T/N	576/64	875/35	1536/24	2000/20
Sample B				
$P_P \pm 95\%$ CL, %	26.3 ± 2.9	29.9 ± 2.0	29.4 ± 2.3	24.8 ± 1.5
Rel. accuracy, %	10.9	6.8	7.7	6
Time, min	14	14	14	14
P_T/N	675/75	1000/40	1472/23	2000/20
Sample C				
$P_P \pm 95\%$ CL, %	46 ± 3.2	46.6 ± 2.5	43.4 ± 2.6	46.3 ± 1.8
Rel. accuracy, %	7	5.4	6	3.9
Time, min	23	23	23	23
P_T/N	873/97	1350/54	1536/24	2000/20

Note: P_T is the total number of grid points; N is the number of fields.
†Confidence limit.

into percent P_P estimates per field (as in Table 6-2) and the mean, standard deviation, 95% confidence limit, and percent relative accuracy were calculated. The total measurement time, including setup and calculations, was determined for each case. The 100-point grid has an advantage in the calculations because the number of P_α hits is the same as the percent P_P; thus, one step in the calculations is avoided.

For the case of a constant number of fields (20), the measurement time increased as the volume fraction increased and as the grid point density increased. As might be anticipated, the percent relative accuracy increased as P_0 increased because P_T increased. For the case of a constant total number of test points ($P_T = 2000$), the relative accuracies were approximately equal. Again, as the volume fraction increased, the relative accuracy increased. However, as the grid point density P_0 decreased, the total measurement time increased because more time was spent moving the stage, refocusing, tabulating the data, and calculating. For a constant measuring time, the higher-point-density grids produced the best accuracy. As the volume fraction increased, the accuracies exhibited less difference because the low-density grids were more efficient for high V_V than for low V_V. The high-density grids are clearly superior for low volume fractions. Counting effort is least for the low-density grids, which becomes more apparent at high V_V. The 25-point grid appears to be a good compromise for use at medium to high volume fractions. If these samples had been less homogeneous, the lower-point-density grids would have demonstrated greater worth.

6-6.6 Summary

Point counting with a systematic two-dimensional grid is the optimum method for estimating the volume fraction of constituents in a microstructure. The statistical analysis procedure is relatively straightforward and easily performed with an inexpensive hand calculator. For low volume fractions, a high-point-density grid, e.g., the 100-point grid, is preferred, while for high volume fractions, a low-point-density grid, such as the 25-point grid, is useful. For heterogeneous structures, it is better to spend less time measuring each field and measure more fields. Thus, the 25-point grid would be preferred in these instances. One should always count the phase with the lowest volume fraction. It is inefficient to point-count a phase with a volume fraction greater than 50 percent. The major phase can always be estimated by difference after point counting the minor phase or phases. Sample preparation must be carefully controlled, with low surface relief, sharp phase delineation, and good contrast. Choice of magnification is always a compromise between surface area and resolution. One should always use the lowest possible magnification at which the location of the test points with respect to the structure can be unambiguously discerned. Field selection should always be done without looking at the structure in order to prevent operator bias. The fields should be spaced systematically over the sample surface. Naturally, the sample must be representative of the specimen.

6-7 GRAIN SIZE

Determination of the grain size of polycrystalline materials is probably the single most important metallographic measurement because of the influence of grain size on properties and behavior. The problem of determining the size of the three-dimensional grains on the basis of planar measurements has intrigued and perplexed researchers for decades. The determination of the spatial size of all of the grains within a given volume is an exceedingly difficult task. Instead, one generally determines a single value and uses it to represent the average planar grain size. This number says nothing about the range of grain sizes present, but it is a useful value.

6-7.1 Grain Shape

Many studies have been conducted to evaluate the shape of grains. Basically, the grains must exhibit a shape that is space filling, and the interfaces between grains must conform to laws governing surface tension. In 1894, Lord Kelvin showed that the optimum space-filling shape with a minimum of surface area is the tetrakaidecahedron (cuboctahedron or truncated octahedron). This figure is a polyhedron with 14 faces. It fulfills the surface tension requirements described by Plateau in 1873 that no more than three grains can meet at an edge and no more than four edges can meet at a corner. However, it does not meet the requirement of 120° dihedral angles between grain boundaries where three adjacent grains meet an edge. This requirement can be satisfied by introducing a slight double curvature to the faces, which changes the surface area about 4 percent. Another shape of interest is the pentagonal dodecahedron with its 12 five-sided faces. Although not a space-filling shape, its features agree well with measurements of actual grains. In practice, however, the grains in a polycrystalline solid exhibit a variety of sizes, shapes, and number of faces. This variability has been demonstrated by numerous studies, e.g., the work of Desch [35], who studied the shapes of β-brass grains after intergranular disintegration in mercury, or the study of Williams and Smith [36], who used stereoscopic microradiography.

In the study by Williams and Smith, the average number of edges per face was 5.02 (further study changed this value to 5.06) and the average number of faces per grain was 12.48 [36]. These average grain characteristics compare closely with the pentagonal dodecahedron. Their results showed that larger grains have a greater number of faces than small grains.

6-7.2 Grain Size Measurement

The dimensions of grains observed on a cross section through the structure is used to determine the planar grain size. Several different measurements can be used to express the grain size:

- Average diameter
- Average area
- Number of grains per unit area
- Average intercept length
- Number of grains per unit volume
- Average diameter based on average grain volume

To add to the confusion, there are a number of ways that grain boundaries can be revealed and there are different types of grains. In quality control studies, steel samples can be processed by a variety of procedures that are designed to decorate the austenite grain boundaries [37, 38]. These methods include the following:

- McQuaid-Ehn carburizing method
- Interrupted-cooling, isothermal transformation, or gradient-quenching method
- Oxidation method
- Copper diffusion method
- Thermal-etching method

These methods are described in specifications covering grain size measurement, such as ASTM Specification E112.

In a steel component that has already been heat-treated, these methods alter the microstructure and, thus cannot be applied. For these samples, etching techniques must be used to preferentially delineate the prior-austenite grain boundaries. Etchants for this purpose are described in Chap. 3. If the steel is predominantly martensitic with a very high hardness, as in the case of most heat-treated tool steels, the sample can be fractured and rated using the Shepherd fracture grain size method.

In low-carbon steels, such as sheet metal, the ferrite grain size is measured because the parent austenite grains cannot be revealed. The ferrite grain size is smaller than the parent austenite grains. Only in rare cases can both the ferrite and austenite grains be revealed in such steels. The morphology of ferrite grains can vary widely, which will influence the validity of the grain size measurement.

The rating of grain size in austenitic material is difficult when annealing twins are present. Annealing twins are ignored in such measurements of grain size even though twin boundaries influence properties and behavior in the same manner as grain boundaries. In structure-property correlations on such material, it has been shown that the total interfacial area correlates better with properties than the grain-boundary interfacial area alone.

In measuring grain size, several procedures can be employed:

- Comparison with standard charts
- Fracture grain size
- Planimetric (Jeffries) method
- Intercept (Heyn) method
- Snyder-Graff intercept method
- Grain size distribution methods

General reviews on grain size measurement are found in Refs. 39 to 42.

Delineation of grain boundaries Methods to reveal austenite grain structures in steels can employ direct observation, e.g., hot-stage microscopy or electron-emission microscopy. Most methods, however, use indirect methods such as those outlined previously in this chapter. Each of these methods has limited applicability and inherent advantages and disadvantages.

The thermal-etching method of heating a polished sample to the desired temperature in a vacuum is similar to hot-stage microscopy except that the sample is observed after it is cooled to room temperature. Thermal grooving occurs at the grain boundaries because of surface tension effects. A vacuum furnace can be used, or the polished sample can be encapsulated in an evacuated glass or quartz tube and heated in an ordinary furnace. Poor grain-boundary contrast is obtained at temperatures just above the upper critical temperature of the steel. Dark-field illumination is useful in the examination of such samples. Thermal etching is applicable to nearly any steel sample and is sometimes referred to as "the method of last resort."

Another variant of thermal etching involves etching of austenite grain boundaries either in a molten salt bath or in molten glass. Salt baths consisting of equal parts NaCl, $BaCl_2$ and $CaCl_2$ have been used. After about 10 min at heat in the bath, the sample is removed and oil-quenched. The adhering salt is removed, and the sample is repolished and etched in picral. This method is widely applicable but tends to produce a finer grain size at the surface than in the interior [37], a common problem with all these surface techniques.

In many steels, it is possible to control the austenite transformation so that the austenite grain boundaries are preferentially decorated with ferrite, cementite, fine pearlite, or bainite and the grain interior is transformed to a different structure. The sample is sectioned, polished, and etched to produce maximum contrast between the grain-boundary phase and the grain interior. When successfully employed, this method is very reliable and objective for grain size measurement. However, considerable experimentation may be required to obtain good results. Fine-grained steels are difficult to decorate in this manner, but the method works extremely well for coarse-grained steels.

Eutectoid carbon steels about 1 in thick can be austenitized and brine-quenched. Between the outer martensitic case and the pearlitic core there is often a region where the pearlite outlines the grain boundaries. Again, coarse-grained steels are more readily evaluated by this method than fine-grained steels. If the steel's hardenability is too great for this method, a gradient quench can be tried. A sample roughly 2 to 3 in long is austenitized, and one end of the sample is immersed in the brine, producing a range of cooling rates. A region can sometimes be found where pearlite outlines the grain boundaries. A Jominy bar often exhibits this effect in the region of the drop-off in hardness.

Pearlite can also be preferentially formed in eutectoid steels in small amounts at the austenite grain boundaries during a short isothermal hold in the region where pearlite forms. Consultation of TTT (time-temperature transformation) diagrams can help remove some of the guesswork associated with this method.

Isothermal transformation can also be applied to decorate grain boundaries with ferrite in hypoeutectoid steels. This method works best with steels with 0.3 to 0.6% carbon. With lower carbon contents, equiaxed ferrite forms. Fine-grained steels, even with optimum carbon content, generally cannot be successfully treated in this way. The gradient-quench method is also useful in producing ferrite grain-boundary networks. Isothermal transformation methods work well with higher-alloy steels.

The oxidation method has been used for many years to delineate austenite grain boundaries. This technique works well with nearly any steel but is limited to austenitization temperatures below about 1900°F (1038°C). Above this temperature, the bulk diffusion rate is too high to preferentially oxidize the grain boundaries, but below 1900°F, grain-boundary diffusion predominates, which permits selective oxidation. A finely ground but unpolished specimen is placed in an electrically heated furnace face up and heated to the desired temperature with free access to air. After a suitable holding time, the sample is quenched to form martensite. The oxide layer is carefully removed, and the sample is polished and etched. The grain boundaries are revealed either by oxide accumulation or by grain-boundary decarburization networks. Excessive grinding will remove the affected layer.

High temperatures can cause excessive scaling with this method. In such cases, the sample is heated in a vacuum or under an inert atmosphere for most of the cycle and air is admitted for a short time (30 s to 15 min have been employed) before quenching. Schreiber and Mennenöh have evaluated the method using seven types of steels[43]. They recommend a 1 h holding time because shorter times produced finer grain sizes. They used a 1-min etch in 15% alcoholic HCl. This method works well for fine-grain-size steels with which many other methods fail.

The most commonly used procedure for decorating austenite grain boundaries is the carburization method developed by McQuaid and Ehn. While originally designed for testing of carburizing steels, it has been subsequently applied to test most carbon and alloy steels. A small sample is pack-carburized for 8 h at 1700°F (925°C), after which it is slowly cooled to room temperature. The sample is cut in half, polished, and etched (generally with nital or picral, but alkaline sodium picrate is far better). At the carburized surface, excess cementite precipitates at the austenite grain boundaries (see Fig. 6-7).

2% Nital

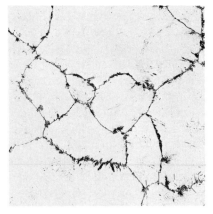

Alkaline Sodium Picrate
–boiling

Alkaline Sodium Picrate
–electrolytic (1A/ cm ^{2}-1 min)

Figure 6-7 Examples of the use of various popular etchants for revealing grain-boundary cementite networks in McQuaid-Ehn carburized test samples (120×).

Steelmakers employ the McQuaid-Ehn test to determine if a steel is "inherently" fine-grained; i.e., it has a grain size number of 5 or greater. Although this technique is a good procedure for carburizing steels that are subjected to similar carburizing cycles, the results can be misleading for steels austenitized at lower temperatures. Steels that exhibit fine-grained structures at normal austenitizing temperatures, e.g., 1500 to 1600°F (816 to 871°C), might be defined as coarse-grained and, thus, unsalable, after the McQuaid-Ehn test. If the test shows that a particular steel is coarse-grained, the steel should be evaluated by the oxidation test at the prescribed austenitization temperature for the grade, assuming that the austenitization temperature is below 1700°F (927°C).

The fracture grain size test, which is discussed later in this chapter, is only suitable for high-hardness steels with a predominantly martensitic structure. This method is widely employed in tests of tool steels. As a test method, it is quite accurate, simple to use, and extremely fast.

Standard chart methods The 1930 revision of ASTM Specification E2 contained the first standard chart for rating grain size. The chart was intended for rating annealed copper and copper alloys containing annealing twins and consisted of 10 micrographs at 75X prepared with a grain contrast etch. Grain sizes were expressed as the average grain diameter in millimeters determined by the Jeffries method. At the time the chart was developed, the ASTM method for defining grain size was not in existence. This chart was criticized on the basis of the picture grading. The grain size portion of ASTM E2 was deleted in 1941. This information was reevaluated and issued as ASTM Specification E79 in 1949 with a chart containing 12 micrographs. ASTM E79 was discontinued in 1963, when all of the grain size methods were incorporated into the current specification, ASTM E112. The current chart has 14 graded micrographs.

In 1932 ASTM established a committee to prepare a grain size chart for rating austenite grain size in steels using the McQuaid-Ehn test. ASTM Specification E19, adopted in 1933, contained a single chart that consisted of eight graded pictures of both the hypereutectoid and hypoeutectoid subsurface zones. Although the chart listed ranges for the number of grains per square inch at 100X for each grain size number, tabular data were not included until the 1938 revision. The ASTM E19 McQuaid-Ehn chart was widely used but severely criticized because of inaccuracies. Most of the grain size pictures depicted finer grain sizes than the ratings given. Measurement methods were not included in ASTM E19. These charts were discontinued in 1961, when ASTM E112 was adopted. They were replaced by a single chart, Plate IV of ASTM E112, illustrating cementite grain-boundary networks in steels for grain sizes 1 to 8.

ASTM established a committee in 1947 to prepare a chart for rating ferrite grain size in steels. ASTM E89 was subsequently introduced in 1949 and contained a chart depicting ferrite grains with sizes from 1 to 8. ASTM E89 introduced formal procedures for measuring the grain size by the Heyn intercept method and also included the Jeffries method. This chart was reasonably accurate. Nital etching had been employed, and numerous poorly etched and unetched grain boundaries were present, a common problem with nital etching of ferrite grains.

ASTM E89 was discontinued in 1961, when ASTM E112 was adopted. A ferrite grain size chart was not included in ASTM E112; instead, a stylized chart depicting grain-boundary etching in a nontwinned alloy was adopted. This chart has wide applicability and is quite accurate.

In 1947, ASTM began a study of grain size rating methods for nonferrous metals other than copper, which culminated in the adoption of ASTM E91 in 1951. The standard incorporated both the Jeffries and Heyn measurement methods and introduced the macro-grain-size scale. Calculation methods for handling nonequiaxed grains were also introduced. Two charts, one for non-twinned grains and one for twinned grains, were provided for comparison ratings. ASTM E91 was also discontinued when ASTM E112 was adopted. ASTM E91 also introduced the basic equation used to establish the ASTM grain size scale:

$$n = 2^{G-1} \tag{6-10}$$

where n is the number of grains per square inch at 100X and G is the ASTM (Timken) grain size number. This relationship can also be expressed as follows:

$$G = \frac{\log n}{\log 2} + 1 \tag{6-11}$$

The adoption of ASTM E112 pulled together all these methods for rating grain size into a single comprehensive standard still in force today after several revisions. The core of ASTM E112 is contained in Table 2 of ASTM E112, which lists the relationships among the ASTM grain size number, the number of grains per square inch at 100X, the number of grains per square millimeter at 1X, the average grain diameter determined by the Jeffries method, and the average intercept length calculated using the Heyn method (see Table 6-5).

Many other countries have also prepared standard methods for rating grain size, and many have adopted the ASTM charts or prepared similar series. Since most of these countries use the metric system, they have established their grain size scales based on the number of grains per square millimeter at 1X rather than on the number per square inch at 100X. For example, the Swedish, Italian, Russian, French, and ISO standards define the grain size number G_m according to the following equation:

$$m = 8(2^{G_m}) \tag{6-12}$$

where m is the number of grains per square millimeter at 1X. This can also be expressed as follows:

$$G_m = \frac{\log m}{\log 2} - 3 \tag{6-13}$$

Grain size numbers calculated with the metric procedure are about 4.5 percent higher than those calculated by the ASTM method, i.e.,

$$G = G_m - 0.045 \tag{6-14}$$

The German standard also uses the metric system, but the calculation yields numbers equivalent to the ASTM system. In this method, the picture serial

Table 6-5 Grain-size data and relationships from ASTM E112

ASTM micro-grain-size number G	"Diameter" of average grain section[†]		Average intercept distance‡ L_3, mm	Intercept count per mm, N_L	Area of average grain section, A, mm²	Calculated no. of grains per mm³, N_V§	Average	
	Nominal d_n, mm	Feret's d_f, mm					Grains per mm² at 1X¶, N_A	Grains per in² at 100X, N_A
00††	0.51	0.570	0.453	2.210	0.258	6.11	3.88	0.250
0	0.36	0.403	0.320	3.125	0.129	17.3	7.75	0.500
0.5	0.30	0.339	0.269	3.716	0.0912	29.0	11.0	0.707
1.0	0.25	0.285	0.226	4.42	0.0645	48.8	15.50	1.000
1.5	0.21	0.240	0.190	5.26	0.0456	82	21.9	1.414
1.7	0.200	0.226	0.177	5.64	0.0400	100	25.0	1.613
2.0	0.18	0.202	0.160	6.25	0.0323	138	31.0	2.000
2.5	0.15	0.170	0.135	7.43	0.0228	232	43.8	2.828
3.0	0.125	0.143	0.113	8.84	0.0161	391	62.0	4.000
3.2	0.120	0.135	0.106	9.41	0.0144	463	69.4	4.480
3.5	0.105	0.120	0.095	10.51	0.0114	657	87.7	5.657
3.7	0.100	0.113	0.089	11.29	0.0100	800	100	6.452
	μm	μm	μm	μm	mm² × 10⁻³			
4.0	90	101	80.0	12.5	8.07	1105	124	8.000
4.5	75	85	67.3	14.9	5.70	1859	175	11.31
4.7	70	79	62.0	16.1	4.90	2331	204	13.17
5.0	65	71	56.6	17.7	4.03	3126	248	16.00
5.2	60	68	53.2	18.8	3.60	3708	278	17.92
5.5	55	60	47.6	21.0	2.85	5258	351	22.63
5.7	50	56	44.3	22.6	2.50	6400	400	25.81
6.0	45	50	40.0	25.0	2.02	8842	496	32.00
6.3	40	45	35.4	28.2	1.60	12 500	625	40.32
6.5	38	42	33.6	29.7	1.43	14 871	701	45.25
6.7	35	39	31.0	32.2	1.23	18 659	816	52.67
7.0	32	36	28.3	35.4	1.008	25 010	992	64.00

	μm	μm	μm	μm	mm² × 10⁻⁶	× 10⁶	× 10³	
7.2	30	34	26.6	37.6	0.900	29 630	1111	71.68
7.5	27	30	23.8	42.0	0.713	41 061	1403	90.51
7.7	25	28	22.2	45.1	0.625	51 200	1600	103.23
8.0	22	25	20.0	50.0	504	0.0707	1.98	128.0
8.3	20	23	17.7	56.4	400	0.1000	2.50	161.3
8.5	19	21	16.8	59.5	356	0.1190	2.81	181.0
9.0	16	18	14.1	70.7	252	0.200	3.97	256.0
9.2	15	17	13.3	75.2	225	0.237	4.44	286.7
9.5	13	15	11.9	84.1	178	0.336	5.61	362.0
10.0	11	13	10.0	100	126	0.566	7.94	512.0
10.3	10	11.3	8.86	113	100	0.800	10.00	645.2
10.5	9.4	10.6	8.41	119	89.1	0.952	11.22	724.1
10.6	9.0	10.2	7.98	125	81.0	1.097	12.35	796.5
11.0	8	8.9	7.07	141	63.0	1.600	15.87	1024
11.4	7.0	7.9	6.20	161	49.0	2.332	20.41	1317
11.5	6.7	7.5	5.95	168	44.6	2.692	22.45	1448
11.8	6.0	6.8	5.32	188	36.0	3.704	27.78	1792
12.0	5.6	6.3	5.00	200	31.5	4.527	31.7	2048
12.3	5.0	5.6	4.43	226	25.0	6.40	40.0	2581
12.5	4.7	5.3	4.20	238	22.3	7.61	44.9	2896
13.0	4.0	4.5	3.54	283	15.8	12.80	63.5	4096
13.5	3.3	3.7	2.97	336	11.1	21.54	89.8	5793
13.8	3.0	3.4	2.66	376	9.0	29.6	111.1	7168
14.0	2.8	3.2	2.50	400	7.88	36.2	127	8192
14.3	2.5	2.8	2.22	451	6.25	51.2	160	10323

†Feret's diameter = height between tangents; $d_f = \bar{A}/\bar{L}_3$. Values of d_n and d_f rounded to digits shown.

‡Value of Heyn intercept or mean free path.

§Computation of N_V based on grains averaging to spherical shape for which $N_V = 0.5659 (N_L)^3$.

¶To obtain grains per mm² at 100X, multiply by 10^{-4}.

††The use of "00" is recommended instead of "minus 1" to avoid confusion.

number K is calculated based on the average number of grains Z per square centimeter at 100X by the following formula:

$$K = 3.7 + 3.33 \log Z \tag{6-15}$$

For example, for K of 5, there are 2.5 grains per square centimeter at 100X, which translates to 16 grains per square inch at 100X, or ASTM 5. The Japanese specifications also use the metric system, but the equation used produces grain size numbers equal to ASTM numbers. The formula used is as follows:

$$m = 2^{G+3} \tag{6-16}$$

where m is the number of grains per square millimeter at 1X.

Of the standard charts prepared by other countries, two should be mentioned. The German chart SEP 1510, which is used for ferritic microstructures that are equiaxed or elongated by cold work, illustrates nontwinned grains that are equiaxed or elongated with axial ratios of $2:1$ and $4:1$. The French NF A04-102 chart for rating the grain size of carburized steels is particularly useful because it depicts the case structure after etching with alkaline sodium picrate, which preferentially darkens the cementite grain-boundary network.

To estimate the grain size of a given specimen, the sample must be carefully polished and then etched in a manner consistent with the chart employed; i.e., if a sample is given a grain contrast etch, the chart used should depict similarly etched samples. Each sample should be rated at several randomly chosen locations, and the average should be computed and rounded to the nearest whole number. The operator should not view the image when selecting the fields, and no attempt should be made to pick out "typical" areas for rating. Unbiased field selection always produces the best results. If the grain structure is not uniform, the number of fields rated should be increased.

Estimates are made by viewing the microstructure through the eyepieces or on a projection screen interspersed with views of the chart. First impressions of the most typical chart picture are usually best. Alternatively, some of the charts may be available as eyepiece reticles, which makes it possible to compare the structure and standard more efficiently. Plate I of ASTM E112 can be obtained as transparencies. These can be held next to the projected image or superimposed over it, thus permitting very good grain size estimates.

Although it is usually best to view the sample at the same magnification as the standard, other magnifications can be used. If the magnification M is greater than the chart magnification M_b, the true grain size number will be greater by a factor Q than the apparent grain size number; the opposite result is obtained if M is less than M_b. For example, suppose that a magnification of 200X is used with an ASTM chart designed for 100X and the apparent grain size number for the sample is ASTM 8.† To calculate Q, the following formula is employed:

$$Q = 6.64 \log \frac{M}{M_b} \tag{6-17}$$

---

† Grain size estimates are usually rounded to the nearest one-half unit.

In this example, M is 200 and M_b is 100; thus Q is 2. Therefore, the ASTM grain size is $8 + 2$, or 10. Using higher magnifications than M_b can be very useful for rating fine-grained samples and can also be used to obtain grain size ratings outside the range of the chart pictures.

Grain size ratings by the comparison method are generally accurate within one ASTM grain size number if the grain structure is uniform and equiaxed. When a sectioning plane cuts through a single-phase grain structure, a variety of grain diameters or areas are observed, even in a sample with a highly uniform grain size, because the sectioning plane can cut through the grains anywhere between the center and the corners. Thus, a range of grain sizes will always be observed.

In some laboratories, the comparison method is used to describe the distribution of grain sizes in a specimen. For example, the operator might describe the grain size of a given sample as 60 percent 7 to 8 and 40 percent 4 to 5. The accuracy of such an estimate is dubious. In many cases, this procedure is used even though the grain structure does not exhibit a true duplex grain structure. In the case of a uniform grain structure, the sectioning plane effect will produce an apparent spread of grain areas that will cover three or four grain size numbers. Apparent grain size distribution ratings of this type cannot be converted by weighting procedures to produce a meaningful ASTM grain size number [39]. True duplex grain size distributions should be evaluated by methods described later in this chapter.

Jeffries planimetric method The planimetric method developed by Jeffries has been used for many years to provide a measure of the number of grains per unit area on the sectioning plane which can be directly related to the ASTM grain size number scale. In recent years, the intercept method has replaced the Jeffries method as the preferred method for measuring grain size because it is simpler to use.

The Jeffries method is generally performed by drawing a circle or rectangle, typically 79.8 mm in diameter (5000 mm^2), on a photomicrograph or on a transparency for a projection screen. The magnification is adjusted to provide at least 50 grains within the measurement area. A count is made of the number of grains completely within the area n_1 and the number of grains intersecting the perimeter of the test area n_2. The total of $n_1 + n_2/2$ is multiplied by the Jeffries factor f for the magnification employed to obtain an estimate of the number of grains per square millimeter at 1X, i.e.:

$$N_A = f\left(n_1 + \frac{n_2}{2}\right) \tag{6-18}$$

where N_A is the number of grains per square millimeter at 1X. The value of f for any magnification M can be found by use of the following equation:

$$f = \frac{M^2}{5000} \tag{6-19}$$

The average grain area $\bar{A}$ is obtained using the following equation:

$$\bar{A} \text{ (mm}^2) = \frac{1}{N_A} \quad \text{or} \quad \bar{A} \text{ (}\mu\text{m}^2) = \frac{10^6}{N_A} \tag{6-20}$$

The mean grain diameter $\bar{d}$ is obtained as follows:

$$\bar{d} \ (\text{mm}) = (\bar{A})^{1/2} = \frac{1}{(N_A)^{1/2}} \tag{6-21}$$

The ASTM grain size number G can be calculated from N_A (no. of grains per square millimeter) using the following relationship:

$$G = \frac{\log N_A}{[\log 2]} - 2.95$$

or, $$G = [3.322 \log N_A] - 2.95 \tag{6-22}$$

Values for $\bar{d}, \bar{A}$, and N_A as a function of G are listed in cols. 2, 6, and 8 of Table 6-5. Figure 6-8 provides an example of the Jeffries procedure. In performing the grain count, it is best to mark off the grains as they are counted in order to obtain an accurate count. Several randomly chosen areas should be selected and measured, and the average calculated. In most work, the grain size number is rounded to the nearest one-half unit.

Triple-point count method Euler's Law, as described by Smith [44], can also be used to determine grain size, although the method is used infrequently. Grain-boundary triple points P within a known area are counted. If a quadruple point, i.e., a 4-ray grain junction, is observed, it is counted as two units. The number of grains per unit area, N_A, is given by the following relationship:

$$N_A = \frac{P/2 + 1}{A_T} \tag{6-23}$$

where A_T is the total measurement area at 1X. The ASTM grain size can be estimated by the triple-point method, as shown in Figure 6-9.

If either the Jeffries or the triple-point count method are used to estimate the number of grains per square inch at 100X rather than the number per square millimeter at 1X, the ASTM grain size number can be calculated from the following:

$$G = \frac{\log N_A}{0.301} + 1 \tag{6-24}$$

where N_A is the number of grains per square inch at 100X. Again, the value of G is generally rounded to the nearest one-half unit. If N_A has been determined in the traditional manner (square millimeters at 1X), Eq. (6-22) is used to calculate G.

If the triple-point count technique is used at a magnification M other than 100X to determine the number of grains per square inch at the magnification of the micrograph [substitute the area of the test grid itself for the test grid area computed to 1X, A_T, in Eq. (6-23)], this value can be converted to the number per square inch at 100X by the following relationship:

$$N_{A(100X, \text{in}^2)} = N_{A(M, \text{in}^2)} \times \left(\frac{M}{100}\right)^2 \tag{6-25}$$

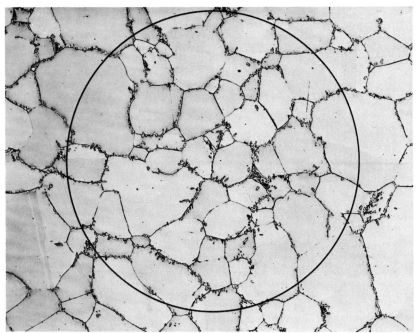

The above circle has a diameter of 79.8 mm for an area of 5000 mm². The micrograph, at 100X, is an austenitic manganese steel that was solution annealed at 1900° F (1038°C) and aged at 1150° F (621°C) to decorate the grain boundaries with fine pearlite. A count is made to determine the number of grains completely within the circle (44) and the number intersecting the circle (25). The Jeffries multiplier for 100X is 2. The number of grains per mm² at 1X is:

$$\text{No. of grains/mm}^2 = (2)(44 + 25/2) = 113$$

The ASTM grain size G, is:

$$G = [3.322 \log(113)] - 2.95 = 3.87 \text{ (round to 3.9 or 4)}$$

Figure 6-8 Example of grain size measurement by the planimetric (Jeffries) method (reduced 25 percent in reproduction).

The Jeffries method can also be modified to produce any desired N_A units. The count total, $n_1 + n_2/2$, is divided by the test grid area computed at the photograph magnification and $N_{A\,(M,\text{in}^2)}$ is obtained, which can be converted to $N_{A(100\text{X},\text{in}^2)}$ using Eq. 6-25. The test area can be converted to the equivalent area at 100X, and this area can be used in the calculation of $N_{A(100\text{X},\text{in}^2)}$, thus eliminating Eq. 6-25.

Heyn intercept method Both the Jeffries and the triple-point count methods require marking of a photograph or overlay to obtain an accurate count. Thus, the methods are slow. Greater measurement speed with the same accuracy can be obtained using intercept counts [45, 46]. Since the test element is a line rather than an area, an accurate count can be made without recourse to marking overlays or pictures. Indeed, grid overlays are perfectly suitable so that it is not necessary to work on photographs. Thus, the intercept method can be used to obtain an accurate estimate of the grain size in a fraction of the time required for the Jeffries method. A good measurement can be made in slightly more time than needed for

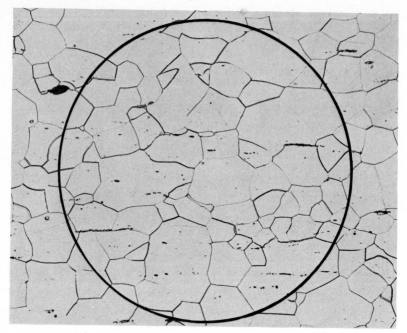

The above circle has a diameter of 79.8 mm for an area of 5000 mm^2. The micrograph is a low-carbon sheet steel, etched with nital, at 500X. The true area is found by dividing the circle radius by 500 and then calculating the area, πr^2. The true area is 0.02 mm^2. The number of triple points within the test area was counted and found to be 141. Hence, the number of ferrite grains per mm^2 at 1X is:

$$\text{No. of grains/mm}^2 = \frac{(141/2) + 1}{0.02} = 3574$$

The ASTM grain size G, is:

$$G = [\log(3574)/0.3] - 2.95 = 8.85 \text{ (round to 8.9 or 9)}$$

The same micrograph was analyzed by the Jeffries method and found to have 61 grains within the test area and 30 intersecting the circle. Hence, the number of ferrite grains per mm^2 is 3800 and the ASTM grain size is 8.94 (round to 8.9 or 9). Using the three-circle template, P_L was 70.5 per mm. Hence, the mean lineal intercept was 0.0142 mm and the ASTM grain size was 8.98 (round to 9). Hence, all three methods produced excellent agreement.

Figure 6-9 Example of grain size determination by the triple-point count method and comparison to planimetric (Jeffries) and intercept (Heyn) measurements (reduced 25 percent in reproduction).

a decent comparison chart rating. The intercept method is ideally suited for measuring nonequiaxed grains, and the number of intercepts per unit length N_L is directly related to the surface area per unit volume S_V of grain boundaries as follows:

$$S_V = 2N_L \tag{6-26}$$

Thus, the intercept technique provides additional insight into the microstructure.

To use the method, a straight or curved line of known length L_T is drawn on a micrograph or a clear plastic overlay or scribed on a ground-glass projection screen or reticle. The magnification is chosen so that the number of grains intercepted by the line N or the number of grain boundaries intersecting the line P can be counted accurately. The line length chosen should produce from 50 to 150 intersections or interceptions per field at the chosen magnification to obtain an accurate estimate of P_L or N_L. A wide variety of test-line patterns are possible with either directed (straight) lines, which can also measure grain elongation, or concentric circles, to obtain a measurement free of anisotropy effects.

If a set of parallel or randomly oriented lines are used and one counts the number of grains intercepted, the ends of the lines usually end within a grain rather than exactly at the grain boundary. A count is made of the grains intercepted by the lines, and if the ends of the lines end within the grains, each end point is counted as one-half an interception. If grain-boundary intersections with the line elements are counted, which is more commonly done, grain-boundary intersections are counted as one point, triple-point intersections are counted as 1½ points, and tangent hits are counted as one-half point. These counting rules pertain to single-phase structures. Procedures for intercept grain size analysis of two-phase structures are described later. For a single-phase grain structure, counting of the number of intercepted grains N or the number of grain-boundary intersections P yields equivalent results that differ at most by one.

For single-phase structures $N_L = P_L$, and either counting method can be used to estimate G. These intercept values are calculated as follows:

$$N_L = \frac{N}{L_T/M} \quad \text{and} \quad P_L = \frac{P}{L_T/M} \tag{6-27}$$

where L_T is the total line length and M is the magnification. The mean intercept length (mean lineal intercept) $\bar{L}_3$ is given by the following relationship:

$$\bar{L}_3 = \frac{1}{N_L} = \frac{1}{P_L} \tag{6-28}$$

This relationship only holds for single-phase microstructures. Columns 4 and 5 of Table 6-5 show the relationship between ASTM grain size and $\bar{L}_3$ and the number of intersections per millimeter. Alternatively, G can be calculated as follows

$$G = [-6.6457 \log \bar{L}_3] - 3.298 \quad (\bar{L}_3, \text{mm}) \tag{6-29}$$

$$G = [-6.6353 \log \bar{L}_3] - 12.6 \quad (\bar{L}_3, \text{in}) \tag{6-30}$$

The average grain diameter $\bar{d}$ from the Jeffries method is about 12.5 percent greater than the mean lineal intercept $\bar{L}_3$ for the same grain size. If enough fields are measured, the grain size by the intercept method is accurate to one-tenth a unit of G.

The relationship between the mean lineal intercept and the ASTM grain size was first shown in ASTM E89. This specification suggested making intercept counts on two sets of perpendicular lines to yield two estimates, N_{L1} and N_{L2}†, to

---

† N_{L1} and N_{L2} in this case are calculated using the test length in inches at M rather than using the line length at 1X.

calculate the number of grains per square inch at 100X from the following equation:

$$N_A(100X, \text{in}^2) = 0.8\left(\frac{M}{100}\right)^2 N_{L1}N_{L2} \tag{6-31}$$

This relationship was also used in ASTM E112 when it was introduced. The current procedure to relate $\bar{L}_3$ and G is based on the average intercept width of a circular grain $\bar{A}$ calculated from Eq. (6-20). The relationship between $\bar{L}_3$ and $\bar{A}$ for a circular grain section is as follows:

$$\bar{L} = \left(\frac{\pi}{4}\bar{A}\right)^{1/2} \tag{6-32}$$

The mean lineal intercept for polygonal grains is slightly larger than this value (0.52 percent greater) and is decreased by grain anisotropy and increased as the range of section sizes increases. The calculated values of $\bar{L}_3$ can be used to back-calculate N_L or P_L using Eq. (6-28). The difference between $\bar{L}_3$ calculated using Eq. (6-31) or (6-32) is very small, with a minor difference at the third place to the right of the decimal.

If sets of perpendicular lines† are used to determine N_L, the number of grains per square millimeter at 1X can be calculated directly as follows:

$$N_A(1X, \text{mm}^2) = 0.8(N_{L,\perp} \; N_{L,\|}) \tag{6-33}$$

where N_L for perpendicular test lines $(N_{L,\perp})$ and for parallel test lines $(N_{L,\|})$ is determined according to Eq. (6-27). G is then calculated by Eq. (6-22). Since the difference in the two methods for relating $\bar{L}_3$ to G is so small, little error is introduced by use of the former method. Perpendicular test lines are useful in evaluating grain elongation and are used in preference to circular test lines when this additional information is desired. The ratio of $N_{L,\perp}/N_{L,\|}$, or $\bar{L}_{3,\|}/\bar{L}_{3,\perp}$, gives a measure of grain elongation.

A useful procedure for determining the average mean lineal intercept for an oriented structure is to use a circular test line as first suggested by Hilliard [45] and later expanded by Abrams [33, 46]. The three-circle template suggested by Abrams has been adopted in ASTM E112. It has a total length of 500 mm and consists of three concentric circles with diameters of 79.58, 53.05, and 26.53 mm. This template is available from ASTM. Tick marks are placed at the north pole of each circle for referencing the beginning and end of each count. A circular test grid can introduce a bias toward overestimating the mean lineal intercept if the number of grains counted is small. The inner circle should not be so small or the magnification so high that the grain count on this circle falls below 15. The bias is insignificant if the number of intersections on the inner circle is 18 or greater. If this level cannot be obtained, the bias can be countered by counting triple-point intersections as 2 rather than as 1½.

---

† One set of lines are parallel to the hot-working axis and the other set are perpendicular to the hot-working axis.

In general, when using the three-circle grid, the magnification should be adjusted to provide about 100 intercepts. If the count is below 70, the magnification should be lowered; if it is above 140, the magnification should be raised. As with all measurements, the fields should be chosen at random without observing the structure. One should space the fields about the surface rather than concentrating them in one location. Five fields usually provide acceptable accuracy. The field estimates of $\bar{L}_3$ are analyzed using the procedure described in the section on point counting. If the standard deviation is high, the grain structure is nonuniform and more fields should be measured. Figure 6-10 shows a grain structure analyzed by the three-circle intercept method.

Nonequiaxed grains When the grain shape is noticeably distorted, grain size measurements should be made on the transverse, longitudinal, and planar (rolling

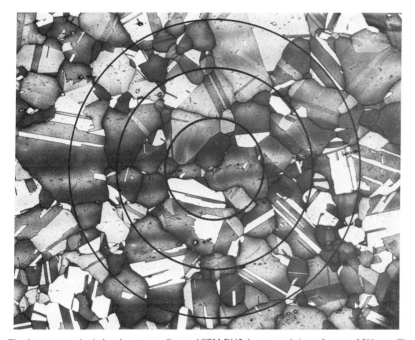

The three concentric circles, drawn according to ASTM E112, have a total circumference of 500 mm. The photograph is a 100X typical field in a nickel-base superalloy (X-750), tint etched. The number of grain boundary intersections (twins ignored) is determined and found to be 63. Hence, P_L is:

$$P_L = 63/(500/100) = 12.6 \text{ mm}^{-1}$$

The mean lineal intercept, $\bar{L}_3$, is:

$$\bar{L}_3 = 1/12.6 = 0.0794 \text{ mm}$$

The ASTM grain size G, is:

$$G = [-6.646 \log(0.0794)] - 3.298 = 4$$

Figure 6-10 Example of grain size measurement by the intercept (Heyn) method using three concentric circles (reduced 25 percent in reproduction).

plane surface) surfaces with respect to the deformation direction. Either the Jeffries or the intercept method can be used, although the latter is preferred.

If a Jeffries count of the number of grains per square millimeter at 1X is made on the three principal planes yielding values of $N_{A,t}$, $N_{A,l}$, and $N_{A,p}$, the number of grains per cubic millimeter N_V is determined from the following equation:

$$N_V = 0.8(N_{A,t} N_{A,l} N_{A,p})^{1/2} \qquad (6\text{-}34)$$

Values of N_V for different grain sizes are given in col. 7 of Table 6-5, or the ASTM grain size be calculated from the following equation:

$$G = [2.214 \log N_V] - 2.74 \qquad (6\text{-}35)$$

Alternatively, an average value of the number of grains per square millimeter at 1X ($\bar{N}_A$) can be calculated† as follows:

$$\bar{N}_A = (N_{A,t} N_{A,l} N_{A,p})^{1/3} \qquad (6\text{-}36)$$

Then G is calculated by Eq. (6-22). Estimates of G for such structures are probably accurate within one-half a unit. The relationship between N_A or N_L and N_V in ASTM E112 was initially based on the following:

$$N_V = (N_A)^{3/2} = 0.7(N_L)^3 \qquad (6\text{-}37)$$

Currently, N_V is calculated only from N_L using a more conservative relationship:

$$N_V = 0.5659(N_L)^3 \qquad (6\text{-}38)$$

If the intercept method is used to evaluate nonequiaxed grains, straight test lines are preferred over the circular grid. The straight lines must be oriented in the following way on the three test planes:

$N_{L,l}$ Parallel to the elongation on the longitudinal plane
$N_{L,t}$ Perpendicular to the elongation on the transverse plane (through-thickness direction)
$N_{L,p}$ Perpendicular to elongation on planar surface (i.e., across the width)

Note that these three test directions are mutually perpendicular. The degree of grain elongation on each plane can be determined by making intercept measurements on each plane in directions perpendicular to each of the above test lines. Then, on each plane, the grain-elongation ratio is determined by dividing the N_L value in the compressed direction by that in the elongated direction.

To determine the ASTM grain size, two equivalent procedures can be employed. The average $\bar{N}_L$ value can be obtained as follows:

$$\bar{N}_L = \frac{1}{3}(N_{L,l} + N_{L,t} + N_{L,p}) \qquad (6\text{-}39)$$

Then, $\bar{N}_L$ is used to calculate $\bar{L}_3$ from Eq. (6-28), and the ASTM grain size is

---

† This method is preferred to estimation of G based on N_V.

calculated from Eqs. (6-29) or (6-30).† Alternatively, N_V can be estimated from the following:

$$N_V = 0.566N_{L,1}N_{L,t}N_{L,p} \tag{6-40}$$

Equation (6-35), or Table 6-5, can then be used to determine G.

Duplex grain structures It is not uncommon to observe duplex grain structures in metals, a condition encountered in partially recrystallized specimens or at the onset of rapid grain growth in aluminum-killed steels. A duplex grain structure exhibits a bimodal frequency distribution of grain area, diameter, or intercept length. Two types of duplex structure can be observed. One type exhibits agglomerations of small grains within a matrix of large grains, or vice versa, while the other exhibits a more continuous dispersion with a small amount of grains scattered throughout the matrix that are outside the normal distribution.

If the duplex condition exhibits well-defined agglomerations of fine and coarse regions, analysis can be handled by determining the volume fraction of the fine and coarse regions by point counting using randomly selected fields. Then, the grain size within each region can be analyzed by selectively measuring each area. This is a reasonably simple procedure, although some subjectivity is involved in the measurement. To perform the analysis, a low magnification is usually used for the point count, although a variety of higher magnifications may be needed for the selective grain size estimates.

The analysis is much more difficult when the duplexity is randomly dispersed throughout the matrix. An average grain size number does not provide insight into the nature of the structure. The standard deviation of the field measurements gives an indication of the duplexity, but it is not as obvious as with the agglomerated duplex condition.

Several investigators suggest that the best procedure for defining the random duplex structure is to develop a size distribution. Such distributions use grain areas, diameters, or intercepts. For manual analysis, a frequency distribution of intercept lengths is easiest to perform. Any measurement parameter can be used with semiautomatic or automatic image analyzers, depending on the machine and its ability to reveal the grain boundaries. ASTM is developing a procedure for measuring duplex grain structures. Underwood has suggested the following method for measuring the frequency distribution of intercept lengths. A grid consisting of a number of straight parallel lines spaced 5 mm apart is superimposed over the microstructure using four orientations: 0°, 45°, 90°, and 135°. Measurements can be made manually or can be made with a semiautomatic tracing device or by image analysis. The intercept lengths are summarized for each orientation according to class intervals. The class intervals are 1 mm wide at the measurement magnification starting at zero and ending with the largest observed intercept. Using the duplex microstructure shown in Fig. 6-11, this method was employed as follows and produced the data listed in Table 6-6. The data for the four orienta-

†This method is preferred to estimates of G based on N_V.

Table 6-6 Lineal analysis of duplex grain structure

Class interval, mm	Orientation				Avg.	Intercept length per class interval	% intercept length per class
	0°	45°	90°	135°			
	Fine-grain region†						
0–1	22	22	19	29	23.0	11.5	0.44
1–2	32	45	53	62	48.0	48.0	1.85
2–3	38	73	59	73	60.75	121.5	4.68
3–4	49	89	88	80	76.5	229.5	8.84
4–5	53	96	73	111	83.25	333.0	12.83
5–6	45	70	54	59	57.0	285.0	10.98
6–7	44	56	53	53	51.5	309.0	11.90
7–8	33	43	49	57	45.5	318.5	12.27
8–9	26	25	31	20	25.5	204.0	7.86
9–10	35	18	17	22	23.0	207.0	7.97
10–11	13	16	13	9	12.75	127.5	4.91
11–12	12	9	9	10	10.0	110.0	4.24
12–13	8	4	3	8	5.75	69.0	2.66
13–14	3	6	1	5	3.75	48.75	1.88
14–15	6	4	2	1	3.25	45.5	1.75
15–16	2	1	2	1	1.5	22.5	0.87
16–17	0	1	0	2	0.75	12.0	0.46
17–18	2	0	0	1	0.75	12.75	0.49
18–19	2	0	0	0	0.5	9.0	0.35
19–20	1	0	0	0	0.25	4.75	0.18
	Coarse-grain region‡						
20–21	0	0	1	1	0.5	10.0	0.39
21–22	0	1	0	0	0.25	5.25	0.20
22–23	0	0	1	0	0.25	5.5	0.21
23–24	0	0	0	0	0	0	0

Interval	428	581	528	606	535.75	2596.0	100.01
24–25	0	0	0	1	0.25	6.0	0.23
25–26	0	0	0	0	0	0	0
26–27	0	0	0	0	0	0	0
27–28	0	0	0	0	0	0	0
28–29	0	0	0	0	0	0	0
29–30	0	0	0	0	0	0	0
30–31	2	1	0	0	0.75	22.5	0.87
31–32	0	0	0	0	0	0	0
32–33	0	0	0	0	0	0	0
33–34	0	0	0	0	0	0	0
34–35	0	1	0	0	0.25	8.5	0.33
35–36	0	0	0	0	0	0	0
36–37	0	0	0	0	0	0	0
37–38	0	0	0	0	0	0	0
38–39	0	0	0	1	0.25	9.5	0.37
Total	428	581	528	606	535.75	2596.0	100.01

Note: Division between fine-grain and coarse-grain regions is an arbitrary division.

†Fine grained region:
Sum of no. of intercepts = 533.25
Sum of intercept lengths = 2528.75
$$L_T = \frac{L}{M} = \frac{2528.75}{424} = 5.964 \text{ mm}$$
$$N_L = \frac{533.25}{5.964} = 89.4 \text{ mm}^{-1}$$
$$\bar{L}_3 = \frac{1}{N_L} = 0.01118 \text{ mm} \qquad \text{ASTM 9.7}$$
$$V_v = \frac{2528.75}{2596}\,100 = 97.4\%$$

‡Coarse grained region:
Sum of no. of intercepts = 2.5
Sum of intercept lengths = 67.25
$$L_T = 0.1586 \text{ mm}$$
$$N_L = \frac{2.5}{0.1586} = 15.76 \text{ mm}^{-1}$$
$$\bar{L}_3 = \frac{1}{N_L} = 0.0634 \text{ mm} \qquad \text{ASTM 4.7}$$
$$V_v = \frac{2.5}{2596}\,100 = 2.6\%$$

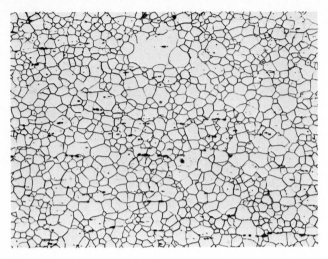

Figure 6-11 Example of a well-dispersed duplex grain structure in a low-carbon steel (150×, etched with nital, Marshall's reagent, and nital). *(Courtesy of A. O. Benscoter, Bethlehem Steel Corp.)*

tions were averaged and are listed in col. 6 of the table. Then, the intercept length per class interval was calculated as shown and is listed in col. 7. Next, the percentage of intercept length per class was calculated and is listed in col. 8. The raw data were separated into fine- and coarse-grained regions after inspection of the frequency data. This separation requires some judgment on the part of the metallographer.

In each region, the number of intercepts and the intercept length are determined. The volume fractions of the fine- and coarse-grained regions are determined by dividing the intercept length in each region by the total intercept length. The intercept length in each region is divided by the magnification, and the number of intercepts is divided by this value to give N_L for each region. Then $\overline{L}_3$ and G are calculated for each region. For the data given in Table 6-6, the results are as follows:

	Fine-grained region	Coarse-grained region
Volume fraction, %	97.4	2.6
N_L, mm^{-1}	89.4	15.76
$\overline{L}_3$, mm	0.01118	0.0634
G	9.7	4.7

The data in Table 6-6 are plotted in Figs. 6-12 and 6-13 using linear and semilog plots of the frequency distribution, respectively.

Two-phase structures Many commercial alloys contain more than one phase or constituent. A classic example is carbon steels, which frequently exhibit ferrite and pearlite. In such steels, it is often important to measure the ferrite grain size.

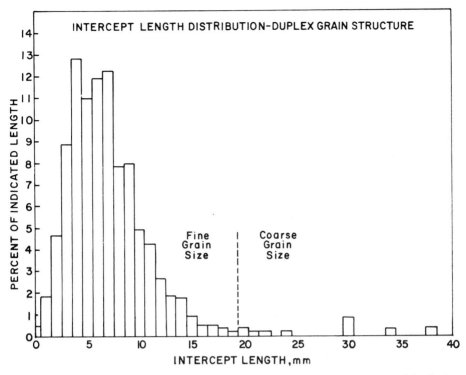

Figure 6-12 Arithmetic frequency histogram of the random intercept measurements of the duplex grain structure shown in Fig. 6-11.

If more than a few percent of pearlite is present, the methods just described to measure grain size must be modified to obtain an accurate grain size estimate. The morphology of the ferrite phase can vary substantially depending on the composition and processing.

If the second phase is similar in size to the matrix phase, comparison charts can be used to estimate the matrix grain size. If the amount of the second phase is low, and is located primarily at the grain boundaries, chart ratings can be performed.

If these conditions are not present or if a more accurate estimate is desired, the planimetric or intercept methods can be used. If the planimetric method is chosen, the number of matrix grains that are within the test area and intersect the perimeter is counted as described previously, but the percentage of the test area containing these grains must also be measured. This can be done by point counting or lineal analysis within the test area. Then the corrected test area is used in the calculations. This method is not very convenient.

The intercept method is simpler and yields excellent results. First, the volume fraction of the matrix is determined, generally by point counting or lineal analysis. This measurement is usually made on the second phase, and the V_V of the matrix phase is determined by difference. Next, the three-circle test grid, or another linear test grid, is applied to the structure, and the number of matrix grains N_α

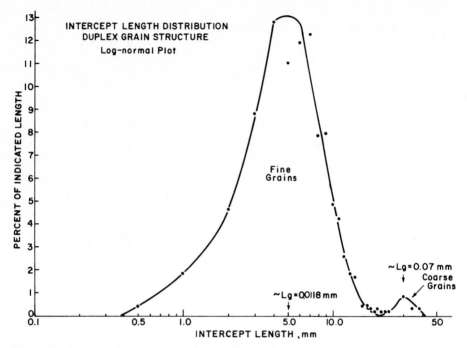

Figure 6-13 Logarithmic frequency distribution curve of the random intercept measurements of the duplex grain structure shown in Fig. 6-11.

intercepted by the test lines is counted. In this case, it is much better to count the number of intercepted grains than to count the number of grain-boundary intersections. These two measurements are not equal for two-phase structures. The mean linear intercept of the matrix (α) phase $\overline{L}_{3,\alpha}$ is calculated according to:

$$\overline{L}_{3,\alpha} = \frac{V_{V,\alpha} L_T}{N_\alpha} \qquad (6\text{-}41)$$

where L_T is the total line length calculated at 1X. An example of the measurement procedure is given in Fig. 6-14.

Snyder-Graff intercept method The prior-austenite grain size of high-speed tool steels is generally in the range of ASTM 9 to 12, a range in which the fracture grain size method described in the next section is insensitive. In this range, the number of grains per unit area changes by a factor of about 10 and the mean intercept length is reduced from 14.1 to 5 μm but the grain size number changes only three units. Grain refinement that is within this range or is finer produces a significant improvement in properties. In an effort to obtain greater sensitivity to these changes, Snyder and Graff developed a modified intercept method, which was introduced in 1938 [47].

The prior-austenite grain size of many high-alloy tool steels in the as-quenched or lightly tempered condition can be revealed simply by etching with nital (2 to 10%). Snyder and Graff found that the addition of 10% HCl to 3% nital

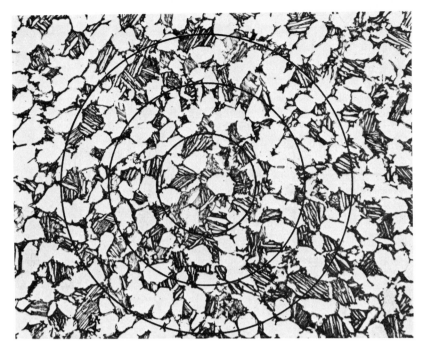

The above microstructure, at 500X , is a sample of Ti-6Al-2Sn-4Zr-2Mo forged at 1750° F (954° C) in the alpha-beta region and annealed at 1775° F (968° C) in the alpha-beta region producing primary alpha (white) and an alpha-beta eutectoid. The sample was etched with Kroll's reagent. Point counting is used to determine the amount of equiaxed alpha, 48.5%. The three concentric circles have a total circumference of 500 mm. A count is made of the number of equiaxed alpha grains intercepted by the three circles, 76. The mean lineal intercept $\overline{L}_{3\alpha}$ is calculated:

$$\overline{L}_{3\alpha} = \frac{(0.485)\,(500/500)}{76} = 0.006382 \text{ mm}$$

The ASTM grain size G, is calculated:

$$G = [-6.646 \log(0.006382)] - 3.298 = 11.29 \text{ (round to 11.3 or 11.5)}$$

Figure 6-14 Example of the determination of grain size in a two-phase alloy using point counting and intercept counting (reduced 25 percent in reproduction).

produced better results. The etched sample is viewed at 1000X. A 5-in (127-mm) line, usually scribed on a ground-glass projection screen or drawn on a clear-plastic overlay, is used as the test element. With certain samples, the structure is viewed at 500X and a 2.5-in line is used. The number of grains intercepted by the line is counted. The average of 10 such measurements is the Snyder-Graff intercept grain size number. Figure 6-15 is an example of the use of the technique. The ASTM grain size can be calculated from the following equation:

$$G = [6.635 \log (S\text{-}G)] + 2.66 \qquad (6\text{-}42)$$

where S-G is the Snyder-Graff intercept count number. To convert the Snyder-Graff intercept count to a mean intercept length, it is multiplied by 7.874 to give N_L as the number per millimeter or by 200 to give N_L as the number per inch and then the reciprocal of N_L is taken. G can then be calculated from $\overline{L}_3$ using either Eq. (6-29) or (6-30), depending on the units used.

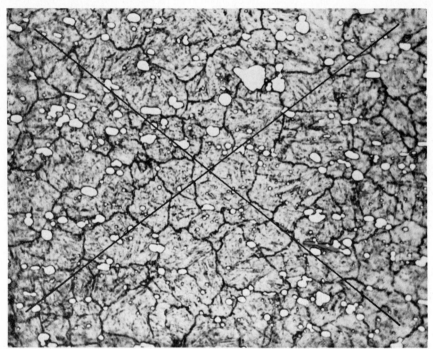

The above micrograph at 1000X (nital) has two 5 in. long lines drawn diagonally to fit the picture size (ten measurements on horizontal lines normally used.) A count of the number of grains intercepted reveals 12 plus $2\frac{1}{2}$ for one line and 13 plus $2\frac{1}{2}$ for the other for an average of 13.5 interceptions. Hence, the Snyder-Graff intercept grain size number is 13.5. To convert to ASTM grain size, two procedures may be used. Equation 6-42 can be used to estimate G.

$$G = [6.635 \log(S\text{-}G)] + 2.66 = 10.16 \text{ (round to 10)}$$

N_L can be determined in two ways,

$$N_L = 13.5 \text{ (5 } 1000) = 2700 \text{ in}^{-1}$$

or,

$$N_L = (13.5)(200) = 2700 \text{ in}^{-1}$$

The mean lineal intercept is 1 $N_L = 0.00037$ in.
The ASTM grain size is:

$$G = [-6.6353 \log(0.00037)] - 12.6 = 10.17 \text{ (round to 10)}$$

Figure 6-15 Example of grain size measurement of M2 high speed steel using the Snyder-Graff intercept method (reduced 25 percent in reproduction).

Fracture grain size For high-hardness, relatively brittle steels, the prior-austenite grain size can be determined simply by comparing a fractured specimen to a set of 10 graded standard fractures numbered 1 to 10 to coincide with the ASTM grain size scale. The technique, which is referred to as the Shepherd fracture grain size method, was introduced by Arpi in 1931. His samples consisted of 5 graded fractures which were expanded to 10 by Shepherd. Figure 6-16 shows the 10 specimens of the Shepherd fracture grain size standards along with scanning electron microscope (SEM) views of the fractures at 50X. Note that intergranular fractures are clearly present in standards 1 to 6. For the finer-grained standards, the amount of intergranular fracture decreases as the grain size number increases. Intergranular fractures have been known to result when coarse-grained, high-hardness, high-carbon steels are fractured, a condition also long recognized in carburized steels. In very fine-grained high-carbon steels, most of the fracture is cleavage when the samples are quite hard.

Vilella and Bain have demonstrated that there is a very close correlation between fracture grain size numbers and prior-austenite grain size ratings after polishing and etching. Grain sizes finer than 10 cannot be rated because the fractures do not produce feature differences discernable by eye. Grain sizes coarser than 1 can be estimated, but the error increases as the grain size goes into the macrorange. However, the need to rate such coarse fractures rarely occurs. Thus, only for the finer grain sizes above 10 are the standards inadequate.

The fracture grain size method can only be used to rate fractures of samples containing high-carbon martensite. Considerable retained austenite can also be present without invalidating results. A flat brittle fracture must be obtained for best results. Brittle fractures exhibiting curvature are more difficult to rate.

Grossman, in a study of the fracture of hardened steels, showed that the nature of the fracture influences the validity of the ratings [48]. While untempered, coarse-grained, high-carbon steels fracture intergranularly, hardened alloy steels, such as AISI 8640, yield only partial intergranular fractures, even at the coarsest grain sizes. Grossman tested samples of AISI 8640 that were quenched from 2000°F and had a prior-austenite grain size of 2 to 3. Samples tempered below 400°F were given a fracture grain size rating of about 5.

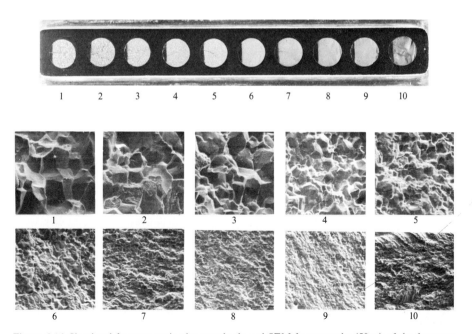

Figure 6-16 Shepherd fracture grain size standards and SEM fractographs (50×) of the fractures.

Tempering at higher temperatures decreased the fracture grain size ratings, producing agreement with a 500°F temper. This work suggested that the fracture grain size method should be limited to brittle, high-carbon steels. Additional standards would be required if the method were to be used for rating other types of steels.

In performing the method, a bar about 1 in thick and several inches long is heat-treated, usually without tempering, and fractured in a press, usually at room temperature. The fracture plane should be transverse to the rolling direction. Lightly tempered samples sometimes require notching or refrigeration to facilitate fracturing.

To illustrate the influence of microstructure and heat treatment on fracture grain size ratings, a series of 1-in diameter, 3-in long samples of AISI 01 tool steel were austenitized for 1 h at the recommended temperature of 1475°F (802°C) and at 1600, 1800, and 2000°F (871, 982, 1093°C). All samples were oil-quenched and fractured. Figure 6-17 shows the fracture appearance, the fracture grain size ratings, hardnesses, SEM views of the fractures at 250X, and the microstructures at 250X. AISI 01 is not aluminum-killed but relies on undissolved spheroidal carbides to prevent grain growth. As the austenitization temperature is increased, the carbide goes into solution and grain growth results. All the samples in this

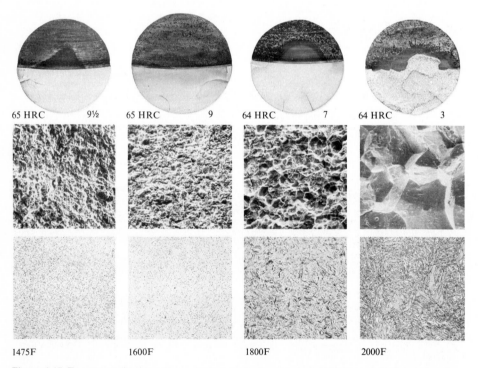

| 65 HRC | 9½ | 65 HRC | 9 | 64 HRC | 7 | 64 HRC | 3 |

1475F   1600F   1800F   2000F

Figure 6-17 Fracture grain size ratings of oil-quenched samples of AISI 01 tool steel samples after austenitizing at progressively higher temperatures. SEM fractographs and microstructures at 250× (picral etch).

figure exhibit valid fracture grain sizes, and the coarser samples exhibit inter-granular fractures.

In failure analysis work, the fracture grain size technique is often applied to tempered samples. Depending on the grade of tool steel, some degree of tempering can be tolerated without invalidating the ratings. Figure 6-18 shows AISI 01 samples austenitized at 1475°F (802°C) with varying degrees of temper from none to 1000°F (538°C). Note that tempering at 600°F (316°C) and above reduced the fracture grain size rating even though all the samples had the same prior-austenite grain size. Tempering changes the toughness of the sample and the nature of the fracture. Note that the flatness of the samples decreases as the tempering temperature increases.

Figure 6-19 illustrates the influence of different matrix structures on the fracture grain size. Since all four samples were austenitized at 1475°F (802°C), they should all exhibit the same prior-austenite grain size. However, microstruc-tures of lower bainite, upper bainite, or very fine pearlite do not produce fractures suitable for rating of the grain size. Note that all the fractures are coarse-cleavage fractures.

Accuracy of grain size estimates Three types of errors can influence grain size estimates [39]. The first type of error is due to experimental limitations, e.g., limited resolution, poor delineation of grain boundaries, overetching, errors in the test line length, miscounting, or improper counting. The extent and influence

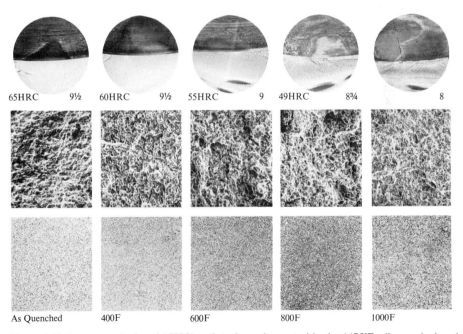

| 65HRC | 9½ | 60HRC | 9½ | 55HRC | 9 | 49HRC | 8¾ | | 8 |

| As Quenched | 400F | 600F | 800F | 1000F |

Figure 6-18 Fracture grain size of AISI 01 tool steel samples austenitized at 1475°F, oil-quenched, and tempered at progressively higher temperatures. SEM fractographs and microstructures at 200× (picral etch).

65 HRC　　9½　　48 HRC　　5½　　34 HRC　　5¼　　4

Oil Quench　　500F-3h　　900F – 30m　　1150F-1h

Figure 6-19 Fracture grain size of AISI 01 tool steel samples austenitized at 1475°F and transformed at different microstructures. SEM fractographs and microstructures at 250× (picral etch).

of these errors are difficult to measure, but in many cases, they are not as significant as other sources of error.

The second source of error involves improper sampling. Best results are always obtained by random sampling. All fields or photomicrographs for ratings must be chosen at random—one should never attempt to pick out "typical" areas for rating. The third source of error involves the representativeness of the measured areas to the whole sample. These last two types of sampling errors usually produce most of the measurement error.

In any measurement, the most efficient method should be used, i.e., the procedure that gives the greatest accuracy for the least effort. To determine the most efficient analysis method, the magnitude of the sampling errors must be determined. The standard deviation of the field measurements is used to quantify sampling errors. It is impossible to determine the population standard deviation σ, but the standard deviation of the observations s approaches that of the population as the number of measurements N becomes very large. As N increases, s decreases. Thus, both the sample homogeneity and the number of measurements alter the standard deviation. For a given level of homogeneity, the number of fields required to obtain a reasonable accuracy must be determined. Each type of measurement requires a certain amount of effort to obtain a desired level of accuracy.

Hilliard found that for a single measurement field, the Jeffries procedure produced a lower standard deviation [39]. However, the Jeffries method is much slower than the intercept method because of the need to keep track of the grains being counted; at equal accuracies the Jeffries method requires 60 percent more time than the intercept method. Hilliard also compared the efficiency of the intercept method to that of the comparison method and assumed for the comparison of efficiency that chart comparison ratings yield an accuracy of 0.5 ASTM units. The time required to obtain this accuracy with the intercept method is no more than is required with the chart comparison rating.

Relationship of $\overline{L}_3$ to other grain parameters The mean intercept length $\overline{L}_3$ has been shown to be quite useful in correlations between grain size and mechanical properties. These correlations hold because $\overline{L}_3$ is directly related to the grain-boundary surface area per unit volume (S_V). It should be recognized that the grain-boundary surfaces control properties and the mean intercept or grain diameter has no intrinsic relationship to properties except for the relationship of $\overline{d}$ and $\overline{L}_3$ to S_V. As the grain size gets smaller, the surface area per unit volume increases.

In a single-phase structure, N_L and P_L are equivalent and $\overline{L}_3$ is the reciprocal of either count. According to Underwood [3], for a single-phase microstructure, the surface-to-volume ratio S_V has been derived at least eight times and is simply expressed as follows:

$$S_V = 2P_L = 2N_L \qquad \text{(single phase)} \qquad (6\text{-}43)$$

S_V has units of square millimeters per cubic millimeter. For the case of discrete particles within a matrix phase, S_V of the particles is the following:

$$S_V = 2P_L = 4N_L \qquad \text{(two phases)} \qquad (6\text{-}44)$$

where $P_L = 2N_L$ for separated particles. In practice, P_L is not precisely $2N_L$ because some test lines produce tangents to particles rather than two intersection points. In making an estimate of S_V for discrete particles, a P_L count is preferred.

Although the relationship between $\overline{L}_3$ and S_V is exact, the relationship between $\overline{L}_3$ and the spatial grain diameter $\overline{D}$ is not. The studies that have been conducted to relate the intercept length to the spatial grain diameter assume a particular grain shape [49]. Thus, these derivations require a constant grain shape which, as has been shown, does not occur. The earliest relationships assumed that the grains were spherical; therefore the spatial grain diameter $\overline{D}$ would be $1.5\overline{L}_3$. If the Kelvin polyhedron is the assumed grain shape, the mean spatial grain diameter is $1.68\overline{L}_3$ [49]. For the Kelvin polyhedron of minimum surface area, the spatial grain diameter has been shown to be $1.74\overline{L}_3$ [49].

6-7.3 Grain Size Distributions

The spatial grain size can be estimated by determination of the planar grain size distribution and calculation of the three-dimensional grain size distribution using appropriate assumptions [1–3, 5, 50–59]. Most of these methods assume that the grain shape is spherical, although a few methods are based on the tetrakaidecahedron or rhombic dodecahedron models. The planar grain size distribution is based on measurements of grain areas, diameters, or chords. An alternate approach for the determination of three-dimensional grain characteristics is serial sectioning. Serial sectioning methods can be applied to both grain and particle spatial characteristics, but in this section, we consider only those methods specifically used for determining volumetric grain size distributions.

In applying these methods, a polished and etched cross section is prepared. The structure must be completely delineated without producing excessive relief otherwise errors will result. Generally the light microscope or photomicrographs are used. For very fine structures, transmission electron microscopy (TEM) replicas may be required to provide the needed resolution. Naturally, the sample must be representative of the bulk conditions, and field selection should be random.

It is impossible to develop a continuous size distribution of the planar grain characteristics. Instead, intervals that divide the range of grain sizes into classes of a finite width must be used to group the measurements. These increments, or intervals, can be linear or geometric. Linear scales are simple to employ. Each class i has the same width, with the first class starting at zero. An interval width is chosen that divides the range of sizes into a convenient number k of classes. Generally, 8 to 12 classes provide optimal results, with 7 as a minimum and 15 as a maximum. Therefore, it is necessary to find the largest grain and measure it to establish the class width and number of classes.

Many studies have shown that grain size distributions are positively skewed if linear scales are used; i.e., they are log-normal. Thus, use of logarithmic or power series scales sometimes produces better results. Linear classes based on the logarithm of the measurement or multiples of $2^{1/2}$ are often used. These two parameters are used when grain areas are measured.

The grains are sized and classified according to the scale chosen until a suitable number of measurements have been made, generally at least 300 to 500. These data are then subjected to a series of calculations to produce an estimate of the number of grains per unit volume, N_V. The calculation methods are based on the probability of a sectioning plane cutting through the plane between the exact center and a grain corner to produce a range of planar grain sizes. It is assumed that the largest grains make up all the grains in the largest size class and produce some of the grains in the smaller size classes as a result of the sectioning effect. On the basis of the number of grains in the largest class and the sectioning probability, the correct number per volume in the largest class is calculated. Then, the grains from the largest class that were originally classed in smaller classes are determined and subtracted from the counts in each of the smaller classes. After this is done, the number of grains in the second largest class is determined, and their contribution to the smaller classes is calculated and subtracted from each class. This procedure is continued until the number per volume in each class $N_{v,i}$ is determined. The sum of the $N_{V,i}$ values gives N_V. The arithmetic mean grain diameter can be calculated from the following equation:

$$\overline{D} = \frac{1}{N_V} \Sigma N_{V,i} D_i = \frac{1}{N_V}(N_{V1}D_1 + N_{V2}D_2 + \cdots + N_{V,k}D_k) \qquad (6\text{-}45)$$

where the subscript i refers to the class number and the subscript k is the number of classes. $\overline{D}$ is the arithmetic mean spatial diameter. The mean grain volume $\overline{V}$ is the reciprocal of N_V. The arithmetic standard deviation of the grain diameter, $s(D)$, is calculated from the following equation:

$$s(D) = \left[\frac{1}{N_V} \Sigma N_{V,i} (D_i - \overline{D})^2 \right]^{1/2} \qquad (6\text{-}46)$$

The arithmetic mean diameter $\overline{D}$ can also be calculated from the following relationship:

$$N_A = \overline{D} N_V \qquad (6\text{-}47)$$

or by Eq. (6-45) employing the midpoints of the size classes for D_i.

The nature of the distribution can be assessed using arithmetic- or logarithmic-probability paper. With either paper, the maximum diameter of each size class is plotted against the percentage of grains with diameters equal to and less than the size class. If a normal distribution is present, a straight-line relationship is observed on the arithmetic-probability paper; if a log-normal relationship is present, a linear relationship is obtained on the log-probability paper. In the latter case, the geometric mean diameter D_g and the geometric standard deviation $s(D_g)$ can be calculated to provide a better description of the data:

$$\log D_g = \frac{\Sigma N_{V,i} \log D_i}{N_V}$$

$$= \frac{N_{V1} \log D_1 + N_{V2} \log D_2 + \cdots + N_{V,k} \log D_k}{N_V} \qquad (6\text{-}48)$$

$$\log s(D_g) = \left[\frac{\Sigma N_{V,i} (\log D_i - \log D_g)^2}{N_V} \right]^{1/2} \qquad (6\text{-}49)$$

From the value of N_V, the ASTM grain size can be estimated using the assumption of spherical grains based on the original N_V values in ASTM E112-63:

$$G = [2.215 \log N_V] - 2.95 \qquad (6\text{-}50)$$

which is slightly different than Eq. (6-35).

Many methods have been developed to determine N_V for grain size and particle-size distribution. Three of the more popular methods are the Schwartz-Saltykov diameter method [1–3], the Saltykov-Johnson area method [2, 3], and the Saltykov area method [55]. The latter method is particularly useful because it eliminates much of the tedium associated with the calculations.

Saltykov has modifed the Saltykov-Johnson area method in order to eliminate the tedious sequential calculations for the sectioning plane influence [55]. The Saltykov area method is considerably faster than the other methods and is amenable to automation. The same size classification scheme is used as in the Saltykov-Johnson method except that the class numbering system (30 to 1) is dropped. In the new method, the factor used is $(10^{-0.1})^n$ where n is 1, 2, 3, etc.

The following restrictions apply:

- Particles or grains can be monodispersed or polydispersed.
- Particles or grains must have the same shape, differing only in size.
- A random plane can intersect a particle or grain only once.
- Particles or grains must be randomly dispersed.

Both spherical and nonspherical particles or grains can be evaluated, but the accuracy is reduced as the shape differs substantially from spherical. The measured sections should contain the largest observed grains or particles.

Saltykov established the method using 12 or fewer size classes; however, we have expanded the analysis to cover 15 size classes. Table 6-7 presents the basic information for 15 size classes from 3.16 to 100 μm. The classification can be extended in either direction as required using the repetitive pattern of the scheme. Column 3 of Table 6-7 lists the limits of section areas (A_{max} to A) for the scheme. This column is a sliding scale. For example, if the largest grain is in the range of 25.1 to 31.6 μm, one can simply slide col. 3 down to this class using A_{max} as the area with a diameter of 31.6 μm. All the smaller size classes will be automatically indexed.

Next, the percentage of the sections within a given group is calculated as the probability that the sectioned grain surface will fall between given class limits [52]:

$$\text{Probability} = d_n - d_{n-1} = \left[1 - \left(\frac{d_{n+1}}{d_{max}} \right)^2 \right]^{1/2} - \left[1 - \left(\frac{d_n}{d_{max}} \right)^2 \right]^{1/2} \tag{6-51}$$

Table 6-7 Basic information for the Saltykov area method

Class number	Diameter, μm	Limits of section areas†	% of sections of given group, N_A
1	100–79.4	1.0–0.6304	60.792
2	79.4–63.1	0.6304–0.3928	16.786
3	63.1–50.1	0.3982–0.2510	8.967
4	50.1–39.8	0.2510–0.1576	5.237
5	39.8–31.6	0.1576–0.0999	3.094
6	31.6–25.1	0.0999–0.0630	1.923
7	25.1–19.95	0.0630–0.0398	1.191
8	19.95–15.85	0.0398–0.0251	0.746
9	15.85–12.59	0.0251–0.0159	0.468
10	12.59–10.0	0.0159–0.010	0.294
11	10.0–7.94	0.010–0.0063	0.186
12	7.94–6.3	0.0063–0.00397	0.117
13	6.3–5.01	0.00397–0.00251	0.073
14	5.01–3.98	0.00251–0.00158	0.046
15	3.98–3.16	0.00158–0.00099	0.029

†Limits are from A_{max} to A.

Note: Third and fourth columns are sliding scales indexed to class number with largest observed grain diameter.

where d_{max} is the largest class diameter and d_n and d_{n+1} are the upper and lower diameters for each class. These probabilities are given in col. 4 of Table 6-7. Again, this is a sliding scale which is indexed to the class with the largest observed grains. These data are used to calculate the contribution each grain makes to each size class. A general equation was developed to calculate $N_{V,i}$ for each class without the laborious correction procedures of the above methods. The general equation for 15 or fewer classes is as follows:

$$N_{V,i} = \frac{1}{D_i}(1.645N_{A,i} - 0.4542N_{A,i-1} - 0.1173N_{A,i-2} - 0.0423N_{A,i-3}$$

$$- 0.01561N_{A,i-4} - 0.0083N_{A,i-5} - 0.0036N_{A,i-6} - 0.0019N_{A,i-7}$$

$$- 0.0009N_{A,i-8} - 0.00044N_{A,i-9} - 0.00036N_{A,i-10}$$

$$- 0.0001N_{A,i-11} - 0.00003N_{A,i-12} - 0.00003N_{A,i-13}$$

$$- 0.00001N_{A,i-14}) \tag{6-52}$$

The calculation of $N_{V,i}$ for a given class is continued until the index of $N_{A,i}$ reduces to zero. To calculate N_{V1} only the first term is needed, while as i increases, the number of terms increases linearly. D_i in Eq. (6-52) is the maximum diameter for the particular class.

To illustrate the technique, 470 grains within a known area of a single-phase grain structure were sized according to the grain class ranges listed in Table 6-7. These data are listed in Table 6-8. The number of grains per unit area for each class, $N_{A,i}$, was measured, and Eq. (6-52) was used to calculate the $N_{v,i}$ values; for example:

$$N_{V1} = \frac{1}{0.063}[(1.645)(24.92)] = 651 \text{ grains/mm}^3$$

$$N_{V2} = \frac{1}{0.0501}[(1.645)(56.07) - (0.4542)(24.92)] = 1615 \text{ grains/mm}^3$$

$$N_{V3} = \frac{1}{0.0398}[(1.645)(186.9) - (0.4542)(56.07) - (0.1173)(24.92)]$$

$$= 7012 \text{ grains/mm}^3$$

The calculation was continued in this fashion, developing the values of N_{V4} to N_{V13}. These data are also given in Table 6-8. The $N_{A,i}$ and $N_{V,i}$ columns were summarized to obtain N_A and N_V. The value of N_V, 149,239 grains per cubic meter, and Eq. (6-50) were used to estimate the ASTM grain size of 8.5, which agreed well with the Jeffries and three-circle measurements. The data in Table 6-8 were plotted in Fig. 6-20, which illustrates the log-normal nature of the data distribution.

Many procedures have been developed to determine grain size distributions through measurements of chord lengths. Aaron et al. [54] used the measurement data and sample of Williams and Smith [36] to compare the accuracy of three

Table 6-8 Grain size analysis by the Saltykov area method

D_{max}		No. of grains observed	$N_{A,i}$ mm^{-2}	$N_{V,i}$ mm^{-3}	% per class
μm	mm				
63.1	0.063	4	24.92	651	0.44
50.1	0.0501	9	56.07	1,615	1.08
39.8	0.0398	30	186.9	7,012	4.70
31.6	0.0316	65	404.95	18,153	12.16
25.1	0.0251	75	467.25	22,312	14.95
19.95	0.01995	94	585.63	34,819	23.33
15.85	0.01585	59	367.57	16,608	11.13
12.59	0.01259	48	299.04	18,141	12.16
10.0	0.010	39	242.97	18,453	12.36
7.94	0.00794	20	124.6	3,662	2.5
6.31	0.0063	13	80.99	3,530	2.4
5.01	0.0050	9	56.07	3,874	2.6
3.98	0.00398	5	31.15	409	0.3
		470	2928.11†	149,239‡	

†N_A
‡N_V

diameter sizing methods, two area sizing methods, and three chord sizing methods to determine N_V, D_g, and $s(D_g)$. All methods produced higher N_V estimates and smaller D_g values than obtained by Williams and Smith by microradiography. Best agreement was obtained with the Schwartz-Saltykov diameter method and the Saltykov-Johnson area method (the Saltykov area method was not developed until after this study). The chord methods overestimated N_V by 30 to 36 percent. The errors produced by these methods are partly due to the need to use a finite number of class intervals. Also, N_V varies with the number of class intervals; as k increases, N_V increases. Williams and Smith [36] used seven class intervals, while in most of the other methods, k was substantially larger.

Hanson has developed a simple equation relating N_A and N_L measurements to N_V [60]:

$$N_V = \left[\frac{2.4150}{(N_A)^{1/2}} - \frac{1.4552}{N_L} \right]^{-3} \tag{6-53}$$

Other formulas have been suggested to relate N_L or N_A to N_V. Underwood has shown that N_V can be estimated from N_L and N_A for the truncated octahedron grain shape by the following equation [3]:

$$N_V = 0.744 \frac{N_A^2}{N_L} \tag{6-54}$$

Calculations of N_V with this equation produce results that are very similar to those calculated using Hanson's equation.

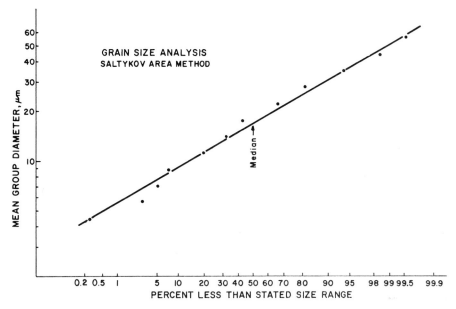

Figure 6-20 Logarithmic-probability plot of corrected grain size data by the Saltykov area method.

The use of serial sectioning for determining N_V overcomes many of the difficulties of the previously described techniques because it does not depend on shape assumptions and is not influenced by anisotropy [58, 59]. However, these methods have seldom been used because of the belief that great effort is required. However, it has recently been shown that as few as 5, but generally 6 to 10, sections are adequate for estimating N_V with acceptable accuracy [59].

6-7.4 Summary

Grain size can be measured by a number of procedures which produce equivalent estimates of the ASTM grain size number. Comparison chart ratings have limited accuracy but are adequate for simple screening purposes. Lineal analysis produces a better estimate of G in about the same time as needed for a good comparison rating. Lineal analysis is considerably faster and perhaps slightly more accurate than ratings using the Jeffries method. The intercept method has the additional advantage that N_L is directly related to the grain-boundary surface area per unit volume (S_V). The intercept method is also better suited for measuring the grain size of two-phase structures, duplex grain structures, or distorted grain structures. The versatility of the intercept method is enhanced through the application of either random (circular) or oriented test lines.

Measurement of grain size distributions and the calculation of N_V, $\overline{V}$, or $\overline{D}$ generally involve grain shape assumptions. These techniques provide considerable information about the grain structure but are tedious to employ without recourse to automatic or semiautomatic devices. Several simple methods for estimating N_V are given which are useful if the full distribution curve is not required. Serial sectioning provides a direct method for determining N_V and requires no assumptions about grain shape. However, for a fine-grained structure, the method presents considerable experimental challenge, although the calculations are quite simple.

6-8 INCLUSION RATING METHODS

Because inclusions can significantly influence material properties and behavior, they have been studied extensively. While the vast majority of this work concerns inclusions in steel, one should not conclude that inclusions do not influence other materials. Inclusions are usually categorized according to origin, i.e., exogenous or indigenous. Exogenous inclusions come from external sources such as slag or refractories. Indigenous inclusions arise from natural processes, such as deoxidation or precipitation of sulfides. Although the word "inclusion" by definition should be used only in reference to the exogenous types, it has been applied to both types. Most inclusion studies concentrate on the indigenous types because they can be controlled by the melting practice and they are more numerous and more predictable in distribution.

Indigenous inclusions are usually classified by composition, such as oxides or sulfides. Carbides and nitrides are not considered to be inclusions because they are more akin to metals than to nonmetals. In a few instances, nitrides have been included in chart methods for rating inclusions. Inclusions are also categorized by size, i.e., microscopic or macroscopic. In general, indigenous inclusions are small—less than 100 μm in diameter (as-cast condition). Macroscopic inclusions are usually exogenous in origin, but small exogenous inclusions are also observed. Thus, one cannot simply state that all indigenous inclusions are microscopic in size and all exogenous inclusions are macroscopic.

In this chapter, only microscopic methods for assessing inclusion content are covered. Broader coverage of techniques for inclusion identification and measurement is available in a recent review [61]. A variety of methods have been used to measure or describe inclusion content. These methods involve the following:

- Chart comparison
- Counting
- Volume fraction determination

Inclusion analysis requires quantification of the amount, size, shape, and distribution of inclusion types. In many cases, it is adequate to sort inclusions as either sulfides or oxides, although precise chemical identification is sometimes necessary. Chemical identification is a simple procedure if an energy- or wavelength-dispersive analytical device is available.

6-8.1 Chart Comparison Methods

Comparison methods using standard charts have been the most widely used procedure for describing inclusion content microscopically [11–14]. These charts pictorially illustrate different inclusion types, sizes, quantities, and distributions. Obviously, all possible combinations cannot be illustrated by a limited number of chart pictures. Also, each picture series depicts only one inclusion type, while a microscopic field of view can contain several types of inclusions. Thus, considerable subjective judgment is required.

In the application of charts for inclusion rating, a number of factors influence the results [62]:

- Amount of hot working and inclusion plasticity
- Amount, location, and orientation of samples
- Sample preparation
- Magnification and resolution
- Area examined per field and per sample
- Field selection

Inclusion malleability is an important aspect of chart formulation. Hot working elongates deformable inclusions, while brittle nondeformable inclusions are strung out in a broken pattern. All degrees of inclusion deformation cannot be depicted. Since charts generally illustrate ingot material after rolling to a certain cross-sectional area, typically about 4 to 6 in^2, materials with much greater deformation, such as sheet metal or wire, are difficult to rate with charts.

In ingot-cast metals, the sulfides and oxides are not randomly distributed but tend to vary from top to bottom and from surface to center. The extent of deoxidation can markedly alter the distribution pattern. This problem, plus the practical difficulty of obtaining random samples, requires systematic sampling at specified test locations. Generally, the top and bottom or top, middle, and bottom of the first, middle, and last ingots teemed on a given steel heat are tested. The plane of polish is taken at midthickness parallel to the hot-working axis in order to assess inclusion plasticity.

Sample preparation is critical. Scratches, pits, comet tailing, and staining must be prevented. Inclusions must be fully retained with minimum relief and smearing must be avoided. Automatic polishing devices are quite helpful. If inclusion lengths are measured, sectioning errors can lead to measurement errors. Allmand and Coleman have shown that deviations of only 6° from the true longitudinal plane can produce appreciable errors in measurement of length [63]. Volume-fraction measurements of inclusions are influenced slightly by the orientation of the plane of polish.

Most standard charts depict fields at 100X magnification, thus providing a large field of view for rapid assessment of a large surface area. For steels with low inclusion content, higher magnifications may be required for detection and classification. It is very difficult to translate ratings at higher magnifications to 100X standards. The use of six or nine samples with a total polished surface area of less than 10 in^2 to rate the inclusion content of a heat of steel that can weigh up to 300 tons presents inherent statistical problems because of the variability of inclusion content. Clearly, one cannot hope to define the content of exogenous inclusions. Other procedures, such as ultrasonics, must be applied to detect these types. For the indigenous types, the probability of detecting the worst condition in a heat with such a small sample area is exceedingly low. As the number of samples increases, the surface area examined increases and the worst-field ratings depict poorer quality.

In examining a sample, the entire polished surface, or a specific area, is usually examined starting at one corner. Contiguous field selection is employed. Ratings can be qualitative, i.e., the operator rates only the worst conditions, or quantitative, i.e., every field is rated. In the United States, ASTM E45 is widely used for rating the inclusion content of steels. This standard covers three chart methods and one nonchart technique The JK (Jernkontoret) chart can be used with most steels, the SAE chart is generally used for low-carbon carburizing steels, and the modified JK chart is used with steels of low inclusion content.

Both JK charts categorize inclusions into four classes—type A (sulfides), type B (aluminates), type C (silicates), and type D (globular oxides). In the past, inclusions were categorized by both morphology and composition, but only morphology is used now. This change was made because nondeforming complex silicates are sometimes observed that exhibit a type B morphology rather than a type C. Since one cannot, however, differentiate sulfides (type A) from deformable silicates (type C) by morphology alone, most users depend on color differences (light gray versus black) to separate sulfides from silicates. Each of the four types are further graded into a thin or thick series with five severity levels. For the JK chart, the severities are 1 to 5; for the modified JK chart, they are ½ to 2½. For each chart, data are provided regarding the total sulfide length, the total B- or C-type stringer length and the total number of globular oxides per field as a function of severity.

Chart methods are generally used in two ways. The simplest procedure is to find the worst fields of each type that are depicted in the chart and rate them. Then, the averages of these ratings on each sample are calculated to represent the heat. The second method requires rating every field within a given area on each sample. The data are summarized in a table listing the number of fields for each possible type, thickness, and severity.

6-8.2 Nonchart Rating Methods

Numerous nonchart methods have been proposed for rating inclusion content [61]. Some of the more significant methods are described here. A few of these methods have been incorporated into standards; e.g., Epstein's technique is Method B in ASTM E45.

Of the many methods described in various standards, only in Japanese Specification JIS G 0555 is a method employed that is based on stereological principles. In this standard, a point-counting procedure is used that is similar to that of Bergh [64] and Bergh and Lindberg [65]. In the Japanese standard, an eyepiece reticle with 20 horizontal and vertical lines is used. Field selection is performed randomly, and at least 30, but preferably 60, fields are measured. The number of grid points occupied by inclusions is counted; 400X magnification is recommended. The percentage of area occupied by the inclusions is determined as follows:

$$d = \frac{n}{pf} \times 100 \qquad (6\text{-}55)$$

where d = index of cleanliness (volume fraction in %)
  n = number of grid points occupied by inclusions
  p = total number of reticle grid points
  f = number of fields

Stereological methods for estimating V_V, N_A, or N_V can be employed to determine inclusion content. Although these methods are quantitative and capable of providing good accuracy, a number of different measurements must be made to describe all the information depicted in charts. For example, a total volume fraction is not as useful as the volume fraction of oxides and sulfides and gives no information about worst-field conditions or elongation. Oxide stringer length is believed to have an important influence on bearing steels and would require a separate measurement. Thus, although stereological methods have the potential for rigorously describing inclusions, manual determination of all the required parameters with adequate accuracy is quite tedious. Future work with image analysis should help overcome this problem.

Manual measurements of the V_V of inclusions require substantial effort to obtain reasonable accuracy because of the extensive field-to-field variation in V_V. This problem is illustrated by the following example. Nine samples containing 0.020 to 0.34% sulfur were evaluated for the total V_V of inclusions using point counting at 500X with a 100-point grid and using lineal analysis with a Hurlbut counter at 1000X [61]. To minimize the problem of nonnormal data distributions, the point count data from 100 fields were grouped into 10 sets, each set consisting of 10 successive measurements. The set averages were used for the statistical analysis. About 1 h per sample was required. For the lineal analysis, eight to ten 15-min traverses were made covering at least 10,000 units on the counter. The L_L values for each run were used to calculate the V_V, the 95 percent confidence limit, and the relative accuracy. The data are plotted in Figs. 6-21 and 6-22. In general, as the volume fraction of inclusions increased, the relative accuracy improved. The trend was influenced somewhat by the fact that some samples were as-cast while others were hot-rolled and by the fact that the amount of oxide in the samples varied. The average relative accuracies were 26.1 percent for point counting and 28.8 percent for lineal analysis. However, the time required for lineal analysis was more than double that of point counting. The accuracy of the lineal analysis was also influenced by the need to work at 1000X rather than 500X.

These same samples were analyzed by image analysis using 16X, 32X, and 80X objectives. Twelve sets of 30 contiguous fields, i.e., 1080 total fields, were measured for each sample with each objective. The area covered at each magnification was 165.8, 42.69, and 6.63 mm^2 for the 16X, 32X, and 80X objectives, respectively. Except for two of the 80X measurements, all results

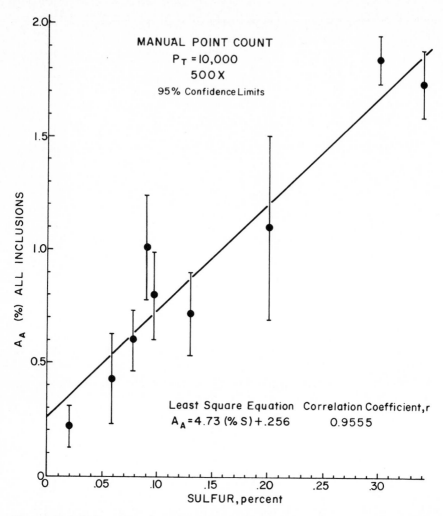

Figure 6-21 Inclusion volume fractions of nine samples of varying sulfur contents evaluated by the manual point-counting method (100 fields with a 100-point test grid at 500× for each sample). *(From Vander Voort, Ref. 61, courtesy of Plenum Press.)*

conformed to a normal distribution. The V_V measurements are shown in Fig. 6-23. The trend line shown is the average of all the data. The relative accuracy improved as the magnification decreased because the field-to-field variability was reduced and more area was covered. However, the 32X objective produced the best estimates of V_V and provided the best compromise between resolution and field size. The average relative accuracies were 5.1, 6.5 and 11.9% for the data from measurements with the 16X, 32X, and 80X objectives. Image analysis provided much better accuracy than either manual method and required about 45 min for each sample.

Image analysis has also been employed to perform JK analyses [66]. The field images are separated into the four basic categories and then subdivided by thin

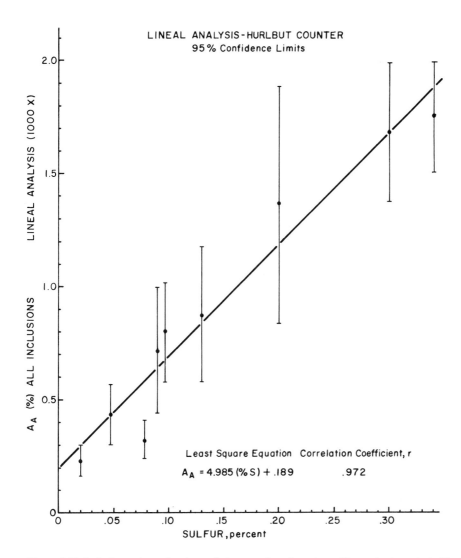

LINEAL ANALYSIS-HURLBUT COUNTER
95% Confidence Limits

Least Square Equation   Correlation Coefficient, r

A_A = 4.985 (%S) + .189   .972

Figure 6-22 Inclusion volume fractions of nine samples of varying sulfur contents evaluated by the lineal analysis technique using a Hurlbut counter (1000×). *(From Vander Voort, Ref. 61, courtesy of Plenum Press.)*

and thick differences; the appropriate measurement is then made to determine the severity. This procedure overcomes one of the primary problems of manual JK ratings—poor reproducibility. The reproducibility of image analysis JK ratings is very good. Both qualitative and quantitative data are obtained.

6-8.3 Inclusion Deformability

Free-machining steels frequently contain high concentrations of manganese sulfide inclusions to provide improved machinability. Many studies have been

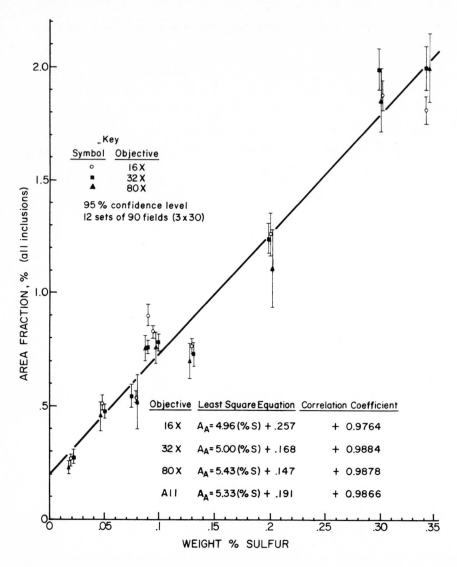

Figure 6-23 Inclusion volume fraction measurements of nine samples with varying sulfur contents using image analysis with $16\times$, $32\times$, and $80\times$ objectives. The trend line shown was plotted by using the least-squares method to fit all the data points. *(From Vander Voort, Ref. 61, courtesy of Plenum Press.)*

conducted showing the influence of sulfide shape and quantity on machinability. Several different procedures have been used to evaluate shape changes in such steels. A simple technique, which is typified by the studies of Carney and Rudolphy [67] and by the studies of Van Vlack [68] consists of measuring length-to-width ratios of sulfides in the ingot, bloom, billet, or bar shapes, i.e., at different stages of hot reduction. Carney and Rudolphy counted and measured length-to-width ratios of sulfides greater than 0.007 mm in length. The relative inclusion size V was calculated from these measurements using the relationship:

$$V = 1.08LW^2 \tag{6-56}$$

The average relative size was calculated using data from at least 50 inclusions per sample.

Analytical procedures for inclusion malleability were introduced by Malkiewicz and Rudnik [69] and were later modified by Maunder and Charles [70]. The initially spherical inclusion is deformed during hot working to an ellipsoid with a length-to-width ratio ($\lambda = b/a$) which is constant for any section parallel to the hot-working axis. Axial inclusion ratios are compared to shape changes of the product due to hot working. The change in product shape is calculated [71] based on the cross-sectional area of the ingot x and the cross-sectional area of the wrought product y by the equation:

$$h = \frac{x^{3/2}}{y^{3/2}} \tag{6-57}$$

where h is the reduction ratio for the steel product. This value is compared to the measured aspect ratio λ to obtain the relative inclusion-to-steel plasticity, i.e., the deformability of the inclusion relative to the steel.

An index of relative deformability υ is defined (69) as follows:

$$\upsilon = \frac{2 \log \lambda}{3 \log h} \tag{6-58}$$

This index is zero for a completely nondeformable inclusion, while it is one if the inclusion deforms as much as the steel. Low amounts of reduction generally produce lower index values than high degrees of reduction, and large inclusions exhibit higher index values than small inclusions.

Brunet and Bellot modified the above equation for steel rolled to flat shapes [72]. Two aspect ratios are calculated: λ, as just discussed, on a longitudinal plane and $\delta = b/c$ where b is defined as the length and c is the width of the inclusion on a transverse plane. The index of deformation υ is calculated by the equation:

$$\upsilon = \frac{\log \lambda + \log \delta}{3 \log h} \tag{6-59}$$

6-8.4 Summary

Measurement of inclusion content presents problems because of the variety of types present, their relatively low content, and the variability of their concentration. Chart methods are widely used because of their simplicity and the usefulness of the data. Many material specifications use these ratings as a basis for acceptance or rejection. Such ratings are well understood by metallurgists, and they provide a useful description of the inclusions present. Stereological data are more precise but are not as readily grasped by the average metallurgist, nor are they used as acceptance criteria in specifications. A volume-fraction measurement is helpful, but additional measurements are needed to describe the inclusions. Future work with image analysis may overcome these difficulties. Automating the chart ratings by image analysis provides excellent reproducibility and accurate, objective severity ratings.

6-9 LINE LENGTH

Estimation of line length per unit area, L_A, based on P_L measurements is accomplished using the following relationship [1–3, 73, 74]:

$$L_A = \frac{\pi}{2}P_L \tag{6-60}$$

For the P_L measurement, straight or curved test lines can be employed as long as they intersect the structure randomly. Concentric circles or spiral test grids have also been used. As an example of the determination of L_A, we can calculate the total circumference lengths of the circular particle intersections in Fig. 6-6. For the 17 circular features, the total circumference length is 413.9 mm. Dividing by the field area, 12,100 mm^2, produces a length per unit area, L_A, of 0.0342 mm/mm^2. The number of intersections of the test lines is 46.5. Dividing by the test line length, 2200 mm, produces a P_L of 0.02114 intersections per millimeter. Using Eq. (6-60), L_A is estimated as 0.033 mm/mm^2, which agrees very well with the calculated perimeter length per unit area.

The total line length per unit volume, L_V, can be estimated using the following relationship [1–3, 73]:

$$L_V = 2P_A \tag{6-61}$$

The number of points of emergence of lines, e.g., dislocations, with a test plane through the sample are counted and expressed in terms of the test plane area. The lines measured can be of any form—straight or curved or continuous or broken.

6-10 SPACINGS

6-10.1 Mean Free Path and Mean Spacing

In the study of structures strengthened by discrete second-phase particles, the mean free path λ has been shown to correlate with strength measurements. The mean free path is the average edge-to-edge distance between particles, i.e., the average uninterrupted distance between all possible pairs of particles. When λ is measured on random section planes, it provides a three-dimensional measurement of the distance between particles. Its usefulness is enhanced because λ does not depend on the size, shape, or distribution of the particles. Prior to the development of a simple stereological method for measuring λ, previous estimates were quite tedious. Gensamer et al. for example, measured the mean free path by drawing straight lines across photomicrographs and measuring the distance between particles and then averaging the results of about 250 measure-ments per sample [75].

Fullman derived the following relationship to estimate the mean edge-to-edge distance λ, between particles or phases in a duplex microstructure [76]:

$$\lambda = \frac{1 - V_V}{N_L} \tag{6-62}$$

where V_V is the volume fraction of the second-phase particles and N_L is the number of particles intercepted per unit length.

The mean center-to-center distance σ, i.e., the mean random spacing, is the reciprocal of N_L. The mean particle intercept length $\overline{L}_3$ is $\sigma - \lambda$. Various mean free path and mean nearest neighbor relationships have been reviewed by Corti et al. [77].

Figure 6-6 can be used to illustrate the calculation of λ, σ, and the mean particle intercept length $\overline{L}_3$. In this example, V_V varied from 6 to 7.3 percent depending on which technique was employed and N_L was 0.01022 intercepts per millimeter. Thus, using Eq. (6-62), the mean free path ranges between 90.7 and 91.98 mm. The mean random spacing $1/N_L$ is 97.85 mm. Thus, the mean particle intercept length, $\sigma - \lambda$, varies between 5.9 and 7.2 mm. Using Eq. (6-32), we can estimate the mean particle intercept length by calculating the areas of the circular sections and relating the mean area to $\overline{L}_3$. This produces an estimate of $\overline{L}_3$ of 6.1 mm, which agrees reasonably well with the measurement results.

6-10.2 Interlamellar Spacing

Measurements of spacing have been applied frequently to lamellar structures, particularly pearlite in steels. Interlamellar spacing measurements have been conducted using a variety of methods. These methods were altered substantially after the introduction of electron microscopy replication procedures.

Determination of the true interlamellar spacing is complicated by the inher-ent variation of the interlamellar spacing within a pearlite colony and by the sectioning plane effect, which produces additional apparent spacing variations. If the sectioning plane is perpendicular to the lamellae, the true spacing and carbide thickness are observed. If the sectioning plane cuts through the lamellae at an angle other than 90°, the apparent spacing (center to center) and the apparent carbide thickness increase. The range of true interlamellar spacings is influenced by the manner in which the pearlite forms and by the composition. The distribu-tion of true interlamellar spacings is wider if the pearlite is formed over a range of temperatures (continuous cooling) than if it is formed at a constant temperature (isothermal).

Early workers in this field used the limitation of resolution of objectives with different numerical apertures, as calculated by Eq. (4-6) in Chap. 4, to estimate the interlamellar spacing. Because the limit of resolution of the light microscope is about 0.2 μm (200 nm), Belaiew concluded that if the true spacing were below this limit, the portion of observed resolvable lamellae could be correlated to the distribution of apparent spacings created by the sectioning plane [78]. In the case of very fine pearlite with a true spacing much less than 0.2 μm, a few areas of resolvable pearlite could be found. The apparent spacing in these areas was much larger than the minimum spacing, and the edges of the carbide exhibited a frayed or broken appearance. With another sample in which all the lamellae were resolvable, he found that this frayed condition was obtained when the sectioning plane was 83° from the plane perpendicular to the lamellae. Thus, according to Belaiew, for very fine pearlite, the apparent spacing of the frayed carbide lamellae can be measured, the angle is assumed to be 83°, and the minimum spacing can be obtained by dividing the apparent spacing of the frayed carbide by the secant of 83°.

Belaiew's assumption of a constant interlamellar spacing was wrong, as was shown by Pellissier et al. [79]. They found that even isothermally transformed pearlite exhibited a statistical distribution of spacings about a mean value S_0. The constancy of S_0 in an isothermally transformed eutectoid steel was examined using 144 randomly chosen photographed (2500X) areas with a total area of 0.35 mm². The total area was subdivided into regions of approximately constant values of S. The spacing intervals S_i were quite small so that a nearly continuous distribution was obtained. Further work showed that 50 random areas would be adequate. If the true spacing S_0 was assumed to be constant and equal to the finest observed spacing, comparison of the distribution of spacings to a theoretical curve based on the same assumption revealed considerable disagreement. Comparison of the experimentally developed distribution curve to a theoretical curve based on the assumption that S_0 was 1.65 times the minimum observed spacing produced good agreement. The value of 1.65 is not a constant and has since been shown to vary with time, temperature, and composition. Asundi and West observed that the mean true spacing was 2 to 2.5 times the minimum spacing [80]. Birkbeck and Wells, working with 0.1 to 0.2% carbon steels, found that the ratio of the mean true spacing to the finest spacing varied between 1.1 and 1.8 [81].

Pearsall developed a simplified method for estimating S_0 based on the resolving power of the optical microscope [79]. The area fraction of unresolvable pearlite using an objective of known resolution S was determined by point counting. Then, the mean true spacing S_0 was calculated as follows:

$$S_0^2 = S^2 (1 - V_V^2) \tag{6-63}$$

where V_V is the fraction of pearlite with an apparent spacing less than S.

Gregory et al. evaluated Pearsall's partial-resolution method for obtaining S_0 and found that best results were obtained when the resolution of the objective was greater than S_0, which produced an unresolved pearlite area fraction of about 0.65 [82]. They also made measurements of S_0 on pearlite colonies observed on two orthogonal polished surfaces and used stereographic projection procedures to calculate S_0. The results by this method agreed well with those by the partial-resolution method.

Brown and Ridley determined the minimum interlamellar spacing using TEM replicas [83]. The magnification was raised until the finest observed lamellae were resolvable. The magnification M was determined using a replica of a diffraction grating of known spacing. The number of lamellae n crossed at right angles to the diameter d_c of a scribed circle on the viewing screen was counted, and the minimum spacing S_{min} was calculated as follows:

$$S_{min} = \frac{d_c}{nM} \tag{6-64}$$

Many researchers have employed this procedure to measure the interlamellar spacing of pearlite. Since the minimum spacing appears to be related to the mean true spacing, either method should be adequate for structure-property correlations, although comparison of the results of different studies may be difficult. It should be mentioned that the technique of looking for the finest spacing introduces a subjective judgment into the analysis and that the finest observed spacing will vary depending on the effort spent in examining the sample. Some authors claim, however, that the minimum spacing is the most reliable and consistent method for determining the interlamellar spacing.

Underwood recommends determination of the mean random spacing $\bar{\sigma}_r$ by applying test lines randomly on the structure of interest in order to intersect the lamellae at all possible angles [3]. The structure is observed with the light microscope or with replicas, depending on the fineness of the pearlite. The total number of intersections of the carbide lamellae with the test line is divided by the total true test line length to obtain N_L. The mean random spacing $\bar{\sigma}_r$ is calculated as follows:

$$\bar{\sigma}_r = \frac{1}{N_L} \tag{6-65}$$

This method has the advantage that N_L is directly related to the surface-to-volume ratio S_V of the carbide. Saltykov [1] has shown that for pearlite with a constant true spacing within each colony, the mean true spacing $\bar{\sigma}_t$ is the following:

$$\bar{\sigma}_t = \frac{\bar{\sigma}_r}{2} \tag{6-66}$$

Although this relationship is not universally exact, it is a reasonably good approximation. Gensamer et al. obtained values between 1.9 and 2.0 in their studies [75].

To illustrate the calculation of the interlamellar spacing of pearlite, an as-rolled sample of AISI 1040 steel was examined and measured using several methods (see Fig. 6-24). The optical micrograph illustrates the fine nature of the pearlite, the influence of the sectioning plane, and the variation in spacing within a colony. Two techniques were used to measure the interlamellar spacing with the light microscope—Belaiew's secant method and Pearsall's partial resolution method.

For Belaiew's secant method, the sample was scanned and a dozen measurements of frayed, highly oblique colonies were made. The average spacing of the

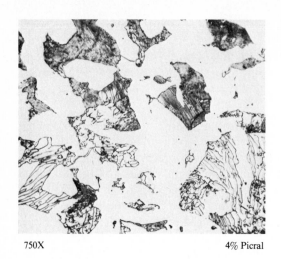

750X   4% Picral

Figure 6-24 Appearance of pearlite lamellae as observed by light microscopy in an as-rolled AISI 1040 carbon steel.

frayed lamallae was 2300 ± 690 mm, with a range from 1000 to 3500 nm. The average value was divided by the secant of 83°, 8.2055, producing 280 nm as an estimate of the true spacing. The 95 percent confidence limit of the true spacing estimate was 84 nm which results in a relative accuracy of 30 percent. Thus, many more measurements would be required to improve the accuracy of the measurement.

Pearsall's partial resolution measurement was made initially with a 100X dry objective with a 0.95 numerical aperture. The resolution of this objective was calculated as 290 nm. Ten fields at 1000X were point-counted using a 100-point test grid to determine the amount of unresolved pearlite; 50.7 percent was unresolved. Equation (6-63) was used to calculate the mean true spacing and yielded a value of 250 nm. A second attempt was made using a 50X dry objective with a 0.85 numerical aperture. This attempt produced an estimate of 195 nm as the mean true spacing, which, as is shown later in this section, is a poor estimate. Therefore, we must agree with Gregory et al. [82] that the amount of unresolved pearlite must be 50 to 65 percent to get a reliable estimate. The first estimate of the mean true spacing, as is shown later in this section, is a good estimate.

Next, TEM replicas were prepared, and two different operators searched for what looked like the finest pearlite colonies. This produced estimates of 175 and 168 nm. If we assume that the finest spacing multiplied by 1.65 is the mean true spacing, as suggested by Pellissier et al. [79], we obtain estimates of 289 and 277 nm. As is shown later in this section, these measurements of the finest spacings were higher than those obtained by more exhaustive examination.

Next, a large number of photographs were made of pearlite colonies on the replicas chosen at random. On each picture, measurements were made using lines drawn perpendicular to the lamellae from center to center of the lamellae. The distance was divided by the magnification and then by N, where N was the number of carbide lamellae intersected by the line, to obtain a directed-spacing measurement. This produced a mean directed spacing of 333 nm for 183 measurements. The finest observed spacing was 124 nm, substantially finer than found previously.

Next, the same photomicrographs were measured using a circular test pattern to produce an estimate of the mean random spacing, as recommended by Underwood [3]. The average of 92 measurements was 508 nm. Using Eq. (6-66), we calculated the mean true spacing as 254 nm, which is quite similar to the estimate using Pearsall's method but is certainly a more precise measurement.

Thin foils were made of the surface adjacent to the replicated surface, and a large number of colonies where the lamellae were perpendicular to the surface were photographed. Again, straight lines were drawn perpendicular to the lamellae, and the colony spacings were determined. The average of 218 such measurements was 254.5 ± 9.0 nm, which agrees extremely well with the estimate of the true spacing made by random measurements on replicas. The finest observed spacing was 100 nm, again much finer than was found in the initial search. The true spacings exhibited a range from 100 to 450 nm.

Using the measurements of the finest observed spacings, either 124 or 100 nm, and the best estimate of the mean true spacing, 254.5 nm, we conclude that the finest spacing times 2 to 2.5 is a good estimate of the true spacing. However, this assumes that considerable effort will be expended in finding the finest spacing. The difference between the 1.65 factor of Pellisier and the 2 to 2.5 factor of Asundi and West [80] and our measurements probably stems from the nature of the pearlite formation; i.e., in Pellisier's study pearlite was formed isothermally which produces a narrower range of spacings than formation by continuous cooling.

To summarize, the best procedure for determining the mean true spacing is to determine the mean random spacing using a random spacing measurement. As few as 15 randomly chosen fields can be used to produce a good estimate of the true spacing. Searching for the finest spacing is a very subjective measurement which is prone to considerable error. This type of measurement is similar in nature to worst-field inclusion ratings—the magnitude of the measurement depends on the amount of time and effort spent searching the sample. Pearsall's partial-resolution measurement appears to be a useful technique when SEM or TEM procedures are unavailable. However, it appears to be quite dependent on the magnification and resolution of the objective used. Thus, the technique must be carefully controlled in order to get good results. Belaiew's secant method is simple to employ, but the accuracy of the measurement is not adequate.

6-11 CONTIGUITY

The degree of contact of the surfaces of similar α particles or grains or between α and β particles or grains in polyphase systems has been found to exert a considerable influence on the properties of certain systems. Gurland has introduced the term "contiguity" to describe the fraction of the surface area of a particle or grain that is shared with other similar particles [84]. The contiguity of α

particles $C_{\alpha\alpha}$ in a β matrix is given by the following equation:

$$C_{\alpha\alpha} = \frac{2S_{V,\alpha\alpha}}{2S_{V,\alpha\alpha} + S_{V,\alpha\beta}} = \frac{4P_{L,\alpha\alpha}}{4P_{L,\alpha\alpha} + 2P_{L,\alpha\beta}} \qquad (6\text{-}67)$$

where $S_{V,\alpha\alpha}$ and $S_{V,\alpha\beta}$ are the interfacial contact area per unit volume between touching $\alpha\alpha$ particles or $\alpha\beta$ particles and $P_{L,\alpha\alpha}$ and $P_{L,\alpha\beta}$ are the number of point intersections per unit length of test line with $\alpha\alpha$ and $\alpha\beta$ interfaces.

6-12 ANISOTROPY

It is not uncommon to encounter microstructures that exhibit preferred orientation. Stereological measurements on such structures can lead to erroneous results unless the test grids are randomly oriented with respect to the anisotropy. However, if the degree of anisotropy is of interest, the test plane orientations are placed with specific reference to the orientation pattern.

The intercept count P_L that uses a directed test line is ideal for assessing anisotropy. Saltykov introduced use of a polar plot of P_L called the "rose of the number of intersections" [1]. A convenient reference location is chosen as the starting point, and test lines are placed at different angles for directed P_L measurements. From the line length and magnification, P_L as a function of the angles is determined and plotted using polar graph paper.

Most microstructures are isometric or partially oriented; fully oriented structures are much less common. Saltykov has suggested a simple approach for determining the degree of orientation Ω that requires only P_L measurements parallel and perpendicular to the orientation axis [1]. The procedure is to divide the length of oriented lines per unit area, $L_{A,\text{or}}$, by the total line length per unit area, i.e.,

$$\Omega = \frac{L_{A,\text{or}}}{L_{A,\text{is}} + L_{A,\text{or}}} = \frac{P_{L,\perp} - P_{L,\parallel}}{P_{L,\perp} + 0.571 P_{L,\parallel}} \qquad (6\text{-}68)$$

where $L_{A,\text{is}}$ is the line length per unit area of randomly oriented, that is isometric, lines and $P_{L,\perp}$ and $P_{L,\parallel}$ are the number of point intersections per unit length on test lines perpendicular and parallel to the orientation axis. Values of Ω vary between 0 (for a completely random system of lines) to 1 (for a completely oriented system of lines). Intermediate values correspond to partially-oriented systems of lines in a plane.

6-13 SHAPE

The description of the shape or form of microstructural elements is the most difficult task encountered in stereology. The problem is straightforward for those particles that conform closely to well-recognized shapes, such as spheres, cubes, ellipsoids, and rods. As soon as the particle shape differs substantially from these geometrical forms, problems arise. The sectioning plane effect complicates the description of shape, since one must deduce the three-dimensional shape from observations of the spatial outline of the particles. Description of the shape of microstructures on the basis of planar observations can lead to erroneous terminology. A classic example of this problem is provided by high-carbon martensite, which has often been referred to as "acicular" martensite since Osmond introduced the description in 1895. A coarse-grained high-carbon sample heat-treated to produce substantial retained austenite when examined on a sectioning plane reveals a needlelike, i.e., acicular, shape for the martensite particles. However, if the sample is scanned, a small number of the martensite particles will appear flat, or platelike, because the sectioning plane has cut through the structure longitudinally. It is now well recognized that high-carbon martensite has a platelike shape in three dimensions. Therefore the term "plate" martensite is a more accurate description than acicular martensite.

Direct approaches to shape determination are serial sectioning, examination on two orthogonal sectioning planes, stereomicroradiography, optical examination during electrolytic dissolution, TEM examination of thin foils, or SEM examination of deeply etched specimens. While these methods are very useful for determining the true shape of structural elements, they do not provide a quantitative description of shape. The study of shape has been applied to many different problems—graphite in cast iron, grains, sediments, minerals, and powders, to name a few. The shape of graphite in cast iron has received considerable attention because of its strong influence on the properties and behavior of cast irons. Numerous standard chart methods have been developed to classify the size, shape, and distribution of graphite. ASTM Specification A247 is widely used for this purpose.

Quantitative techniques for evaluating graphite shape have been proposed. One approach for flake graphite uses the ratio of the area fraction to the square of the perimeter to define a shape factor [85]. Another approach to defining a shape factor is to divide the area of a graphite particle by the area of a circle circumscribing the particle [86]. The greater the ratio, the more spherical the particle. The mean of a number of such measurements did not correlate as well with the properties as a modified approach which placed greater emphasis on the extremes:

$$SF_{mod} = (SF_{avg} \, SF_{min} \, SF_{max})^{1/3} \qquad (6\text{-}69)$$

where SF is a shape factor.

Hausner has used three approaches to evaluate particle shapes [87]. The first approach was to draw a box around the particle. The ratio of the length to the width of the box is a measure of the particle elongation. The second approach was to divide the particle area A by the area of the box as a way of defining the bulkiness of the particle. The third approach was to divide the square of the particle circumference L_P by $4\pi A$ to define a shape factor (SF):

$$SF = \frac{(L_P)^2}{4\pi A} \qquad (6\text{-}70)$$

For a sphere, the value of the shape factor is 1, and it increases as the particle becomes less spherical. Most users of this type of shape factor prefer the inverse of this equation so that values between 0 and 1 result, with the maximum value applying to a perfect sphere, i.e., a circle in cross section.

Fischmeister has examined the various indirect shape factors that have been proposed and has concluded that there is only one simple combination of stereological measurements that depends exclusively on the planar shape and is not influenced by the volume fraction, size, or size distribution [88]. This shape factor equation is the following:

$$SF = \frac{2}{3\pi} \frac{(P_L)^2}{V_V N_A} \tag{6-71}$$

This shape index gives a value of 1 for a sphere and increases for more complex shapes. In the case of an open structure, tangent counts must be employed. This is accomplished by sweeping a line of constant orientation across the section and counting the number of tangent points per unit area, $\overline{T}_A$, that touch regions of positive $(+)$ and negative $(-)$ curvature. The shape factor equation for this special case is as follows:

$$SF = \frac{4}{3\pi} \frac{(P_L)^2 V_V}{(T_A^+ - T_A^-)} \tag{6-72}$$

As an example of the application of shape factors, three common types of graphite—nodular, compacted, and flake—were analyzed by making 500 to 1000 individual image analysis measurements of the area and perimeter of the particles and computing the shape factor [inverse of Eq. (6-70)] of each particle. The data were grouped into 10 classes from 0 to 1 and plotted as a frequency distribution as shown in Fig. 6-25. The two flake graphite samples from the top and bottom of a large casting had an average shape factor of about 0.4, with most of the shape values confined to the lower 6 shape classes. The compacted graphite had an average shape factor of about 0.6, with most of the shape values between the third and eighth classes. The nodular graphite had an average shape factor of about 0.83, with most of the measurements in the upper four classes.

6-14 PARTICLE SIZE

Measurement of particle size has challenged workers in many fields [89]. Many different procedures have been developed involving counting methods, sedimentation methods, and separation techniques. Many of these methods do not involve microscopy. These different methods do yield somewhat different results depending on the size range of the particles and the influence of shape. The microscopic techniques are quite similar to those previously described for measuring grain size distributions. Indeed, many of the grain size distribution methods can be applied

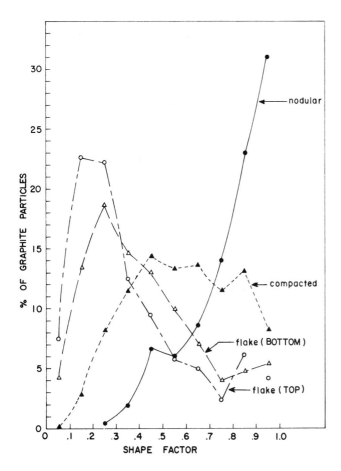

Figure 6-25 Frequency histogram of shape factors measured on flake, compacted, and nodular graphite samples.

to particles, and many of the particle size distribution methods can be used for analyzing grain size distributions. Only microscopic-based techniques are described in this section. Figure 6-26 illustrates the types of measurements employed to size particles or grains.

While the majority of the microscopic methods are based on the assumption that the particles or grains are spherical, De Hoff [4, 6, 90–92] has developed procedures for ellipsoidal particles that are simpler than those used in the early work of Wicksell. The ellipsoid of revolution is a versatile mathematical shape model, with the sphere, rod, and plate as special cases. The axial ratio q of the minor-to-major axis defines the shape of the ellipsoid. The first step in the analysis is to determine if the ellipsoids are prolate (elongated) or oblate (flattened). This is done by comparing the largest observed equiaxed section to the largest most elliptical section. The shape is prolate if the diameter of the equiaxed section is

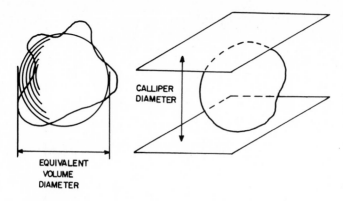

QUANTITIES FOR SIZING IRREGULAR SPATIAL FEATURES.

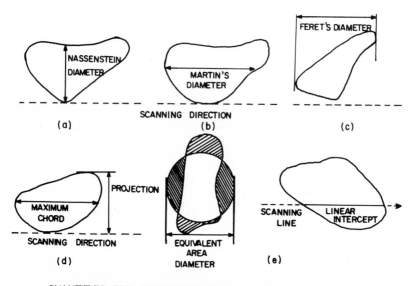

QUANTITIES FOR SIZING IRREGULAR PLANAR FEATURES

Figure 6-26 Illustration of measurement procedures used to size particles. *(From Exner, Ref. 57, courtesy of the American Society for Metals and The Metals Society.)*

approximately equal to the small axis of the most elliptical section. The shape is oblate if the diameter of the equiaxed section is approximately equal to the long axis of the most elliptical particle. Next, the axial ratio q of the most elongated section is measured. If one knows the particle shape, i.e., prolate or oblate, and the axial ratio q, the shape factor $k(q)$ is determined using Fig. 6-27.

Next, the largest section in the plane of polish is found and a measurement is made of the minor axis if it is prolate or the major axis if it is oblate. The largest

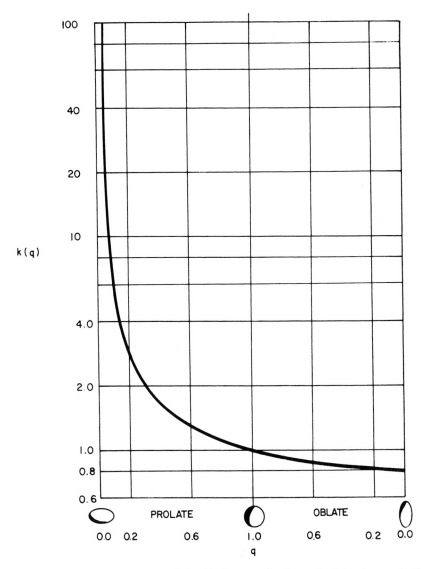

Figure 6-27 Graph showing the relationship between the observed axial ratio q to the shape factor $k(q)$. Graph is used for size classification of ellipsoidal particles. *(From De Hoff, Refs. 4 and 6, copyright American Society for Testing and Materials, reprinted with permission.)*

axial diameter is divided by k, where k is between 8 and 15 in order to define a convenient class interval width Δ. Then, the appropriate dimension of a large number of particle sections (250 to 1000) within a known area is measured. These measurements are grouped into the size classes chosen and the number of observations per class is divided by the area measured to determine $N_{A,i}$ per class. The Saltykov coefficients (see Refs. 4 and 91), $\beta\,(i,j)$, are used for the k classes to calculate the value of $N_{V,j}$ according to the following equation [4, 91]:

$$N_{V,j} = \frac{1}{k(q)\Delta} \sum_{i=j}^{k} N_{A,i}\, \beta(i,j) \tag{6-73}$$

In an alternate procedure, DeHoff used the linear intercept method to estimate the size distribution of ellipsoidal particles in a manner that is simpler than the method just described [4, 6]. A shape factor k_4 is determined using Fig. 6-28 in the same manner as described for determining the shape factor $k(q)$, i.e., one determines whether the particles are prolate or oblate and measures the axial ratio q of the largest observed section. The chord lengths intersecting a large number of particles in a known area are determined using a linear test pattern. The longest observed chord L_{max} is identified and L_{max} is divided by k, the number of size classes (8 to 15) defining a convenient class width Δ. The chord lengths are classified into the appropriate classes and the number of chords per class is divided by the total test line length to obtain the number of chords per unit length per class, $N_{L,j}$. Then, using the values of k_4, Δ, and $N_{L,j}$, the number of particles per unit volume for each class, $N_{V,j}$, is calculated:

$$N_{V,j} = \frac{N_{L,j-1}}{2k_4(j-1)\Delta^2} - \frac{N_{L,j}}{2k_4\, j\Delta^2} \tag{6-74}$$

This calculation is performed for each class, and N_V is calculated by summation.

Hilliard et al. have described a general procedure for determining grain and particle size that is based on the moments of the size distribution and incorporates shape factors for a variety of commonly encountered shapes [93]. The technique is applicable to both single-phase (contiguous) structures or multiphase (noncontiguous) structures. Only simple counting measurements—V_V, P_L, N_L, and N_A— are required. The method permits the estimation of the mean caliper diameter or the mean linear intercept. The former represents the volumetric diameter, while the latter is a planar dimension. The equation for the moments of the grain size distribution is used to define a variety of average grain sizes $D_{m,n}$. These average diameters are weighted using the number of particles, a linear dimension, the number per unit area, the surface area, or the grain volumes. The average diameter of particles changes depending on the nature of the measurement. For example, higher values of $D_{m,n}$ average diameters are obtained as m and n are increased. To illustrate this, we can calculate three particle diameters for the ideal structure shown in Fig. 6-6. The average of the diameters of the 17 circular sections is 7.75 mm. If we total the areas of the 17 circles, calculate the average area, and then calculate the diameter of the average area, we obtain 8.14 mm. Finally, if we assume that each is a sphere and that they have all been intersected at their maximum diameter, we can calculate the average sphere volume and obtain an average diameter of 8.59 mm. Note that as we went from a simple linear measurement to two- and three-dimensional quantities, the average diameter increased. This is due to the difference in the way each particle is weighted. The choice of the appropriate diameter depends on the type of correlation desired.

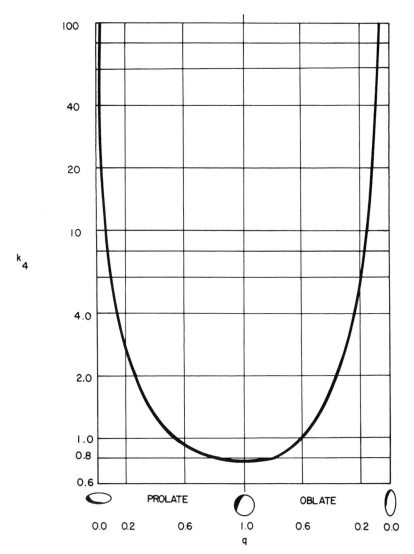

Figure 6-28 Graph relating the observed axial ratio q to the shape factor k_4. Graph is used for sizing of ellipsoidal particles by linear intercept length measurements. *(From De Hoff, Refs. 4 and 6, copyright American Society for Testing and Materials, reprinted with permission.)*

6-15 ELECTRON MICROSCOPY TECHNIQUES

The techniques described in this chapter can be applied to replicas examined in the transmission electron microscope (TEM) or to polished sections examined in the scanning electron microscope (SEM). However, their application to thin foils examined in the TEM is more limited. These techniques can be used if the foil thickness t is small compared to the structure element ($t <$ one-tenth the feature diameter). If the foil thickness is equal to or greater than the size of the structural elements of interest, the image can be made up from particles within the foil thickness as well as from particles intersecting the top and bottom surfaces. Thus, the projected foil image contains more information than normally obtained with reflected-light microscopy. Because there is no way to separate the sources of the information, there are no simple, universal relationships that apply in such cases. An additional problem—particle overlap, or the "Holmes effect"—can produce additional complications in the analysis. Only limited corrections are possible. Many of the relationships used with thin foils require measurement of the foil thickness. However, the foil thickness is not uniform, which also introduces error.

If the volume fraction is very low, particle overlap is a minor source of error and the stereological procedures can be employed with knowledge of the foil thickness t to develop quantitative measurements [94–101]. Extraction replicas can be used to develop particle size distributions, mean size, and standard deviations [96, 99]. However, because 100 percent of the particles cannot be extracted and the percentage of extracted particles varies from sample to sample, volume fractions cannot be estimated with accuracy. Particles varying between about 10 and 1000 nm in diameter can be sized using extraction replicas. Very small particles are best measured with thin foils.

In the analysis of TEM samples, one must recognize that the area examined is very small. Thus, the measurement is not necessarily representative of the bulk condition. One should always use the lowest possible magnification and examine randomly selected areas from a number of locations. Measurements with replicas present no unusual problems. The methods used are identical to those for optical reflected-light microscopy except that the very high magnifications employed and the small test areas influence the statistical measurement accuracy.

The SEM covers the same magnifications as the light microscope and much of the range covered by the TEM. However, sample preparation procedures are identical to those for light microscopy. Although it has been common practice to etch samples more deeply for SEM observation in order to improve image contrast, deep etching is not always necessary with a modern instrument. For high-magnification measurements, a light etch is desired for best accuracy. Indeed, many samples can be examined successfully without etching if there is adequate atomic number difference between the phases to produce an acceptable backscattered electron image. Deep-etching increases the apparent size, volume fraction, and number of second-phase particles, while decreasing their spacing. Deep-etched samples are useful for shape and size studies, but any attempt to extract other information will lead to erroneous conclusions. When attempting to make measurements from SEM images or photographs, one should avoid tilting the sample with respect to the beam because it complicates analysis.

6-16 QUANTITATIVE FRACTOGRAPHY

The development of fracture replication methods and direct fracture examination in the SEM have stimulated progress in the quantification of fracture morphology and in the correlation of fracture morphology with properties and service performance. Prior to the development of these methods, observations were limited to optical examination, generally at low magnifications, of the fracture or of fracture profiles.

Since most fracture surfaces are nonplanar, the light microscope is of limited value except for fracture profile measurements. Replication techniques are difficult to use with ductile fractures, but they do have an advantage in that the replica collapses somewhat, thus presenting a more planar appearance. SEM observation is direct and free of replication artifact problems; thus, interpretation and sample preparation are simpler. The resolution of the modern SEM is no longer a limiting factor as with earlier instruments. Image distortion still exists, but it is a minor problem. If measurements are to be made in the SEM, one should avoid tilting the sample even though there is some loss of image contrast and resolution, otherwise corrections must be made for tilting.

When making measurements on a fracture, the direction of observation should be normal to the fracture. For a flat brittle fracture, this is relatively simple. However, not all fractures are flat and normal to the specimen surfaces. In the case of a shear fracture, it is sometimes possible to cut the sample below the fracture so that the cut surface is parallel to the fracture face, thus simplifying sample orientation in the SEM. In TEM examination of replicas, the specimen holder aligns the replica normal to the beam.

It is sometimes important to determine the length of a crack in a partially fractured sample. If the sample is sectioned in a direction parallel to the crack-growth direction on a plane perpendicular to the fracture, measurement of the projected and true crack lengths can be made on the polished plane. The projected length is simply the straight-line distance between the origin and the crack tip. The total true crack length is the sum of all of the branches of the crack and its undulating surface. The true crack length L_t is the length per unit area, L_A, times the surface area enclosing the crack, A_T. The length per unit area is determined by a P_L count and is calculated using Eq. (6-60). The number of intersections of the crack with a linear test pattern of known length applied in a random fashion within the enclosing test area is counted to determine P_L and to calculate L_A. The value of L_A is multiplied by A_T to determine the total true crack length L_t, i.e.,

$$L_t = \frac{\pi}{2} P_L A_T \qquad (6\text{-}75)$$

The basic stereological relationships given previously are not directly applicable to quantitative fractography because the fracture surfaces are nonplanar. In addition, even with relatively flat fracture surfaces, the orientation of surface elements is not random with respect to a single viewing angle [102]. Thus, procedures for partially oriented surfaces must be employed [3].

One can study fracture topography using vertically oriented sections cut through the fracture. Measurements are made of the fracture profile on the polished vertical section. Edge protection by plating of the fracture surface is recommended. Fracture trace lengths can be measured manually or they can be measured with the aid of semiautomatic tracing devices such as the Zeiss MOP-3.

Manual measurements of the fracture profile can be made using a plastic overlay ruled with evenly spaced parallel test lines [102, 103]. P_L is determined as a function of orientation of the grid test line. Underwood and Chakrabortty used 12 different orientations, each 15° apart [102]. The trace length L_t is calculated as follows:

$$L_t = \frac{\pi}{2} \overline{P_L(\theta)} A_T \qquad (6\text{-}76)$$

where $\overline{P_L(\theta)}$ is the average of the number of grid intersections per unit grid length of the 12 measurements and A_T is the true area of the arbitrarily chosen test area enclosing the fracture trace. With the semiautomatic tracing device, L_t is obtained directly by tracing the fracture surface within a known area with an electronic pencil.

The true fracture profile length L_t is used to calculate the linear roughness parameter R_L, defined by Pickens and Gurland [104] as follows:

$$R_L = \frac{L_t}{L'} \qquad (6\text{-}77)$$

where L' is the projected length of the fracture profile in the test area A_T where L_t is measured. As the fracture surface roughness increases, R_L increases.

One can also plot a rose of the number of intersections of the fracture profile [102]. The degree of orientation of the fracture trace can also be evaluated using Eq. (6-68) and measurements of P_L perpendicular and parallel to the orientation direction [102]. The fracture profile characteristics can be assessed by determination of R_L, use of the rose of the number of intersections, and determination of the degree of orientation.

To determine true spatial fracture feature measurements from projected measurements on vertically oriented SEM fractographs, the R_L measurements are combined with measurements on vertical and parallel longitudinal fractographs in the crack propagation direction [102]. The fracture surface roughness S_A is defined as follows [102]:

$$S_A = \frac{S_t}{A'_T} \qquad (6\text{-}78)$$

where S_t is the true fracture surface area and A'_T is the projected area of the SEM fractograph. As the fracture surface roughness increases, S_A increases. S_A is related to R_L according to the following equation [102]:

$$S_A = \frac{4}{\pi} R_L \qquad (6\text{-}79)$$

The true fracture surface area S_t is determined as follows [102]:

$$S_t = \frac{4}{\pi} R_L A_T'$$ (6-80)

where A_T' is the projected area with dimensions consistent with L'.

Underwood and Chakrabortty have shown how the average area of fracture features can be determined [102]. In their study, fracture facet areas were determined, but the method can be applied to other features as well. The mean projected area of facets, $\overline{A}_{facets}'$, is given as follows:

$$\overline{A}_{facets}' = A_A' / N_A'$$ (6-81)

where A_A' is the area or point fraction of facets determined by point counting on the projected image and N_A' is the number of facets per unit projected area on the SEM fractographs. They postulated that the projection ratio S_A for the entire fracture surface should equal the corresponding projection ratio of the facets (or other features), that is,

$$S_{A,fracture} = A_{A,facets}'$$ (6-82)

where

$$A_{A,facets}' = \frac{\overline{A}_{facets}}{\overline{A}_{facets}'}$$ (6-83)

that is, $A_{A,facets}'$ equals the ratio of the mean true facet area to the mean projected area. Substitution yields the following:

$$\overline{A}_{facets} = S_{A,fracture} \overline{A}_{facets}'$$ (6-84)

or,

$$\overline{A}_{facets} = \frac{4}{\pi} R_L \overline{A}_{facets}'$$ (6-85)

Thus, by combining the surface roughness profile R_L determined on a vertical section through the fracture with a measure of the projected area of the facets made on vertical SEM fractographs, the average true facet (or feature) area can be determined.

Estimation of the average striation spacing on fatigue fractures is the most common fractographic measurement. The striation spacing is a function of the applied stress; however, striations are not present on all fatigue fractures. At very low or at very high crack growth rates, the fracture process does not result in the formation of striations. For some materials, striations are not formed or are observed on only a fraction of the surface even when the crack growth rate is optimum for striation formation. Under certain conditions of loading, the fracture features are destroyed or artifacts are produced which complicate the analysis.

Striation spacings can be measured by direct examination of fractures in the SEM or by using replicas examined in either the SEM or the TEM. The resolution of modern SEMs is sufficient to resolve the finest striations. Specimen tilting in the SEM is commonly employed to improve image contrast; however, tilting distorts the projected image and introduces a variation in magnification across the field. Many fractographers prefer to use replicas, despite the many advantages of the SEM, because of the flatness of the replica image, the good contrast obtained without tilting, and the nondestructive nature of replication.

The fracture surface is examined at regular intervals across the center of the fracture in the crack propagation direction from the origin to the final rupture zone. If replicas are used, the shadowing direction is used to locate the crack propagation direction. At each location of known distance from the origin, several fractographs are taken. The average spacing at each location should be based on measurements of at least 50 striations. Considerable spacing variability can be encountered; when this occurs, the number of striations measured should be increased.

Several procedures have been used to make striation spacing measurements, partly because of differences in the appearance of the striations [103]. A commonly used procedure is to draw several parallel lines across each fractograph in the crack propagation direction. In many cases, these lines will be perpendicular to the striations, although some misorientation can be observed. The test line length is measured and divided by the magnification to obtain L', the projected length of the test line on the fracture surface. The mean projected striation spacing $\bar{\sigma}'$ is calculated using the following equation:

$$\bar{\sigma}' = \frac{L'}{N} \tag{6-86}$$

where N is the number of striations intersected by the line. For best results, N should be 10 or greater. This process is repeated for each test line drawn on each fractograph in order to compute an average striation spacing. In this measurement, the spacing is that of the projected image. The fractograph area is a projected image of the fracture surface in which the fracture surface area is larger than the projected image area [103].

When using this procedure, if the striations are not perpendicular to the test line, the striation spacing will be overestimated. Because the projected spacing underestimates the true spacing, these two errors offset each other to some degree. With replicas, the projected image is closer to the true surface area than with an SEM image because the replica flattens on the grid. For SEM images, corrections can be made by determining the ratio of the true fracture profile length to the projected length by examination of a section cut perpendicular to the fracture surface in the crack growth direction. If the test lines drawn on the fractograph are oriented perpendicular to the striations rather than parallel to the crack growth direction, the striation spacing will be underestimated.

Measurements of the average striation spacing made between the origin (stage II crack initiation site) and the beginning of the final rupture zone are used to plot a graph of the number of striations per unit length (inverse of the spacing) versus distance. This curve can be integrated either mathematically or graphically to determine the number of striations during stage II crack growth. No information can be obtained for the number of cycles prior to stage II crack initiation. Because each cycle during crack growth corresponds to a stress cycle of sufficient magnitude to produce crack growth, the number of cycles of sufficient magnitude to produce crack growth can be estimated (ignoring load interaction effects). The stress intensity range ΔK at any location along the fatigue crack can be estimated based on the average striation spacing.

6-17 IMAGE ANALYSIS

Development of automatic image analyzers and semiautomatic tracing devices (see Fig. 6-29) has greatly increased the use of stereological principles for determining microstructural characteristics [105–114]. These devices reduce the tedium associated with manual measurements, a prime factor in retarding the implementation of these methods. Measurement statistics are also improved because more measurements can be performed in less time. Also, with on-line computer analysis capability, a more thorough statistical analysis of the measurement data can be accomplished. Most such devices have automatic stage movement that provides random field selection, which helps prevent operator bias.

Use of these instruments does require greater attention to sample preparation, since the analyzer lacks the human ability to separate microstructural features that are not unambiguously defined by black-and-white contrast differences. Etching techniques that are adequate for qualitative structural assessment or manual measurements are not always suitable for image analysis. Instead, the operator must rely heavily on selective etching or staining techniques, as described in Chap. 3. The method chosen must produce a clear, distinct contrast difference between phases or constituents of interest because these devices rely primarily on gray-level differences for structural discrimination. Because of the difficulty of image discrimination with certain structures, several semiautomatic tracing devices have been developed in which the operator controls the detection with a light pen. Such features are also available with some image analyzers.

As with most quantitative measurements, the magnification chosen influences the measurements. For example, volume-fraction and length measurements are clearly influenced by magnification. This problem arises partly from the nature of the detection. The television screen contains a great number of picture points with a finite area and a fixed shape. Measurements are made by adjusting the gray-level threshold detection system for the specific gray level of the feature to be detected. The picture points within the constituent of interest are colored white, i.e., detected, and these are compared to the total number of picture points to determine the volume fraction. The number of contiguous detected (white) picture points in a horizontal line is compared to the total number of picture points on a horizontal scan to develop length measurements. In adjusting the threshold, one must just fill out the constituent of interest to get an accurate measurement.

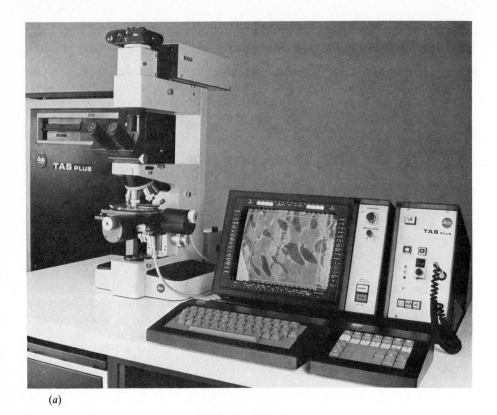

(a)

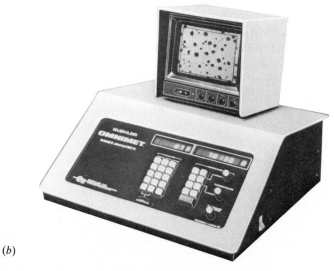

(b)

Figure 6-29 (*a*) Leitz TAS PLUS automatic image analyzer. *(Courtesy of E. Leitz Inc.)* (*b*) Omnimet Image Analyzer. *(Courtesy of Buehler Ltd.)* (*c*) MOP-30 digital semiautomatic tracing device for image analysis. *(Courtesy of C. Zeiss, Inc.)*

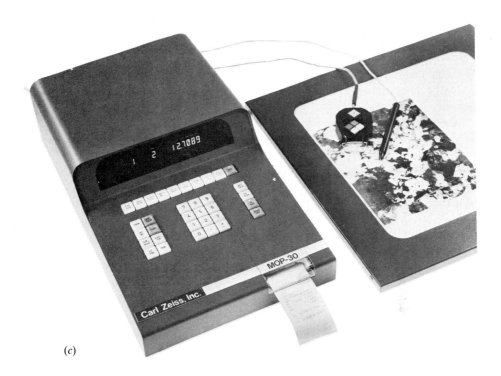

(c)

Since the picture points have a finite size, the smaller the feature with respect to the picture point size, the greater the error associated with the measurement. In such cases, the proper delineation of the feature is very critical. Area and perimeter measurements of small particles can be highly inaccurate. The problem is often complicated by the presence of a slightly different gray level at the perimeter of the constituent because of relief. If the gray level at the phase boundary is shared by some other constituent, proper detection is not possible and a compromise must be used. Proper setting of the threshold detection is somewhat subjective at times and is a major source of error and lack of reproducibility. Use of a "flicker" mode, i.e., alternation between the detected and undetected image, is quite helpful for correct threshold establishment. Automatic detection systems are available on most instruments. They are generally useful on structures that are easily detectable but are not as useful for more complex situations.

Most image analyzers employ minicomputers that can be used to control all the machine functions and analyze the resulting data. Thus, measurements can be performed and a complete analysis of the data prepared in a fraction of the time required for similar manual measurements. By employing the basic stereological counting procedures, most of the manually performed measurements can be conducted automatically. The major restriction is still the need to use particular sample preparation techniques that permit detection of the desired features.

Stereological measurements can be field measurements or measurements of individual features. Field-specific measurements include the classic V_V, P_L, N_L, and N_A counts used to calculate $\overline{L}_3$, L_A, λ, etc. Feature-specific measurements imply that each detected particle or grain is measured individually. Individual measurements are ideal for sizing, calculation of N_V, and shape measurements.

Development of image analyzers has greatly stimulated interest in stereology and the application of stereology to structure-property correlations. Unfortunately, image analyzers are quite expensive, although some relatively low-cost, reasonably versatile instruments have been introduced.

6-18 APPLICATIONS

Quantitative measurement of microstructures is of great importance in quality control studies and in structure-property correlations. Many examples have been provided in this book of the use of these measurements in quality control. Quantitative measurements are of great value to the physical metallurgist in the study of phase transformations and kinetics. Failure analysts also find microstructural measurements useful in both the fractographic and the metallographic studies required to understand the nature of the failure and its causes. Structure-property correlations have received considerable attention in recent years, partly because of the development of stereological methods and the improvements made in image analysis. The subject is so vast that it cannot be reviewed adequately in this chapter. Instead, a number of excellent review articles are listed in the references, which should provide the interested reader with a good introduction to the literature in this field [115–122].

6-19 SUMMARY

For many years, metallurgists have primarily relied on qualitative descriptions of microstructures or ratings based on comparison charts. In general, comparison charts lack the sensitivity needed to accurately define differences between samples. Grain sizes can be rated with reasonable accuracy using standard charts as long as the chart is properly graded, as long as the sample preparation produces a well-defined grain structure, and as long as the grain size distribution is uniform, equiaxed, and similar in etch appearance to the chart pictures. Greater accuracy can be obtained by the intercept measurement technique in a time barely exceeding that required for a good comparison rating.

By proper application of simple stereological counting methods, the microstructural characteristics can be accurately and fully described. These measurements can then be used for quality evaluations, determination of conformance to specifications, growth or transformation kinetic studies, or structure-property correlations. The literature also contains numerous examples of non-stereological-based structure parameters which should be avoided. This chapter has presented most of the commonly used stereological parameters and measurement techniques and a description of the practical problems associated with their use. Further information on these and more complex relationships can be found in the cited references.

While a great deal has been achieved in the development of a systematic system for quantification of microstructures, much more is possible. Indeed, the field of stereology is still in its infancy, with promise of tremendous future potential.

REFERENCES

1. Saltykov, S. A.: *Stereometric Metallography,* 2d ed., Metallurgizdat, Moscow, 1958 (Armed Services Technical Information Agency rough-draft translation ADC 267-700 and 267-701); 3d ed., 1970 (German translation of 3d ed. by VEB Deutscher Verlag für Grundstoffindustrie, Leipzig, 1974).
2. De Hoff, R. T., and F. N. Rhines (eds.): *Quantitative Microscopy,* McGraw-Hill Book Company, New York, 1968.
3. Underwood, E. E.: *Quantitative Stereology,* Addison-Wesley Publishing Company, Inc., Reading, Mass., 1970.
4. De Hoff, R. T.: "Quantitative Microstructural Analysis," *Am. Soc. Test. Mater., Spec. Tech. Publ. 430,* 1968, pp. 63–95.
5. Weibel, E. R.: *Stereological Methods,* vol. 1, *Practical Methods for Biological Morphometry,* 1979; vol. 2, *Theoretical Foundations,* Academic Press, Inc., London, 1980.
6. De Hoff, R. T.: "Quantitative Metallography," *Techniques of Metals Research,* vol. II, pt. 1, Interscience Publishers, a division of John Wiley & Sons, Inc., New York, 1968, pp. 221–253.
7. Saller, H. A., R. F. Dickerson, and G. E. Lind: "Grain Size Chart for Uranium," Battelle Memorial Institute Rep. BMI-66, June 1, 1951.
8. Berglund, T.: "Grain Size Charts for Ferritic and Austenitic Structures," *Jernkontorets Ann.,* vol. 137, no. 11, 1953, pp. 767–784 (BISI no. 1171).
9. Brandis, H., and K. Weibking: "Considerations on Metallographic Grain Size Determination Methods," *DEW Tech. Ber.,* vol. 7, no. 4, 1967, pp. 215–226 (BISI no. 6536).
10. Brandis, H., and K. Wiebking: "Grain-Size Determination of Steels by the Comparative Method," *DEW Tech. Ber.,* vol. 8, no. 3, 1968, pp. 124–127.
11. Walker, G. W.: "Rating of Inclusions ('Dirt Chart')," *Met. Prog.,* vol. 35, February 1939, pp. 167, 169, 170.
12. Diergarten, H.: "Classification of Roller Bearing Steels According to Inclusion Content," *Arch. Eisenhuettenwesen,* vol. 10, 1936, pp. 197–210 (HB no. 556).
13. Rinman, B., H. Kjerrman, and B. Kjerrman: "Chart for the Estimation of Inclusions in Steel," *Jernkontorets Ann.,* vol. 120, 1936, pp. 199–226.
14. Barteld, K., and A. Stanz: "Microscopic Examination of Specialty Steels for Non-Metallic Inclusions with Reference Inclusion Charts," *Arch. Eisenhuettenwesen,* vol. 42, 1971, pp. 581–597.
15. Everest, A. B.: "International Proposals for Cast Iron Graphite Classification," *Mod. Cast.,* vol. 41, April 1962, pp. 86–93.
16. Cura, R.: "Microstructure Standards for Malleable Iron," *Mod. Cast.,* vol. 51, May 1967, pp. 199–229.
17. Nelson, J. A.: "A Guide for Visual Area-Fraction Estimates," *Prakt. Metallogr.,* vol. 8, 1971, pp. 310–313.
18. Ryntz, E. F.: "Reference Microstructures for Visual Estimation of Iron Carbide Content in Nodular Iron," American Foundrymen's Society, CR 7503; *Trans. Am. Foundrymen's Soc.,* vol 82, 1974, pp. 551–554.
19. "Reference Microstructures for Measurement of Pearlite and Ferrite Content in Ductile Iron Microstructures," *Trans. Am. Foundrymen's Soc.,* vol. 82, 1974, pp. 545–550.

20. Hull, F. C.: "A New Method for Making Rapid and Accurate Estimates of Grain Size," *Trans. Am. Inst. Min. Metall. Eng.*, vol. 172, 1947, pp. 439–451.

21. Koebel, N. K.: "Methods for Determining the Degree of Carburization or Decarburization and Evaluating Controlled Atmospheres," *Controlled Atmospheres*, American Society for Metals, Cleveland, 1953, pp. 128–158.

22. Sedriks, A. J.: "Austenitic Manganese Steel: A Technique for Measuring the Extent of Decarburization," *J. Iron Steel Inst.*, vol. 204, 1966, pp. 142–145.

23. Dawes, C.: "The Measurement of the Depth of a Carburized Case," *Metallurgia*, vol. 64, November 1961, pp. 217–219.

24. Saur, R. L.: "Sources and Magnitude of Errors in the Measurement of Coating Thickness with the Double-Beam Interference Microscope," *J. Test. Eval.*, vol. 2, March 1974, pp. 87–90.

25. Gore, J. K., and J. J. Glass: "The Practical Application of Statistics to the Quality Control of Electroplated Products," *48th Annual Tech. Proc.*, American Electroplaters' Society 1961, pp. 115–119.

26. "Microscopical Method of Measuring Coating Thickness: An Interlaboratory Comparison," *Plating*, vol. 59, 1972, pp. 320–323.

27. Ogburn, F.: "Microscopical Measurements of Thickness: Manipulation of the Microscope," *Plating*, vol. 59, 1972, pp. 1155–1157.

28. "Report of Subcommittee III on Conformance Tests—Part 1: Thickness Determination of Electrodeposits," *Proc. Am. Soc. Test. Mater.*, vol. 60, 1960, pp. 207–217.

29. Ogburn, F.: "Coating Thickness—Its Measurement and Its Significance," *Properties of Electrodeposits, Their Measurement and Significance*, Electrochemical Society, Princeton, N.J., 1975, pp. 229–245.

30. Ogburn, F., T. R. Shives, and C. H. Brady: "Calibration of a Filar Micrometer," *J. Matls.*, vol. 6, no. 1, 1971, pp. 60–66.

31. Hilliard, J. E.: "Volume-Fraction Analysis by Quantitative Metallography," General Electric Research Laboratory Report 61-RL-2652M, March 1961 (see also: Chap. 3 in Ref. 2).

32. Hilliard, J. E., and J. W. Cahn: "An Evaluation of Procedures in Quantitative Metallography for Volume-Fraction Analysis," *Trans. Am. Inst. Min. Metall. Eng.*, vol. 221, 1961, pp. 344–352.

33. Abrams, H.: "Practical Applications of Quantitative Metallography," *Am. Soc. Test. Mater., Spec. Tech. Publ. 504*, 1972, pp. 138–182.

34. Mathieu, O., et al.: "Measuring Error and Sampling Variation in Stereology: Comparison of the Efficiency of Various Methods for Planar Image Analysis," *J. Microsc.*, vol. 121, pt. 1, 1980, pp. 75–88.

35. Desch, C. H.: "The Solidification of Metals from the Liquid State," *J. Inst. Met.*, vol. 22, 1919, pp. 241–276.

36. Williams, W. M., and C. S. Smith: "A Study of Grain Shape in an Aluminum Alloy and Other Applications of Stereoscopic Microradiography," *Trans. Am. Inst. Min. Metall. Eng.*, vol. 194, 1952, pp. 755–765; vol. 197, 1953, pp. 741–743.

37. Skarek, J., and K. Ciha: "Comparative Investigation and Evaluation of Different Methods of Determining Austenitic Grain Size," *Neue Huette*, vol. 6, 1961, pp. 301–309 (BISI no. 2589).

38. Iancu, P.: "Comparison Between the Austenitic Grain Sizes Obtained by Various Methods," *Metalurgia*, vol. 22, 1970, pp. 695–701 (BISI no. 9254).

39. Hilliard, J. E.: "Grain-Size Estimation," General Electric Research Laboratory Report no. 62-RL-3133M, December 1962.

40. "Standard Method for Measuring the Austenite Grain Size in Steel," Special Report no. 5, Nov. 4, 1965, Japan Society for Promotion of Science.

41. Schückher, F.: "Grain Size," *Acta Polytech. Scand.*, 1966, Chap. 54, pp. 1–102 (see also Ref. 2, pp. 201–265).

42. Woodhead, J. H.: "The Statistical Errors in Grain Size Measurement," *Quantitative Analysis of Microstructures in Medicine, Biology and Materials Development*, Dr. Riederer-Verlag, Stuttgart, 1975, pp. 265–276.

43. Schreiber, D., and S. Mennenöh: "Contribution to the Determination of Austenite Grain Size by the Oxidation Method," *Arch. Eisenhuettenwes*, vol. 32, 1961, pp. 857–861.

44. Smith, C. S.: "Grain Shapes and Other Metallurgical Applications of Topology," *Metal Interfaces,* American Society for Metals, Cleveland, 1952, pp. 65–113.

45. Hilliard, J. E.: "Estimating Grain Size by the Intercept Method," *Met. Prog.,* vol. 84, May 1964, pp. 99–100, 102.

46. Abrams, H.: "Grain Size Measurement by the Intercept Method," *Metallography,* vol. 4, 1971, pp. 59–78.

47. Snyder, R. W., and H. F. Graff: "Study of Grain Size in Hardened High Speed," *Met. Prog.,* vol. 33, 1938, pp. 377–380.

48. Grossman, M. A.: "Toughness and Fracture of Hardened Steels," *Trans. Am. Inst. Min. Metall. Eng.,* vol. 167, 1946, pp. 39–79.

49. Thompson, A. W. : "Calculation of True Volume Grain Diameter," *Metallography,* vol. 5, 1972, pp. 366–369.

50. Johnson, W. A.: "Estimation of Spatial Grain Size," *Met. Prog.,* vol. 49, January 1946, pp. 87–92, 92B.

51. Kostron, H.: "The Metallographic Measurement of Grain Size," *Arch. Metallkund.,* vol. 3, 1949, pp. 193–203; vol 3, 1949, pp. 229–242.

52. Bergh, S., and O. Lindberg: "On the Microscopic Determination of the Number and Distribution of Nonmetallic Inclusions," *Jernkontorets Ann.,* vol. 146, 1962, pp. 862–868 (HB no. 5772).

53. Paulus, M.: "Method of Study of Granular Structure," *Met. Corros. Ind.,* no. 448, 1962, pp. 447–468; no. 449, 1963, pp. 14–34.

54. Aaron, H. B., R. D. Smith, and E. E. Underwood: "Spatial Grain-Size Distribution from Two-Dimensional Measurements," *First International Congress of Stereology,* Vienna, April 18–20, 1963, pp. 16-1 to 16-8.

55. Saltykov, S. A.: "The Determination of the Size Distribution of Particles in an Opaque Material from Measurement of the Size Distribution of their Sections," *Stereology,* Springer-Verlag New York Inc., New York, 1967, pp. 163–173.

56. Shephard, R. G.: "An Examination of the Relative Convenience and Expected Errors in the Various Methods for Determining Grain Size Distribution in Metals and Ceramics," Atomic Energy Research Establishment-R6268, United Kingdom Atomic Energy Authority, January 1970.

57. Exner, H. E.: "Analysis of Grain- and Particle-Size Distributions in Metallic Materials," *Int. Metall. Rev.,* vol. 17, 1972, pp. 25–42.

58. Rhines, F. N., K. R. Craig, and D. A. Rousse: "Measurement of Average Grain Volume and Certain Topological Parameters by Serial Section Analysis," *Metall. Trans.,* vol. 7A, 1976, pp. 1729–1734.

59. Patterson, B. R., and F. N. Rhines: "Serial Section Estimate of Number Per Unit Volume," *Microstructural Science,* vol. 7, Elsevier Publishing Company, New York, 1979, pp. 457–462 (see also B. R. Patterson: "The Grain Size Distribution of Aluminum," Ph.D. thesis, University of Florida, Gainesville, 1978).

60. Hanson, K. L.: "Determination of Grain Density in Space-Filling Geometries from Measurable Two-Dimensional Parameters," *Acta Metall,,* vol. 27, 1979, pp. 515–521.

61. Vander Voort, G. F.: "Inclusion Measurement," *Metallography as a Quality Control Tool,* Plenum Press, Plenum Publishing Corporation, New York, 1980, pp. 1–88.

62. Allmand, T. R.: "A Review of Methods for Assessing Nonmetallic Inclusions in Steel," *J. Iron Steel Inst.,* vol. 190, 1958, pp. 359–372.

63. Allmand, T. R., and D. S. Coleman: "The Effect of Sectioning Errors on Microscopic Determinations of Non-Metallic Inclusions in Steels," *Met. Mater.,* vol. 7, 1973, pp. 280–283.

64. Bergh, S.: "Quantitative Microscopic Determination of the Inclusions in Steel," *Jernkontorets Ann.,* vol. 146, 1962, pp. 924–934 (HB no. 5980).

65. Bergh, S., and O. Lindberg: "Routine Appraising of the Micro-Slag Contents in Steel by the Size-Measurement–Point Counting Method," *Jernkontorets Ann.,* vol. 149, no. 4, 1965, pp. 150–156.

66. Vander Voort, G. F.: "Automating the JK Inclusion Analysis," *Microstructural Science,* vol. 10, Elsevier Publishing Company, New York, 1982, pp. 277–290.

67. Carney, D. J., and E. C. Rudolphy: "Examination of High Sulphur Free-Machining Ingot, Bloom and Billet Sections," *J. Met.,* vol. 5, 1953, pp. 999–1008.

68. Van Vlack, L. H.: "Correlation of Machinability with Inclusion Characteristics in Resulphurized Bessemer Steels," *Trans. Am. Soc. Met.,* vol. 45, 1953, pp. 741–757.
69. Malkiewicz, T., and S. Rudnik: "Deformation of Non-Metallic Inclusions during Rolling of Steel," *J. Iron Steel Inst.,* vol. 201, 1963, pp. 33–38.
70. Maunder, P. J. H., and J. A. Charles: "Behavior of Non-Metallic Inclusions in a 0.2% Carbon Steel Ingot During Hot Rolling," *J. Iron Steel Inst.,* vol. 206, 1968, pp. 705–715.
71. Waudby, P. E.: "Factors Controlling the Plasticity of Silicate Inclusions during Hot Working," *Scand. J. Metall.,* vol. 3, 1974, pp. 151–152.
72. Brunet, J. C., and J. Bellot: "Deformation of MnS Inclusions in Steel," *J. Iron Steel Inst.,* vol. 211, 1973, pp. 511–512.
73. Smith, C. S., and L. Guttman: "Measurement of Internal Boundaries in Three-Dimensional Structures by Random Sectioning," *Trans. Am. Inst. Min. Metall. Eng.,* vol. 193, 1953, pp. 81–87; vol. 193, 1953, p. 1561.
74. Schoeck, G.: "Correlation between Dislocation Length and Density," *J. Appl. Phys.,* vol. 33, 1962, pp. 1745–1747.
75. Gensamer, M., et al.: "The Tensile Properties of Pearlite, Bainite and Spheroidite," *Trans. Am. Soc. Met.,* vol. 30, 1942, pp. 983–1020.
76. Fullman, R. L.: "Measurement of Particle Sizes in Opaque Bodies," *Trans. Am. Inst. Min. Metall. Eng.,* vol. 197, 1953, pp. 447–452; vol 197, 1953, pp. 1267–1268; vol. 200, 1954, p. 664.
77. Corti, C. W., P. Cotterill, and G. A. Fitzpatrick: "The Evaluation of the Interparticle Spacing in Dispersion Alloys," *Int. Metall. Rev.,* vol. 19, 1974, pp. 77–88.
78. Belaiew, N. T.: "On the Structure of Nodular Troostite," *J. Iron Steel Inst.,* vol. 124, 1931, pp. 195–214.
79. Pellissier, G. E., et al.: The Interlamellar Spacing of Pearlite," *Trans. Am. Soc. Met.,* vol. 30, 1942, pp. 1049–1086.
80. Asundi, M. K., and D. R. F. West: "The Kinetics of Pearlite Growth in Binary Aluminium Bronzes," *J. Inst. Met.,* vol. 94, 1966, pp. 19–23.
81. Birkbeck, G., and T. C. Wells: "Pearlite Morphology in Three Low-Carbon Steels," *Trans. Am. Inst. Min. Metall. Eng.,* vol. 242, 1968, pp. 2217–2220.
82. Gregory, B., H. T. Hall, and G. Bullock: "Measurement of the Interlamellar Spacing of Pearlite," *Trans. Am. Soc. Met.,* vol. 54, 1961, pp. 106–110, 743–746.
83. Brown, D., and N. Ridley: "Rates of Nucleation and Growth and Interlamellar Spacing of Pearlite in a Low-Alloy Eutectoid Steel," *J. Iron Steel Inst.,* vol. 204, 1966, pp. 811–816.
84. Gurland, J.: "The Measurement of Grain Contiguity in Two-Phase Alloys," *Trans. Am. Inst. Min. Metall. Eng.,* vol. 212, 1958, pp. 452–455.
85. Miyata, S., and M. Kikuchi: "Quantitative Analysis of the Graphite Structure in Cast Iron by a Statistical Method," *Trans. Natl. Res. Inst. Met.,* vol. 16, no. 3, 1974, pp. 25–31.
86. Capeletti, T. L., and J. R. Hornaday: "Nodular Iron Shape Factor—A New Approach to Quantifying Graphite Morphology," *Trans. Am. Foundrymen's Soc.,* vol. 82, 1974, pp. 59–64.
87. Hausner, H. H.: "Characterization of the Powder Particle Shape," *Planseeber. Pulvermetall.,* vol. 14, 1966. pp. 75–84.
88. Fischmeister, H. F.: "Shape Factors in Quantitative Microscopy," *Z. Metallkunde,* vol. 65, 1974, pp. 558–562.
89. Allen, T.: *Particle Size Measurement,* 3d ed., Chapman & Hall, Ltd., London, 1981.
90. De Hoff, R. T., and F. N. Rhines: "Determination of Number of Particles Per Unit Volume from Measurements Made on Random Plane Selections: The General Cylinder and the Ellipsoid," *Trans. Am. Inst. Min. Metall. Eng.,* vol. 221, 1961, pp. 975–982.
91. De Hoff, R. T.: "The Determination of the Size Distribution of Ellipsoidal Particles from Measurements Made on Random Plane Sections," *Trans. Am. Inst. Min. Metall. Eng.,* vol. 224, 1962, pp. 474–477.
92. De Hoff, R. T.: "The Determination of the Geometric Properties of Aggregates of Constant-Size Particles from Counting Measurements Made on Random Plane Sections," *Trans. Am. Inst. Min. Metall. Eng.,* vol. 230, 1964, pp. 764–769.
93. Hilliard, J. E., J. B. Cohen, and W. M. Paulson: "Optimum Procedures for Determining

Ultrafine-Grain Sizes," *Ultrafine-Grain Ceramics, Proc. 15th Sagamore Army Materials Res. Conf.,* Syracuse University Press, 1970, pp. 73–98.

94. Hilliard, J. E.: "The Counting and Sizing of Particles in Transmission Microscopy," *Trans. Am. Inst. Min. Metall. Eng.,* vol. 224, 1962, pp. 906–917.

95. Crompton, J. M. G., R. M. Waghorne, and G. B. Brook: "The Estimation of Size Distribution and Density of Precipitates from Electron Micrographs of Thin Foils," *Br. J. Appl. Phys.,* vol. 17, 1966, pp. 1301–1305.

96. Ashby, M. F., and R. Ebeling: "On the Determination of the Number, Size, Spacing and Volume Fraction of Spherical Second-Phase Particles from Extraction Replicas," *Trans. Am. Inst. Min. Metall. Eng.,* vol. 236, 1966, pp. 1396–1404.

97. Goldsmith, P. L.: "The Calculation of True Particle Size Distributions from the Sizes Observed in a Thin Slice," *Br. J. Appl. Phys.,* vol. 18, 1967, pp. 813–830.

98. Sellars, C. M., and A. F. Smith: "Measurement of Particle Size, Volume Fraction, and Foil Thickness from Electron Microscopic Observations," *J. Mater. Sci.,* vol. 2, 1967, pp. 521–528.

99. Mukherjee, T., W. E. Stumpf, and C. M. Sellars: "Quantitative Assessment of Extraction Replicas for Particle Analysis," *J. Mater. Sci.,* vol. 3, 1968, pp. 127–135.

100. Underwood, E. E.: "The Stereology of Projected Images," *J. Microsc.,* vol. 95, pt. 1, 1972, pp. 25–44.

101. Weibel, E. R., and R. P. Bolender: "Stereological Techniques for Electron Microscopic Morphometry," *Principles and Techniques of Electron Microscopy,* vol. 3, Van Nostrand Reinhold, Company, Inc., New York, 1973, pp. 237–296.

102. Underwood, E. E., and S. B. Chakrabortty: "Quantitative Fractography of a Fatigued Ti-28V Alloy," *Am. Soc. Test. Mater., Spec. Tech. Publ. 733,* 1981, pp. 337–354.

103. Underwood, E. E., and E. A. Starke: "Quantitative Stereological Methods for Analyzing Important Microstructural Features in Fatigue of Metals and Alloys," *Am. Soc. Test. Mater., Spec. Tech. Publ. 675,* 1979, pp. 633–682.

104. Pickens, J. R., and J. Gurland: "Metallographic Characterization of Fracture Surface Profiles on Sectioning Planes," *Proc. 4th Intern. Cong. for Stereology,* National Bureau of Standards Special Pub. 431, 1976, pp. 269–272.

105. Moore, G. A.: "Recent Progress in Automatic Image Analysis," *J. Microsc.,* vol. 95, pt. 1, 1972, pp. 105–118.

106. Cole, M.: "Instrument Errors in Quantitative Image Analysis," *Microscope,* vol. 19, 1971, pp. 87–112.

107. Gahm, J.: "Instruments for Stereometric Analysis with the Microscope—Their Application and Accuracy of Measurement," *Advances in Optical and Electron Microscopy,* vol. 5, Academic Press, Inc., New York., 1973, pp. 115–161.

108. Hougardy, H. P.: "Instrumentation in Automatic Image Analysis," *Microscope,* vol. 22, 1974, pp. 5–25.

109. Underwood, E. E.: "Stereology in Automatic Image Analysis," *Microscope,* vol. 22, 1974, pp. 69–80.

110. Hougardy, H. P.: "Measurement of the Performance of Quantitative Image Analysing Instruments," *Prakt. Metallogr.,* vol. 12, 1975, pp. 624–635.

111. Hougardy, H. P. "Recent Progress in Automatic Image Analysis Instrumentation," *Microscope,* vol. 24, 1976, pp. 7–23.

112. Exner, H. E.: "Programmable Semiautomatic Instruments for Quantitative Structure Analysis and Other Geometric Evaluations in the Materials Laboratory," *Prakt. Metallogr.,* vol. 15, 1978, pp. 15–22.

113. Lee, R. J., and J. F. Kelly: "Overview of SEM-Based Automated Image Analysis," *Scanning Electron Microscopy, 1980,* part I, SEM Inc., AMF O'Hare (Chicago), pp. 303–310.

114. Lee, R. J., et al.: "Quantitative Metallography by Computer-Controlled Scanning Electron Microscopy," *J. Met.,* vol. 33, March 1981, pp. 20–25.

115. Underwood, E. E.: "Microstructure and Properties," *An Atomistic Approach to the Nature and Properties of Materials,* John Wiley & Sons, Inc., New York, 1967, pp. 432–451.

116. Rhines, F. N.: "Microstructure-Property Relationships in Materials," *Metall. Trans.,* vol. 8A, 1977, pp. 127–133.

117. Rhines, F. N.: "Use of the Global and Topological Parameters in Microstructure-Property Correlation," *Microstructure Science,* vol. 8, Elsevier Publishing Company, New York, 1980, pp. 123–139.
118. Freiman, S. W.: "Applied Stereology," *Characterization of Ceramics,* Marcel Dekker, Inc., New York, 1971, pp. 555–579.
119. Nazare, S., and G. Ondracek: "Automatic Image Analysis in Materials Science," *Microscope,* vol. 22, 1974, pp. 39–58.
120. Fischmeister, H. F.: "Applications of Quantitative Microscopy in Materials Engineering," *J. Microsc.,* vol. 95, pt. 1, 1972, pp. 119–143.
121. Amstutz, G. C., and H. Giger: "Stereological Methods Applied to Mineralogy, Petrology, Mineral Deposits and Ceramics," *J. Microsc.,* vol. 95, pt. 1, 1972, pp. 145–164.
122. De Hoff, R. T., and E. D. Whitney: "Quantitative Microscopy in the Characterization of Ceramic Materials and Processes," *Ceramic Microstructures '76,* Westview Press, Boulder, Colo., 1977, pp. 81–100.

ETCHANTS FOR REVEALING MACROSTRUCTURE

Macroetchants for aluminum and aluminum alloys

Material	Etch composition	Remarks
Al	10 mL HF 15 mL HCl 90 mL H_2O	Flick's etch. Immerse for 10–20 s, dip in HNO_3, rinse, and dry. 180-grit ground surface is best.
Al	27 mL HNO_3 24 mL HCl 39 mL H_2O	Etch by immersion of sample (Grabin and Rabkin).
Al Al alloys	15 mL HF 45 mL HCl 15 mL HNO_3 25 mL H_2O	Tucker's etch. Etch by immersion of sample. General purpose etch. Finely ground surface not required.
Al Al alloys	10–20 g NaOH 100 mL H_2O	Use at 60–70°C for 5–15 min, dip in HNO_3 to remove smut. Good-general purpose etch. Finely ground surface not required.
Al Al-Cu alloys Al-Si alloys	1 mL HF 1.5 mL HCl 2.5 mL HNO_3 95 mL H_2O	Etch by immersion of sample (Dix and Keller).
Al-3%Ag alloy Al alloys	12 mL HCl 12 mL HNO_3 6 mL HF 90 mL H_2O	Modified Tucker's etch. Etch by immersion of sample, dip in HNO_3 to remove smut (Stewart and coworkers).

Macroetchants for aluminum and aluminum alloys *(continued)*

Material	Etch composition	Remarks
Al Al-Cu alloys	10 mL HF 15 mL HCl 25 mL HNO$_3$ 50 mL H$_2$O	Etch by immersion of sample (Barker).
Al alloys	Conc. NaOH	Use hot. Reveals recrystallized areas (Bennett).
Al alloys	60 mL HCl 30 mL HNO$_3$ 5 mL HF 5 mL H$_2$O	Poulton's etch. Reveals grain structure.
High-purity Al Al-Mg alloys	20 mL glycerin 30 mL HCl 2 mL saturated aq. FeCl$_3$ solution 7 drops HF 0.5–1 mL HNO$_3$	Etch by immersion of sample. Reveals grain structure. Color filters employed to increase contrast (Beck and coworkers).
Al-Mn alloys	6 mL glycerin 25 mL HCl 3 mL saturated aq. FeCl$_3$ solution 7–10 drops HF 2–3 mL HNO$_3$	Etch by immersion of sample for 10–20 s. Reveals grain structure. Color filters employed to increase contrast (Beck and coworkers).
Al alloys	1 part HCl 1 part HF 1 part H$_2$O	Immerse sample for a few minutes (Boss).
High-purity Al	15 mL HCl 85 mL H$_2$O	Couple externally to an austenitic stainless steel rod dipped in same solution (galvanic couple); adjust cathode-to-anode areas to give a good etch in 5 min (Servi).
Al Al alloys	100 mL HCl 100 mL HNO$_3$ 25 mL HF 100 mL H$_2$O	Swab etch. Good for welds.
Al alloys	75 mL HCl 25 mL HNO$_3$ 5 mL HF	Use fresh solution at room temperature by immersion or swabbing of sample. Develops grain structure. Does not require finely ground surface. Can dilute etching solution with 25% H$_2$O to slow etching.
Al alloys (except high-Si castings)	15 mL HCl 5 mL HNO$_3$ 5 mL HF 75 mL H$_2$O	Dilute Tucker's etch. Immerse sample at room temperature in etch.
Al Al alloys	100 mL HNO$_3$ 50 mL HCl 1.5 mL HF	Concentrated Keller's etch. Very vigorous.

Macroetchants for aluminum and aluminum alloys *(continued)*

Material	Etch composition	Remarks
Al Al alloys	1 part HNO_3 1 part HCl 1 part 1–2% HF solution (in H_2O)	Very vigorous (Van Lancker).
Al-Si alloys	15 g cupric chloride 100 mL H_2O	Hume-Rothery etch. Good for high-Si alloys. Use ground surface. Immerse sample 5–10 s, brush off copper deposit or dip in a 1:1 solution of HNO_3 and H_2O.
Al-Cu-Si alloys	15 mL HNO_3 10 mL HCl 5 mL HF 70 mL H_2O	Conc. Keller's etch. Dip in HNO_3 to remove smut.
Al-Cu-Mg-Ni alloys	20 mL HCl 15 mL HNO_3 5 mL HF 60 mL H_2O	Zeerleder's etch. Dip in HNO_3 to remove smut.
Al-Si alloys	10 mL HF 90 mL H_2O	Good for high-Si alloys (Keller).
Al-Cu alloys	15 mL H_2SO_4 5 mL HF 80 mL H_2O	Good for billet structures (Van Lancker).
Al alloys	5 mL HF 15 mL HCl 20 mL HNO_3 60 mL H_2O	Good for most Al alloys. Swab etch. Remove deposits by swabbing sample lightly with HNO_3 (Mott and Thompson).
Al alloys	2 mL HF 24 mL HNO_3 72 mL H_2O	Good for most Al alloys (Arrowsmith and coworkers).
Pure Al	5.5 mL H_2SO_4 100 mL H_2O	Reveals surface defects. Immerse sample from few seconds to minutes.

Al
Al alloys
	Solution a
	  50–200 g NaOH
	  1000 mL H_2O
	Solution b
	  1 part HNO_3
	  1 part H_2O
		Caustic etch to reveal early damage by fatigue cracking. Dip in solution a for 3–15 min at room temperature. Rinse in water and immerse briefly in solution b. Wash and dry. For larger parts, swab surface with 400 g NaOH per liter of water for 30–60 min. Any insoluble residue can be removed with solution b (Boone).

Al alloy forgings	40 g $FeCl_3$ 13 g cupric ammonium chloride 1000 mL H_2O	Use hot (80–95°C). Immerse sample for 2-min periods until sufficient depth of etch is obtained. Wash and immerse in 45% aq. HNO_3 at room temperature to remove surface deposit. Surface adequate for "nature printing."

Macroetchants for aluminum and aluminum alloys *(continued)*

Material	Etch composition	Remarks
Al-Cu-Mg castings	1 g NaOH 100 mL H_2O	Use polished surface. Immerse sample in solution at room temperature for 15 min. This produces a dull-gray color. Rinse with water and immerse in cold water for 10 min. This lightens the surface film. After drying, the film has a brass or bronze hue and the grains appear bright (Kapernick).
Very pure Al	808 mL orthophosphoric acid 1660 mL Carbitol 320 mL HF 128 g anhydrous boric acid 72 g oxalic acid 1012 mL H_2O	Use aluminum tank for anodizing and graphite cathode. Gently agitate solution (35°C). Raise current density to about 5 A/in^2 for about 30 s. Drop voltage until the current density is 0.5 A/in^2. Hold for 105 s. Transfer sample to cool water. This produces an anodic film that reveals grain structure (Hone and Pearson).

Macroetchants for beryllium

Material	Etch composition	Remarks
Be	10 mL HCl 4 g NH_4Cl 90 mL H_2O	Works best on coarse-grained Be. Swab or immerse sample at room temperature for a few minutes.
Be	10 mL HCL 2 g NH_4Cl 2 g picric acid 90 mL H_2O	Use when the above etch does not work. Use in same manner. Fine-grained Be difficult to macroetch.
Be	25 mL H_2SO_4 500 mL H_3PO_4 59 g CrO_3	Produces a grain-boundary etch. Etch at 100°F for a few seconds to minutes.

Macroetchants for bismuth and antimony and their alloys

Material	Etch composition	Remarks

Bi-Sn alloys
Sb-Pb alloys
	Solution a
	160 mL H_2O
	40 mL HNO_3
	30 mL acetic
	    acid
	Solution b
	400 mL H_2O
	1 mL acetic
	    acid
		Etch with solution a at 100°F. Repolish until surface becomes bright. Then etch with solution b for 1–2 h.

Pure Sb alloys
Sb-Bi alloys
	Solution a
	220 mL H_2O
	80 mL HNO_3
	Solution b
	300 mL H_2O
	45 g am-
	    monium
	    molybdate
		Mix equal parts of solutions a and b before use. Etch for up to a few minutes.

Sb Bi	100 mL H_2O 25 g citric acid 10 g ammonium molybdate	Etch for up to a few minutes.

Macroetchants for cobalt and cobalt alloys

Material	Etch composition	Remarks
49%Co-49%Fe-V alloy Some Stellites	50 mL HCl 50 mL H_2O	Good for general structure. Immerse sample in hot (60–80°C) solution for 30 min. Rinse in hot water.
HS-31 HA-151 N-155	50 mL HCl 10 mL HNO_3 10 g $FeCl_3$ 100 mL H_2O	Good for general structure and grain size. Swab sample until desired contrast is obtained.
HA-36	2 g cupric ammonium chloride 5 g $FeCl_3$ 5 mL HNO_3 50 mL HCl 80 mL H_2O	Good for general structure and grain size. Swab sample until desired contrast is obtained.
Co Co alloys	Solution a Saturated solution of $FeCl_3$ in HCl Solution b Add 5% HNO_3 to solution a prior to use.	Use at room temperature. After etching dip sample in 1:1 solution of HCl and H_2O.
Co Co alloys	Solution a 21 mL H_2SO_4 15 mL HCl 21 mL HNO_3 21 mL HF 22 mL H_2O Solution b 40 mL of a solution of 1 g $CuCl_2·2H_2O$ and 5 mL H_2O 40 mL HCl 20 mL HF	Etch sample 5 min in solution a and then 5 min in solution b.
Nimonic Ni-Cr-Co alloys Ni-Cr-Co-Mo alloys	5 mL HF 3 mL HCl 50 mL alcohol "pinch" of sodium hyposulfite	Use boiling.
Co-Ni-Fe high-temperature alloys	25 mL H_2O 50 mL HCl 25 mL HNO_3	Immerse sample at room temperature for 10–30 min.

Macroetchants for copper and copper alloys

Material	Etch composition	Remarks
Cu Brass	10 mL HNO_3 90 mL H_2O	Reveals grain structure and cracks. Immerse sample at room temperature for a few minutes.
Cu Cu-Al alloys Brass	50 mL HNO_3 50 mL H_2O	Develops grain contrast. Agitate sample to prevent pitting. Immerse sample at room temperature for a few minutes. Remove smut on Al bronze by dipping in HNO_3.
Cu Brass	30 mL HCl 10 g $FeCl_3$ 120 mL H_2O or ethanol	Develops grain contrast. Immerse sample at room temperature for a few minutes.
Cu Cu alloys	50 mL HNO_3 5 g $AgNO_3$ (or 0.15–0.5 g) 50 mL H_2O	Produces a brilliant deep etch. Etch by immersion of sample.
Si brass Bronze	40 g CrO_3 7.5 g NH_4Cl 50 mL HNO_3 8 mL H_2SO_4 100 mL H_2O	Etch by immersion of sample.
Brass	1 part 10% $FeCl_3$ in H_2O 1 part 5% CrO_3 in saturated brine 2 parts 20% acetic acid in H_2O	Reveals strain pattern.
Cu Cu alloys	25 g $FeCl_3$ (or 5 or 10 g) 25 mL HCl (or 10 mL) 100 mL H_2O	Acid aqueous ferric chloride. Develops grain contrast. Requires a good surface.
Cu Cu alloys	59 g $FeCl_3$ 2 mL HCl 96 mL ethanol	Alcoholic ferric chloride. Wash with alcohol or acetone rather than water to avoid staining.
Cartridge brass	Solution a 1 part 30% NH_4OH 1 part H_2O Solution b 3% H_2O_2 (25–35 vol % of solution a) Solution c 1 part HNO_3 1 part H_2O	Reveals flow lines. Use a ground surface. Cover specimen with solution a under a chemical hood. Add solution b to increase etch volume by 25–35%. Do not let reaction get too violent. Cover and let stand for 12 h. Rinse with water. Brush solution c onto specimen. When flow lines are visible, rinse in water and dry (Carlson).

Macroetchants for copper and copper alloys *(continued)*

Material	Etch composition	Remarks
Cu Cu alloys	5 g $Fe(NO_3)_2$ 25 mL HCl 70 mL H_2O	Requires a polished surface. Swab sample for 3–4 min, then immerse for 15–60 s (Slepian and Prohaska).
Cu Cu alloys	Conc. HNO_3	Rapid etch for rough surfaces. Contrast can be improved by a small addition of $AgNO_3$.

Brass	Solution a
	  1 g $Hg(NO_3)_2$
	    ·$8H_2O$
	  100 mL H_2O
	Solution b
	  1 mL HNO_3
	  100 mL H_2O
		Verifies stresses in brass. Use equal parts of solutions a and b. Time until cracking indicates stress level.

Cu Brass	10–25 g ammonium persulfate 100 mL H_2O	Good general etch. Immerse sample for a few seconds to a few minutes.
Cu High-Cu alloys Phosphor bronze	2 g $K_2Cr_2O_7$ 4 mL saturated aq. NaCl solution 8 mL H_2SO_4 100 mL H_2O	Immerse specimen for 15–30 min, then swab with fresh solution. Reveals grain boundaries and oxide inclusions.
Cu Cu alloys	75 mL HNO_3 25 mL acetic acid	Use fresh solution. Specimen should be dry before use.
Brass containing beta phase	1 part 0.880 ammonia 2 parts 2.5% aq. ammonium persulfate 1 part water	Reveals grain size (Cibula).

Macroetchants for iron and steel

Material	Etch composition	Remarks
Fe Most steels	1 part HCl 1 part H_2O	Developed by Uddeholm. Use at 160–180°F. Immerse sample for 10–60 min. General-purpose etch. Use with cut or ground surfaces. Most commonly used deep etch.
Fe Most steels	38 mL HCl 12 mL H_2SO_4 50 mL H_2O	Watertown Arsenal etch. Use at 160–180°F. Immerse sample for 10–60 min. Good contrast obtained. Can be used for stainless steel. Use with cut or ground surfaces.
Fe Most steels	9 parts HCl 3 parts H_2SO_4 1 part H_2O	Use at 160–175°F for 2 h. Use with cut or ground surfaces (Waring and Hofamman).
Fe Most steels	1 parts HCl 3 parts H_2SO_4 6 parts H_2O	Use at 160–175°F for 30 min or more. Use with cut or ground surfaces (Sauver).
Fe Most steels	1 part H_2SO_4 6 parts HCl 2 parts H_2O	Etch by immersion of sample in solution heated to 80°C.
Fe Most steels	1 part HCl 2 parts H_2SO_4 3 parts H_2O	Use at 160–175°F for 30 min or more. Use with cut or ground surfaces.
Fe Most steels	500 mL HCl 70 mL H_2SO_4 180 mL H_2O	Use at 160–175°F for 1–2 h. Use with cut or ground surfaces (Keshian).
Fe Most steels	10 g iodine 20 g KI 100 mL H_2O	Developed by Reinhardt. Used in early studies of macrostructure. No longer used.
Fe Most steels	10 mL 10 N iodine solution 100 mL ethanol	Developed by Osmond and used in early studies of macrostructure. No longer used.
Fe Most steels	25 mL HNO_3 75 mL H_2O	Use cold. Good for large sections that cannot be immersed. Use with ground surfaces (Sauver).
Fe Most steels	10–15 mL HNO_3 85–90 mL H_2O or alcohol	Use cold. Good general-purpose etch. Use with ground surfaces.
Fe Most steels	10 g ammonium persulfate 90 mL H_2O	Use cold by immersion or swabbing of sample with polished surface. Good general etch (Rawdon).
Alloy steels	50 mL HCl 25 mL HNO_3 25 mL H_2O	Dilute aqua regia. Immerse sample for 10–15 min at room temperature. Good for high-alloy steels, Fe-Co high-temperature alloys, and Ni-based high-temperature alloys.

Macroetchants for iron and steel *(continued)*

Material	Etch composition	Remarks
Fe Most steels	1–6% HNO_3 in alcohol (1% zephiran chloride can be added)	Use cold by immersion of sample with polished surfaces. Good general-purpose etch.
Fe Most steels	4% picric acid in alcohol (zephiran chloride can be added)	Use cold by immersions of sample with polished surface. A few milliliters of HCl can be added for higher-alloy steels. Good general-purpose etch.

Cast iron	Solution a
	  2.5 g ammonium persulfate
	  100 mL H_2O
	Solution b
	  Solution a plus 1.5 g KI
	Solution c
	  Solution b plus 1.5 g $HgCl_2$
	Solution d
	  Solution c plus 15 mL H_2SO_4
		Swab 15 min with solution a, then 10 min with solution b, then 5 min with solution c, then 5 min with solution d. Reveals dendritic structure (Austin and Lipnick).

Fe
Most steels
	Solution a
	  5 mL HNO_3
	  95 mL alcohol
	Solution b
	  10 mL HCl
	  90 mL H_2O
		Etch 5 min in solution a, then dip 1 s in solution b. Use polished sample. Good for revealing decarburization, carburization, and depth of hardening.

High-alloy steels	16 g $CuSO_4 \cdot 5H_2O$ 50 mL H_2O 100 mL HCl	Use at 71–77°C for 30 min or more with ground surface.
Maraging steel	60 mL lactic acid 20 mL HNO_3 10 mL HCl	Use at room temperature. Discard after use (Piearcy and coworkers).
Nitriding steels	15 mL ammonium persulfate 85 mL H_2O	Use at 160°F for 10 min. Reveals flow times (Burg and Weiss).
Fe Low-alloy steels	2 g picric acid 25 g NaOH 100 mL H_2O	Use boiling with polished sample. Reveals dendritic pattern (Sauver and Krivobok).
Fe Most steels Stainless steel	1 g picric acid 10 mL HCl 100 mL alcohol	Vilella's reagent. Immerse sample at room temperature. Use polished surfaces.

Macroetchants for iron and steel *(continued)*

Material	Etch composition	Remarks
High-alloy steels	2 parts HCl 1 part HNO_3 3 parts glycerol	Developed by Vilella. Use fresh solution with polished surface. Warm sample in water before etching. Repolishing and reetching sometimes improves contrast.
High-alloy steels	10–40 mL HNO_3 4–10 mL HF 86–50 mL H_2O	Use at 160–180°F.
High-alloy steels Stainless steel	50 mL HCl 50 mL H_2O 20 mL H_2O_2 (30%)	Mix HCl and H_2O, heat to 160–170°F. Immerse sample and add H_2O_2 in steps when foaming stops. Do not mix. Produces brilliant etch.
Austenitic stainless steels	50 mL HCl 25 mL saturated aq. $CuSO_4$ solution (or 10 g $CuSO_4$ in 50 mL H_2O)	Marbles reagent. Solution can be heated. Good general etch.
Fe Low-alloy steels	Saturated aq. picric acid solution plus small amount of wetting agent.†	Use polished surface. Etch up to 25 min at room temperature. A few percent HCl can be added to etch higher-alloy steels. Good for welds.
Austenitic stainless steel	10 g CrO_3 90 mL H_2O	Use electrolytically with polished surface. Platinum or stainless steel cathode, 60–100°F, 6 V dc, 1 A/in², 2–7 min. Good for welds (Miller and Houston).
Stainless steel	20 mL ethylene glycol 20 mL HNO_3 100 mL ethanol	Use electrolytically with polished sample. Use stainless steel cathode, 3 A/in². Instantaneous contact made with specimen. Current density cut in half. Light repolishing sometimes required before a 15–30 s etch with anode and cathode in contact. Reveals flow lines. Also useful for Co-based and Ni-based alloys (Buchheit).
High-speed steel	23 mL H_2O 20 mL HCl 10 mL HNO_3	Dilute aqua regia. Immerse sample for 5–6 s in water at 180–200°F, then in the cold etchant for about 10 s. Reveals soft spots (Shepherd).
Fe-3.25% Si alloy	30 mL HCl 1 mL HF 69 mL H_2O	Reveals secondary recrystallization (Philip and Lenhart).
Nitralloy	10 mL HCl 2 mL HNO_3 88 mL H_2O	Use ground surface. Immerse sample for up to 60 min at 180°F. Reveals alumina distribution. (V. T. Malcolm).
Fe Most steels	20 mL HNO_3 10 mL H_2SO_4 20 mL H_2O	Nitrosulfuric acid etch. Reveals as-cast structure and grain size in cast steels (Loria).

†Such as Teepol or sodium tridecylbenzene sulfonate.

Macroetchants for iron and steel *(continued)*

Material	Etch composition	Remarks
Austenitic stainless steel Ni-based alloys	Solution a 15 g $(NH_4)_2SO_4$ 75 mL H_2O Solution b 250 g $FeCl_3$ 100 mL HCl Solution c 30 mL HNO_3	Lepito's no. 1 etch. Combine solutions a and b, then add solution c. Immerse sample in solution at room temperature. Use fresh. Reveals grain structure.
Nitrided steels	250 mL H_2O 109 g ammonium persulfate 1 g Maccanol (wetting agent) 10 drops of saturated aq. sodium thiocyanate solution	Used to detect "white layer" on surfaces of nitrided steels after grinding. Clean surface and brush on etchant. Areas with white layer are not attacked (Weiss and Burg).
Austenitic stainless steel	5 mL bromine 95 mL methanol	Etch samples containing stress-corrosion cracks in the solution for about an hour at room temperature. Crack pattern vividly revealed (Nielsen).
Steels	60 mL HNO_3 15 mL HCl 25 mL H_2O	Use with ground surfaces. Scrub surface clean and swab with 50% aq. HCl (Smith).
High-speed steel	30 g ammonium persulfate 6 mL HF 6 mL H_2O_2 58 mL H_2O	Use fresh solution, add $(NH_4)_2S_2O_8$ to the solution last. Swab solution on sample. Use a ground surface. Use at room temperature (Cremisio).

Macroetchants for lead and lead alloys

Material	Etch composition	Remarks

Pb
Most alloys
	Solution a
	250 mL H_2O
	140 mL
	  NH_4OH
	60 mL HNO_3
	100 mL molyb-
	  dic acid
	Solution b
	960 mL H_2O
	400 mL HNO_3
	Solution c
	100 mL glacial
	  acetic acid
		Add solution a to solution b (never solution b to solution a) and let precipitate redissolve, then add solution c. Swab sample until desired contrast is obtained. Alternate method to make etch: dissolve molybdic acid in water, add ammonium hydroxide, filter, then add solution b only.

Pb-Sb alloys	Solution a
	30 mL glacial
	  acetic acid
	40 mL HNO_3
	16 mL H_2O
	Solution b
	1 mL glacial
	  acetic acid
	400 mL H_2O
		Requires well-polished surface. Etch with solution a at 42°C, then repolish until bright. Etch with solution b for 1–2 h.

Pb-Sb alloys	Solution a 80 mL HNO_3 220 mL H_2O Solution b 45 g $(NH_4)_2MoO_4$ 300 mL H_2O	Russell's reagent. Mix a 1:1 solution of solutions a and b immediately before application. Immerse specimen in solution (room temperature) until desired contrast is obtained.
Pb-Sb alloys	10 g $(NH_4)_2MoO_4$ 25 g citric acid 100 mL H_2O	Voce's reagent. Immerse specimen in solution (room temperature) until desired contrast is obtained.

Pb-Sb alloys	70–80 mL acetic
	  acid
	30–20 mL
	  $H_2O_2(30\%)$
		Worner and Worner's reagent. Immerse sample in solution† (room temperature) a few second until desired contrast is obtained. Sample should be dry before immersion.

Pb	80 mL H_2O 20 mL HNO_3	Swab sample for 10 min. Produces grain contrast.

†A freshly prepared mixture can cause pitting. It is recommended to allow the etch to work on some lead wire or foil for several seconds before etching the specimen. If the wire or foil exhibits a smooth, bright surface, the etch is ready for use. If the surface of the wire or foil has a dull appearance, add more H_2O_2. If the surface is pitted, add acetic acid. Contrast is improved through use of polarized light.

Macroetchants for lead and lead alloys *(continued)*

Material	Etch composition	Remarks

Pb
Most Pb
  alloys
	4 parts glycerol
	1 part glacial
	  acetic acid
	1 part HNO$_3$
		Add HNO$_3$ immediately before use. Heat solution to 80°C. Alternate etching and repolishing may be required. Reveals grain boundaries. For Pb-Sn alloys, double the amount of glycerol (Vilella and Beregekoff).

Pb-Sb-Cu alloys	5 mL acetic acid 95 mL alcohol	Immerse polished specimen in solution (room temperature) for 20 min. Produces grain contrast (Gregory and coworkers).

Pb-As-Sn-Bi
  alloys
	16 g
	  (NH$_4$)$_2$MoO$_4$
	20 mL NH$_4$OH
	75 mL HNO$_3$
	100 mL H$_2$O
		Etch with this solution followed by Voce's reagent. Produces grain contrast (Gregory and coworkers).

Pb	7 parts acetic
	  acid
	1 part
	  H$_2$O$_2$(30%)
	1 part H$_2$O
	1 part ethanol
		Polish chemically, then etch in solution for 4–5 s. Dry and reetch three or four times. Contrast improved at low magnification using polarized light. A sensitive tint plate produces brilliant color contrast (Gifkins and Nicholls).

Pb Pb alloys	3 parts glacial acetic acid 4 parts HNO$_3$ 16 parts H$_2$O	Use fresh at 40–42°C. Immerse sample for 4–30 min. Good results obtained by etching with solutions a and b of first etchant in this table followed by this etchant for about 6 min. Swab with running water (Bassett and Snyder).
Pb Pb alloys	50 mL HNO$_3$ 50 mL H$_2$O	Etch in boiling solution. Reveals grain structures (Cibula).

Macroetchants for magnesium and magnesium alloys

Material	Etch composition	Remarks
ZK60A	5–25 mL acetic acid 95–75 mL H_2O	Immerse sample in solution at room temperature until desired contrast is obtained. Alloys with zinc may form smut on surface which can be removed by dip in a 1:1 solution of HF and H_2O. Reveals flow lines (Bassett and Snyder).
Mg Mg alloys	10 g tartaric acid 90 mL H_2O	Immerse sample in solution at room temperature for up to about 3 min. Reveals flow lines (Hess and George).
AZ31B AZ61A AZ80A	20 mL acetic acid 80 mL H_2O 5 g $NaNO_3$	Immerse sample in solution at room temperature for 1–5 min. Reveals flow lines (Dow Chemical Co.).
AZ61A AZ80A	5 g picric acid 100 mL alcohol 10 mL H_2O 5 mL acetic acid	Immerse sample in solution at room temperature for up to 3 min. Use finely ground surface. Reveals grain size and flow lines (George).
AZ21 AZ31	3.5 g picric acid (or 6 g) 70 mL alcohol 10 mL H_2O 10 mL acetic acid	Same as above etch (Dow Chemical Co.).
ZK60A	2.5 g picric acid (or 6 g) 50 mL alcohol 20 mL H_2O 5 mL acetic acid (or 20 mL)	Same as above etch (Dow Chemical Co.).
Mg-Al-Zn-Mn alloys (C-Alloy)	10–20 mL HNO_3 90–80 mL H_2O	Immerse sample in solution at room temperature for up to 5 min. Remove smut with a 1:1 solution of HF and H_2O. Reveals flow lines and internal defects (Hess and George).
Mg-Al-Zn-Mn alloys (C-Alloy)	75 mL ethylene glycol 24 mL H_2O 1 mL HNO_3	Glycol etch. Reveals grain structure. Immerse sample in solution at room temperature until desired contrast is obtained (McCabe and Sharp).
All Mg alloys	60 mL ethylene glycol 20 mL acetic acid 19 mL H_2O 1 mL HNO_3	Immerse sample in solution at room temperature until desired contrast is obtained. Reveals grain structure (George).
Mg alloys	180 g $Na_2Cr_2O_7$ 180 mL HNO_3 H_2O to make 1000 mL	Immerse sample in solution at room temperature until desired contrast is obtained. General-purpose etch for revealing defects.

Macroetchants for magnesium and magnesium alloys *(continued)*

Material	Etch composition	Remarks
Mg alloys	280 g CrO_3 25 mL HNO_3 10 mL HF H_2O to make 1000 mL	Immerse sample in solution at room temperature until desired contrast is obtained. Reveals abnormal grain growth and surface defects.
Mg alloys	4 g picric acid 100 mL alcohol 0.7 mL H_3PO_4	Immerse sample in solution at room temperature repeatedly to obtain desired contrast by staining. Reveals segregation of intermetallic compounds and cracking. Use finely ground surface (George).
Mg alloys	2–10 g ammonium persulfate 100 mL H_2O	Immerse sample in solution at room temperature until desired contrast is obtained. Reveals flow lines (Montgomery).
Mg-Al-Zn-Mn alloys	100 mL ethanol saturated with picric acid 10 mL acetic acid	Use fresh solution to reveal grain structure (Montgomery).
Mg alloys	12 g CrO_3 15 mL HNO_3 85 mL H_2O	Immerse sample in etch. Reveals grain size (Montgomery).
Mg alloys	24 g sodium acid phosphate 4 g potassium ferricyanide 1000 mL H_2O	Use finely ground specimen. Immerse specimen in solution at room temperature for 40 min to 2 h. Reveals flow lines (Dearden).

Macroetchants of nickel and nickel alloys

Material	Etch composition	Remarks
Ni	10 g $CuSO_4$ 50 mL HCL 50 mL H_2O	Marble's reagent. Immerse sample in solution at room temperature (3–10 min) until desired contrast is obtained. Reveals grain structure.
Low-Ni alloys	10 g $CuSO_4$ 20 mL HNO_3 10 mL H_2O	Immerse sample in solution at room temperature for 20–30 min. Reveals grain structure.
High-Ni alloys	50 mL HNO_3 50 mL H_2O	Immerse sample in solution at room temperature for 20–30 min. Reveals flow lines and defects.
Ni-Cr-Fe alloys	50 mL HNO_3 50 mL acetic acid (75 mL HCl addition can be made)	Lepito's no. II etch. Immerse sample in hot solution. Reveals grain structure. Can also be applied by swabbing. Good for welds.
Ni alloys	50 mL saturated aq. $CuSO_4$ solution 50 mL HCl	Modified Marble's reagent. Apply by swabbing sample.
Ni alloys	100 mL HCl 100 mL H_2O 40 mL $H_2O_2(30\%)$	Mix HCl and H_2O, then heat to 160–170°F. Immerse sample in solution and add H_2O_2 in several steps (allow foaming to stop). Do not mix.
Ni alloys	Solution a 15 g ammonium persulfate 75 mL H_2O Solution b 250 g $FeCl_3$ 100 mL HCl Solution c 30 mL HNO_3	Lepito's no. I etch. Combine solutions a and b, then add solution c. Immerse samples in solution at room temperature. Use fresh solution. Reveals grain structure.
Ni Ni alloys	1 part HNO_3 3 parts HCl	Aqua regia. Etch by immersion of sample at room temperature (3–10 min).
Nickel alloys	Solution a 4 g copper ammonium chloride 25 mL H_2O Solution b 15 g $FeCl_3$ 50 mL HCl	Adler's etch. Works best with smooth ground surfaces. Mix solutions a and b. Dip or swab sample for 5–60 s. Deep etching reveals flow lines.
Maraging steel	60 mL lactic acid 20 mL HNO_3 10 mL HCl	Use at room temperature. Discard after use (Piearcy and coworkers).

Macroetchants of nickel and nickel alloys *(continued)*

Material	Etch composition	Remarks
TD-nickel TD-NiCrAl Inconel MA-754	70 mL HCl 30 mL H_2O_2	Reveals general structure (Wittenberger).
Ni Ni alloys	Conc. HNO_3	Immerse specimen 3–5 min to reveal structure or longer to reveal porosity and flow lines (Sinizer).
Ni Ni alloys	Conc. HCl	Etch by immersion of sample at room temperature for up to 1 h. Produces grain contrast (Rawdon and Lorentz).
Ni-based superalloys	80 mL HCl 2 mL HNO_3 11 mL H_2O 16 g $FeCl_3$	Widely used for pickling and macroetching of superalloys. Produces grain contrast. Preheat sample in hot water (180°F) for a few minutes before etching.
Ni-based superalloys	80 mL HCl 13 mL HF 7 mL HNO_3	"Heppenstall" etch. Used to reveal freckles. Preheat sample by immersing in hot (180°F) water for a few minutes. Then immerse in etch at room temperature. Use above etch to remove surface deposit.

Macroetchants for noble metals

Material	Etch composition	Remarks
Silver	10 mL HNO_3 90 mL alcohol	Etch sample at room temperature for a few minutes. Produces grain contrast.

Gold
Platinum
  alloys
Palladium
  alloys
	66 mL HCl
	34 mL HNO_3
		Etch sample in hot solution for a few minutes. Produces grain contrast. Use fresh solution.

Ruthenium
Osmium
Rhodium
Ruthenium,
  osmium,
  and
  rhodium
  alloys
	50 mL lactic acid
	20 mL HNO_3
	30 mL HF
		Immerse sample in solution at room temperature. Produces grain contrast.

Ruthenium
Osmium
Rhodium
Ruthenium,
  osmium,
  and
  rhodium
  alloys
	30 mL HCl
	15 mL HNO_3
	30 mL HF
		Immerse specimen in solution at room temperature. Produces grain contrast.

Platinum
Platinum
  alloys
	80 mL of
	  saturated aq.
	  NaCl solution
	20 mL HCl
		Etch sample electrolytically at 6 V for a few minutes. Produces grain contrast.

Macroetchant for polymers

Material	Etch composition	Remarks

Phenol
  formaldehyde
	75 mL dimethyl
	  sulfoxide
	25 mL HNO_3
		Immerse sample 4 h at 75–80°C. Rinse with water, then acetone, and dry (Gaulin and Richardson).

Macroetchants for refractory metals

Material	Etch composition	Remarks
Molybdenum Tungsten Vanadium Niobium Tantalum	30 mL HCl 15 mL HNO_3 30 mL HF	Immerse samples in solution for 5–20 min at room temperature.
Molybdenum Tungsten Vanadium	15 mL HF 35 mL HNO_3 75 mL H_2O	Immerse samples in solution at room temperature for 10–20 min.
Tungsten Vanadium Niobium Tantalum	10 mL HF 30 mL HNO_3 50 mL lactic acid	Immerse sample in solution at room temperature for 1–40 min.
Chromium	10 mL H_2SO_4 90 mL H_2O	Immerse sample in boiling solution for 2–5 min.
Chromium plating	120–240 g NaOH 3.75–15 g potassium pyrophosphate 1000 mL H_2O	Electrochemical reverse-etch process for detecting abrasive grinding of hard Cr plating developed by Grumman Aerospace Corp. Use for Cr plating on high-strength steel. Use electrolytically at room temperature at 12 V dc, 0.62 A/cm^2, 45 s (Messler and Maller).

Macroetchants for silicon

Material	Etch composition	Remarks
Si-B-P alloys	2 parts 20% aq. HF 98 parts HNO_3	Use polished specimen. Etch reveals P-N barrier (Pfann and Scaff).
Si-B-P alloys	5 g NaOH 100 mL H_2O	Use warm with polished sample. Reveals grain structure (Pfann and Scaff).

Macroetchants for tin and tin alloys

Material	Etch composition	Remarks
Tin	1–5% HCl in alcohol	Etch by immersion of sample.
Sn-Sb-Cu alloys Sn-Sb-Cu-Pb-Ni alloys	Saturated aq. ammonium polysulfide solution	Immerse sample in solution at room temperature for 20–30 min. Use glass container under a chemical hood. Remove deposit by swabbing under running water. For low-Sn alloys and high-Cu alloys, etch as described and then immerse in 1:1 solution of H_2O_2 and NH_4OH. Reveals grain structure (Drake).
Tin Sn-Sb alloys Sn-Sb-Pb alloys	10 mL HCl 90 mL H_2O	Etch sample electrolytically. Use 5 s for common tin and 20 s for pure tin. For Sn-Sb-Pn alloys, etch for 2 s. Use platinum electrode (Weaver).
Sn-Sb-Pb alloys	1 mL silver nitrate 99 mL H_2O	Etch by immersion of sample. Rub smut off under running water.
Tin alloys	100 mL H_2O 2 mL HCl 10 g $FeCl_3$	Etch for 30 s to 5 min.
Tin	10 g ammonium pursulfate 100 mL H_2O	Etch by immersion of sample (Homer and Plummer).
Sn-Pb alloys	1 part HNO_3 1 part acetic acid 8 parts glycerin	Etch by immersion of sample (Urquhart and coworkers).
Sn-Pb alloys	Conc. HCl	Etch by immersion of sample (Haworth and Oliver).

Macroetchants for titanium and titanium alloys

Material	Etch composition	Remarks
Titanium alloys	20 mL HCl 40 mL HF 40 mL H_2O	Immerse specimen in solution at 120–150°F for 20–30 min. If smut forms immerse in 30% H_2SO_4 for 3 min.
Ti-7%Al-4%Mo alloy	42 mL HNO_3 8 mL HF 50 mL H_2O (or 10 mL HF and 40 mL HNO_3)	Immerse specimen in solution at 120–150°F for 20–30 min.
Iodide Ti	60 mL $H_2O_2(30\%)$ 30 mL H_2O 10 mL HF	Use under hood, swab sample at room temperature until desired contrast is obtained.
Ti-4%Al-4%Mn alloy	10 mL HF 90 mL H_2O	Reveals flow lines (Ogden and Holden).
Ti-4%Al-4%Mn alloy	50 mL HF 50 mL glycerin	Reveals flow lines (Ogden and Holden).
Ti-6%Al-4%V alloy Ti-5%Al-2.75%Cr-1.25%Fe alloy Ti-2.25%Al-3.75%Mn alloy	0.5 mL HF 1.5 mL HCl 2.5 mL HNO_3 95 mL H_2O	Keller's etch. Reveals flow lines and general structure.
Ti alloys Ti-7%Mn alloy	5 mL HF 35 mL HNO_3 60 mL H_2O	Reveals flow lines and general structure (Ogden and Holden).
Ti-3%Al alloy Ti-13%V-11%Cr-3%Al alloy Ti-6%Al-4%V alloy	1.5 mL HF 3 mL HNO_3 95.5 mL H_2O	Reveals general structure (Ogden and Holden).
Ti-5%Al-2.5%Sn alloy	1.5 mL HF 15 mL HNO_3 83.5 mL H_2O	Reveals general structure (Ogden and Holden).
Alpha-beta alloys	50 mL HCl 50 mL H_2O	General-purpose macroetch (Ogden and Holden).
Ti alloys	200 mL H_2O 2 mL HF 10 g $Fe(NO_3)_3$ $\cdot 9H_2O$ 35 g oxalic acid	Heat solution to 120–140°F, immerse sample for up to a few minutes. Good for welds.

Macroetchants for titanium and titanium alloys *(continued)*

Material	Etch composition	Remarks
Ti alloys	Solution a Agitated solution of dry acid salt (e.g., MacDermid Metex Acid Salt M-629, 16 oz/gal at room temperature Solution b 15 oz/gal solution of trisodium phosphate Solution c 35 mL HNO_3 2.5 mL HF 62.5 mL H_2O	"Blue-etch anodize" technique. Mask all steel parts of anodizing fixture. Vapor-degrease parts. Immerse in heavy-duty alkali cleaner for 1–2 min at 120–180°F. Rinse in cold water. Immerse in solution a for 1.5 min. Rinse in cold water. Attach anodizing fixture and rinse in water. Immerse in solution b at 70°F and agitate. Anodize at 30 V for 30 s. Turn on current after immersion. Do not agitate. Rinse in water. Remove from fixture and rinse. Immerse in solution c to remove most of blue color and improve color contrast. Time varies from 2–25 s depending on alloy. Rinse in water and dry. Segregation revealed by color pattern (Baron and Snell).
Ti alloys	75 mL H_2O 15 mL HNO_3 10 mL HF	Swab sample for 2 min at room temperature. Reveals flow lines, grain structure, and segregates. Good general-purpose macroetch (Hendrickson and Sparks).

Macroetchants for zinc and zinc alloys

Material	Etch composition	Remarks
Zn alloys (Cu-free)	50 mL HCl 50 mL H_2O	Immerse sample in solution at room temperature for about 15 s. Wipe under running water to remove smut. Repeat until desired contrast is obtained. Produces grain contrast.
Zn alloys (with Cu)	20 g CrO_3 1.5 g Na_2SO_4 (or 3.5 g Na_2SO_4 $\cdot 10H_2O$) 100 mL H_2O	Palmerton etch. Immerse in solution until desired contrast is obtained. Produces grain contrast.
Zn Zn alloys	Conc. HCl	Produces grain contrast (Anderson and Rodda).
Zinc-rich alloys	5 mL HCl 95 mL alcohol	Produces grain contrast.

Macroetchants for zirconium and hafnium

Material	Etch composition	Remarks

Zr
Hf
High-Zr
  alloys
High-Hf
  alloys
	45 mL H_2O
	45 mL HNO_3
	8–10 mL HF
	(ethanol some-
	  times sub-
	  stituted for
	  H_2O)
		Chemically polish sample with solution by swabbing then stain sample in the solution diluted with 3–5 parts H_2O. When the desired contrast is obtained, remove sample and wash in water. Sample can also be heat-tinted (750°F for 5 min) rather than stained. Reveals grain contrast (Cain).

Zr
Hf
Low-Zr
  alloys
Low-Hf
  alloys
	45 mL
	  H_2O_2(30%)
	45 mL HNO_3
	10 mL HF
		Apply by swabbing sample at room temperature. Rinse 10 s after yellow vapor forms. Use under hood.

Zircalloy-2 Hf	30 mL HNO_3 5 mL HF 70 mL H_2O	Same as above.

MACROETCHANTS BASED ON COPPER-CONTAINING COMPOUNDS— FOR ETCHING OF IRON AND STEEL

Etch name and/or developer	Composition									
	Water, mL	Alcohol, mL	CuCl₂, g	NH₄Cl, g	FeCl₃, g	HCl, mL	SnCl₂, g	MgCl₂, g	Picric acid, g	Ni(NO₃)₂, g
Heyn	1000		51	32						
Humfrey	1000		74	46						
Whiteley	1000		1.2		200	50				
Dickenson	1000		6		80	100				
Rosenhain and Haughton	1000		1		30	80				
Stead's no. 1†	10	900	10			100	0.5			
Stead's no. 2	200	1000	50			20		40		
Comstock		1000	10			10		40		
LeChatelier's no. 1	180	1000	10			20		40		
LeChatelier's no. 2		1000	10			20		40		
Oberhoffer	100	500	1		30	15–25			5	
Fry's no. 1	500	150	8			50	0.5			
Fry's no. 2	480	200	40			150				
Canfield‡	400	600	6		24	200				
Fry's no. 4	48		450			600				20
Meyer and Eichholz no. 1	500		200		200	300				
Meyer and Eichholz no. 2	1000	1000	60		60	100				

Composition

Etch name and/or developer	Water, mL	Alcohol, mL	CuCl₂, g	NH₄Cl, g	FeCl₃, g	HCl, mL	SnCl₂, g	MgCl₂, g	Picric acid, g	Ni(NO₃)₂, g
Wazau	400		180			720				
Schrader	500	100	6		6	10			5	
DeSy	250	500	1.5		3	50	1			
Flinn	500	100	20			50				
Jin		500	8		30	36	4			
Marts and Capes	1000		92	58		5				
Griffis and Spretnak	30	120	30			35				
Warke and McCall		120			2	5			4	
Adler§	25					50				
Bish	80		36		15	144				
Taub¶	157					76				

Note: Le Chatelier's no. 1 also known as the LeChatelier-Lemoine reagent and Le Chatelier's no. 2 is also known as the LeChatelier-Dupuy reagent.

† Dissolve salts in a small amount of hot water.

‡ 4 mL HNO₃ can be added.

§ Reagent also contains 4 g copper ammonium chloride. Dissolve copper ammonium chloride in water, then add ferric chloride and hydrochloric acid.

¶ Reagent also contains 1 g anhydrous AuCl₃.

MACROETCHANTS FOR REVEALING STRAIN PATTERNS IN NONFERROUS METALS

Material	Etchant Composition	Comments
Al-Mg alloys Al-Cu-Mg alloys	10% aq. H_3PO_4 solution	Polished sample etched for 5–20 min at room temperature. Strain pattern revealed by gray to black shading (Morris and coworkers).
Al	20 mL HCl 20 mL HNO_3 5 mL HF 40 mL H_2O 15 mL ethanol	Before straining, the samples are annealed for 4 h at 450°C, then furnace-cooled. After loading, the samples are mechanically polished and etched by immersion (Mequid).

Ni-based superalloys
Mar-M200
Udimet-700
	Etchant:
	  67 mL lactic acid
	  22 mL HNO_3
	  11 mL HCl
	Electropolish:
	  87 mL methanol
	  8 mL H_2SO_4
	  3 mL HNO_3
	  2 mL HF
	Etchant:
	  Solutionized
	    Udimet-700
	  50 mL HNO_3
	  50 mL HCl
	Electropolish:
	  87 mL methanol
	  13 mL H_2SO_4
	Etchant:
	  Solutionized and
	    aged Udimet-700
	  50 mL lactic acid
	  33 mL HCl
	  17 mL HNO_3
	Electropolish
	  87 mL methanol
	  13 mL H_2SO_4
		Samples are chemically etched and electropolished for a short time. Current density for electropolishing is 1.6 A/in^2. The etch should be "overaged"—add the HNO_3 to the HCl and let stand until yellow. Then add other chemicals, if specified. Current density for electropolishing of solutionized or solutionized and aged Udimet-700 is 4.8 A/in^2 (Gell and Field).

ELECTROLESS AND ELECTROLYTIC PLATING PROCEDURES

Electroless Nickel

Electroless nickel is the most commonly used plating material in metallographic edge preparation schemes. A very wide range of materials have been coated in this way. For metals, the procedures [19]† used can be categorized as follows:

1. *Direct plating.* Iron, cobalt, nickel, ruthenium, palladium, osmium, iridium, and platinum.
2. *Galvanic initiation.* Copper, silver, gold, beryllium, aluminum, carbon, vanadium, molybdenum, tungsten, chromium, selenium, titanium, and uranium.
3. *Cannot be plated.* Bismuth, cadmium, tin, lead, and zinc (electroplate with copper, then use electroless nickel).

A wide variety of nonmetals such as plastics, wood, glass, carbide, silicon, and porcelain have also been plated.

The following are examples of electroless nickel formulas:

Formula 1	*Formula 2*
45 g nickel chloride	37.3 g nickelous sulfate
11 g sodium hypophosphite	26.4 g sodium hypophosphite
100 g sodium citrate	15.9 g sodium acetate

†References in App. D are from Chap. 2.

50 g ammonium chloride
1000 mL distilled water

pH 8.5–9, use at 194–212°F
Plating rate, 0.015 mm/h

5–6 drops sulfuric acid
1000 mL distilled water

Use at 180–190°F
Plating rate, 0.01 mm/h

Electroless Copper Plating [20]

Solution A
170 g Rochelle salt, $KNaC_4H_4O_6 \cdot 4H_2O$
50 g NaOH
35 g $CuSO_4 \cdot 5H_2O$
1000 mL distilled water

Solution B
37% formaldehyde, wt %

Procedure: Mix 5 parts solution A and 1 part solution B at 20 to 30°C just before use. Plastics can be coated with copper, but their surface must first be sensitized. This can be done using a 0.1% by weight solution of methyl ethyl ketone at room temperature. Copper is deposited at 0.0001 mm/h. A uniform film can be formed in about 15 min.

Electroless Silver Plating (W. Peacock, U.S. Patent no. 2,214,476) [20]

Solution A
9.6 g $AgNO_3$
4.4 g NH_3 (as NH_4OH)
1000 mL distilled water

Solution B
19.2 g hydrazine sulfate
4.8 g NaOH
1000 mL distilled water

Procedure: Mix equal parts of solutions A and B. To decrease the speed of reduction, eliminate the NaOH and increase the NH_4OH. The technique is used for coating nonconductors prior to electroplating.

Electrolytic Copper Plating [21]

The following technique is used to produce a copper strike on metals that cannot be plated with electroless nickel directly.

Electrolytic Copper Strike
22.5 g cuprous cyanide, $Cu_2(CN)_2$
33.7 g sodium cyanide, NaCN
15.0 g sodium carbonate, Na_2CO_3
0.2 g sodium thiosulfate, $Na_2S_2O_3 \cdot 5H_2O$

Procedure: Use at 90–100°F for 1 to 2 minutes at 4 to 6 V. The pH of the solution should be between 12.0 and 12.5. Do not allow the pH to fall below 12.0 Use sodium hydroxide to raise the pH. The free cyanide content is maintained at 7.5 g/L.

Electrolytic Iron Plating

Electrolytic Iron [22]
288 g ferrous chloride
57 g sodium chloride
1000 mL distilled water

Procedure: Filter before use. Mix cold. Rotate sample (cathode) at about 50 r/min. Use Armco iron for anode, about 4 by 1 by ½ in size. Operate at 70 to 100°C and use a current density of 5 to 38 mA/cm^2. Extended operation produces evaporation losses and requires water additions to maintain a constant bath level.

Electrolytic Iron [54]
375 g ferrous chloride
187.5 g calcium chloride
1000 mL distilled water

Procedure: Vapor-degrease sample in trichloroethylene and cathodic-clean for 15 s in hot metasilicatetrasodium phosphate—Calgon solution. Use a current density of 60 mA/cm^2 at 90°C and a pH of 1.0.

Electrolytic Nickel Plating

Electrolytic Nickel (U.S. Patent no. 2,532,283-4)
30 g nickel chloride, $NiCl_2·6H_2O$
10 g sodium hypophosphite, $NaH_2PO_2·H_2O$
10 g sodium citrate, $Na_3C_6H_5O_7·5½H_2O$
1000 mL distilled water

Procedure: Use at 190 to 200°F and adjust pH to between 4 and 6. Cobalt can be electroplated by substituting cobalt chloride for nickel chloride.

ELECTROMECHANICAL POLISHING PROCEDURES

Material	Electrolyte	Comments
Iron Iron-carbon alloys	20 g ammonium sulfate 100 cm^3 alumina, conc. 900 mL water†	1–10 min. Do not use when pH drops below 5 (Just and Altgeld).
Iron Iron-carbon alloys Low-iron alloys	20 g ammonium sulfate‡ 12 g ammonium chloride 100 cm^3 alumina, conc. 900 mL water	As above (Just and Altgeld).
Cast irons (gray, white, or nodular)	25 g ammonium sulfate 80 cm^3 alumina, conc. 1000 mL water	Use 0.01–0.015 A/cm^2 for 180–240s. Addition of 1% ammonium citrate produces better results. Stop when pH is less than 5; pH of 8 best for white iron. Decrease current density during polishing (Prakash).
Niobium	3% H_2O_2 Alumina	Use cyclic current, 0.01 A/cm^2 for 5 min (Dickinson).
Molybdenum	3% $K_3Fe(CN)_6$ Alumina	Use reverse polarity, 0.01 A/cm^2 for 5 min (Dickinson).
	3% H_2O_2 Alumina	Use cyclic polarity, 0.01 A/cm^2 for 5 min (Dickinson).

Material	Electrolyte	Comments
Rhenium	Sat. $NaClO_3$ Alumina	Use cyclic polarity, $0.1 A/cm^2$ for 2 min (Dickinson).
Rhenium-tungsten alloys	Sat. $K_3Fe(CN)_6$ Alumina	Use normal or cyclic polarity, 0.04 A/cm^2 for 2 min (Dickinson).
ThO_2-tungsten	3% H_2O_2 Alumina	Use cyclic polarity (Dickinson).
	Sat. $NaClO_3$ Alumina	Use cyclic polarity (Dickinson).
	Sat. $K_3Fe(CN)_6$ Alumina	Use normal polarity, silk cloth, 0.04 A/cm^2, 5 min (Dickinson).
Tungsten	Sat. $K_3Fe(CN)_6$ Alumina	Use normal polarity, 2 min, 0.04 A/cm^2 (Dickinson).
	3% H_2O_2 Alumina	Use cyclic polarity, 3 min, 0.04 A/cm^2 (Dickinson).
Ruthenium	300 mL 1% aq. NaOH 200 mL ¼-μm alumina	For 1 cm^2 area, use 40 mA at 10 V ac for 10 min. For electron–beam-melted samples, use 50 mA at 20 V ac (Piotrowski and Accinno).
Universal	12% sodium thiosulfate 19% potassium thiocyanate	Samples preground to 600-grit SiC. No abrasive added (Stone).

†For all recipes, when water is specified, use distilled water

‡Use this electrolyte when pitting results with the above electrolyte.

ATTACK POLISHING PROCEDURES

Material	Attack-polishing solution	Comments
Aluminum	0.5 wt % NaOH in water	Add dropwise to the charged cloth (Samuels).
Beryllium	Alumina in warm solution of 20% oxalic acid and water	Used after 600 grit (Bonfield and coworkers).
Beryllium	5% oxalic acid in water Alumina on cloth	Use with 1750 r/min wheel. Apply small amount of abrasive and solution. As polishing progresses, add solution only. Near end, add water, a few drops at a time, to moisten the cloth. CP Fe_2O_3 is better but slower than alumina (Udy and coworkers).
Beryllium	Solution 1 $\quad$ 10% oxalic acid $\quad$ 0.3-μm alumina Solution 2 $\quad$ 100 mL water $\quad$ 14 mL H_3PO_4 $\quad$ 1 mL H_2SO_4 $\quad$ 20 g CrO_3 $\quad$ 0.05-μm alumina	Two-step procedure. Dilute 1 part solution 2 with 10 parts water before use. Use silk cloth with solution 1, synthetic suede cloth with solution 2. Use 1200 r/min wheel with solution 2. Add solution dropwise and polish 15–30 s (Boyd).

Material	Attack-polishing solution	Comments
Beryllium	Magnesia suspended in H_2O_2 (30%)	Mix fresh. Charge wheel heavily. Used when Mg-rich particles are present. Slow, requires a few minutes (Udy and coworkers).
Beryllium	200 cm³ 0.05-μm alumina 600 mL water 20 mL 10% CrO_3 in water	Used with vibratory polisher, short-nap cloth, 24-h polish (Calabra and Jackson).
Beryllium	10 g oxalic acid 100 mL water	Used with two grades of alumina on silk cloths (Woods).
Bismuth	30% HNO_3 in glycerol Gamma alumina	Add gamma alumina to solution (Anderson).
Bismuth	50 mL HNO_3 150 mL glycerol Rouge or alumina abrasives	Used with Terylene-covered laps. Polish for 3–5 min. Good for polarized-light work (Haddrell and coworkers).
Chromium	15 g acetic acid 150 mL H_2O Rouge or alumina abrasives	Used with Terylene-covered laps. Polish for 5–10 min (Haddrell and coworkers).
Chromium	1% oxalic acid in 1:1 solution of ethyl alcohol and water Alumina abrasive	(Ogleby.)
Chromium Tungsten	75 mL water 15 g 0.05-μm alumina 1 g CrO_3	Near end of polish, flush with water and finish without solution (Anderson).
Cr-Si alloys (2–76 atomic wt % Si)	5% CrO_3 in water Alumina abrasive	Grind through 600 grit, use with nylon cloth (Chang).
Copper Brass (high Zn content)	Aq. ammonium persulfate 10–15 g/L (for copper) 15–30 g/L (for brass) MgO abrasive	Insert plastic between cloth and wheel to prevent pitting. Use skid-polish technique. Good for Al or Zn also (Samuels).
Copper	2–10% CrO_3 in water Rouge or alumina abrasives	Use napped cloth (Buchheit and coworkers).
Copper	1% ferric nitrate in water Alumina or colloidal silica abrasives	Use with medium-nap cloth.
Copper	5 g $Fe(NO_3)_3$ 25 mL HCl 370 mL water Gamma alumina	Attack-polish for 3 min, wash off wheel, add solution only and polish for 2–5 s (Slepian and Prohaska).
Cu-30%Zn alloy	12 g/L aq. ammonium persulfate MgO abrasive	Skid-polish for 20 min with high-nap cloth (Cocks and Taplin).

Material	Attack-polishing solution	Comments
Cu-Pb alloys	Aq. solution of CrO_3 and HCl	Concentrations and abrasive not given (Grange).
Gold	5–10% CrO_3 in water Rouge or alumina abrasives	Use napped cloth (Buchheit and coworkers).
Gold	12.5 g potassium iodide 100 mL water Alumina abrasive	Add a few drops of etch to charged cloth (Buchheit and coworkers).
Hafnium	4–30 drops HF to 100 mL of alumina-water suspension	Use napped cloth (Woods).
Hf-V alloys Hf-Cr alloys	5% CrO_3 in water Gamma alumina	(Rudy and St. Windisch.)
Lead telluride	50% H_2O_2 (30%) 50% glacial acetic acid Alpha alumina	Use twill-jean cloth on glass plate. Saturate cloth with solution and abrasive. Polish 2–3 min. Wash cloth, apply etch only, polish 2–3 min. Wash with warm water, then acetone or alcohol, dry (Schmidt).
Magnesium	20 mL of 2% potassium dichromate 150 mL sat. boric acid 15 drops HNO_3 Alumina	Other recipes in reference for specific Mg alloys (Haddrell, Ref. 39, Chap. 2).
Molybdenum	10 g NaOH 30 g $K_3Fe(CN)_6$ 100 mL water	1 part etch to 5 parts C-RO polishing compound. Use for 3–5 sec (Coons).
Moylbdenum Tungsten	Solution 1 15 g fine alumina 5 mL of 20% CrO_3 in water Solution 2 10 g rouge abrasive 35 mL water 5 mL of 20% CrO_3 in water	Rough-polish with napped cloth on 1750 r/min wheel with solution 1. Use heavy pressure, recharge. Final polish with napped cloth on 250–500 r/min wheel with solution 2 (Buchheit and coworkers).
Molybdenum	2 g/L $CuSO_4 \cdot 5H_2O$ in water 20 mL NH_4OH	Abrasive not specified. Polish 15–20 min (Miller and Sass).
Mo-C alloys	5% CrO_3 in water Gamma-alumina abrasive	Use napped cloth (Rudy and coworkers).
Molybdenum Niobium Tantalum Tungsten	5% KOH in water Alumina abrasive	Prepolish to 1-μm diamond (Hodkin and coworkers).

Material	Attack-polishing solution	Comments
Nickel	4 g cupric sulfate 20 mL HCl 20 mL water	Marble's reagent. Dilute 1 part etch to 10 parts water. Apply to napped cloth charged with gamma alumina. Use very light pressure, 500 r/min wheel speed (Beland).
Ni alloys Some alloy steels	2.5 g copper chloride 50 mL water 50 mL HCl	Dilute 1 part etch to 10 parts water. Charge billiard cloth with abrasive, add small amount of etch. Insulate cloth from wheel (O'Mara).
Niobium	15 g gamma alumina 35 mL water 5 mL of 20% CrO_3 in water	Use napped cloth, 1750 r/min wheel. Finish polishing without etch on slow wheel, napped cloth (Buchheit and coworkers).
Niobium Tantalum	200 mL water 10 mL H_2SO_4 3 mL HNO_3 2 mL HF	Use stainless steel wheel. Add etch, then alumina to cloth. As polishing progresses, flush with water and finish with alumina only (Anderson).
Niobium Tantalum	450 mL water 15 mL HF 5 mL HNO_3 10 mL H_2SO_4	Use as above but works best with automatic devices (Anderson).
Nb-Hf alloys	50 mL H_2O_2 (30%) 10 mL HNO_3 1 drop HF Gamma alumina	Use with Hf-rich alloys. Use gamma-alumina abrasive (Taylor and Doyle).
Nb-Hf alloys	50 mL lactic acid 30 mL HNO_3 5 mL HF Gamma alumina	Use with Nb-rich alloys. Use with gamma-alumina (Taylor and Doyle).
Nb-Mo-C alloys	5% CrO_3 in water Gamma alumina	Add solution, amount not specified, to almunia-water suspension (Taylor and coworkers).
Platinum Palladium	10 g rouge abrasive 35 mL water 5 mL of 20% CrO_3 in water	Final polish with napped cloth on 250 r/min wheel (Buchheit and coworkers).
Rhenium	15 g fine alumina 35 mL water 5 mL of 20% CrO_3 in water	Rough polish with slurry on napped cloth, 1750 r/min wheel. Final polish without etch, napped cloth, 250 r/min wheel (Buchheit and coworkers).

Material	Attack-polishing solution	Comments
Re-Hf alloys	50 mL H_2O_2(30%) 50 mL HNO_3 5 mL HF	Add solution to gamma alumina–water suspension, concentration not given (Taylor and coworkers).
Ruthenium Rhodium Iridium Osmium	15 g fine alumina 35 mL water 5 mL of 20% CrO_3 in water	Use napped cloth, 1750 r/min wheel. Final polish with solution on napped cloth, 250 r/min wheel (Buchheit and coworkers).
Silicon	Alpha alumina in 3–5% solution of CrO_3 and water	Use silk-covered bronze wheel at 1150 r/min, firm pressure (Coons).
Ag-Sn-Hg alloys	Dilute aq. solution of ammonium persulfate	Concentration and abrasive not given. Add a few drops of ammonia during polishing (Gaylor).
Tantalum	15 g fine alumina 35 mL water 5 mL of 20% CrO_3 in water	Use napped cloth, 1750 r/min wheel, medium to heavy pressure. Recharge periodically (Buchheit and coworkers).
Tantalum	Solution 1 2–5% aq. CrO_3 Alumina abrasive Solution 2 50 mL lactic acid 30 mL HNO_3 2 mL HF	Use napped cloth, 1750 r/min wheel with solution 1. Follow with chemical polishing with solution 2. (Buchheit and Brady).
Tantalum	Solution 1 2–5% aq. CrO_3 Alumina abrasive Solution 2 30 mL lactic acid 10 mL HNO_3 10 mL HF	Use wax lap instead of cloth with solution 1. Follow with chemical polishing with solution 2 (Vaughan and coworkers).
Tantalum	100 mL acetic acid 60 mL HNO_3 3 mL HF Alpha alumina	Polish through 6-μm diamond. Add solution to napped cloth, add dry abrasive. Use 30 lb/in^2 pressure for 8 min, 10 lb/in^2 for 1 min (Lott).
Thorium	Solution 1 10% oxalic acid in water Alumina abrasive Solution 2 10 mL HNO_3 1 mL HF 98 mL water Rouge or alumina abrasive	Use solution 1 for rough-polishing step, add abrasive to etch. Use solution 2 for final polishing step. Add etch to cloth charged with abrasive (Buchheit and coworkers).

Material	Attack-polishing solution	Comments
Titanium	15 g fine alumina 35 mL water 5 mL of 20% CrO_3 in water	Charge napped cloth with slurry, use 1750 r/min wheel. Heavy pressure initially, decrease gradually. Etch with Kroll's reagent. Final polish without CrO_3 on 500 r/min wheel, napped cloth, light, firm pressure (Buchheit and coworkers).
Titanium	0.3-μm alumina suspended in 5% aq. oxalic acid	Use for 3 min (Titanium Metals Corp.).
Titanium	10 g gamma alumina 15 drops HF 15 drops HNO_3 100 mL water	Use for 1 min, napped cloth (Sylvania Met. Lab.).
Titanium	1% HF in water Gamma alumina	Moisten napped cloth with solution, add gamma alumina (Rem-Cru Titanium, Inc.).
Titanium	1% HF in water Gamma alumina	Insulate wheel surface, use napped cloth. Moisten cloth with solution, add dry abrasive. If the surface is dull, add more abrasive. Followed by electropolish.
Titanium	5% oxalic acid in water Two grades of alumina	Alumina abrasives suspended in water plus small amount of liquid soap and a few drops of reagent. Polish, etch, repolish (Craver).

Tungsten	Solution 1
	  8–10 g alpha alumina
	  10 mL of 20% CrO_3 in water
	  150 mL water
	Solution 2
	  3.5 g $K_3Fe(CN)_6$
	  0.2–0.3 g NaOH
	  150 mL water
		Two-step process. Rough polish with solution 1 on 1750 r/min wheel covered with Metcloth and silk. Polish, etch, repolish. Final polish with solution 2 on 250–550 r/min wheel covered with Metcloth. Add gamma alumina, moisten with solution 2 (Yih and Wang).

Tungsten	10 g gamma alumina 3.5 g $K_3Fe(CN)_6$ 1 g NaOH 150 mL water	Pregrind to 600-grit SiC. Add solution to velvet cloth, polish for about 15 s (Woods).
Tungsten	1 g $CuSO_4 \cdot 5H_2O$ 20 mL NH_4OH 1000 mL water	Add a few drops of solution to wheel charged with abrasive, polish for 15–20 min (Miller and Sass).

Material	Attack-polishing solution	Comments
Tungsten	30 g rouge abrasive 30 g CrO_3 100 mL water	Intermediate polish. Swab-etch with a solution of 70 mL lactic acid, 20 mL HNO_3, and 10 mL HF. If deformation is present, repeat polish with light pressure (Lott).
Tungsten	1 part water 1 part NH_4OH 1 part H_2O_2 (30%) (add last) (use under hood, with rubber gloves)	Two-step process. Pregrind to 600-grit SiC. Insulate wheel, add 1-μm alumina to Kitten Ear cloth. Pour solution onto abrasive, mix. Polish 4–5 min with heavy pressure. Final polish: Kitten Ear cloth with alpha alumina and solution, light pressure. Repeat, if necessary, with gamma alumina (Newton and Olson).
Uranium	5% suspension of H_2O_2 (30%) in fine alumina slurry	Use Terylene cloth (Ambler and Slattery).
Uranium	50 g CrO_3 100 mL water 10 mL HNO_3 Alumina	Use Terylene-covered wheel, 20–30 min (Haddrell and coworkers).
Uranium	30 mL HF 30 mL HNO_3 60 mL water 5–8 g fine alumina	Swab surface with conc. HNO_3 immediately after polishing (Metz and Woods).
U-Mo-Ti alloys	100 g CrO_3 118 mL water Gamma-alumina abrasive	Attack-polish sample, follow by electropolishing (Bauer and coworkers).
UO_2 Carbide-coated graphite Pyrolitic graphite	30 g gamma alumina 140 mL H_2O_2 (30%)	Polish with slurry on Texmet or Pellon for 4–5 min, 5–6 lb pressure on mount. Wet cloth with water before adding slurry. Follow with 30-s polish on Microcloth, same load. Wash with water immediately to prevent staining (Filer and Asaud).
UO_2 U_3Si	H_2O_2 (30%) Chromic oxide abrasive (concentrations not give)	Use freshly prepared Cr_2O_3 abrasive. Grind UO_2 through 600-grit SiC before attack polishing; Polish U_3Si to 1-μm diamond before attack polishing (Ambler).

Material	Attack-polishing solution	Comments
UO_2 UO_2CeO_2	50 g CrO_3 10 mL HNO_3 70 mL water 30 cm^3 alumina or chromic oxide abrasive	Grind through 600-grit SiC. Attack polish on coarse felt, 10-min maximum. Final polish with fine alumina on napped cloth (Hunlich).
Vanadium	15 g fine alumina 35 mL water 5 mL of 20% CrO_3 in water	Charge 1750 r/min wheel, napped cloth, with solution. Use medium to heavy pressure, recharge as needed. Polish for short time without CrO_3, medium pressure. Follow with electropolishing (Buchheit and coworkers).
Vanadium	60 g rouge abrasive 60 g CrO_3 200 mL water	Boil solution 20 min before use. If deformation is present after attack polishing, swab-etch with 1 part HF, 1 part HNO_3, and 2 parts water, repeat polish and etch until deformation is removed (Lott).
V-O alloys	15 g gamma alumina 35 mL water 5 mL of 20% CrO_3 in water	For alloys with more than 5% oxygen. Used 8-in wheel, 1150 r/min (Henry and coworkers).
Zirconium	50 mL HNO_3 150 mL glycerol Alumina abrasive	Use terylene cloth, 1–10 min (Haddrell and coworkers).
Zirconium	4–30 drops HF added to 100 mL polishing solution	(Roth.)
Zirconium	1% HF 0.5% HNO_3 in water	(Roth.)
Zirconium	3–10% oxalic acid in water	(Roth.)
Zirconium	50% HNO_3 in water Few drops HF or fluosilicic acid	(Roth.)
Zirconium	Slurry of chromic oxide abrasive plus ½% aq. HF	Use freshly prepared Cr_2O_3. Polish sample through 6-μm diamond before attack polishing. Near end of polish, dilute with water (Ambler).
Zircalloy-2 Hafnium	200 mL water 200 mL HNO_3 72 drops HF	Add about 5–10 mL of solution to wheel charged with alumina abrasive (Westinghouse).

Material	Attack-polishing solution	Comments
Zr$_3$Al-based alloys	Slurry of chromic oxide abrasive in water plus a few drops of ½% aq. HF	Use freshly prepared Cr$_2$O$_3$. Dilute with water as polishing progresses (Ambler and coworkers).
Minerals	10 g rouge abrasive 35 mL water 5 mL of 20% CrO$_3$ in water	Use with napped cloth. For galena, dilute with 10 parts water (Buchheit; Cameron and Van Rensburg).
Pyrolytic graphite	2% CrO$_3$ in water Gamma alumina	Polish to 1-μm diamond. Attack-polish with slurry on napped cloth, heavy pressure. Final polish with MgO on Rayvel (Lott).
Pyrolytic graphite	5% CrO$_3$ in water	Polish through 1-μm diamond. Add solution to automatic polishing device charged with C-RO abrasive, 325-g weight, 10 min (Coons).
Cermets Sintered carbides	7–10% CrO$_3$ in water plus H$_3$PO$_4$ (<1%)	Attack-polish with rouge on 1750 r/min wheel. Add a few drops of solution periodically (McBride).
Silicon carbide	20% CrO$_3$ in water Gamma alumina	Polish through 1-μm diamond. Attack-polish on Texmet or Pellon cloth (Robinson and Gardner).
Borides of Hf, Nb, Ti, V, or Zr	10–20 g abrasive 10 g K$_3$Fe(CN)$_6$ 10 g KOH 100 mL water	(Rudy and St. Windisch.)
Tungsten boride	10 g NaOH 35 g K$_3$Fe(CN)$_6$ 150 mL water	Add solution to cloth charged with Cer-Cro abrasive (Coons).

Note: In all cases, when water is specified, use distilled water.

CHEMICAL POLISHING SOLUTIONS

Material	Chemical polishing solution	Comments
Alumina	H_3PO_4	Use at 425°C; remove sample from mount before polishing, 2–3 min required (Alford and Stephens).
Alumina	Borax glass	Use at 800–900°C, rotate sample periodically for about 5 min. Dissolve adherent glass with dilute acid (King).
Alumina-0.04% Cr	H_3PO_4	Heat sample slowly in gas flame to 425°C, then immerse in acid at 425°C for 1–2 min (Janowski and Conrad).
Aluminum	60 mL H_2SO_4 30 mL H_3PO_4 10 mL HNO_3	Use at 100°C for 2–5 min (Montgomery and Craig).
Aluminum	25 mL H_2SO_4 70 mL H_3PO_4 5 mL HNO_3	Use at 85°C for 30 s to 2 min. Good for alloys with intermetallic phases (Herenguel and Segond).

Material	Chemical polishing solution	Comments
Al-Mg alloys Al-Mg-Si alloys Al-Zn-Mg alloys Al-Cu-Mg alloys	Solution a 30–60 mL H_3PO_4 60–30 mL H_2SO_4 5–10 mL HNO_3. Solution b 70–90 mL H_3PO_4 25–5 mL H_2SO_4 3–8 mL HNO_3 Solution c 90 mL H_3PO_4 10 mL HNO_3	Use solution a at 95–120°C, good for preliminary polish. Use solution b at 85–110°C, good for final polish. Use solution c at 85°C, etches grain boundaries (Herenguel and Segond).
Aluminum	70 mL H_3PO_4 15 mL acetic acid 15 mL water	Use at 100–120°C for 2–6 min (Meyer and Brown).
Aluminum	83 mL H_3PO_4 15 mL acetic acid 5 mL HNO_3	Use at 100–105°C for a few min (Spahn).
Aluminum	70 mL H_3PO_4 3 mL HNO_3 12 mL acetic acid 15 mL water	Use at 100–120°C, 2–6 min. Good for many Al alloys. (Meyer and Brown).
Aluminum	90 mL H_3PO_4 5 mL HNO_3 5 g sodium nitrate 0.2 g copper nitrate	Grind through 600-grit SiC, immerse in solution at 90°C for 4 min (Ciha).
Aluminum	80 mL H_3PO_4 15 mL H_2SO_4 5.5 mL HNO_3	Grind through 600-grit SiC, immerse in solution at 95°C for 4 min (Ciha).
Aluminum	77.5 mL H_3PO_4 16.5 mL H_2SO_4 6 mL HNO_3 3.9 g $CuSO_4{\cdot}5H_2O$ 1000 mL water	Use for 1½–2 min. Temperature not given, probably about 100°C (Arrowsmith and coworkers).
Aluminum	47.7 mL H_3PO_4 6.4 mL HNO_3 6.0 mL acetic acid 25.0 mL H_2SO_4 12.5 mL water 0.3 g $Ni(NO_3)_2$	Use at 90–110°C for 30–120 s. Good for Al alloys (De Jong).
Pure Al Al-1%Si-1%Fe-0.1%Cu alloy	15 mL HNO_3 4 mL HCl 46 mL H_3PO_4	Use at 100°C for 8–10 min (De Jong).

Material	Chemical polishing solution	Comments
Beryllium	44 mL H_3PO_4 3 mL H_2SO_4 13 mL water 7 g CrO_3	Use at 49°C (120°F). Removes 1 mil (25 μm) in 20 min (Black and Faust).
Cadmium	2 parts H_2O_2 (30%) 2 parts ethanol 1 part HNO_3	Immerse sample in solution for 2 min—always add HNO_3 to ethanol when preparing solution (Gilman and De Carlo).
Cd-1.5%Zn alloy	320 g CrO_3 20 g Na_2SO_4 1000 mL water	If staining occurs, use above solution (Stoloff and Gensamer).
Cadmium Cd-Ag alloys (up to 3% Ag)	Solution a 1 part H_2O_2 (3%) 1 part NH_4OH Solution b 2 mL HF 28 mL HCl 50 mL water Solution c 25 mL water 25 mL H_2O_2 25 mL NH_4OH	Immerse or gently swab with solution a for 1 min to remove grinding scratches. Follow with very fine diamond on satin, 500 r/min, for 15 min. Wipe with a solution of HCl and ethanol, swab with solution b for 50–60 s. Remove surface deposit by immersing in solution c for 30 s (Dudrova and Copova).
Cadmium	3–6 g $K_2Cr_2O_7$ 100 mL HNO_3	Prepolish through alumina. Use solution at 40–60°C, immerse sample for 8–10 s, wash with water. Repeat cycle 6–7 times until polished (de Gregorio).
Cobalt	40 mL lactic acid 30 mL HCl 5 mL HNO_3	Good for Co alloys also (Morral).
Cobalt	1 part acetic acid 1 part HNO_3	(Morral.)
Copper Alpha brass	55 mL H_3PO_4 20 mL HNO_3 25 mL acetic acid	0.5 mL HCl can be added. Use at 55–80°C for 2–4 min. Agitate solution (Pray and coworkers).
Copper	6 mL HNO_3 65 mL acetic acid 27 mL H_3PO_4	Grind samples through 600-grit SiC. Immerse in solution at 60°C for 1 min (Pisek).
Copper	80 mL H_2SO_4 20 mL HNO_3 1 mL HCl 55–60 g CrO_3 200 mL water	Use at 20–40°C for 1–3 min. Good for Cu alloys also (Meyer and Dunleavey).
Cu-8%Al alloy Cu-0.5%Be alloy Cu-5%Al-2%Si alloy	1 part HNO_3 1 part H_3PO_4 1 part acetic acid	Use at 60–70°C for 1–2 min (De Jong).

Material	Chemical polishing solution	Comments
Cu-4.85%Si alloy	30 mL HNO_3 10 mL HCl 10 mL H_3PO_4 50 mL acetic acid	Use at 70–80°C for 1–2 min. Agitate sample (De Jong).
Alpha brass	17 mL HNO_3 17 mL H_3PO_4 66 mL acetic acid	Use at 50°C for 30–120 s (Camenisch).
OFHC copper Cu-Zn alloys (10–15% Zn) Cu-7.5%Al alloy	57 mL H_3PO_4 20 mL HNO_3 16 mL acetic acid	Use at 50–60°C for 20 s (Blau).
Gallium arsenide	5 mL HCl 5 mL HNO_3 40 mL glycerin	Suspend sample in solution, agitate lightly to dislodge bubbles. Polishing rate is 0.37 mg/(cm²·min) (Packard).
Gallium phosphide	100 mL methanol Saturate with chlorine	Use under hood, 5–20 min (Fuller and Allison).
Germanium	15 mL HF 25 mL HNO_3 15 mL acetic acid 3–4 drops bromine	Use at 20°C for 5–10 s (Haynes and Shockley).
Iron Low-carbon steels	30 mL HNO_3 70 mL HF 300 mL water	Use at 60°C (Beaujard).
Iron Low-carbon steels	25 g oxalic acid 10 mL H_2O_2 (13 g) 1 drop H_2SO_4 (0.1 g) 1000 mL water	Grind through 600-grit SiC. Immerse sample for 5 min at 20°C (Marshall).
Iron Low-carbon steels Fe-20%Ni-5%Mn alloy	80 mL H_2O_2 (30%) 15 mL water 5 mL HF	Prepolish sample through 6-μm diamond. Swab with fresh solution at 20–25°C for 4–10 s. Flush immediately with cold water (Christ and Smith).
Iron Low-carbon steels Low-alloy steels	3 mL HF 97 mL H_2O_2 (30%)	Adjust HF concentration to obtain gas evolution. Good for thinning TEM samples (Rzepski and coworkers).
Steels (0.1–0.8%C, up to 3% alloys)	14 mL HF 100 mL H_2O_2 (30%) 100 mL water	The finer the mechanical polish, the smaller the pits produced. Use a fresh, cold solution. Immerse sample for 3–30 s and shake vigorously. Rinse in 30% H_2O_2 (Plichta).

Material	Chemical polishing solution	Comments
Cast iron Low-alloy steels	70 mL H_2O_2 (30%) 5 mL HF 40 mL H_2O	Use at 15–25°C (Gramzow and Heim).
Carbon steel	7 parts oxalic acid (100 g/L) 1 part H_2O_2 (100%) 20 parts water	Grind to 0-grade emery or equivalent. Immerse sample 15 min at 35°C (Graham and coworkers).
Low-carbon steels Magnesium	90 mL H_2O_2 (30%) 10 mL water 15 mL H_2SO_4	Use at 25°C for 2–5 min (Kawamura).
Carbon steels	Solution a 25 g oxalic acid 1000 mL water Solution b 100 vols. H_2O_2	Use fresh for 30 min. Ratio of solution a to b varies with carbon content (see Fig. 2-23 in Chap. 2) (Hallett and coworkers).
Pure iron	5 mL HF 70 mL H_2O_2 (30%)	Grind through 600-grit SiC. Immerse in solution at 20°C for 25–45 s (Chia).
Fe-3%Si alloy	100 mL H_3PO_4 115 mL H_2O_2 (30%)	Grind through 600-grit SiC. Immerse in solution at 25°C for 8–10 min. Cool during use (Chia).
Stainless steel	% by weight: 30% HCl 40% H_2SO_4 5.5% titanium tetrachloride 24.5% water	Use by immersion of sample at 70–80°C for 2–5 min. Can add 0.5% HNO_3 to solution (Uhlig).
Low-carbon steels	3 parts H_3PO_4 1 part H_2SO_4 1 part HNO_3	Use at 85°C (Conn).
Low-carbon steels	1 part H_2O_2 (30%) 2 parts 20% oxalic acid in water	Used at 30–70°C (Kawamura).
Medium-carbon steels	10 parts H_2O_2 (30%) 10 parts water 1 part HF	Use at room temperature (Kawamura).

Material	Chemical polishing solution	Comments
Steels	Solution a 3 parts H$_2$O$_2$ (30%) 10 parts water 1 part HF Solution b 1 part H$_3$PO$_4$ 15 parts water	Steels > 0.3% Carbon: Grind to 150 grit, immerse in solution a for 15–25 s, wash with water, clean with solution b with cotton, wash in water, dry (de Magalhaes and coworkers). Steels 0.15–0.30% carbon: Grind to 320 grit, immerse in solution a for 12–18 s, then same procedure as for steels > 0.3% carbon (de Magalhaes and coworkers). Steels < 0.15% carbon: Grind to 600 grit, immerse in solution a for 3–5 s, then same procedure as for steels > 0.3% carbon (de Magalhaes and coworkers). Extra soft sheet steels: Grind to 200 grit, immerse in solution a for 3–5 s, mechanical-polish with chromium oxide, then with alumina (de Magalhaes and coworkers).
Iron Fe-Si alloys	6 mL HF 94 mL H$_2$O$_2$ (30%)	Use at room temperature. Wash in successive baths of H$_2$O$_2$, water, and ethanol, dry (Wiesinger).
Austenitic stainless steel	4 parts HNO$_3$ 1 part HCl 1 part H$_3$PO$_4$ 5 parts acetic acid	Use at 70°C for 3 min (de Jong).
Austenitic stainless steel	4 parts HNO$_3$ 3 parts HCl 5 parts acetic acid	First passivate surface by dipping in boiling 4% aq. H$_2$SO$_4$. Then chemical-polish at 70°C for 1 min (de Jong).
Pure lead	20 mL acetic acid 30 mL H$_2$O$_2$ 50 mL methanol	(Gifkins and Corbitt.)
Pure lead Lead alloys	75 mL acetic acid 25 mL H$_2$O$_2$	Pour solution rapidly over sample (50 mL in 3–4 s) in a random pattern. Quickly wash in running water, rinse with alcohol, dry. Repeat until good polish is obtained (Gifkins).
Lithium fluoride	H$_3$PO$_4$	Use at 60–120°C for 6–12 h; cool to ambient temperature, rinse in water, ethanol, and anhydrous ether (Scott and Pask).
Magnesium	10 mL HNO$_3$ 90 mL methanol	Use at 20°C (Grall).
Magnesium	0.4 g potassium dichromate 6 g boric acid 140 mL water 15 drops HNO$_3$	Use for 1–2 min. Good for polarized-light work (Haddrell).

Material	Chemical polishing solution	Comments
Magnesium Mg-MgO alloys (0–5%MgO)	8 mL HNO_3 12 mL HCl 100 mL ethanol	Grind to 600-grit SiC. Use at 20°C for 30 s (Ciha).
Pure nickel	3 parts HNO_3 1 part H_2SO_4 1 part H_3PO_4 5 parts acetic acid	Grind through 600-grit SiC. Use at 85–95°C for less than 1 min. Wash immediately in water (De Jong).
Pure nickel Ni-Co alloys	65 mL acetic acid (ice-cooled) 35 mL HNO_3 0.5 mL HCl	Fine grinding not required for pure Ni. Use at 20°C for 2–4 min. For Ni-Co alloys, grind through 600-grit SiC, use at 20°C for 1–2 min (Fox, U.S. Patent no. 2,680,678).
Niobium Vanadium Tantalum	6 g $FeCl_3$ 30 mL HCl 120 mL water 16 mL HF	Use at room temperature, 1 min for V, 2 min for Nb, 3 min for Ta (Eary and Johnston).
Niobium Vanadium Tantalum	30 mL water 30 mL HNO_3 30 mL HCl 15 mL HF	Use at room temperature.
Platinum	20 mL HF 5 mL HNO_3	Use hot (temperature not specified) under hood.

Rare earth
metals
Erbium
Dysprosium
Gadolinium
Holmium
Lanthanum
	Solution a
	20 mL lactic
	acid
	5 mL H_3PO_4
	10 mL acetic
	acid
	15 mL HNO_3
	1 mL H_2SO_4
	Solution b
	10 mL H_3PO_4
	10 mL lactic
	acid
	30 mL HNO_3
	20 mL acetic
	acid
		Solution a
		  Polish through 3-μm diamond. Do not add water to solution. Swab sample gently for 10–15 s (good for samples with low amount of inclusions) (Roman).
		Solution b:
		  Etches with a slight chemical polishing action. Use for samples with larger amounts of inclusions. Polish through ½–1 μm diamond, then use solution a for 2–3 s (Roman).

Cerium	20 parts of solution a above 10 parts dimethyl-formamide (inhibits oxidation)	Do not add water to solution. Use for 10–15 s (Koch and Picklesimer).
Silicon	93 mL HNO_3 70 mL HF 17 mL water 30 mL acetic anhydride 30 mL acetic acid	Use at 20°C for 10–15 min. Discard after use (Butlinelli).

Material	Chemical polishing solution	Comments
Silicon	20 mL HNO_3 5 mL HF	Use at 20°C for 5–10 s (CP-4 Reagent).
SiO_2	1 part HF 2 parts acetic acid 3 parts HNO_3	Stir solution (Balk and coworkers).
Silver	100 g CrO_3 65 mL water 5 drops HCl	Polish to 6-μm diamond, swab with solution (rinse frequently with water) for about 5 min. If a film forms, swab with H_3PO_4 (Levinstein and Robinson).
Silver	21 g NaCN 78 g H_2O_2 (30%) 1000 mL water	Use at 32°C for a few seconds. When gas evolution begins, remove and wash with 37.5 g NaCN per liter of water. Immerse in chemical polish and repeat cycle until polished (Soderberg).
Ag-30%Zn alloy	4 g Cr_2O_3 7.5 g NH_4Cl 150 mL HNO_3 52 mL H_2SO_4 Water to 1 L	Use at 60°C (Chase etch).
Sodium	5–50% methanol in acetone	Use at room temperature for less than 10 s. Dip in pure acetone, wash immediately in petroleum ether. Place in mineral oil for viewing (Isaacs and Singer).
Tantalum	2 parts acetic acid 5 parts H_2SO_4 1 part HF	(Vermilyea.)
SnTe	0.35 g I_2 40 mL ethanol (or methanol) 10 mL water 4 mL HF	To prepare solution dissolve iodine in ethanol (or methanol). Add water, then add HF. Prepolish sample to Linde A abrasive. Saturate cloth with solution. Lightly rub sample over wet cloth in figure-eight motion for 15–20 min. Add solution periodically. Rinse in methanol, then water, dry (Norr).
Iodide titanium	60 mL H_2O_2 (30%) 30 mL water 8–10 mL HF	Swab for 30–60 s (Cain).
Titanium	1 part HF 1 part HNO_3	Immerse sample and agitate vigorously. When polishing action becomes violent, continue for about 10 s. Discard solution when it turns green (Cain).
Titanium	30 mL HF 70 mL HNO_3	Polish through gamma alumina. Chemical-polish for 10 s (Rice and coworkers).
TiO_2	KOH	Heat to 650°C, immerse sample (remove from mount) for 8 min (Hirthe and Brittain).

Material	Chemical polishing solution	Comments
Zinc	20 g CrO_3 95 mL water 5 mL HNO_3 4 g zinc sulfate	Use at 20°C for 2–5 min. Use fresh solution. Discard when done. Hold sample vertical to minimize pitting. Remove chromic acid film by dip in 5–7% aq. HCl (Miller).
Zinc	1 part HNO_3 1 part H_2O_2 (30%) 1 part ethanol	Immerse sample for about 2 min. When preparing solution always add HNO_3 to ethanol (Gilman and De Carlo).
Zinc	43 mL H_2O_2 27 mL H_2SO_4 900 mL water	Immerse for 30's (Soderberg).
Zinc Cadmium	200 g $Na_2Cr_2O_7$ 6–9 mL H_2SO_4 1000 mL water	Use at 20°C for 5–10 min (Soderberg).
Zinc	200 g CrO_3 15 g Na_2SO_4 52.5 mL HNO_3 950 mL water	Use at 20–30°C for 10–30 s (Soderberg).
Zinc	25 wt% CrO_3 10 wt% HCl 65 wt% water	Use at 20–30°C for 10–30 s (Soderberg).
Zirconium Zircaloys Hafnium	45 mL HNO_3 45 mL glycerol 8–10 mL HF	Use under hood. Swab (preferred) or dip sample. A few seconds after contact, NO_2 is given off (do not inhale)—polishing has started. Continue 5–10 s (Cain).
Zirconium Zr-2½%Nb alloy Zircaloy-2 Zircaloy-4 Hafnium	45 mL NHO_3 45 mL water 8–10 mL HF	Use as above (Cain).
Zirconium Hafnium	45 mL H_2O_2 (30%) 45 mL HNO_3 8–10 mL HF	Use as above (Cain).
Zircaloy-2 Hafnium	70 mL water 30 mL HNO_3 2–5 mL HF	Use as above (Cain).

Zr-Cr-O
  alloys
Zr alloys
  other than
  Zircaloys
	45 mL lactic acid
	45 mL HNO_3
	8 mL HF
		Polish to 6-μm diamond (Rumball and Elder).

Material	Chemical polishing solution	Comments
Zircaloy-4	50 mL HNO_3 50 mL water 10 mL HF	(Aqua and Owens.)
Zirconium	15 mL HF 80 mL HNO_3 80 mL water	Use for 2 min (Mackay).

Note: When water is specified, always use distilled water.

ELECTROLYTIC POLISHING SOLUTIONS

Solutions for aluminum and alloys

Electrolyte composition	Conditions				Comments
	Current density	Voltage, dc	Temp., °C	Time, min	
1. 22mL perchloric acid 78 mL anhydrous acetic acid 3–5 g/L Al per liter of solution (dissolve Al in solution before use)	5–6 A/dm^2	50–80	<45	15	Degrease sample, pretreat with NaOH or HF solution. Remove film by washing in cold water. Good for Al-Cu alloys.
2. 20 mL perchloric acid 70 mL acetic anhydride	3–5 A/dm^2	50–100	<50	15	Use aluminum cathode. Dangerous! Good for Al-Cu alloys (Jacquet).
3. 20 mL perchloric acid 80 mL ethanol with 3% ether	1–4 A/cm^2	110– 120	<35	<20 s	Good for Al-Mg alloys, not suitable for Al-Si (<2% Si) alloys (DeSy and Haemers).

Solutions for aluminum and alloys *(continued)*

Electrolyte composition	Conditions				Comments
	Current density	Voltage dc	Temp., °C	Time, min	
4. 200 mL perchloric acid 1000 mL ethanol	0.15–0.3 A/cm^2	10	<25	2	Good for most Al alloys, except for Al-Cu and Al-Si alloys. Relatively safe. Black film forms. Peel off after 1–1½ min, electropolish for 1 min more (Perryman and Blade).
5. 400 mL H$_3$PO$_4$ 380 mL ethanol 250 mL water	35 A/dm^2	50–60	42–45	4–6	Good for Al-Mg alloys (Perryman).
6. 400 mL H$_3$PO$_4$ 380 mL ethanol 200 mL water	0.15–0.35 A/cm^2 0.15–0.35 A/cm^2	27–30 27–30	30–40 42–45	4–6	Good for Al-Ag alloys. Bath age affects operating conditions (Larke and Wicks).
7. 1 part HNO$_3$ 2 parts methanol	0.1–1 A–cm^2	4–7		10–12	Good for Al-Si and Al-U alloys. Polish for 2 min, rotate anode, repeat until polished. Can be explosive! Do not substitute ethanol for methanol (Waisman).
8. 1 part fluoboric acid 20 parts water	0.3–0.8 A/cm^2	15–35	18–20	20–60 s	Struers A2 electropolishing solution (Hagemann).
9. 62 mL perchloric acid 700 mL ethanol 100 mL butyl cellosolve 137 mL water	3.85 A/cm^2			20 s	Mix ethanol and water, add perchloric carefully. Immediately before use, add butyl cellosolve. Pump electrolyte. For Al and Al-Al$_3$Ni alloys (Lemkey and coworkers).

Solutions for aluminum and alloys *(continued)*

Electrolyte composition	Conditions				
	Current density	Voltage dc	Temp., °C	Time, min	Comments
10. 5 mL perchloric acid 95 mL acetic acid		25–60	Room temp.	2	Pregrind to 3/0 paper. Cool bath, stir. Relatively safe. Reveals grain boundaries. Use for high-purity Al (Serviand Grant).

Note: When water is specified, always use distilled water.

Solution for antimony

Electrolyte composition	Conditions				
	Current density	Voltage dc	Temp., °C	Time, min	Comments
1. 300 mL methanol 50 mL H_2SO_4 30 mL HCL		6–10	Room temp.	2–4	Use for pure Sb. Use platinum for cathode and anode lead wires. Polish through to a fine abrasive. Agitate electropolishing solution. Do not touch polished surface with cotton (Coons).

Solutions for beryllium

Electrolyte composition	Conditions				Comments
	Current density	Voltage dc	Temp., °C	Time, min	
1. 100 mL H$_3$PO$_4$ 30 mL H$_2$SO$_4$ 30 mL glycerol 30 mL ethanol	2–4 A/cm^2				Good for polarized-light work (Mott and Haines).
2. 28 mL per-chloric acid 200 mL acetic anhydride	0.1 A/cm^2		<28		Slowly stir bath (Jacquet).
3. 350 mL ethanol 100 mL per-chloric acid plus water to $d = 1.20$ 100 mL butyl cellosolve	75–90 A/dm^2	50		30–45 s	Anode and cathode horizontal. Move sample rapidly during polishing. Pregrind to 600 grit (Jacquet).
4. 2 ml HCl 2 mL HNO$_3$ 2 mL perchloric acid 94 mL ethylene glycol	0.1 A/cm^2	10–16	Room temp.	2½	Use stainless steel cathode, 7-mm anode-to-cathode spacing, moderate stirring. Etch at 5 V for 5–7 s. Samples preground to 600-grit SiC (Wheeler and Price).
5. 4 mL H$_2$SO$_4$ 4 mL HCl 20 mL HNO$_3$ 200 mL ethy-lene glycol		15		Several minutes	(Coons.)

Solutions for bismuth

Electrolyte composition	Conditions				Comments
	Current density	Voltage dc	Temp., °C	Time, min	
1. 20 mL H$_3$PO$_4$ 40 mL H$_2$SO$_4$ 40 mL water	1 A/cm^2				Suitable for polarized-light work (Mott and Haines).
2. 300 mL ethanol 300 mL H$_3$PO$_4$ 90 mL HCl	0.23 A/cm^2		Room temp.	>5	Grind to 600 grit with light pressure. Etch, regrind with 600 grit. Wash in alcohol and electropolish (pumped electrolyte). If twin artifacts are present, regrind with 600-grit SiC and repeat electropolish (Hare and Mallon).
3. 200 mL methanol 50 mL H$_2$SO$_4$ 50 mL HCl 20 mL ethylene glycol		6–10		2–4 (or more)	Use platinum for cathode and anode lead wires. Polish samples mechanically to a fine abrasive. Electropolish with agitated solution. If a frosty film appears, add HCl a few drops at a time to the solution. Never touch the surface with cotton (Coons).

Solutions for cadmium

Electrolyte composition	Conditions				Comments
	Current density	Voltage dc	Temp., °C	Time, min	
1. 120 g potassium cyanide 1000 mL water 20 g cadmium hydroxide	0.12–0.25 A/cm²	2.5–5	Room temp.		Use sheet iron cathode. Do not stir (Liger).
2. 450–500 mL H₃PO₄ 550–500 mL water	~5 A/dm²	2	Room temp.	30	Good for polarized-light studies (Phillips and Thompson).
3. 40 mL H₃PO₄ 40 mL glycerol 20 mL water	0.4 A/cm²	8–9	Room temp.	5–10	Good for polarized-light studies (Mott and Haines).
4. 200 mL perchloric acid 700 mL ethanol 100 mL butyl cellosolve	High	70–80	Room temp.	15 s	Good for alloys containing Ni, Ag, or Cu (Jacquet).
5. 200 mL perchloric acid 800 mL acetic anhydride	0.6–1.0 A/cm²	25–35	35–55		Use cadmium cathode. Bath age influences optimum conditions. Dangerous. Explosive! (Honeycombe.)

Solutions for chromium

Electrolyte composition	Conditions				
	Current density	Voltage dc	Temp., °C	Time, min	Comments
1. 50 mL perchloric acid 1000 mL acetic acid	0.12–0.30 A/cm^2	30–50	Room temp.	2–3	Pregrind to 00 grit. Use flat cathode, 50-cm^2 area, several centimeters from sample (1–15 cm^2 area). Can lower voltage to 25–35 V by addition of 5–15% water (Jacquet).
2. 64 mL H$_3$PO$_4$ 15 mL H$_2$SO$_4$ 21 mL water	1.5 A/cm^2	18	22–120		Stir bath or agitate sample. Mixing order: water, H$_3$PO$_4$, H$_2$SO$_4$ (Lorking).
3. 5 g ZnCl$_2$ 15 g AlCl$_3$·6H$_2$O 200 mL methanol 30 mL H$_2$SO$_4$	1–2 A		Room temp.	2	Use sample size of about 10 by 10 mm. Grind through 600-grit SiC. Use platinum cathode and anode lead wires. Agitate cathode. Dissolve salts in methanol, add H$_2$SO$_4$ slowly (Coons and Iosty).
4. 100 mL perchloric acid 1000 mL acetic acid	5 A/in^2	29	40–50		Relatively safe (Hook and Adair).

Solutions for cobalt and alloys

Electrolyte composition	Conditions				Comments
	Current density	Voltage dc	Temp., °C	Time, min	
1. 50 mL HCl 50 mL ethanol	2.5 A/cm^2	8–9	20	30–90 s	Use stainless steel cathode. Bluish-green anode film dissolves in water. Slight etching (Mott and Haines).

2. 5 g ZnCl$_2$
   15 g AlCl$_3$·6H$_2$O
   200 mL methanol
   30 mL H$_2$SO$_4$
	1–2 A		Room temp.	2	Use 10 by 10 mm sample size. Grind to 600 grit. Use platinum for cathode and anode lead wires. Agitate cathode. Dissolve salts in methanol, add H$_2$SO$_4$ slowly (Coons and Iosty).

3. 100 mL perchloric acid
   142 mL water
   758 mL methanol
	9 A/cm^2	48	Room temp.	3 s	For Vitallium. Used 1-cm^2 area, ground to 600 grit. Stainless steel or Vitallium cathode, vertical, 25-mm spacing. Agitate and cool solution during use (Perry).

4. H$_3$PO$_4$, conc.	1–2 A/dm^2	1–1.5	20	5–10	Produces slight etching. Solid black anode film can be wiped off with cotton. Produces a rise in current density to 12–16 A/dm^2 (Elmore).

5. 14 mL water
   75 mL ethanol
   6 mL perchloric acid
	10–12 A/in^2	6–10	25–55	10–20 s	For Co-Cr-Fe-Ni alloys (Morral).

Solutions for copper and alloys

Electrolyte composition	Conditions				
	Current density	Voltage dc	Temp., °C	Time, min	Comments
1. H_3PO_4	0.7–1.0 A/cm^2	1.6–2.0	Room temp.	5–10	For Cu-Co and Cu-Fe alloys. Use copper cathode, 12-mm spacing (Jacquet).
2. H_3PO_4	1–2 A/dm^2	1.8–2.0	Room temp.	15–30	For bronze, Cu-Al and Cu-Al-Pb alloys. Not good for high-tin alloys.
3. 38 mL H_3PO_4 62 mL ethanol	2–7 A/dm^2	2–5	Room temp.	10–15	For Cu-Pb alloys, good up to 30% Pb.
4. 100 mL HNO_3 200 mL methanol	0.75–1.50 A/cm^2	40–50 (ext.)	20–30	<1	Good for Cu and Cu alloys, many other metals. Use stainless steel gauze cathode. Cooling required (Kuhn).
5. 70 mL H_3PO_4 30 mL water 200 g/L CrO_3	250–775 A/dm^2		<30	30 s	For Cu and 30% Zn alloy.
6. 25–55% H_3PO_4 in water	2.5–3.0 A/dm^2	1–2	Room temp.	10–15	For Cu and 30% Zn, alpha-beta, and beta alloys. Grind to 600 grit. Specimen horizontal, cathode above or vertical, 12–50-mm spacing. Cathode area at least 10 times sample. Works best with some Cu in solution. Filter occasionally, do not agitate. Remove sample quickly with current on (Foss and Shiller).

Solutions for copper and alloys *(continued)*

Electrolyte composition	Conditions				Comments
	Current density	Voltage dc	Temp., °C	Time, min	
7. Solution a 670 mL H$_3$PO$_4$ 100 mL H$_2$SO$_4$ 230 mL water	0.1 A/cm^2	2–2.2	Room temp.	15	For either solution, use copper cathode, 2 cm above sample (face up, horizontal). No agitation. Pre-polish mechanically. Etch at 0.8 V about 30 s. Use solution a for Cu-O alloys and alloys of Cu and Sn up to 6% Sn, solution b for Cu-9%Sn alloys (Perryman).
Solution b 470 mL H$_3$PO$_4$ 200 mL H$_2$SO$_4$ 330 mL water	0.1 A/cm^2	2–2.2	Room temp.	15	
8. 150 mL H$_3$PO$_4$ 75 mL lactic acid 75 mL propionic acid 30 mL H$_2$SO$_4$ 30 mL water		5–10	20–25	5	Use copper cathode. Anode gently agitated. Good for tin bronzes and beryllium bronzes.
9. 370 mL H$_3$PO$_4$ 560 mL glycerol 70 mL water	0.16 A/cm^2		50–70		For nickel-silver alloys, nickel, copper, Inconel, and alpha brass (Evans and Lloyd).
10. 133 mL acetic acid 7 mL water 25 g CrO$_3$		10–12	35–40	5	For Cu-Au and Cu-Au-Zn alloys. Use fresh with platinum cathode (Linke).
11. 67.5 g potassium cyanide 15 g potassium sodium tartrate 15 g potassium ferrocyanide 18.5 mL H$_3$PO$_4$ 2.5 mL NH$_4$OH Water to 1000 mL	1 A/cm^2	45–50	55–62	1–4	For Cu-Au (AuCu$_3$) alloys. Solution is very unstable, good for only 10–15 min (color changes and precipitate forms). Use under a hood, stir vigorously (Bakish and Robertson).

Solutions for copper and alloys *(continued)*

Electrolyte composition	Current density	Voltage dc	Temp., °C	Time, min	Comments
12. 250 mL H$_3$PO$_4$ 250 mL ethanol 50 mL propanol 500 mL water 3 g urea	0.8 A/cm^2			50 s	Add H$_3$PO$_4$ to other liquids, then dissolve urea. Pump electrolyte (Buehler Ltd.).
13. 30 mL HNO$_3$ 900 mL methanol 300 g cupric nitrate	1.05 A/cm^2			15 s	For bronzes. Dissolve cupric nitrate in methanol (heat slowly). Cool solution, add HNO$_3$ carefully. Pump electrolyte. Slight etch (Buehler Ltd.).

Solutions for germanium

Electrolyte composition	Current density	Voltage dc	Temp., °C	Time, min	Comments
1. 500 mL glycerol 50 mL ethanol 50 mL water Saturate with potassium fluoride	0.01 A/cm^2		20	30	Can use 10 A/dm^2 at 80°C (Brouillet).
2. 1000 mL glycerol 10–30 g ammonium hydrogen fluoride	50–100 A/dm^2		80		Specimen horizontal a few millimeter below surface of electrolyte. Uneven current distribution (Epelboin and Froment).

Solutions for gold

Electrolyte composition	Conditions				Comments
	Current density	Voltage dc	Temp., °C	Time, min	
1. 25 g thiourea 3 mL H_2SO_4 10 g acetic acid	1.5–3.5 A/dm^2		20–45		(Jacquet.)
2. 95 mL water 20 g sucrose 20 g KCN 2 g K_2CO_3	10–20 A/in^2				For Au-Cd alloys. Good for polishing and etching (Birnbaum and Read).
3. 67.5 g KCN 15 g potassium sodium tartrate 15 g potassium ferrocyanide 22.5 g H_3PO_4 1000 mL water	1.5 A/cm^2	9–10	>60	1–2	Use stainless steel, graphite, or platinum cathode. Solution is toxic, use under a hood. Agitate sample rapidly. Solution decomposes rapidly (Kushner).
4. 75 g KCN 16 g potassium sodium tartrate 19 g potassium ferrocyanide 16 g H_3PO_4 4 g copper cyanide 3.5 mL NH_4OH 1000 mL water	1.5–2.0 A/cm^2	>12	60	1–2	Use as with electrolyte no. 3 (Kushner).

Solutions for hafnium

Electrolyte composition	Conditions				
	Current density	Voltage dc	Temp., °C	Time, min	Comments
1. 50 mL perchloric acid 1000 mL acetic acid		18	20	6 s	Used to polish wires. Use successive immersions of a few seconds with agitation (Rudy and St. Windisch).
2. 5 g $ZnCl_2$ 15 g $AlCl_3 \cdot 6H_2O$ 200 mL methanol 5 mL H_2SO_4	1–2 A		Room temp.	2	Use 10 by 10 mm sample size, ground to 600 grit. Use platinum for cathode and anode lead wires. Agitate cathode. Dissolve salts in methanol, add H_2SO_4 slowly (DeSy and Haemers, Coons and Iosty).

Solutions for indium

Electrolyte composition	Conditions				
	Current density	Voltage dc	Temp., °C	Time, min	Comments
1. 100 mL HNO_3 200 mL methanol	0.30 A/cm^2	40–50 (ext.)	20	1–2	Cool during use (Goss and Vernon).
2. 50 mL HNO_3 20 mL HCl 750 mL Carbitol	0.3–0.6 A/cm^2	40–60	20		Used for In and In-Tl alloys. For In, use Al cathode. Remove solid film with 10% HF. For In-Tl alloys, use at 100°C, austenitic stainless steel cathode. Use at 20°C for In (Guttman).

Solutions for iron and steel

Electrolyte composition	Conditions				Comments
	Current density	Voltage dc	Temp., °C	Time, min	
1. 185 mL H_3PO_4 765 mL acetic anhydride 50 mL water	0.04–0.06 A/cm^2	50 (ext.)	<30	4–5	Wide applicability. Age solution 24 h before use. Use Fe or Al cathode, 20 times as large as sample. For gamma stainless steel and Fe-3%Si alloys, use 0.1 A/cm^2 (Merchant, DeSy, and Haemers).
2. 54 mL perchloric acid 146 mL water 800 mL ethanol plus 3% ether	4 A/cm^2	110 (ext.)	<35	15 s	Good for many metals. Use Fe or austenitic stainless steel cathode. Pump electrolyte. Cool (DeSy and Haemers).
3. 200 mL perchloric acid 700 mL ethanol 100 mL butyl cellosolve or glycerol	100 A/dm^2	40–47		15 s	Pump electrolyte. Good for Fe-Si alloys (Knuth-Winterfeldt).
4. H_3PO_4, conc.	0.6 A/dm^2	0.15–2.0	Room temp.	9–10	For Fe or Fe-Si alloys. Use Fe cathode. Use fine mechanical polish to minimize inclusion attack.
5. 37 mL H_3PO_4 56 mL glycerol 7 mL water	77.5 A/dm^2		100–120	5–10	For stainless steel. Etching results if temperature is too low (Evans and Lloyd).
6. H_3PO_4, conc.	15.5 A/dm^2		40–93		For stainless steel.
7. 420 mL H_3PO_4 470 mL glycerol 150 mL water	1.5–20 A/dm^2		100	8–15	For stainless steel (Uhlig).

Solutions for iron and steel *(continued)*

| Electrolyte composition | Conditions | | | | |
	Current density	Voltage dc	Temp., °C	Time, min	Comments
8. 60 mL lactic acid 25 mL H₃PO₄ 25 mL mono-chloracetic acid (100 g/100 mL water) 30 mL ammonium citrate (50 g/100 mL water) 20 mL acetic acid 40 mL HCl 40 mL H₂SO₄		5–6	Room temp.	5	For stainless steel. Grind samples to 600-grit SiC. If polished further, electropolish for 2 min. Use stainless steel cathode. Gently agitate sample (Bassi).
9. Solution a 60 mL lactic acid 20 mL H₃PO₄ 30 mL sodium acetate (50 g in 100 mL water) 15 mL HCl 20 mL H₂SO₄ Solution b 40 mL lactic acid 40 mL acetic acid 15 mL H₃PO₄ 10 mL sodium acetate (50 g in 100 mL water) 10 mL HCl 10 mL H₂SO₄	10 15			5 5	For austenitic Mn steels. Use as with electrolyte no. 8. Remove brown anode film with water. To etch, dry sample, place in solution a at 1 V for 30–60 s. Solution b has less tendency to form brown deposit. Etch in solution b at 1 V for 30 s (Bassi).

Solutions for iron and steel (*continued*)

Electrolyte composition	Conditions				Comments
	Current density	Voltage dc	Temp., °C	Time, min	
10. 25 g CrO$_3$ 133 mL acetic acid 7 mL water	0.09–0.22 A/cm^2	20	17–19	6	Wide applicability. Dissolve CrO$_3$ in solution using water bath at 60–70°C. Samples mounted in Bakelite can be safely electropolished. Grind to 600 grit. Cool bath during use. Will attack inclusions and cracks. Etch stainless steel samples at 0.025 A/cm^2 for 5–20 min. For graphitic samples, follow with fine mechanical polish. Store solution in airtight bottle (Morris).
11. 50 mL perchloric acid 750 mL ethanol 140 mL water	0.3–1.3 A/cm^2	8–20	Room temp.	20–60 s	For steels, stainless steel. Add perchloric acid last carefully. Rinse immediately after polishing. (Waisman).
12. 335 mL perchloric acid 665 mL acetic anhydride	6–7 A/dm^2		<30	>4	For stainless steel. Dissolve 0.5% Al in bath. Agitate solution. Dangerous, explosive! (Pellisier and coworkers, Jacquet).
13. 1000 mL acetic acid 50 mL perchloric acid 5–15 mL water (optional)	0.01 A/cm^2	45 (ext.)	25		Wide applicability. Best polishing without water. Can produce preferential attack in two-phase alloys (Jacquet).

Solutions for iron and steel (*continued*)

Electrolyte composition	Conditions				
	Current density	Voltage dc	Temp., °C	Time, min	Comments
14. Solution a 650 mL H_3PO_4 150 mL H_2SO_4 150 mL water 50 g CrO_3	66–100 A/dm^2		40–60	3–7	For carbon steels up to 1.1% C. Surface passivation is greatest with solution c, least with solution a (Tiranskaya).
Solution b 800 mL H_3PO_4 150 mL H_2SO_4 50 mL water 100 g CrO_3	33–66 A/dm^2		60	5–6	
Solution c 1000 mL H_3PO_4 200 g CrO_3	12–33 A/dm^2		60–80	5–8	
15. 1 part HNO_3 1 part acetic acid	5–6 A/cm^2		Room temp.	1–3 s	For maraging stainless steels. Use stainless steel cathode, 33-mm separation. Etch at 0.5–0.7 A/cm^2 for 1–3 s. Reveals grain boundaries in nonaged samples (Il'ina and Strueva).
16. 62 mL perchloric acid 700 mL ethanol 100 mL butyl cellosolve 137 mL water	1.2 A/cm^2			20 s	Wide applicability, including high- and low-carbon steels and high-speed steels. Add perchloric acid carefully to ethanol and water. Add butyl cellosolve immediately before use. Rinse immediately after electropolishing (Buehler Ltd.).

Solutions for iron and steel *(continued)*

Electrolyte composition	Conditions				Comments
	Current density	Voltage dc	Temp., °C	Time, min	
17. 75 g citric acid 12 mL perchloric acid 800 mL ethanol 100 mL propanol 3 mL water 60 mg sodium thiocyanate	1.6 A/cm^2			10 s	For cast irons. Dissolve citric acid and sodium thiocyanate in ethanol. Add propanol and water. Then, add perchloric acid carefully. Follow with fine mechanical polish (graphite in relief) (Buehler Ltd.).
18. 15 g citric acid 20 mL HNO$_3$ 450 mL ethanol 450 mL methanol 60 mL water 75 g ferric nitrate 75 g manganese nitrate 3 g urea	2.6 A/cm^2			10	For Fe, low-carbon steels. Dissolve salts in methanol. Dissolve citric acid and urea in water and add to above mixture. Add ethanol, then nitric acid. Place in large flask and use water bath to heat solution to boiling. Precipitation begins at 55°C, settling occurs at boiling point (65°C). Remove from water bath when boiling begins and cool to ambient temperature. Precipitate redissolves in 7–24 h, solution is clear and dark brown (Buehler Ltd.).
19. 500 mL H$_3$PO$_4$ 500 mL H$_2$SO$_4$ 20 mL lactic acid	1.5–2.75 A/in^2		40–60		For low-carbon steels. Can use 450 mL H$_3$PO$_4$ and 550 mL H$_2$SO$_4$ or 600 mL H$_3$PO$_4$ and 400 mL H$_2$SO$_4$ (Krishman and coworkers).

Solutions for iron and steel (*continued*)

Electrolyte composition	Conditions				Comments
	Current density	Voltage dc	Temp., °C	Time, min	
20. 5 mL perchloric acid 95 mL acetic acid	8–10 A/in^2				For Fe and 30% Ni alloy, steel welds. Alternate solution is 33 mL perchloric acid and 1000 mL acetic acid, 120 V, 0.2–0.3 A/cm^2, 3–8 s (Krauss and Cohen).
21. 40% H_2SO_4 46% H_3PO_4 4% dextrose 10% water	23–70 A/dm^2		28–40	5–10	For carbon steels. Etch at 12–16 A/dm^2 for 10 min (Imboden and Sibley).

Solutions for lead and alloys

Electrolyte composition	Conditions				Comments
	Current density	Voltage dc	Temp., °C	Time, min	
1. 650–750 mL acetic acid 350–250 mL perchloric acid	20–25 then 1–2 A/dm^2	25–35 (ext.)	<30	3–5	For Pb, Pb-Sn, and other alloys. Horizontal electrodes. Copper cathode. Can be used for Sn and bearing metals (Jacquet).
2. 20 mL perchloric acid 80 mL ethanol plus 3% ether	0.5–2 A/cm^2	70–110 (ext.)	<25	10–30 s	Optimum conditions vary with alloy. Vigorous stirring, cool bath (DeSy and Haemers).
3. 700 mL acetic acid 300 mL perchloric acid	0.4–0.6 A/cm^2	10		2–5	For alloys with low Ag content. Use stainless steel cathode. Etch at 2 V (Heidenreich).
4. 315 mL acetic acid 60 g sodium acetate 80 mL water	0.05–0.12 A/in^2	50–60 (ext.)	20–30	4–10	Not good for alloys with more than 0.1% As or 0.2% Sb. Use graphite or platinum cathode, about 5 cm from vertical anode (Jones and Thirsk).
5. 315 mL acetic acid 32 g sodium acetate 108 mL water	0.05–0.1 A/cm^2			2	For Pb and dilute alloys. After electropolish, dip in 3:1 acetic acid and H_2O_2 (30%) solution to remove black surface film (Gregory and coworkers).
6. 60 mL perchloric acid 590 mL methanol 350 mL butyl cellosolve	3.1 A/cm^2				Add perchloric acid carefully to other liquids. Use cyclic polishing with 10–20 s intervals (Buehler Ltd.).

Solutions for magnesium and alloys

Electrolyte composition	Conditions				Comments
	Current density	Voltage dc	Temp., °C	Time, min	
1. 375 mL H_3PO_4 625 mL ethanol	4.5–5 A/dm^2	1–3	Room temp.	10	Current density drops to 0.5 A/dm^2 as polishing progresses. When an anode film forms, wash it off quickly to prevent pitting. Inadequate for polarized-light studies (Jacquet).
2. 10 mL HCl 90 mL butyl cellosolve	2 A/dm^2	10–15	20–30	1–2	After initial polarization, the voltage can be reduced to 5 V with 1 A/dm^2 current density. Good for polarized-light studies (Black).
3. 400 mL H_3PO_4 380 mL ethanol 200 or 250 mL water	0.2 A/cm^2	10	20–50	2	Use Mg cathode. Remove sample with current on. If a film forms during washing, remove with dilute HNO_3 swab (Larke and Wicks).
4. 800 mL ethanol 80 mL butyl cellosolve 160 g sodium thiocyanate	1.3 A/cm^2			10 s	Dissolve sodium thiocyanate in ethanol, add butyl cellosolve last (Buehler Ltd.).
5. 20 g sodium thiocyanate 100 mL ethanol 10 mL butoxyethanol 10 mL water 10 g EDTA (Na^+ salt form)		23	20		After electropolishing, wash in alcohol jet (Gradwell).
6. 700 mL acetic acid 300 mL perchloric acid	1.5 A/dm^2	20–30	<30	1–2	Use stainless steel or nickel cathode (Black).

Solution for manganese and alloys

Electrolyte composition	Conditions				
	Current density	Voltage dc	Temp., °C	Time, min	Comments
1. 100 mL H$_3$PO$_4$ 100 mL glycerol 200 mL ethanol	0.28–0.5 A/cm^2	18		15	For Mn and Mn and 12% Cu alloy. Pregrind to 4/0 paper. After polishing, remove sample quickly and wash in alcohol (Basinski and Christian).

Solutions for molybdenum and alloys

Electrolyte composition	Conditions				Comments
	Current density	Voltage dc	Temp., °C	Time, min	
1. 50–60 mL HCl 20–30 mL H$_2$SO$_4$ 150 mL methanol	65–70 A/dm^2	12	50	30 s	For as-cast Mo (no C). Avoid water in bath or a detrimental surface oxide will form (Coons).
2. 25 mL H$_2$SO$_4$ 175 mL methanol	0.8–1.2 A/cm^2	15–20	<25	1	For Mo. Mix carefully. Use stainless steel cathode, no agitation. Good for wide range of Mo alloys. Slight enlargement of pores (Coons).
3. 5 mL H$_2$SO$_4$ 1.25 mL HF 93.75 mL methanol	4.4 A/cm^2	50–70	<25	6–12 s	Also good for W, Nb, and Ta. Pregrind to 600-grit SiC. Solution improves with age. Pump electrolyte (Cortes).
4. 5 g ZnCl$_2$ 15 g AlCl$_3$·6H$_2$O 200 mL methanol 30 mL H$_2$SO$_4$	1–2 A		Room temp.	2	Use 10 by 10 mm sample size, grind to 600-grit SiC. Use platinum for cathode and anode lead wires. Agitate cathode. Dissolve salts in methanol, add H$_2$SO$_4$ slowly (Coons and Iosty).
5. Solution a 35 mL H$_2$SO$_4$ 140 mL water		12	50	25–35 s	Use solution a for Mo, solution b if carbides are present. Grind samples to 600-grit SiC. Use stainless steel cathode. Blue molybdic oxide film is present after solution a, sometimes after solution b. Remove with 10-s dip in NH$_4$OH (Coons).
Solution b 50 mL HCl 20 mL H$_2$SO$_4$ 150 mL methanol	0.65–0.70 A/cm^2	24	50	25–35 s	

Solutions for molybdenum and alloys *(continued)*

Electrolyte composition	Conditions				
	Current density	Voltage dc	Temp., °C	Time, min	Comments
6. 47 mL perchloric acid 600 mL methanol 360 mL butyl cellosolve 13 mL water	3.4 A/cm^2			20 s	Mix methanol and water, add perchloric acid carefully. Add butyl cellosolve immediately before use (Buehler Ltd.).
7. 100 mL H$_3$PO$_4$ 20 mL H$_2$SO$_4$ 40 mL water 0.25 g molybdic anhydride	0.6–0.9 A/cm^2	8	70		Freshly prepared solution appears milky, since only part of the molybdic anhydride is dissolved. Stir solution before and during use. Use stainless steel cathode. Removes 9.4 μm/min (Zamin and coworkers).

Solution for neptunium

Electrolyte composition	Conditions				
	Current density	Voltage dc	Temp., °C	Time, min	Comments
1. 8 parts H$_3$PO$_4$ 4 parts glycerin 4 parts ethanol		10	Room temp.	3	Grind samples through 600-grit SiC, then 6 μm diamond on nylon. Solution not satisfactory for etching (Richter).

Solutions for nickel and alloys

Electrolyte composition	Conditions				Comments
	Current density	Voltage dc	Temp., °C	Time, min	
1. 185 mL perchloric acid 765 mL acetic anhydride 50 mL water		50	<30		Allow solution to age for 24 h before use. Use Fe or Al cathode (Jacquet and Rocquet).
2. 370 mL H_3PO_4 560 mL glycerin 70 mL water	9–12 6–7 8–10 20 A/in^2			1 1–2 2–4 2–4	For Ni 200 and Ni 270 For Monel 400. For Inconel 625. For Incoloy 800, not good for Inconel 718 or Inconel 600 (Evans and Lloyd).
3. 1 part HNO_3 2 parts methanol	0.75–1.5 A/cm^2			25 s	Used for Monel 400, 404, 405 and K-500. A black film forms prior to polishing. Do not permit water to enter the solution (Woodard).
4. 25 mL H_3PO_4 25 mL HNO_3 50 mL water	115 A/in^2			5–10 s	Used for Inconel 600 and X-750. Cool solution, stir (Rosenberg).
5. 40 mL perchloric acid 450 mL acetic acid 15 mL water	0.1 A/cm^2	15	<25		For Nimonic alloys (Jacquet).
6. 390 mL H_2SO_4 290 mL water	0.39 A/cm^2	60	<35	4–6	Use nickel cathode. Rotate cathode to reduce pitting. Will not etch samples at lower voltage (Hothersall and Hammond).
7. 15% H_2SO_4 64% H_3PO_4 21% water (% by weight)	1 A/in^2	2.5–2.8	70		For Nimonic alloys (Lorking).

Solutions for nickel and alloys *(continued)*

Electrolyte composition	Conditions				Comments
	Current density	Voltage dc	Temp., °C	Time, min	
8. 133 mL acetic acid 25 g CrO_3 7 mL water	0.23–0.29 A/cm^2				Dissolve CrO_3 in solution using a water bath at 60–70°C. Will etch samples at 0.05–0.06 A/cm^2 (Morris).
9. 5 g $ZnCl_2$ 15 g $AlCl_3·6H_2O$ 200 mL methanol 30 mL H_2SO_4	1–2 A		Room temp.	2	Use 10 by 10 mm sample, grind to 600-grit SiC. Use platinum for cathode and anode lead wires. Agitate cathode. Dissolve salts in methanol, add sulfuric acid slowly (Coons and Iosty).
10. 10 mL perchloric acid 90 mL acetic acid	8–12 A/cm^2			30–90 s	Used for Inconel X (Begelow and coworkers).

Solutions for niobium and alloys

Electrolyte composition	Conditions				
	Current density	Voltage dc	Temp., °C	Time, min	Comments
1. 175 ml HF 175 mL HNO$_3$ 650 mL water	0.2–0.5 A/cm^2	12–30	<50	10	Use platinum crucible for cell and cathode (Cottin and Haissinsky).
2. 150 ml HF 850 mL H$_2$SO$_4$	0.04 A/cm^2		25–60		Use platinum cathode (Maddin and Chen).
3. 5 mL H$_2$SO$_4$ 1.25 mL HF 93.75 mL methanol	4.6–5.4 A/cm^2	50–60	<25	10–20 s	Pump electrolyte. Maximum area polished is 38 mm^2. Solution improves with age (Cortes).
4. 170 mL HNO$_3$ 50 mL HF 5 g citric acid 510 mL methanol	5 A/cm^2	100–150		40 s	Pump electrolyte. Solution produces etching at low circulation rates, no current, 2–3 min (Krudtaa and Stokland).
5. 18 mL HF 34 mL H$_2$SO$_4$ 48 mL lactic acid	0.20 A/cm^2	4.2			Polish through alumina abrasive. Cool bath externally with ice. Use graphite cathode 1.27 cm from anode (Pelleg).
6. 20 mL HF 20 mL H$_2$SO$_4$ 60 mL water		40	60		For Nb-H alloys. Mechanically polish to alpha alumina before electropolishing (Chung and Stoloff).

Solutions for palladium

Electrolyte composition	Conditions				Comments
	Current density	Voltage dc	Temp., °C	Time, min	
1. NaCl or KCl	1 A/cm^2	3	950		Fused salt electrolyte (Rowland).
2. NaCl plus 48 atomic wt % KCl		2	700		Fused salt electrolyte (Brouillet).

Solutions for platinum

Electrolyte composition	Conditions				Comments
	Current density	Voltage dc	Temp., °C	Time, min	
1. NaCl or KCl	0.15 A/cm^2	1.5	1020		Use Ni crucible as cell and cathode (Rowland).
2. NaCl plus 48 atomic wt % KCl		2	700		Use platinum cathode (Brouillet).
3. 1 part H$_2$SO$_4$ 1 part HNO$_3$ 1 part H$_3$PO$_4$	0.2–0.5 A/cm^2		20–30		Use 50 Hz alternating current. Good for small surfaces (5–10 mm^2) (Linke).

Solutions for plutonium

Electrolyte composition	Conditions				Comments
	Current density	Voltage dc	Temp., °C	Time, min	
1. 1 part H_3PO_4 1 part diethylene glycol		5		5–10	Polish sample through diamond, then electropolish. Good for polarized-light studies (Richter).
2. 10 mL HNO_3 90 mL diethylene glycol		7		5	Not good for polarized-light studies, but surfaces brilliant and pit-free and inclusions not attacked (Cochran).

Solutions for rhenium

Electrolyte composition	Conditions				Comments
	Current density	Voltage dc	Temp., °C	Time, min	
1. 5 g $ZnCl_2$ 15 g $AlCl_3 \cdot 6H_2O$ 200 mL methanol 50 mL H_2SO_4	1–2 A		Room temp.	2	Use 10 by 10 mm sample size. Grind to 600-grit SiC. Use platinum for cathode and anode lead wires. Agitate cathode. Dissolve salts in methanol, add sulfuric acid slowly (Coons and Iosty).
2. 350 mL ethanol 175 mL perchloric acid 50 mL butoxyethanol	6 A/cm^2	50			Use platinum cathode. Produces some grain-boundary etching (Churchman).

Solutions for silver

Electrolyte composition	Conditions: Current density	Voltage dc	Temp., °C	Time, min	Comments
1. 4 g silver cyanide 4 g potassium cyanide 100 mL water		1.5 or 3.0	Room temp.		Some experimentation required to obtain optimum results. Use two polishing steps, 10 min each. Stir solution. Clean on wet velvet between polishes (Mc G. Tegart).
2. 6 g potassium ferrocyanide 6 g sodium cyanide 100 mL water	0.15–0.25 A/cm^2	6	Room temp.		Agitate slowly (Hogaboom).
3. 35 g AgCN 30–70 g KCN 38–40 g K_2CO_3 1000 mL water	1.1 1.0 A/dm^2	1.5 2.5–3.0	20	20 10	Use silver for cathode and anode lead wire. Samples not preground. Find optimum conditions by trial. Slow stirring (Shuttleworth and coworkers).
4. 200 mL H_3PO_4 200 mL ethanol 400 mL water	60 A/in^2	5			For AgMg alloys (Mukherjee and Dorn).

Solutions for tantalum and alloys

Electrolyte composition	Conditions				
	Current density	Voltage dc	Temp., °C	Time, min	Comments
1. 90 mL H$_2$SO$_4$ 10 mL HF	0.1–0.2 A/cm^2	12–20	35–45	9–10	Use graphite or platinum cathode. Cool bath during use. Etch at 0.02 A/cm^2 for 10 min (Wensch and coworkers).
2. 170 mL HNO$_3$ 50 mL HF 30 g ammonium fluoride 510 mL methanol	3.5 A/cm^2	100–150	Room temp.	40–120 s	Pump electrolyte. Etches at zero current, low flow rate, 2–3 min (Krudtaa and Stokland).
3. 100 mL HF 100 mL HNO$_3$ 350 mL water	0.02–0.15 A/cm^2		35–50		Film formation causes current oscillation (Jacquet).
4. 5 mL H$_2$SO$_4$ 1.25 mL HF 93.75 mL methanol	4.6–5.4 A/cm^2	60–80	Room temp.	15–25 s	Pregrind samples to 600-grit SiC. Maximum area polished was 38 mm^2. Pump electrolyte. Solution improves with age (Cortes).

5. Solution a
  9 parts methanol
  6 parts 2-butoxyethanol
  1 part perchloric acid
Solution b
  9 parts H$_2$SO$_4$
  1 part HF
					Solution a used for most solid-solution Ta-Zr alloys, solution b for Ta-rich solid-solution alloys (Williams and coworkers).

Solutions for thorium and alloys

Electrolyte composition	Conditions				Comments
	Current density	Voltage dc	Temp., °C	Time, min	
1. 20 mL perchloric acid 70 mL acetic acid 5 mL water	0.6 A/cm^2		10	7–12	Pregrind samples. Longer polishing times produce grain-boundary etching and pitting (Smith and Honeycombe).
2. 2 parts perchloric acid 9 parts butyl cellosolve 9 parts ethanol					For Th, U, Zr, or Nichrome (Haines and Mott).
3. 1 part H$_3$PO$_4$ 1 part acetic acid	>0.16 A/cm^2				For Th-C alloys with less than 0.5% C (Wilhelm and Chiotti).
4. 3 N HNO$_3$ plus 1% KF	1 A/cm^2				For Th-Nb and Th-Ti alloys. Etch in solution at 0.1 A/cm^2 (Carlson and coworkers).

Solutions for tin and alloys

Electrolyte composition	Conditions				
	Current density	Voltage dc	Temp., °C	Time, min	Comments
1. 194 mL perchloric acid 806 mL acetic anhydride	9–15 A/dm²	25–40	15–22	8–10	For Sn and Sn-Sb and most Sn alloys. Use tin cathode, 2 cm from anode. Stir, especially if polishing continues more than 10 min. Use with care! (Jacquet).
2. Perchloric acid ($d = 1.6$)	0.4 A/cm²	50–60	<35	10–15 s	Use Al cathode, cool solution. Rotate specimen. Dangerous. Etches grain boundaries. Good for polarized-light work (Puttick).
3. 35% H_2SO_4 65% water	0.13 A/cm²	30			Use Al cathode. Remove sample with current on, wash in running water, dry (Faust).
4. 20 mL perchloric acid 80 mL ethanol plus 3% ether	0.5–2.0 A/cm²	110 (ext.)	<35		Agitate and use a cooling bath (De Sy and Haemers).
5. 100 mL fluoboric acid (purified, 48–50%)	400 A/dm²	4–5	15	20 s	For Sn and dilute Sn-Pb alloys. Fresh electrolyte must be activated using a bulk tin anode, 5-cm² area, for 30 min at 120 A/dm². Pregrind samples to 600-grit SiC. Expose area 0.33 cm², tilt 45° to electrolyte flow, 4 cm from stainless steel (25-cm² area) cathode. After polishing, etch in solution at 5 A/dm² for 3–30 s (Whelan).

Solutions for tin and alloys *(continued)*

Electrolyte composition	Conditions				Comments
	Current density	Voltage dc	Temp., °C	Time, min	
6. 63 mL perchloric acid 300 mL acetic acid 13 mL water	9–15 A/dm^2	20–30	25	10	Use tin cathode, anode vertical. Stir solution (Perryman).
7. 62 mL perchloric acid 700 mL ethanol 100 mL butyl cellosolve 137 mL water	3.9 A/cm^2			20 s	Add perchloric acid carefully to mixture of ethanol and water. Add butyl cellosolve immediately before use (Buehler Ltd.).

Solutions for titanium and alloys

Electrolyte composition	Conditions				
	Current density	Voltage dc	Temp., °C	Time, min	Comments
1. 90 mL ethanol 10 mL *n*-butyl alcohol 6 g anhydrous aluminum chloride 28 g anhydrous zinc chloride	0.16–0.8 A/cm²	30–60 (ext.) 20–25	Room temp.	1–6	Stir gently. Very corrosive solution but not explosive. Stable for about 1 week. Produces some surface relief (Rem-Cru Titanium, Inc.).
2. 764 mL acetic anhydride 184 mL perchloric acid 48 mL water	20–25 A/dm²	40–60 (ext.)	Room temp.	45–60 s	Use sample a few square centimeters in area. Place sample horizontal, face down, just below the bath surface. Cathode vertical or horizontal, several centimeters from sample. Move anode rapidly during polish. Use with care! (Jacquet.)
3. 200 mL perchloric acid 350 mL ethanol 100 mL butyl cellosolve	2–4 A/dm²	30	Room temp.	30 s	Electrolyte can be pumped. Remove gas bubbles adhering to surface (Knuth-Winterfeldt).
4. 36 mL perchloric acid 390 mL methanol 350 mL ethylene glycol 24 mL water		30–50	5–10	10–40 s	Excellent results reported. Safe solution. Pump electrolyte (P. R. Mallory & Co.).
5. 5 g ZnCl₂ 15 g AlCl₃·6H₂O 200 mL methanol 10 mL H₂SO₄	1–2 A		Room temp.	2	Use 10 by 10 mm sample size. Grind to 600-grit SiC. Use platinum cathode and anode lead wires. Agitate cathode. Dissolve salts in methanol, add sulfuric acid slowly (Coons and Iosty).

Solutions for titanium and alloys (*continued*)

Electrolyte composition	Conditions				Comments
	Current density	Voltage dc	Temp., °C	Time, min	
6. 1 part perchloric acid 20 parts acetic anhydride	1 A/cm^2		<4	4	Pregrind to 600-grit SiC. Etch promptly after electropolishing (Leighly).
7. Solution a 90 mL ethanol 10 mL *n*-butyl alcohol 6 g aluminum chloride 25 g zinc chloride Solution b 175 mL methanol 25 mL H$_2$SO$_4$	1–5 A/in^2	30–60 80 (ext.) 20–40 (ext.)	23–30	1–6 5 s 30–60 s	For alpha-beta alloys. Can be single-step process using only solution a (see first set of conditions) or two-step process (see second set of conditions). Sample preground to 3/0 paper. Electropolish in solution a, then transfer to solution b without washing or drying. Pump electrolyte (Solution a developed by Rem-Cru Titanium, Inc.) (Coons).
8. 1000 mL acetic acid 60 mL perchloric acid	30–40 A/dm^2	30	20	2	For Ti without carbides. Use Ti cathode, 3-cm anode-to-cathode spacing. Stir solution. Pregrind sample to 3/0 grade emery (Sutcliffe and coworkers).
9. 60–65 mL H$_2$SO$_4$ 20–25 mL HF 10–20 mL glycerin	0.7–2.0 A/cm^2	14–20	25–35	2–5	Use Ti cathode with area 10 times the anode area. Remove sample from solution with the current on (Peksheva and Vorontsov).

Solutions for titanium and alloys *(continued)*

Electrolyte composition	Conditions				Comments
	Current density	Voltage dc	Temp., °C	Time, min	
10. 390 mL methanol 350 mL ethylene glycol 60 mL perchloric acid	9 A	35	<30	15 s	Used a 6-mm diameter area, grind through 0 grade emery paper. Keep cool (Mallory-Sharon Metals Corp.).
11. 11.1 mL HF 59.0 mL lactic acid 24.6 mL H_2SO_4 3.6 mL dimethyl sulfoxide 1.7 mL glycerin	0.1 A/cm^2		24–35		For pure Ti. Pregrind sample. Use graphite cathode, 0.8-cm spacing. Effects of cold work removed after 1 h electropolish. Cool with ice bath (Pelleg).

Solutions for tungsten and alloys

Electrolyte composition	Conditions				
	Current density	Voltage dc	Temp., °C	Time, min	Comments
1. 100 g NaOH 1000 mL water	3–6 A/dm^2	6	20	20–30	Agitate solution. Use stainless steel cathode (Hughes and Coomes).
2. 10 g NaOH 100 mL water 100 mL glycerine		20		5–10	Samples preground with 180 and 320 SiC, then 0 and 3/0 emery. Electropolishing time reduced if samples are diamond-polished. Etch at 6 V for a few seconds (Coons and Gleason).
3. 5 mL H$_2$SO$_4$ 1.25 mL HF 93.75 mL methanol	4.4 A/cm^2	50–70	Room temp.	8–15 s	Pregrind samples to 600-grit SiC. Agitate solution (Cortes).
4. 20 g NaOH 30 g sodium tungstate 1000 mL water	4 A/cm^2	21	20	2	For WC-Co alloys. Use copper or graphite cathode (Miyoshi and Kurihara).

Solutions for uranium and alloys

Electrolyte composition	Conditions				
	Current density	Voltage dc	Temp., °C	Time, min	Comments
1. 28 mL H_3PO_4 28 mL ethylene glycol 44 mL ethanol		15–20			Good polish, emphasizes different phases with minor coloring. UO_2 is strongly attacked (Mott and Haines).
2. 1 part H_3PO_4 1 part glycerol 1 part ethanol	0.1–0.2 A/cm^2		20	30–40 or 5–10	Good for routine examination. Use U, Pt, or steel cathode. Keep solution cool and free of water. Stirring not necessary. Times listed are for ground versus diamond-polished surfaces (Mott and Haines).
3. 50 mL H_3PO_4 100 mL H_2SO_4 100 mL water	0.5–0.75 A/cm^2		20	5–10	Use U or Pt cathode. Continuously remove anodic layer during polishing by wiping with a camel's hair brush. Inclusions are not significantly attacked. Very good for polarized-light studies. Etch at 0.15 A/cm^2, remove anodic film by brushing or with alcohol, then continue etch for 8 min at one-fortieth the normal current density (Mott and Haines).
4. 10 g pyrophosphoric acid 10 g CrO_3 40 mL H_3PO_4 100 mL H_2SO_4 200 mL water	0.25 A/cm^2	10		2	For alloy of U and 2% Zr. Produces good polish for many U alloys. Inclusions not significantly attacked (Mott and Haines).

Solutions for uranium and alloys *(continued)*

Electrolyte composition	Conditions				
	Current density	Voltage dc	Temp., °C	Time, min	Comments
5. 1 part 118 g CrO$_3$ in 100 mL water 4 parts acetic acid	2.5–4 A/in^2	24–30	Room temp.	5–10 s	Use stainless steel cathode. Best to cool below ambient temperature. Pregrind samples to 600-grit SiC. Good for polarized-light studies (Saller and coworkers).
6. 40 g CrO$_3$ 60 mL water 200 mL acetic acid	3.2 A/cm^2	50			Good for U alloys with less than 30 atomic wt % Ti and V. Pregrind to 3/0 emery. Use 2–4 immersions of 8-s duration. Develops structure. Attacks two-phase structures. Follow with fine mechanical polish (Buzzard and coworkers).
7. 50 mL H$_3$PO$_4$ 80 mL ethanol 50 mL ethylene glycol	0.01 A/cm^2	18–20	21	5–15	Use stainless steel cathode (Blumenthal).
8. 20 mL H$_2$SO$_4$ 80 mL methanol plus a few drops of water		10–20		few seconds	Good for U alloys with greater than 30% V (Jacquet).
9. 65 mL lactic acid 45 mL H$_3$PO$_4$ 30 mL water 10 mL dioxane		5–25			For U and 5% "fission" alloys. Etch at 3 V for 10 s (Cheney).
10. 50–100 mL perchloric acid 1000 mL acetic acid	5–10 A/dm^2	50–60 (ext.)	20	5	Use stainless steel cathode (Mott and Haines).
11. 50 g CrO$_3$ 60 mL water 600 mL acetic acid		60	20	1	For U-C alloys. Follow mechanical polish with electropolish. Etch at 10 V for 15 min (Pruna and coworkers).

Solutions for vanadium and alloys

Electrolyte composition	Conditions				Comments
	Current density	Voltage dc	Temp., °C	Time, min	
1. 50–100 mL perchloric acid 900–950 mL acetic acid	15–25 A/dm^2	25–30	<35	1–2	Use stainless steel cathode. May need a second electropolish, use same conditions, fresh solution. Pitting can occur (Kinzel).
2. 5 g ZnCl$_2$ 15 g AlCl$_3 \cdot 6H_2O$ 200 mL methanol 30 mL H$_2$SO$_4$	1–2 A		Room temp.	2	Use 10 by 10 mm sample size. Grind to 600-grit SiC. Use platinum for cathode and anode lead wires. Agitate cathode. Dissolve salts in methanol, add sulfuric acid slowly (Coons and Iosty).
3. 10 mL HF 37 mL H$_2$SO$_4$ 52 mL lactic acid 1 mL glycerin	0.026 A/cm^2	3.2		100	Use graphite cathode, 1.2 cm from anode. Pre-grind sample. Etch at 2 V for 2–3 min (Pelleg).
4. 47 mL perchloric acid 600 mL methanol 360 mL butyl cellosolve 13 mL water	3.1 A/cm^2		20	10-s intervals	Mix methanol and water, add perchloric acid carefully. Add butyl cellosolve immediately before use. Polish using 10-s cycles, repeat several times. Pump electrolyte (Buehler Ltd.).

Solutions for vanadium and alloys *(continued)*

Electrolyte composition	Conditions				
	Current density	Voltage dc	Temp., °C	Time, min	Comments
5. Solution a 1 part 100 g CrO$_3$ in 118 mL water 3 parts acetic acid Solution b 20 mL H$_2$SO$_4$ 80 mL methanol plus a few drops water	20 A/in^2	50 10–20	20 20	30–60 s few seconds	For 0–30 atomic wt % V alloys: electropolish with solution a, relief-polish with stannic oxide on billiard cloth, then etch with solution a at 6–10 V. For 30–100 atomic wt % V alloys: mechanical-polish with stannic oxide, then electropolish with solution b (Seller and Rough).

Solutions for zinc and alloys

Electrolyte composition	Conditions				Comments
	Current density	Voltage dc	Temp., °C	Time, min	
1. 250 g KOH 1000 mL water	16 A/dm²	4–6	Room temp.	15	Agitate solution with air or nitrogen. Use copper cathode (Vernon and Stroud).
2. 200 g CrO₃ 1000 mL water	2.5–3.5 A/cm²	60 (ext.)	20	40–45 s	Good for brass also. Use nickel, zinc, or platinum gauze cathode. Rinse in solution and then water to prevent staining (Rodda).
3. 20 mL perchloric acid 80 mL ethanol (plus 3% ether—optional)	60–300 A/dm²	20–100 (ext.)	<35	10 s	Pump electrolyte. Determine optimum conditions by trial (de Decker and Krijff).
4. 375 mL H₃PO₄ 625 mL ethanol	1.5–1.9 A/dm²	2–3.5	Room temp.	45	Use electrodes horizontally. May need to shake anode to dislodge gas bubbles (Jacquet).
5. 1 part H₃PO₄ 1 part ethanol	1.5–2.5 A/dm²	2.5–3.5	20	60 or more	Can reduce time by polishing through diamond (Jacquet).
6. 200 g CrO₃ 15 g sodium sulfate 1000 mL water	2.6–7 A/cm²				Cool solution. Space electrodes 12–25 mm apart (Jacquet).
7. 160 g sodium thiocyanate in 80 mL butyl cellosolve 800 mL ethanol 20 mL water					For Zn-Al alloys (Alden and Schadler).

Solutions for zinc and alloys *(continued)*

Electrolyte composition	Conditions				Comments
	Current density	Voltage dc	Temp., °C	Time, min	
8. 20 wt % H_2SO_4 in water (Use 650 mL total)	0.3 A/cm^2	2.5	20	60–120	Not good for Zn alloys. Position sample horizontally about 1.5 in (38 mm) off bottom of beaker. Use nickel or platinum foil cathode on inside wall of beaker. A light-gray film forms on anode. After 1–2 h, increase to 7–9 V for 20–60 s to remove the film. Remove sample with current on and plunge into water, dry (Powers and Jerabek).

Solutions for zirconium and alloys

Electrolyte composition	Conditions				
	Current density	Voltage dc	Temp., °C	Time, min	Comments
1. 50 mL perchloric acid 175 mL acetic acid 100 mL ethylene glycol	>1 A/cm²	30–50 (ext.)	<30	20–30 s	Use stainless steel cathode. Good for polarized-light studies (Mott and Haines).
2. 10 mL perchloric acid 100 mL acetic acid	~15 A/dm²	12–18		45 s	Anode and cathode horizontal. Anode face down. After polishing, immerse in 4–8% acetic acid solution to remove surface film. Results may not be reproducible (Roth).
3. 10 mL perchloric acid 100 mL methanol 60 mL butyl cellosolve	1.2 A/cm²	30		3–25 s	Stir rapidly. For Zr-Mo alloys, use 6.5 A/cm² for 30 s (Domagala and coworkers).
4. 20 mL HF 10 mL HNO₃ 200 mL glycerol		9–12	24		(Jacquet.)
5. Solution a 1 part HCl 3 parts ethanol	1 A/cm²			10–20 s	Grind through 2/0 emery. Reveals grain structure.
Solution b 450 mL ethanol 70 mL water 25 mL perchloric acid	1 A/cm²			10–20 s	Use solution a or b (Roberson).

Solutions for zirconium and alloys *(continued)*

Electrolyte composition	Conditions				Comments
	Current density	Voltage dc	Temp., °C	Time, min	
6. 5 g $ZnCl_2$ 15 g $AlCl_3 \cdot 6H_2O$ 200 mL methanol 5 mL H_2SO_4	1–2 A		Room temp.	2	Use 10 by 10 mm sample size. Grind through 600-grit SiC. Use platinum for cathode and anode lead wires. Agitate cathode. Dissolve salts in methanol, add sulfuric acid slowly (Coons and Iosty).
7. 350 mL ethanol 100 mL per-chloric acid 50 or 100 mL butyl cellosolve		30 (ext.)		10–20 s	Sample 0.3–1 cm^2 size. Good results in Disa-Electropol but not in a single cell (Jacquet).
8. 1000 mL acetic acid 50–100 mL per-chloric acid	0.6–0.8 A/cm^2 0.15 A/cm^2	60 (ext.) 40–50 (ext.)	20 <30	30–60 s 45 s	For high-purity Zr, not good for Zr alloys. Rinse sample in 4–8% acetic acid and water solution (Jacquet, Roth).
9. 191 mL acetic anhydride 46 mL perchloric acid 12 mL water	60–80 A/dm^2	50 (ext.)	Room temp.	40–60 s	Pregrind samples. Immerse sample vertically and agitate during polishing (Jacquet).
10. 2 mL perchloric acid 6 mL water 92 mL methanol		40	−75		For Zr_3Al (Schulson and Trottier).

General-purpose solutions

Electrolyte composition	Conditions				Comments
	Current density	Voltage dc	Temp., °C	Time, min	
1. 144 mL ethanol 10 g $AlCl_3 \cdot 6H_2O$ 45 g anhydrous $ZnCl_2$ 16 mL n-butyl alcohol 32 mL water	5–30 A/dm^2	15–25	Room temp.	1	For Al, Cr, Co, Ni, stainless steel, Sn, Ti, and Zn. Use stainless steel cathode. Polish 1 min, remove for 45 s to break down passive film formed on Al. Repeat cycle until a good polish is obtained (~5 cycles). Good only for small samples (Jacquet; Hopkins and coworkers).
2. 1 mL perchloric acid 99 mL methanol			−76 to +25		Polishes 50 different metals, not good for Pt and Tl. Optimum conditions must be determined for each metal. Dry ice–acetone cooling bath used, stainless steel cathode. Cool sample in solution before polishing. Remove with current on. Rinse thoroughly with several successive ethanol baths. Add 5 mL HF for Au and Ta (Hopkins and coworkers).
3. 5 or 20% perchloric acid in methanol			<20		Good for most metals. Optimum conditions must be found by experimentation for each metal (Gabe).

General-purpose solutions (*continued*)

Electrolyte composition	Conditions				Comments
	Current density	Voltage dc	Temp., °C	Time, min	
4. 100 mL HNO₃ 200 mL methanol	1–2 A/cm²	40–50 (ext.)	20	30–60 s	For Al, Cu and alloys, In, Fe and steels, Ni and alloys, and Zn. Use stainless steel cathode. Dangerous solution. Cool with external ice bath, polish for short periods only. Best to use a lower current density of 0.1 A/cm² to control polishing rate (Pellisier and coworkers).
5. 200 mL perchloric acid 800 mL ethanol	1–4 A/cm²	110 (ext.) 35–70	35	10–30 s	For Al and alloys, cast irons, steels, Pb and alloys, Ni and alloys, Sn, and Zn and alloys. Use stainless steel or copper cathode. Produces etching. Good for small surfaces only. Agitate rapidly. Can add 100 mL glycerin and reduce ethanol to 700 mL (DeSy and Haemers).

ETCHANTS FOR REVEALING MICROSTRUCTURE

Etchants for aluminum and alloys

Etchant composition†	Comments
General-purpose etchants	
1. 0.1–10 mL HF 90–100 mL water	General-purpose reagent. Attacks $FeAl_3$, other constituents outlined. Grain contrast usually poor. The 0.5% concentration of HF is very popular.
2. 2.5 mL HNO_3 1.5 mL HCl 1.0 mL HF 95 mL water	Keller's reagent, very popular general-purpose reagent for Al and Al alloys, except high-Si alloys. Immerse sample 10–20 s, wash in warm water. Can follow with a dip in conc. HNO_3. Outlines all common constituents, reveals grain boundaries in certain alloys.
3. 2.5 mL HNO_3 1.0 mL HCl 1.5 mL HF 95 mL water	Modified Keller's reagent, used on Al-Cu-Mg-Si alloys. Use as with Keller's reagent above.
4. 10 mL HNO_3 1.5 mL HCl 1.0 mL HF 87.5 mL water	Modified Keller's reagent. Immerse sample 15–30 s, Heat-treated tempered alloys reveal high grain contrast, while artifically aged tempered alloys produce low grain contrast.
5. 0.5 g sodium fluoride 1 mL HNO_3 2 mL HCl 97 mL water	Modified Keller's reagent, used to detect precipitation in age-hardened alloys. Immerse sample first in 25% aq. HNO_3 at 160°F (70°C) for 1 min, wash and then immerse in etch for 1 min, wash, and dry.

†In all reagents when water is specified, distilled water should be used. Reagent-grade chemicals, acids, bases, solvents, etc. should be used for best results. See comments on laboratory safety in Chap. 2.

Etchants for aluminum and alloys *(continued)*

Etchant composition	Comments
General-purpose etchants *(continued)*	
6. 12.5 mL HNO$_3$ 2.5 mL HF 85 mL water	General-purpose immersion etch.
7. 1–2 g NaOH 100 mL water	Commonly used etch for pure Al and many Al alloys. Swab sample 5–10 s, can be heated to 122°F (50°C). Use fresh. Rinse samples in 5% aq. HNO$_3$. Outlines constituents except Al$_3$Mg$_2$ and (AlCrFe).
8. 3 parts glycerin 1 or 2 parts HF 1 part HNO$_3$	Vilella's reagent, general-purpose reagent. Immerse sample first in boiling water, then in etch for up to 15 s.
9. 0.5–25 g NaOH 1 g zinc chloride 100 mL water	General-purpose etch, reveals grain structure. 0.5, 1, 5, or 25 g NaOH have been used. Etch time varies up to a few minutes.
10. 94 mL water 1 g NaOH 4 mL 0.5% aq. zinc chloride 4 mL 0.5% aq. stannous chloride 1 g sodium carbonate	Bossert's etch for Al and Al-Cu-Mg alloys. Use fresh. Immerse sample 3–5 min. Remove smut with dip in conc. HNO$_3$. For annealed or cold-worked alloys.
11. Solution a 12 g NaOH 100 mL water Solution b 2–3 drops HF 100 mL water	Used to reveal the grain structure of Al. Immerse sample a few seconds in solution a, then 2–3 minutes in solution b.
12. 15 mL HF 10 mL H$_3$PO$_4$ 60 mL water	Reagent for Al-Mg alloys. Produces grain contrast under polarized light.
13. 2 g NaOH 5 g NaF 93 mL water	Etch for 2XXX and 7XXX wrought alloys and Al-Cu and Al-Zn cast alloys. Immerse 2–3 min. Reveals grain structure, cold working, or recrystallization.
14. 5 mL HF 10 mL H$_2$SO$_4$ 85 mL water	Etch to study degree of recrystallization in 6XXX alloys. Immerse sample 30 s.
15. 5 mL acetic acid 1 mL HNO$_3$ 94 mL water	Etch to study degree of recrystallization in 7XXX alloys. Immerse sample 20–30 min.
16. 84 mL water 15.5 mL HNO$_3$ 0.5 mL HF 3 g CrO$_3$	Graff and Sargent etch for grain size of 2XXX, 3XXX, 6XXX, and 7XXX wrought alloys. Immerse sample 20–60 s with mild agitation.
17. 100 mL water 10 mL HCl 10 mL HF	Boss's etch for grain contrast. Immerse sample at room temperature.

Etchants for aluminum and alloys *(continued)*

Etchant composition	Comments

General-purpose etchants (continued)

Etchant composition	Comments
18. 60 mL water 10 g NaOH 5 g $K_3Fe(CN)_6$	Modified Murakami's etch (Klemm) used to reveal precipitates and grain boundaries in Al-Si alloys (but not in Al-Mg-Si alloys).
19. 10 g NaOH 90 mL water	Etch to reveal grain structure in Al-Zn-Mg-Cu alloys. Colors $NiAl_3$ and $(Fe,Co,Ni)_2Al_9$ brown, $FeAl_3$ unaffected. Immerse sample 5–20 s at 160°F (70°C), then dip in conc. HNO_3 to remove stain.
20. 2 g NaOH 4 g Na_2CO_3 94 mL water	Etch for pure Al, reveals grain structure. Immerse sample at room temperature for 60 s.

Anodizing solutions

Etchant composition	Comments
21. 10 mL H_2SO_4 90 mL water	Lacombe and Beaujard's anodizing solution for superpure Al. Electrolytic, 1.5 A/dm^2, 30 min at 59°F (15°C).
22. 12% disodium acid phosphate and 0.4% H_2SO_4 in water	Keller and Geisler's anodizing solution for Al alloys. Electrolytic, 18 V dc, 3–5 min.
23. 350 mL H_3PO_4 132.5 mL Carbitol 5 mL HF 12.5 mL water	Anodizing solution of Hone and Pearson. Electropolish sample in solution. Start at 50 V dc at 20°C. After a few seconds, the current density rises to about 6 A/in^2. Agitation reduces the current density to about 2.5 A/in^2; continue at this level for a few seconds to 1–2 min. To anodize, use 20 V at 20°C. A few seconds after immersion, raise voltage slowly to 50 V, producing about 100 mA/in^2. The current density will slowly drop to about 50 mA/in^2 in 20 min. Agitate sample. Wash in hot water, dry. Examine in polarized light; can use sensitive tint. For pure Al.
24. 808 mL H_3PO_4 1660 mL Carbitol 320 mL HF 128 g anhydrous boric acid 72 g oxalic acid 1012 mL water	Improved anodizing solution of Hone and Pearson. To anodize, use gentle agitation, 35 ± 1°C (95°F), must control temperature. Start at 5 A/in^2 for about 30 s. Decrease voltage until current density is 0.5 A/in^2, hold for 105 s. Remove and cool in water. Do not use hot water. Rinse 1 min, dry. To minimize heating, can start anodize at 30 V, about 250 mA/in^2 for 5 min. Used to study grain orientations in high-purity Al. Use polarized light.
25. 50 mL methanol 50 mL water 2 mL HF	Phillips' anodizing solution for pure Al and Al-Mg alloys. Electrolytic, 30 V dc, 1–2 min, Al cathode. Grain contrast revealed under polarized light.

Etchants for aluminum and alloys *(continued)*

Etchant composition	Comments
	Anodizing solutions *(continued)*
26. 1.8% fluoboric acid in water	Barker's anodizing method for grain structure. Use Al cathode, 13 cm of anode and cathode immersed in solution, 10 mm apart. Use 0.5–1.5 A/in^2, 30–45 V dc. For most alloys and tempered alloys, 20 s at 1 A/in^2 and 30 V at 20°C is sufficient. Stirring not needed. Rinse in warm water, dry. Use polarized light; sensitive tint helpful.
27. 50 mL H_3PO_4 50 mL water	Anodizing solution of Cole and Brooks, applicable to most Al alloys. Use electropolished sample. Anodize at 2.5 A/dm^2 for 20–120 s, Pt or Al cathode, 23°F ($-5°C$), stir solution. Can use alcohol instead of water. Use polarized light.
	Color etchants
28. 200 g CrO_3 20 g sodium sulfate 17 mL HCl 1000 mL water	Beraha's tint etch. Preetch sample with 10% aq. NaOH followed by 50% aq. HNO_3. Rinse in water and dip immediately into reagent for 1–5 s. Rinse and dry. Colors matrix grains, outlines inclusions and precipitates.
29. 100 mL water 10 mL HF	Heat solution to boiling, saturate with molybdic acid. Cool and use cold. Develops brilliant colors.
30. 20 mL water 20 mL HNO_3 3 g ammonium molybdate	Add 20–80 mL ethanol before use. Develops brilliant colors. For Al and alloys.
31. 5 g ammonium molybdate 10 g sodium thiosulfate 20 mL ammonia (0.91 density) 200 mL water	Franchini color etch for Al-Si-Cu-Ni cast alloys. Immerse sample at 20°C for 5–8 min. Colors matrix revealing segregation, granular Si is dark blue to brownish violet.
	Selective etchants for constituents
32. 10 drops HNO_3 10 drops HF 10 drops 10% aq. $K_4Fe(CN)_6$ 5 mL H_2O_2 (30%) 100 mL water	Panseri's etch to detect constituents containing Fe. Use fresh. Immerse sample 20–60 s. Colors Fe deep blue; intensity of blue depends on Fe content.
33. 1–2% HNO_3 in ethanol or 5–10% HNO_3 in methanol	For Al-Mg alloys. Colors Al_3Mg_2 brown (15 min in 1% nital).
34. 25 mL HNO_3 75 mL water	Use at 160°F (70°C) for 40 s. See Table 3-1 for responses. Used for Al and most alloys, particularly Al-Cu alloys. A 2-min etch reveals grain boundaries in Al-Zn alloys.
35. Conc. HNO_3	Immerse sample 10 s at 20°C. Al_6CuMg_4, colored green-brown, Al_2CuMg outlined.

Etchants for aluminum and alloys *(continued)*

Etchant composition	Comments
Selective etchants for constituents *(continued)*	
36. 0.5–1.5 g picric acid 100 mL water	Immerse sample 10–20 min at 20°C. Darkens $CuAl_2$.
37. 4 g picric acid 100 mL ethanol	Immerse sample 10–20 min at 20°C. Darkens $CuAl_2$, other constituents unaffected.
38. 20 mL H_2SO_4 80 mL water	Use at 160°F (70°C) for 30 s. See Table 3-1 for responses.
39. 10 mL H_3PO_4 90 mL water	Immerse sample 1–3 min at 122°F (50°C) or use electrolytically, 1–8 V, 5–10 s, stainless steel cathode. For Al-Mg alloys, immerse samples cold up to 30 min; Colors Mg_2Si black, Al_3Mg_2 light gray, AlFeMn dark gray.
40. 10 g NaOH 100 mL water	Use at 160°F (70°C), immerse sample 5 s. See Table 3-1 for responses.
41. 20 g NaOH 100 mL water	Immerse sample at 20°C for 30 s. Attacks $FeAl_3$. Clean surface in conc. HNO_3.
42. 20 g NaOH 100 mL ethanol	More gentle than aq. 20% NaOH. Same results.
43. 25 g $Fe(NO_3)_3$ 100 mL water	Swab sample for 30 s. See Table 3-1 for responses.
44. 0.5 mL HF 100 mL water	Swab sample for 15 s. See Table 3-1 for responses.
45. 0.5 mL HF 1.5 mL HCl 2.5 mL HNO_3 95.5 mL water	Modified Keller's reagent. Immerse sample for 15 s at 20°C. See Table 3-1 for responses.
46. 5–10 g ferric sulfate 100 mL water	Immerse sample 45 s to 3 min. Colors $CuAl_2$ brown.
47. 3 g KOH 3 g potassium carbonate 100 mL water	Used to distinguish $FeAl_9Ni$ (blue) from $NiAl_3$ (brown).
48. 5–20 g CrO_3 100 mL water	For Al-Mg alloys. Colors Al_3Mg_2 brown.
49. 90 mL water 4 mL HF 4 mL H_2SO_4 2 g CrO_3	For Al and Al-Si and Al-Cu alloys. Immerse sample 10 s. Colors Si gray blue and Mg_2Si violet
50. 0.25 g sodium thiosulfate 100 mL water	For cast alloys. Colors $CuAl_2$ brown to black, $FeAl_3$ unattacked.
51. 2–3 g sodium molybdate 5 mL HCl 1–2 g ammonium bifluoride 100 mL water	Beraha's etch. Immerse sample at 20°C until surface is colored. Colors $CuAl_2$ slightly, AlCuFeMn script blue, $FeSiAl_5$ brown-blue, $NiAl_3$ or FeNiAl brown. Matrix unaffected.

Etchants for antimony and bismuth

Etchant composition	Comments
1. 70 mL water 30 mL HCl 5 mL H_2O_2 (30%)	For Sb and lean alloys. Immerse sample up to a few minutes.
2. 30 mL acetic acid 10 mL H_2O_2 (30%)	For Sb and alloys. Immerse sample up to a few minutes.
3. 100 mL water 30 mL HCl 2 g $FeCl_3$	For Sb, Bi, and alloys. Immerse sample up to a few minutes.
4. 100 mL water 25 mL HCl 8 g $FeCl_3$	For Sb-Pb, Bi-Sn, and Bi-Cd alloys.
5. 30 mL water 15 mL HCl 50 mL 16% aq. sodium thiosulfate 3 mL 10% aq. CrO_3	Czochralski's etch for Sb. Add CrO_3 solution just before use. Produces grain contrast.
6. 50 mL water 50 mL HCl	For Sb, Bi, and alloys. Immerse sample 1–10 min. For bismuth telluride, immerse sample 2 min, wash in 10% aq. acetic acid, rinse, dry.
7. 100 mL glycerol 25 mL HNO_3 25 mL acetic acid	For Sb-Pb alloys. Can reduce amounts of nitric and acetic acids. Immerse sample up to a few minutes.
8. 95–98 mL ethanol 2–5 mL HNO_3	For Bi-Sn eutectic alloys and Bi-Cd alloys. Can add a few drops of zephiran chloride. Immerse sample.
9. 90 mL methanol 10 mL HNO_3	For Bi-Sn, Bi-Cd, and Bi-Pb eutectics. Immerse sample, do not swab it. Do not store etch.
10. 100 mL water 5 g $AgNO_3$	For Bi. Immerse sample.
11. 97 mL water 3 mL HCl	For Bi-In alloys.
12. 100 mL water 30 g potassium iodide 10 g iodine	For Bi-Cd alloys.
13. 50 mL water 25 mL acetic acid 25 mL HNO_3	For Bi-Sn alloys (5–25% Sn).

Etchants for antimony and bismuth *(continued)*

Etchant composition	Comments
	Electrolytic etchants
14. H_3PO_4	For pure Bi; use at 3–4V dc, 10A/in².
15. 5 g CrO_3 100 mL water	Coons' electrolytic etchant for alloy of Bi and 5% Sb. Use at 10 V dc for 30–60 s.
	Stain etch
16. 1 g NaOH 35 g $K_3Fe(CN)_6$ 150 mL water	For iodine-doped bismuth telluride.

Etchants for beryllium

Etchant composition	Comments
1. 100 mL water 0.5–2 mL HF	Immerse sample 1–15 s.
2. 95 mL water 5 mL H_2SO_4	Immerse sample 1–15 s; results inconsistent (Kehl).
3. 90 mL ethanol 10 mL HCl	Immerse sample 10–30 s.
4. 90 mL ethanol 10 mL HF	Immerse sample 10–30 s. Aging of etchant improves etch response (Udy and coworkers).
5. 25 mL glycerin 5 mL HF 5 mL HNO_3	Immerse sample 15 s.
6. 15 mL glycerin 15 mL HF 5 mL HNO_3	Modified "fluor regia"; immerse sample 30 s, wash, dry, etch in 5% nital for 2 s, immerse in solution 10 s, wash and dry.
7. 20 g oxalic acid 100 mL water	Use boiling up to 16 min (Bonfield and coworkers). Also used at 3 g per 100 mL. Bright-field illumination reveals grain boundaries and precipitates.
8. 50 mL water 20 mL NH_4OH 3 mL H_2O_2	For Be-Ag alloys (Boyd).

	Electrolytic etchants
9. 2 mL HCl 2 mL HNO_3 2 mL $HClO_4$ 94 mL ethylene glycol	Etch at 5 V dc for 5–7 s, stainless steel cathode. Can use solution for polishing (10–16 V dc, 20°C, 0.1 A/cm^2) (Wheeler and Price).
10. 2 mL HCl 98 mL ethylene glycol	Use at 50–59°F (10–15°C), stainless steel cathode, ~ 70 V dc, 1–4 min. If structure not etched, reduce to 6–8 V for 3–5 s. Stir solution, wash sample in boiling water. Can examine under bright-field illumination (Grotzky and Fraikor).
11. 100 mL H_3PO_4 30 mL glycerol 30 mL ethanol 2.5 mL H_2SO_4	Grain-boundary etch. Cathode covered with cotton, and specimen swabbed lightly in circular pattern. Use stainless steel cathode, 25 V dc for 1–3 min (30-s cycles) at < 50°F (10°C). Polarized light improves contrast (Calabra and Jackson).
12. 294 mL ethylene glycol 4 mL HCl 2 mL HNO_3	For Be and alloys; use stainless steel cathode, 13–20 V dc, 6 min, 86°F (30°C).

	Heat tint
13. Heat in air at 1652°F (900°C) for 30 min.	Structure developed at 900°C, grain boundaries at slightly higher temperatures (Williams and Jones).

Etchants for cadmium

Etchant composition	Comments
1. 98 mL ethanol 2 mL HNO$_3$	For Cd and alloys (1–3% nital used).
2. 100 mL water 10 g CrO$_3$	For Cd and Cd solders. Immerse sample 1–10 min. Outlines grains.
3. 100 mL water 25 mL HCl 8 g FeCl$_3$	For Cd-Sn and Cd-Zn eutectics.
4. 100 mL ethanol 10 mL HCl 5 g FeCl$_3$	For Cd alloys.

Etchants for chromium and alloys

Etchant composition	Comments
1. 20 mL HNO_3 60 mL HCl	Aqua regia. For Cr and alloys. Immerse or swab sample up to 1 min. Use under a hood with care, do not store.

2. Solution a
    100 mL water
    10 g KOH
    Solution b
    100 mL water
    10 g $K_3Fe(CN)_6$
	Murakami's reagent. For Cr and alloys. Mix solutions a and b. Use fresh, can immerse sample for up to 1 min.

3. 30 mL HCl
    15 mL HNO_3
    45 mL glycerol
	"Glyceregia." For Cr and alloys. Immerse sample up to a few minutes.

4. 200 mL water
    6 g $K_3Fe(CN)_6$
    1 g NaOH
	For Cr-Mo alloys, up to 80% Cr. Immerse sample, wash with hot water, then alcohol, dry.

5. 30 mL HF 10 mL HNO_3	"Fluor regia." For Cr and alloys. Swab sample about 10 s.

6. 80 mL water
    10 mL HF
    10 mL HNO_3
	For chromium silicide.

7. 75 mL water
    2 g CrO_3
    25 mL H_2SO_4
	For Cr and alloys. Use at 176°F (80°C) to boiling.

Electrolytic etchants	
8. 10 g oxalic acid 100 mL water	Use at 6 V dc, 2–5 s, stainless steel or Pt cathode.
9. 90–95 mL water or ethanol 5–10 mL HCl	For Cr alloys. Use at 5–10 V dc, up to a few minutes, stainless steel cathode. Excellent etchant.
10. 95 mL acetic acid 5 mL perchloric acid	For Cr and alloys. Use at 30–50 V dc, 15 s, stainless steel or Pt cathode. Keep cool.
11. 90 mL water 10 mL HF	For Cr alloys, chromium silicide. Use at 5–10 V dc.
12. 95 mL water 5 mL H_2SO_4	For Cr, use at 2–3 V dc. For Cr alloys, use at 5–10 V dc.

Etchants for cobalt and alloys

Etchant composition	Comments
1. 90 mL methanol 10 mL HNO_3	For Co and Co-Fe alloys. Immerse sample for up to 30 s (1–50% nital has been used). Do not store.
2. 15 mL HNO_3 15 mL acetic acid 60 mL HCl 15 mL water	For Co and alloys. Age 1 h before use. Immerse sample for up to 30 s. Excellent etchant.
3. 7.5 mL HF 2.5 mL HNO_3 200 mL methanol	General etch for Co and alloys. Immerse sample 2–4 min (Coons).
4. 100 mL HCl 5 mL H_2O_2 (30%)	For Co hard-facing alloys and high-temperture alloys. Use under a hood. Use fresh. Immerse sample a few seconds.
5. 5 mL HNO_3 200 mL HCl 65 g $FeCl_3$	For Co high-temperature alloys. Immerse sample a few seconds. Use under a hood.
6. 50 mL water 50 mL HCl 10 g $CuSO_4$	Marbles reagent. For Co high-temperature alloys. Immerse or swab sample for up to 1 min. Can add a few drops of H_2SO_4 to increase activity.
7. 100 mL water 100 mL HCl 200 mL methanol 5 mL HNO_3 7 g $FeCl_3$ 2 g cupric chloride	For Co-Fe magnetic alloys. Immerse or swab sample for 10–15 s.
8. 100 mL water 1 mL acetic acid 1 mL HNO_3	For Co-Sm alloys. Immerse sample a few seconds.
9. 100 mL water 2 mL HF 5 mL H_2O_2 (30%)	For Co-Ti alloys (Koch and Jipson).
10. 3 parts HNO_3 1 part HCl	For Co-Pt alloys (48–54 atomic % Co) (Newkirk and coworkers).
11. 95 mL water 1 g KOH 4 g $KMnO_4$	For Alloy C73 (Co, 40.7%Cr, 2.4%C). Colors M_7C_3 gray and $M_{23}C_6$ black (Scarlin).

12. Solution a
  1 g mercuric chloride
  99 mL water
Solution b
  35 g sodium bisulfite
  100 mL water
	Etch with solution a for 30 s or with solution b for 2 min to distinguish between Co metal, cobalt oxide, and sulfides. Both stain the Co matrix brown, oxide remains dark gray, cobalt sulfide remains yellowish and MnS remains bluish gray.

13. 30 mL water 10 mL HCl 10 mL HNO_3	For cobalt boride.
14. 100 mL water 15 g CrO_3	For cobalt silicide. Add 5 drops HCl before using.

Etchants for cobalt and alloys *(continued)*

Etchant composition	Comments
15. 25 mL water 50 mL HCl 15 g FeCl₃ 3 g cuprous ammonium chloride	For Co and Co-Al alloys.
16. 25 mL water 25 mL acetic acid 50 mL HNO₃	For Co alloys.
17. 80 mL lactic acid 10 mL H₂O₂ (30%) 10 mL HNO₃	For Co alloys (Battelle).

	Tint etch

18. Solution a
  HCl and water (1:1) (stock
    solution)
Ingredient b
  0.6–1 g potassium
    metabisulfite
Ingredient c
  1–1.5 g FeCl₃
	Beraha's tint etch for Co-based alloys. Add ingredient b to 100 ml of stock solution a, then add ingredient c. Immerse sample at 20°C for 60–150 s, agitate sample. Matrix is colored, carbides and nitrides are unaffected.

	Electrolytic etchants
19. 100 mL water 5–10 mL HCl	For Co and Co high-temperature alloys. Use at 3 V dc, 2–10 s, graphite cathode. Pitting sometimes occurs.
20. 100 mL water 2–10 g CrO₃	For Co hard-facing alloys. Use at 3 V dc for 2–10 s.
21. 100 mL water 5 mL HCl 10 g FeCl₃	For Co and Co-Al alloys. Use at 6 V dc, few seconds, stainless steel cathode.

22. Solution a
  100 mL water
  2 g CrO₃
Solution b
  85 mL water
  4 g NaOH
  10 g KMnO₄
	For Co hard-facing alloys and Co high-temperature alloys. Use solution a at 3 V dc for 2 s. Rinse in water and immerse sample in solution b for 5–10 s. Use solution b fresh.

23. 140 mL HCl 1 g CrO₃	For Co high-temperature alloys. Use at 3 V dc for 2–10 s.
24. 100 mL HCl 0.5 mL H₂O₂ (30%)	For Co high-temperature alloys. Use at 4 V dc for 3–5 s.
25. 940 mL water 45 mL HNO₃ 15 mL HCl	For Co. Use stainless steel cathode, 3.5 V dc, 0.75 A/cm², 15 s, 20°C (Perry).

Etchants for copper and alloys

Etchant composition	Comments
	General-purpose etchants
1. 25 mL NH$_4$OH 25 mL water 25–50 mL H$_2$O$_2$ (3%)	General-purpose grain-contrast etch for Cu and alloys (does not always produce grain contrast). Use fresh, add peroxide last. Swab sample 5–45 s.
2. 60 mL NH$_4$OH 30 mL H$_2$O$_2$ (3%)	See comments about etchant no. 1.
3. 40 mL NH$_4$OH 40 mL water 20 mL H$_2$O$_2$ (3%)	See comments about etchant no. 1.
4. 50 mL NH$_4$OH 50 mL H$_2$O$_2$ (3%)	See comments about etchant no. 1.
5. 50 mL NH$_4$OH 10 mL H$_2$O$_2$ (3%)	See comments about etchant no. 1.
6. 25 mL NH$_4$OH 25 mL water 20 mL H$_2$O$_2$ (3%)	Selective etch for Al bronze (Mack and Shurman). Age 2–9 days in loosely stoppered bottle. Darkens delta first, then faintly attacks the acicular eutectoid.
7. 10 g ammonium persulfate 100 mL water	General-purpose etch for Cu and alloys. Immerse 3–60 s. Reveals grain boundaries but is sensitive to crystallographic orientation.
8. 3 g ammonium persulfate 1 mL NH$_4$OH 100 mL water	General-purpose etch for Cu and alloys, particularly Cu-Be alloys.
9. 1 g KOH 20 mL H$_2$O$_2$ (3%) 50 mL NH$_4$OH 30 mL water	General-purpose etch. Dissolve KOH in water, slowly add NH$_4$OH, then peroxide. Use fresh, immerse sample 3–60 s.
10. 5 g Fe(NO$_3$)$_3$ 25 mL HCl 70 mL water	Excellent general-purpose etch, reveals grain boundaries well. Immerse sample 10–30 s (Slepian and Prohaska).
11. 2–2.5 N NaOH 1–2% ethylenediamine 100 g/L K$_3$Fe(CN)$_6$	For Cu and alloys. Immerse sample 1–3 min (Greene and Teterin).
12. 2 g K$_2$Cr$_2$O$_7$ 4 mL sat. aq. NaCl 8 mL H$_2$SO$_4$ 100 mL water	For Cu and alloys. Use by immersion or swabbing of sample. Can substitute 1 drop HCl per 25 mL of solution for the saturated NaCl. Sometimes followed by a grain-contrast etch. For Cu-Ti alloys, add 5 mL HF.
13. Sat. aq. CrO$_3$ (about 60 g per 100 mL H$_2$O)	For Cu and alloys. Immerse or swab sample for 5–30 s.
14. 10 g CrO$_3$ 2–4 drops HCl 100 mL water	For Cu and alloys. Add HCl before use. Immerse sample 3–30 s.

Etchants for copper and alloys *(continued)*

Etchant composition	Comments
General-purpose etchants *(continued)*	

15. 40 g CrO_3
    7.5 g NH_4Cl
    50 mL HNO_3
    1900 mL water

For beta brass.

16. 40 g HNO_3
    25 g CrO_3
    35 g water

For Al bronze, discriminates β' from β.

17. Solution a
    3 g CrO_3
    15 mL water
    1 mL HCl
    Solution b
    6 mL NH_4OH
    2 mL H_2O_2 (3%)

Pondo's reagent. Pour solution b into solution a; vigorous reaction—use under hood. Swab sample briskly but lightly for 30–40 s. Good for annealed samples. To etch cold-worked samples, dilute with extra 20% water, etch extra 10 s.

18. 25 g CrO_3
    2 mL HCl
    2 mL H_2SO_4
    500 mL water

For alloy of Cu, 25% Pb, and 0.75% Ag. For alloy of Cu, 25% Pb, and 1% Sn, use 5 mL HCl and 5 mL H_2SO_4.

19. 10 g cupric ammonium chloride
    100 mL water

For Cu and alloys. Ad NH_4OH until the solution is basic.

20. Solution a
    1 g $FeCl_3$
    10 mL HCl
    100 mL water
    Solution b
    5 g $FeCl_3$
    10 or 50 mL HCl
    100 mL water
    Solution c
    8 g $FeCl_3$
    25 mL HCl
    100 mL water
    Solution d
    25 g $FeCl_3$
    25 mL HCl
    100 mL water
    Solution e
    20 g $FeCl_3$
    5 mL HCl
    1 g CrO_3
    100 mL water

General-purpose reagents for most Cu and Cu alloys. Use by immersion or swabbing of sample. Can be used after dichromate etchant (e.g., etchant no. 12) to develop grain contrast. These etchants are often used stepwise until the proper degree of etch attack is obtained. Use solution b with 50 mL HCl to attack Pb in Cu-Pb alloys, including those with high Sn. Use solution g for Al bronze. Use solution h for alpha brass. Use solution i for Cu-Sn-As alloys (Maes and de Strycker).

Etchants for copper and alloys *(continued)*

Etchant composition	Comments
General-purpose etchants *(continued)*	

Solution f
  5 g $FeCl_3$
  10 mL HCl
  1 g $CuCl_2$
  0.1 g $SnCl_2$
  100 mL water
Solution g
  5 g $FeCl_3$
  15 mL HCl
  60 mL ethanol
Solution h
  2 g $FeCl_3$
  30 mL water
  5 mL HCl
  60 mL ethanol
Solution i
  2.5 g $FeCl_3$
  1 mL HCl
  100 mL ethanol

Etchant composition	Comments

21. Solution a
  3% iodine in methanol
Solution b
  3 parts HCl
  1 part HNO_3
	For Cu-Au alloys. Use solution a to reveal grain boundaries. Use solution b to develop grain orientation contrast. Hold sample 1–2 cm *above* solution b. Vapors of fresh aqua regia produce etching in 2–10 s. Do not wash, blow dry (Bakish and Robertson).

22. 20 mL H_2O_2 (30%)
  25 mL water
  50 mL NH_4OH
  5 mL 20% aq. KOH
	For Cu-Si alloys. Add peroxide before use, immerse sample 2–30 s (Smith).

23. 40 mL H_2O_2 (3%)
  58 mL water
  2 g KOH
  100 mL NH_4OH
	For Cu-Si-Zn alloys (Pops).

24. 2 g $K_2Cr_2O_7$
  1 g NaF
  3 mL H_2SO_4
  100 mL water
	Crowell's reagent for Cu-Sn-Ag dental alloys. Attacks beta (AgSn) phase.

25. 10 g sodium thiosulfate 100 mL water	For Al bronze. Reveals γ_2 but not β. Immerse sample 90–150 s with agitation (Aldridge).

26. 20 mL HNO_3
  30 mL acetic acid
  30 mL acetone
	For Cu-Ni-Al alloys. Attacks alpha solid solution vigorously (Alexander).

27. 1 part HNO_3
  1 part acetic acid
  4 parts glycerin
	Vilella's reagent for Cu-Pb alloys. Swab sample lightly for short time; removes smeared Pb, sharply defines Pb areas. Longer etch reveals structure in Pb.

Etchants for copper and alloys *(continued)*

Etchant composition	Comments
General-purpose etchants *(continued)*	

28. 15 mL NH_4OH
    15 mL H_2O_2 (3%)
    15 mL water
    4 pellets NaOH
	For Cu-Be alloys. Add NaOH last.

Polarized-light etchants	

29. 5 parts NH_4OH
    5 parts water
    4 parts H_2O_2 (3%)
	For high-purity alloy of Cu and 10% Zn. Swab sample, produces response to polarized light (Reed-Hill and coworkers).

30. 2 g $FeCl_3$
    30 mL water
    10 mL HCl
    60 mL ethanol
	For Cu and Cu-Zn and Cu-Sn alloys. Immerse sample 1–2 min. Surface responds to polarized light (Barker).

Tint etchants	

31. 50 mL sat. aq. sodium
    thiosulfate
    1 g potassium metabisulfite
	Klemm's I reagent. Immerse sample 3 min or more for beta brass, up to 60 min for alpha brass.

32. 50 mL sat. aq. sodium
    thiosulfate
    5 g potassium metabisulfite
	Klemm's II reagent. Immerse sample 6–8 min or more for alpha brass.

33. 5 mL sat. aq. sodium
    thiosulfate
    45 mL water
    20 g potassium metabisulfite
	Klemm's III reagent. Immerse sample 3–5 min for bronze alloys.

34. 240 g sodium thiosulfate
    30 g citric acid
    24 g lead acetate
    1000 mL water
	Beraha's lead sulfide tint etchant for Cu and alloys. Dissolve in given order in water. Allow each to dissolve before adding next (this is difficult to obtain in practice). Age in dark bottle at 20°C for at least 24 h. Do not remove precipitate. When stock solution turns gray or black after prolonged storage, discard. Preetch sample with a general-purpose grain-boundary etchant. Immerse sample in solution until sample surface turns violet to blue. Colors enhanced with polarized light.

35. 200 g CrO_3
    20 g anhydrous sodium sulfate
    17 mL HCl
    1000 mL water
	Beraha's tint etch for Cu, brass, or bronze alloys. Dip sample 2–20 s. Can dilute to slow down rate of attack.

36. 300 mL ethanol
    2 mL HCl
    0.5–1 mL selenic acid
	Beraha's tint etch for brass and Cu-Be alloys. Keep in dark bottle. Preetch sample with grain-boundary etchant. Immerse sample until surface is violet to blue. Use plastic tongs. Use 0.5 mL selenic acid if color changes too quickly.

Etchants for copper and alloys *(continued)*

Etchant composition	Comments

Tint etchants *(continued)*

Etchant composition	Comments
37. 0.1 g AgNO$_3$ 10 mL HNO$_3$ 90 mL water	Color etch of de Jong used on OFHC copper, 10 s at 20°C. Use on electrolytically or chemically polished samples. Examine with light that is almost cross polarized.

Electrolytic etchants

Etchant composition	Comments
38. 1 g CrO$_3$ 100 mL water	For Cu-Al and Cu-Be alloys. Use at 6 V dc, 3–6 s, Al cathode (1.5 and 3 V also used) (Coons and Blickwede.)
39. 3 g FeSO$_4$ 0.4 g NaOH 10 mL H$_2$SO$_4$ 190 mL water	Use at 8–10 V dc (0.1 A) for 5–15 s. Darkens beta in alpha-beta brass.
40. 5 mL acetic acid 10 mL HNO$_3$ 85 mL water	For Cu-Ni alloys. Use at 1.5 V dc, 20–60 s, Pt lead wires. Use under hood, do not store.
41. 1 g ammonium acetate 3 g sodium thiosulfate 7 mL NH$_4$OH 1300 mL water	For cold-worked brass. Use at 0.3 A/cm^2 for 5–30 s.
42. 50 mL HNO$_3$ 50 mL water	For Cu-Bi alloys. Use at 0.8 V dc.
43. 0.25 g sodium thiosulfate 100 mL water	Used to detect deformation in alpha brass. Use at 6 V dc. Immerse sample at full voltage. Can improve sensitivity by adding 25 ppm NaCl. (Developed by Jacquet, modified by Samuels.)
44. 10 mL H$_3$PO$_4$ 90 mL water	For pure Cu. Use at 1–8 V dc for 5–10 s.

Potentiostatic etchants

Etchant composition	Comments
45. 1 *N* NaOH	For alpha-beta brass. Use at 77°F (25°C), −530 mV vs. SCE (saturated calomel electrode) for 30 s for beta and −320 mV for 60 s for alpha.
46. Conc. H$_3$PO$_4$	For alloy of Cu and 5% Be, use −350 to +100 mV vs. SSE (saturated sulfate electrode). For alloy of Cu and 1% Zr, use +100 mV for 30 s. Cu$_3$Zr darkened, matrix etched. For alloy of Cu, 0.3% Be, and 2% Ni, use −280 mV for 45–60 s. For pure Cu, use −350 mV for 30 s to reveal grain boundaries. Longer times color grains. At +100 mV for 120 s the grains are colored according to their orientations (Mance).

Etchants for copper and alloys *(continued)*

Etchant composition	Comments
	Potentiostatic etchants *(continued)*
47. 2–2.5 *N* NaOH (8–10%) 1–2 vol % ethylenediamine (0.1 *M* KCN can also be used)	For brass, use -0.35 to -0.45 V vs. SCE for 1–3 min (Greene and Teterin).
48. 50% aq. citric acid	For pure Cu, use -130 mV vs. SSE for 420 s. For alloy of Cu and 0.5% Be, use $+1500$ mV for 90 s or $+3000$ mV for 30 s. For alloy of Cu and 1% Zr, use -130 mV for 90 s. For alloy of Cu, 0.3% Be, and 2% Ni, use $+3000$ mV for 30 s (Mance and coworkers).

Etchants for germanium

Etchant composition	Comments
1. 5 mL water 25 mL HNO$_3$ 25 mL HF	For Ge and alloys. Immerse sample up to about 20 s. Do not contaminate bath with other metals.
2. 50 mL water 10 mL sodium peroxide	For Ge. Best results with warm solution.
3. 1 part water 1 part HF 1 part HNO$_3$	For Ge. Popular etchant (Risuer).
4. 100 mL ethanol 5 mL HCl 1 g picric acid	For Ge-In alloys. Etch sample up to a few minutes.
5. 1 part HF 1 part HNO$_3$	For Ge and alloys. Immerse sample up to a few minutes.
6. 40 mL water 10 mL HF 10 mL H$_2$O$_2$ (30%)	For Ge and alloys. Immerse sample 1–3 min. Do not contaminate bath with other metals.
7. Conc. HNO$_3$	For Ge. Can be diluted with water or mixed with HCl. Immerse sample up to a few minutes.
8. 50 mL water 50 mL HCl 20 g FeCl$_3$	For Ge and alloys. Immerse sample up to a few minutes in boiling solution. Excellent etch, produces grain contrast.
9. 40 mL water 40 mL HF 20 mL HNO$_3$ 2 g AgNO$_3$	Westinghouse WAg etch for Ge and alloys. Immerse sample 30–120 s. Reveals grain boundaries, produces etch pits.
10. Conc. H$_2$O$_2$ (30%)	For Ge. Use hot. Attacks grains at different rates according to their orientations.
Electrolytic etchant	
11. 100 mL water 10 g oxalic acid	For Ge and alloys. Use stainless steel cathode, 4–6 V dc, 10–20 s. Reveals grain boundaries.

Etchants for gold

Etchant composition	Comments
1. 60 mL HCl 40 mL HNO$_3$	For gold and high-noble metal alloys. Use under hood. Immerse sample up to 60 s. Equal parts of each acid also used.
2. 60 mL HCl 20 mL HNO$_3$	Aqua regia. For pure gold. Use boiling for up to 30 min.
3. 1–5 g CrO$_3$ 100 mL HCl	For pure Au and alloys. Swab or immerse sample for up to 60 s.
4. 0.1 g CrO$_3$ 10 mL HNO$_3$ 100 mL HCl	Chemical polish and etch for pure Au and alloys. Swab sample for up to 60 s.
5. 5 mL HNO$_3$ 25 mL HCl 30 mL water	For Au and alloys. Use hot. In Au-Ag alloys, a chloride film forms which can be removed with ammonia.
6. 100 mL water 100 mL H$_2$O$_2$ (3%) 32 g FeCl$_3$	For Au-Cu-Ag alloys. Immerse sample for up to a few minutes.
7. 1 part 10% aq. KCN 1 part 10% aq. ammonium persulfate	For Au and alloys. Use fresh, heat if needed, etch up to 3 min. Use under a hood, avoid fumes! (20% solutions have also been used).
8. 15 mL HNO$_3$ 15 mL acetic acid 70 mL glycerin	For Au-Pb-Sn alloys. Darkens Pb, does not attack Sn. Colors AuSn$_4$ golden brown, AuSn$_2$ and AuSn unattacked. Swab sample with 50% aq. HNO$_3$, AuSn$_2$ colored light brown (Prince).

9. Solution a
  50 g potassium iodide
  30 g iodine
  50 mL water
Solution b
  conc. NH$_4$OH
Solution c
  10 mL NH$_4$OH
  10 mL water
  2 mL H$_2$O$_2$ (30%)
	Used to differentiate hard Au electroplate from soft Au electroplate. Mix equal parts of solution a and water, swab sample for 2 s, rinse and dry. Use solution b to remove stains, swab sample 3 s, rinse and dry. Use solution c to etch copper substrate, swab sample for 2–3 s, rinse and dry (Paskowski).

Electrolytic etchants	
10. 5 g KCN 100 mL water	For Au and alloys. Use under hood, avoid fumes! Use 1–5 V ac, 0.5–1.5 A/cm^2, 60–120 s, Pt cathode.
11. Conc. HCl	Grain contrast etch for Au. Use 5 V ac, Pt cathode, 60–120 s.

Etchants for indium

Etchant composition	Comments
1. 40 mL water 10 mL HF 10 mL H_2O_2 (30%)	For In and In-Sb and In-As alloys. Immerse sample 5–10 s.
2. 100 mL ethanol 5 mL HCl 1 g picric acid	Vilella's reagent. For In and lean alloys. Immerse sample up to a few minutes (Carapella and Peretti). If Bi is present, increase amounts of alcohol and HCl.
3. 10 mL water 50 mL HF 50mL HNO_3	For In-Sb alloys. Immerse sample 5–10 s. Do not contaminate bath with other metals.
4. 65 mL water 10 mL HNO_3 20 mL HF 3 mL sat. aq. NaCl 1 g potassium dichromate 5 mL H_2SO_4	For In and lean alloys.

5. Solution a
    90 mL water
    10 g CrO_3
Solution b
    100 mL water
    2 g potassium dichromate
    4 mL sat. aq. NaCl
    7 mL H_2SO_4
Solution c
    80 mL water
    20 g $FeCl_3$
    1 g sodium sulfate
	For In-rich alloys. Mix equal parts of solutions a, b, and c.

6. Solution a
    90 mL water
    10 g CrO_3
Solution b
    6 g $K_2Cr_2O_7$
    20 mL H_2SO_4
    12 mL sat. aq. NaCl
    300 mL water
	For In-Zn alloys. Mix equal parts of solutions a and b.

7. 97 mL water 3 mL water	For In-Bi alloys (Henry and Badwick).

	Electrolytic etchants
8. Conc. H_3PO_4	For pure In. Use 3–4 V dc, 10 A/in^2 (Henry and Badwick).
9. 75 mL Carbitol 5 mL HNO_3 2 mL HCl	For In-Ti alloys (0–25% Tl). use 3 V dc (Guttman).

Etchants for iridium

Etchant composition	Comments
	Electrolytic etchants
1. 20 mL HCl 25 g NaCl 65 mL water	For Ir alloys. Use 20 V ac, 1–2 min, graphite cathode, Pt lead wires.
2. 90 mL ethanol 10 mL HCL	For Ir. Use 10 V dc, 30 s, graphite cathode.
3. 90 mL water 5–20 mL HCl	For Ir. use 0.02–0.1 A/cm^2, graphite cathode, 30–180 min. Reveals grain boundaries.
4. 80 mL water 20 mL H$_2$SO$_4$	For Ir. Use 1–5 V ac, 0.05–0.2 A/cm^2, graphite cathode, up to 60 min.
5. Solution a 40 g NaCl 100 mL water Solution b Conc. HCl	For Ir. Use 20 V ac, 1–2 min, graphite cathode, Pt lead wires. Mix 4 parts of solution a to 1 part solution b (Buchheit and coworkers).

Etchants for iron and steel

Etchant composition	Comments
	General-purpose etchants
1. 1–10 mL HNO_3 90–99 mL methanol or ethanol	Nital. Most common etchant for Fe, carbon and alloy steels, cast iron. Reveals alpha grain boundaries and constituents. The 2% solution is most common, 5–10% used for high-alloy steels (do not store). Use by immersion of sample for up to about 60 s (Boylston).
2. 4 g picric acid 100 mL ethanol	Picral. Recommended for structures consisting of ferrite and carbide. Does not reveal ferrite grain boundaries. Addition of about 0.5–1% zephiran chloride improves etch rate and uniformity (Igevski).
3. 100 mL amyl alcohol 5 g picric acid	Goerens' amyl picral. Recommended for etching very fine pearlite. Use under hood, do not store.
4. 100 mL water 0.5 g picric acid	Etch for producing contrast between as-quenched martensite and ferrite and other transformation products. Use at 160–170°F (71–77°C) for 15–20 s (Coons). Saturated solution also used in the same manner.
5. 0.5–5 mL HNO_3 100 mL amyl alcohol	Amyl nital. For pearlite steels, low concentrations for galvanized steels. Use under hood. Sometimes more sensitive than nital. Do not store.

6. Solution a
  1 part 2% nital
  1 part 4% picral
Solution b
  100 mL alcohol
  0.2 mL HNO_3
  0.3 g picric acid
Solution c
  10 parts 4% nital
  1 part 4% picral
Solution d
  78 mL 4% picral
  2 mL HNO_3
  20 mL water
	Combinations of nital and picral. Use by immersion of sample. Solution c is Kourbatoff no. 4 reagent used to differentiate between austenite, martensite, and tempered martensite and to determine the depth of nitrided layers. Solution d is Bolton's reagent for gray cast iron, immerse sample about 4 s.

7. 100 mL ethanol 5 mL HCl 1 g picric acid	Vilella's reagent. Good for ferrite-carbide structures. Produces grain contrast for estimating prior-austenite grain size. Results best on martensite tempered at 572–932°F (300–500°C). Occasionally reveals prior-austenite grain boundaries in high-alloy steels. Outlines constituents in stainless steels.
8. 10 g picric acid 100 mL alcohol	Superpicral. Above saturation limit. Need to heat to get picric in solution. Immerse sample for up to 1 min or more. Used with high-alloy steels, tool steels, and stainless steels.
9. 10 g picric acid 5 drops HCl 100 mL alcohol	Supersaturated solution. Must heat to get in solution. Immerse sample for up to a minute or more. Use following same procedures as for etchant no. 8, HCl improves etch attack rate.

Etchants for iron and steel *(continued)*

Etchant composition	Comments
	General-purpose etchants *(continued)*

10. 10 g ammonium persulfate 100 mL water	Swab or immerse sample up to 5 s. Reveals ferrite grain boundaries, sometimes produces grain contrast.

11. Solution a
  5 mL H_2SO_4
  8 g oxalic acid
  100 mL water
Solution b
  H_2O_2 (30%)
	Marshall's reagent (Hawkins). Mix equal parts of stock solution a with solution b. Use fresh, 1–3 s. Etch has short life. A 3-s preetch with nital is useful if no reaction occurs with Marshall's reagent. A 20-s postetch with nital increases etch attack. Uniform ferrite grain-boundary etch. Colors cementite, attacks inclusions. Reveals prior-austenite grain boundaries in martensitic low-carbon steels. Hold sample vertical in solution to reduce pitting.

12. 100 mL alcohol 5 g $FeCl_3$	For tempered steels (Igevski).

13. 1 g $FeCl_3$
  2 mL HCl
  0.3 mL zephiran chloride
  100 mL alcohol
	Etch for bainitic steels, 1–5 min.

14. 2.5 g $FeCl_3$
  5 g picric acid
  2 mL HCl
  90 mL ethanol
	For high-Cr cast irons, etch sample about 15 s by immersion.

15. 5 g $FeCl_3$
  5 drops HCl
  100 mL water
	General-purpose etchant. Sometimes reveals prior-austenite grain boundaries in martensitic medium-carbon steels.

16. 40 mL HCl
  5 g $CuCl_2$
  30 mL water
  25 mL alcohol
	General-purpose etchant. Swab sample for up to a minute.

17. 20 mL HCl
  65 mL ethanol
  15 mL water
  1 g $CuCl_2$
	For high-speed steels and martensitic stainless steels (Amberg).

18. Solution a
  40 mL glycerin
  10 mL HNO_3
  20 mL HF
Solution b
  30 mL glycerin
  5 mL HNO_3
  10 mL HF
Solution c
  30 mL ethanol
  30 mL amyl alcohol
  5 mL water
  30 mL HCl
  5 g $FeCl_3$
	Etchants for high-Si irons and steels. Immerse sample for up to a few minutes. Solution c is etch of Kriz and Poboril.

Etchants for iron and steel *(continued)*

Etchant composition	Comments
	General-purpose etchants (continued)
19. 30 mL water 25 mL ethanol 40 mL HCl 5 g CuCl$_2$	Fry's reagent for detection of cold working in steels. Best results after aging steels at 302–392°F (150–200°C).
20. 20 mL HNO$_3$ 80 mL sat. aq. sodium nitrate 1–2 g potassium persulfate	For high-Si irons. Immerse sample at 180–200°F (82–93°C) for 10–30 s (Schneidewind and Harmon).
21. 25 mL acetic acid 15 mL HNO$_3$ 15 mL HCl 5 mL water	For Fe-Al alloys. Swab sample for a few seconds. Use fresh, do not store.
22. 75 mL glycerin 15 mL water 5 mL HF 5 mL HNO$_3$	For Fe-Al alloys. Immerse sample for up to 3 min. Stains can be removed by light repolishing.
23. 100 mL water 2–4 mL H$_2$SO$_4$	Reveals austenite in quenched and tempered steels. Martensite darkened, attacks MnS, pits ferrite. Sometimes reveals prior-austenite grain boundaries.

24. Solution a
   100 mL alcohol
   3 mL HNO$_3$
Solution b
   90 mL ethanol
   10 mL HCl
Solution c
   100 mL ethanol
   2 mL NH$_4$OH
	For austenitic Mn steels. Etch in solution a for 15 s, rinse, dry. Etch in solution b for 15 s, rinse, dry. Etch in solution c for 15 s, rinse, dry. Repeat three times.

25. Solution a
   98 mL ethanol
   2 mL HNO$_3$
Solution b
   20 g sodium metabisulfite
   100 mL water
	For austenitic Mn steels. Etch in solution a for 5 s, rinse, dry. Etch in solution b until surface is darkened. Produces excellent grain contrast, reveals depth of surface decarburization.

26. 3 parts glycerin 3 parts HCl 1 part HNO$_3$	"Glyceregia." For high-alloy steels, austenitic Mn steels, stainless steels. Use fresh, do not store. For slower action, use 2 parts HCl.
	Special etchants
27. 80 mL water 20 g NaOH 4 mL bromine	Colors Fe$_3$P. Use fresh, under a hood. Handle carefully. Use by immersion of sample (Portevin).

Etchants for iron and steel *(continued)*

Etchant composition	Comments
	Special etchants *(continued)*
28. 15 mL HCl 20 mL water 1 g $CuCl_2$ 5 g picric acid 135 mL ethanol	Noren's reagent for detecting cracks in weld heat-affected zones.
29. 10 mL HNO_3 90 mL water	For the study of slip in single crystals of Fe containing 2.8–5.5% Si. Electropolish samples immediately before etching, for 10 s with agitation, then rinse in distilled water, then alcohol, dry (Roche and Rieu).
30. Sat. picric acid in ethanol	To develop substructure in massive cementite. Etch for 15 s. Then, heat-tint at 1200°F (650°C) for 8 min until surface is purple-red, air or water cool. Heat-tint time and temperature are critical (Kindle and Trout).
31. Solution a (alkaline sodium picrate) 2 g picric acid 25 g NaOH 100 mL water Solution b 1–2% nital	Line-etching technique for grain-oriented Fe-Si alloy sheet steel. Electropolish samples and etch in boiling solution a for 20–30 min, then etch in solution b for 3–5 min (Schatt, Friede).
32. Solution a 944 mL water 14.2 g $CuSO_4$ 7.4 mL H_2SO_4 Solution b (pH 5) 1 g sodium sulfide 100 mL water 1 mL HNO_3	To darken martensite for maximum contrast with retained austenite. Dilute stock solution a with 10 parts water. Sample must be well polished. Immerse or gently swab sample for 5–10 s. To increase contrast, apply a few drops of solution b or swab gently with solution b for 5–20 s. Surface colored light brown to black. Solution b without HNO_3 has shelf life of about 1 month. After adding HNO_3, solution b is good for about 6 h (Klimek).
33. 100 mL water 1 g ammonium persulfate 1 g picric acid	To detect recovery in partially recrystallized low-carbon steels. Examine with polarized light (Winsteard and Kot).
	Overheating and burning
34. Sat. aq. ammonium nitrate	Electrolytic etch. Etch at 6 V dc, 0.1 A/cm², 2-cm spacing, Pt or stainless steel cathode, up to 3 min. Has limited life. Overheated steels—white boundaries outline grains. Burned steels—black boundaries outline grains. Works best on fully heat-treated steels tempered to maximum toughness (Preece and coworkers).

Etchants for iron and steel *(continued)*

Etchant composition	Comments
Overheating and burning *(continued)*	
35. 10 mL H_2SO_4 10 mL HNO_3 80 mL water	Nitrosulfuric (Wesley Austin) etch. Immerse sample for 30 s, swab surface with cotton under water. Repeat process three times. Lightly repolish. Overheated steels—white boundaries outline grains. Burned steels—black boundaries outline grains (Slagg and De Belin).
36. 50 mL sat. aq. sodium thiosulfate 1 g potassium metabisulfite	Klemm's I reagent. Immerse sample 45–60 s. Overheated steels—white grain boundaries. Burned steels—zone around grain-boundary oxide inclusions remains white.
Coatings on steel	

37. Solution a
  0.3 g picric acid
  10 mL ethanol
  50 mL water
Solution b
  0.075 g picric acid
  13 mL ethanol
  53 mL water
Solution c
  0.068 g picric acid
  20 mL ethanol
  50 mL water
Solution d
  0.075 g picric acid
  13 mL ethanol
  35–60 mL water
Solution e
  0.075 g picric acid
  18 mL ethanol
  60 mL water
Solution f
  5 drops HNO_3
  50 mL amyl alcohol
Solution g
  0.5 g $K_3Fe(CN)_6$
  50 mL water
  10 mL ethanol
  2 mL NH_4OH
	Etchants for hot-dipped galvanized steels. Use solution a for regular coatings, 3–6 s. Use solution b for tight and extra tight coatings, 3–6 s. Use solution c for coatings formed with immersions of 1 min or longer, etch 10–90 s. Use solution d for galvannealed samples, 10–30 s. Use solutions e, f, and g for Zn-Al coatings, etch 3–6, 10–30, and 15–30 s, respectively (Rowland).

38. Solution a
  1 drop HNO_3
  2 drops HF
  25 mL glycerin
Solution b
  1 drop HF
  100 mL methanol
	For tin-coated steels. Etch in solution a for 60 s with agitation to reveal the Fe-Sn alloy layer. For heavy tin coatings and thick alloy layers, use solution b for 3–15 s with agitation (Romig and Rowland).

Etchants for iron and steel *(continued)*

Etchant composition	Comments

Coatings on steel *(continued)*

Etchant composition	Comments
39. 10 g KOH 　　10 g $K_3Fe(CN)_6$ 　　80 mL water	Murakami's reagent. For TiC-coated steel (Zouhar and coworkers).
40. 100 mL ethanol 　　1 g iodine 　　1 drop HCl	For tin-plated steels.
41. 200 mL water 　　20 g CrO_3 　　1.5 g Na_2SO_4	For galvanized steel or cadmium coatings. To 30 mL of the solution, add 70 mL water. Rinse specimen with cold water, swab 1 s with solution, wash and dry (St. Joseph's Lead Co.).
42. 1 part HNO_3 　　4 parts acetic acid	For nickel deposits on steel, reveals structure of nickel.

Oxygen enrichment etchants

Etchant composition	Comments
43. 10 g $KMnO_4$ 　　10 g NaOH 　　10 g Na_2CO_3 　　4 g $K_2Cr_2O_7$ 　　100 mL water	Alkaline chromate etch (Hall) to detect oxidation in steel. Heat etch to a boil, immerse sample faceup, hold 10–40 min until surface is brownish blue to purple-blue, wash, dry. Use fresh. Oxygen-enriched areas appear white.
44. 16 g CrO_3 　　145 mL water 　　80 g NaOH	Alkaline chromate etch (Fine) to detect oxidation in steel. Dissolve CrO_3 in water, then carefully add NaOH. Heat to a boil, 244–248°F (118–120°C), immerse sample faceup for 7–20 min, rinse in cold water, dry. Use fresh. Oxygen-enriched areas appear white.

Dual-phase steel etchants

Etchant composition	Comments
45. 2 g ammonium persulfate 　　2 mL HF 　　50 mL acetic acid 　　150 mL water	Martensite is darkened, retained austenite is lighter than ferrite (Rigsbee and Vander Arend).
46. Solution a 　　4 g picric acid 　　100 mL methanol 　　Solution b 　　8 g CrO_3 　　40 g NaOH 　　72 mL water	Etch first with picral solution a, then use solution b boiling. Martensite is stained black, "old" ferrite gray, "new" ferrite white (Lawson and coworkers).
47. Solution a 　　1 g sodium metabisulfite 　　100 mL water 　　Solution b 　　4 g picric acid 　　100 mL ethanol	Mix equal parts of solutions a and b. Etch for 7–12 s. Surface colored blue-orange. Bainite is black, ferrite tan, martensite white (Le Pera).

Etchants for iron and steel *(continued)*

Etchant composition	Comments
	Dual-phase steel etchants *(continued)*

48. Solution a
  2 mL HNO$_3$
  98 mL ethanol
Solution b
  10 g sodium metabisulfite
  100 mL water
	Preetch 1–2 s in nital solution a, then for 20 s in solution b. Martensite is dark, ferrite off white, austenite white (Marder and Benscoter).

49. 50 mL sat. aq. sodium
  thiosulfate
  1 g potassium metabisulfite
	Klemm's I. Immerse sample 60–90 s until surface is violet. Light preetch with nital is helpful. Ferrite is light or dark blue, martensite brown and black, retained austenite white.

	Prior-austenite grain size etchants

50. 100 mL ethanol
  1 g picric acid
  5 mL HCl
	Vilella's etch. Works best on martensite tempered at 572–932°F (300–500°C). Immerse sample at room temperature. Sometimes produces grain contrast (results can be improved with several polish-etch cycles). For high-alloy steels, grain-boundary attack is sometimes obtained. HCl sometimes added to 4% picral.

51. 80 mL ethanol
  1 g picric acid
  10 mL HCl
  10 mL HNO$_3$
	Schrader's modification of Vilella's etch, generally used for high-alloy steels. Immerse sample at 20°C.

52. 5 g FeCl$_3$ 100 mL water	Miller and Day's etch for low-carbon steels. 1–10 g FeCl$_3$ has been used. Contrast best when martensite is tempered at 300–400°F (149–204°C). Immerse sample at 20°C for 2–6 s.

53. 1 g FeCl$_3$
  5 drops–5 mL HCl
  100 mL water
	For medium-carbon steels. Immerse sample at 20°C for up to 30 s. Occasionally successful.

54. Sat. aq. picric acid plus small amount of a wetting agent	Bechet and Beaujard's etch. Most successful etchant, good for martensitic and bainitic steels. See Chap. 3 on use. Many wetting agents have been used, sodium tridecylbenzenesulfonate is one of most successful. Use at 20–100°C. Swab or immerse sample for 2–60 min. Etch in ultrasonic cleaner. Additions of 0.5 g CuCl$_2$ per 100 mL solution or about 1% HCl have been used for higher-alloy steels to produce etching. Room temperature etching most common. Lightly back-polish to remove surface smut.

55. 10 g picric acid
  20 drops HCl
  20 drops Teepol (wetting
  agent)
  1000 mL water
	Used for high-purity martensitic Fe-C alloys. Amount of HCl can be critical (Krahe and Desnoues).

Etchants for iron and steel *(continued)*

Etchant composition	Comments

Prior-austenite grain size etchants *(continued)*

Etchant composition	Comments
56. 34 g sodium bisulfite 100 mL water	Used to reveal grain boundaries in fine-grained, heavily deformed steels. Immerse sample 1–2 s to produce a thin, cinnamon-yellow film, examine with dark-field illumination (Popova and Malashenko).
57. 50 mL HCl 25 mL HNO_3 1 g $CuCl_2$ 150 mL water	Used for 18% Ni maraging steels (Spaeder and coworkers).
58. 100 mL sat. aq. picric acid 2 g Calsoft-90 2 g ammonium persulfate 6 drops H_2O_2	Used to reveal grain boundaries in partly or fully recrystallized HSLA steels water-quenched after rolling. Reveals extent of recrystallization and size of grains (Winsteard and Kot).
59. 35 g ammonium persulfate 10 mL HCl 100 mL water	For martensitic stainless steels. Electrolytic etch at 6–10 V dc for a few seconds. Tempering at 1112–1292°F (600–700°C) may be required (Viswanathan).
60. 2 g picric acid 25 g NaOH 100 mL water	Alkaline sodium picrate. Best etch for McQuaid-Ehn carburized samples. Darkens grain-boundary cementite. Use boiling for 1–2 min or electrolytically at 6 V dc, 0.5–2 A/in^2, 30–120 s. Often effective for high-carbon steels when no apparent grain-boundary film is present.
61. 10 mL HCl 3 mL HNO_3 80–100 mL alcohol	For high-speed steels (Leitner and Kostler). Also used for as-quenched high-carbon steels. Examine under polarized light. Sensitive tint emphasizes grain contrast effect. Also used to etch samples treated by oxidation method (Riedl).
62. 10–15 g chromium anhydride 10–20 g aluminum sulfate or ammonium persulfate 100 mL water	For untempered high-Si steels. Use electrolytically, 0.01 A/cm^2, 20–30 min.
63. 25 g $FeCl_3$ 25 mL HCl 100 mL water	For martensitic stainless steels.
64. 2–30 g oxalic acid 100 mL water	For high-speed steels. Electrolytic, 2–12 A/cm^2, 6–50 V dc, 2–60 s, stainless steel cathode. For alloy steels and tool steels, use 0.2–0.3 A/cm^2 (Zablotskii and coworkers).
65. 3 g picric acid 100 mL xylene 10 mL ethanol	For quenched and tempered steels (Werner.)
66. 40 mL HCl 10 mL H_2SO_4 50 mL water	For as-cast alloy steels. Use boiling (Brammar and coworkers).

Etchants for iron and steel *(continued)*

Etchant composition	Comments

Prior-austenite grain size etchants (continued)

Etchant composition	Comments
67. 20 mL HNO_3 　　10 mL H_2SO_4 　　70 mL water	For as-cast alloy steels. Immerse sample 5–20 s. Use under hood. Remove smut with cotton under running water.
68. 6 mL HNO_3 　　100 mL alcohol 　　1 mL zephiran chloride	Used on temper-embrittled as-cast steels (Loria).
69. 80 mL water 　　28 mL 10% aq. oxalic acid 　　4 mL H_2O_2 (30%)	For quench and tempered low-carbon steels (Swarr and Krauss).
70. 400 mL water 　　5 mL HCl 　　10 g $FeCl_3$ 　　10 mL zephiran chloride	For martensitic stainless steels and high-Cr alloy steels (GE Turbo-chrome etch).
71. 10 mL H_2O_2 　　40 mL HCl 　　50 mL water	For AFC 77 martensitic stainless steel (Webster).
72. 100 mL HCl 　　120–140 mL ethanol 　　8 g $FeCl_3$ 　　7 g $CuCl_2$	For tool steels. Etch 10–120 s. Remove gray surface deposit with cotton moistened with 4% alcoholic HCl.
73. 50 mL HNO_3 　　50 mL acetic acid	For martensitic age-hardenable stainless steels. Electropolish in solution at 5–6 A/cm^2, 1–3 s, 20°C. Then etch at 0.5–0.7 A/cm^2, 1–3 s (Il'ina and Strueva).
74. 1 part sat. aq. picric acid 　　1 part 50 g NaOH in 100 mL 　　　water	For hypoeutectoid and hypereutectoid alloy steels. Etch boiling for 8–10 min. Wash in boiling water, dry (Pumphrey).
75. 10 mL HCl 　　6 mL acetic acid 　　1 g picric acid 　　100 mL ethanol	For high-speed steels (Vescovi and Timo).
76. 50 mL ethanol 　　1 mL ammonia 　　1 mL HCl 　　3 g picric acid 　　1 g copper ammonium chloride	For austenite grains in cast iron or steels treated by the oxidation method (Riedl).
77. 15 mL HCl 　　85 mL ethanol	For etching samples treated by the oxidation method. Nital is suitable if decarburization is present along the grain boundaries (Hawkes).

Etchants for iron and steel *(continued)*

Etchant composition	Comments

Etchant composition	Comments

78. Solution a
    50 g picric acid
    250 mL purified ethyl ether
  Solution b
    10 mL zephiran chloride
    240 mL water
	Etch of Cohen and coworkers to reveal temper embrittlement. Mix solutions a and b, shake thoroughly, store overnight in tightly stoppered bottle. Carefully pour off top layer into a beaker and dilute with one-third volume ether. Etch 1–15 min. May require alternate etch-polish cycle. McLean and Northcott substituted CATB or aryl EPG for zephiran chloride. Grain boundaries not revealed in deembrittled steels.

79. Solution a
    6 g picric acid
    150 mL water
  Solution b
    10 mL zephiran chloride
    300 mL purified ethyl ether
	Etch of Rucker for revealing temper embrittlement. Mix solutions a and b, shake solution, store in a tightly stoppered bottle at least 12 h. Carefully pour off top layer and dilute with one-half volume ether. Etch 1–15 min. Grain boundaries not revealed in deembrittled steels.

80. 100 mL sat. aq. $KMnO_4$ 10 g KOH	Klemm's etch for temper-embrittled steels. Etch at 158°F (70°C) for 1 min. Examine with dark-field illumination.

81. 50 g picric acid
    250 mL ethyl ether
    240 mL water
    13 mL zephirol
	Etch of del Corral and de Castro y Mosquera (modification of etch of Eilender and Mintrop).

82. Sat. aq. picric acid	Etch first suggested by McLean and Northcott. Add about 1 g (or 1%) of a wetting agent, e.g., sodium tridecylbenzenesulfonate or Teepol. Will still reveal grain boundaries in deembrittled steels. P must be present. Very popular etch for prior-austenite grain boundaries.

Etchant composition	Comments

83. 45 g Na_2CO_3
    55 mL water
    10 g sodium dichromate
	Beaujard's tint etch. Use at 100°C.

84. 40 g Na_2CO_3
    60 mL water
    15 g sodium nitrate
	Beaujard's tint etch. Use at 100°C. Produces brighter tints than etchant no. 83. Color of ferrite varies with orientation, martensite is blue. Reveals chemical segregation.

85. 60–80 mL 35% aq. sodium bisulfite
    40–20 mL water
    (21–28% aq. $NaHSO_3$)
	Beaujard and Tordeux's tint etch. Use at 20°C, 10–25 s. Reveals grain boundaries and ferrite orientations. As-quenched martensite blackened. Reveals segregation. Light preetch with nital helpful.

Etchants for iron and steel *(continued)*

Etchant composition	Comments
	Tint etchants *(continued)*
86. 50 mL sat. aq. sodium thiosulfate 1 g potassium metabisulfite	Klemm's I reagent. Use at 20°C for 40–100 s. Reveals P segregation (white), colors ferrite (blue or red), cementite and austenite unaffected, colors martensite brown. Light nital preetch helpful. Can reveal overheating. Produces line etching in ferrite. Useful for many nonferrous alloys.
87. 50 mL sat. aq. sodium thiosulfate 5 g potassium metabisulfite	Klemm's II reagent. Use at 20°C for 30–90 s. P-rich regions darkened when etched >15 s. For austenitic Mn steels, γ yellow to brown or light to dark blue, α-martensite dark brown, ϵ-martensite white. Useful for many nonferrous alloys.
88. Solution a 25 mL HNO_3 75 mL ethanol Solution b 35 g $NaHSO_3$ or $Na_2S_2O_5$ 100 mL water	Tint etch for Fe-Ni massive martensite (Benscoter and coworkers). Preetch with solution a for 10 s (not needed if sample is electropolished). Stain with solution b for 2 min at 20°C. Do not store solution a.
89. 1 g $Na_2S_2O_5$ 100 mL water	Tint etch for lath or plate martensite (Benscoter and coworkers). Use at 20°C for 2 min.
90. 10 g potassium metabisulfite 100 mL water	Darkens untempered martensite, carbides and phosphides unaffected. Lightly preetch sample with nital, immerse in etchant solution 1–15 s.
91. 8–15 g sodium metabisulfite 100 mL water	Darkens as-quenched martensite, carbides and phosphides unaffected. Lightly preetch sample with nital, immerse in etchant solution about 20 s.
92. 30 g acetone sodium bisulfite 100 mL water	Tint etch for lath martensite (Benscoter and coworkers). Immerse sample for up to 2 min. Lightly preetch with nital. Polarized light enhances results.
93. Solution a 80 g sodium thiosulfate 60 g ammonium nitrate 1000 mL water Solution b 1 part HNO_3 2.5 parts H_3PO_4	Beraha's tint etch for ferrite. Before use, heat 100 mL of solution a to 158–167°F (70–75°C) and add 0.4–0.5 mL of solution b with vigorous stirring. Reagent becomes turbid and is useful for 15 min. Preetch with nital, then immerse sample in reagent, moving it slowly until the surface turns dark blue, usually 1–3 min. Wash and remove any loosely adhering sulfur particles. Ferrite colored dark red or blue, cementite and phosphide sharply outlined and clear, sulfides brightened.
94. 20 g anhydrous sodium pyrophosphate 13 mL H_3PO_4 3 g sodium molybdate 6 g sodium nitrate 1000 mL water (Final pH 3.5–4)	Beraha's stain etch for pearlitic steels and cast iron. Solution is stable for 48 h (for stock solution, leave out the sodium nitrate). Use light nital preetch. For grain contrast in low-carbon steels, etch 5–20 s; for gray iron, etch 45–90 s; for high-magnification work, etch <30 s. Carburized, nitrided, or electroplated layers unaffected.

Etchants for iron and steel *(continued)*

Etchant composition	Comments
	Tint etchants (continued)

95. 10 g $Na_2MoO_4 \cdot 2H_2O$
     1000 mL water

Beraha's tint etch for cast iron. Before use, add HNO_3 to produce pH of 2.5–3.0 (about 0.4 mL HNO_3 per 100 mL solution). Preetch with nital. Immerse sample in solution for 20–30 s. Phosphide and cementite yellow-orange, ferrite bright. For low-carbon steel, add 100 mg NH_4FHF per 100 mL of solution. Preetch with nital, immerse sample in etching solution 45–60 s. Carbide yellow-orange, ferrite white. For medium-carbon steel, use 200 mg NH_4FHF.

96. 3 g potassium metabisulfite
     100 mL water

Beraha's tint etch to reveal chemical and physical heterogeneities in iron and steel. Use at 20°C for 1–15 min; 3–6 min reveals general structure, 10–15 min discloses heterogeneities. Colors ferrite, martensite, bainite, and pearlite, sulfides brightened. Etch good for several hours.

97. 3 g potassium metabisulfite
     10 g anhydrous sodium thiosulfate
     100 mL water

Beraha's tint etch for iron and steel. Immerse sample 1–15 min. Nital preetch reduces etch time. Acts similarly to etchant no. 96.

98. 5–10 mL HCL
     1000 mL water

Beraha's tint etch for iron, steels, and tool steels. Before use, add 1 g potassium metabisulfite per 100 mL solution. Good for a few hours. For most work, 6 mL HCl is sufficient. For deep etching, use 10 mL HCl (reveals substructure, martensite grain boundaries, flow lines). Agitate strongly during etching, then hold motionless until surface is colored, 10–60 s total time. Colors ferrite, martensite, bainite, pearlite. Carbide, nitride, and phosphide unaffected.

99. Solution a
     100 mL ethanol
     2 mL HCl
     1 mL selenic acid
     Solution b
     100 mL ethanol
     1–2 mL HCl
     0.5 mL selenic acid
     Solution c
     100 mL ethanol
     10 mL HCl
     3 mL selenic acid

Beraha's tint etch for cast iron, steels, tool steels. Nital preetch optional. Use solution a or c for cast iron (15–30 s); solution b for cast iron (use 2 mL HCl, 7–10 min), steel, tool steel, and martensitic or PH stainless steels. Ferrite and austenite bright; phosphides, nitrides, and carbides are colored. Solution a colors phosphide red-brown or violet. Preetch with nital before using solution b; phosphide colored blue or green, cementite colored red, blue, or green, and ferrite colored yellow or brown. Preetch with nital for 2 min before using solution c; phosphide colored red-brown, cementite and ferrite bright.

Etchants for iron and steel *(continued)*

Etchant composition	Comments
	Tint etchants *(continued)*
100. 240 g anhydrous sodium thiosulfate 30 g citric acid 20–25 g cadmium chloride 1000 mL water	Beraha's cadmium sulfide tint etch for Fe, steel, and ferritic and martensitic stainless steel. Dissolve in order shown. Allow each to dissolve before adding next. Allow to age 24 h at 20°C in a dark bottle. Before use, filter 100 mL of solution to remove precipitates. Use at 20°C, good for 4 h. Preetch with a general-purpose reagent. Etch 20–90 s. For steels, after 20–40 s only ferrite is colored, red or violet. Longer times color all constituents: ferrite is colored yellow or light blue, phosphide brown, carbide violet or blue. For stainless steels, immerse sample 60–90 s; carbides are colored red or violet-blue, matrix yellow, colors of ferrite vary. Sulfides red-brown after 90 s.

101. Solution a
  100 mL water
  3 g potassium metabisulfite
  1 g sulfamic acid
Solution b
  100 mL water
  6 g potassium metabisulfite
  2 g sulfamic acid
Solution c
  100 mL water
  3 g potassium metabisulfite
  2 g sulfamic acid
Solution d
  100 mL water
  3 g potassium metabisulfite
  2 g sulfamic acid
  0.5–1 g ammonium bifluoride
	Beraha's tint etchants for cast iron, steels, tool steels, Mn steels, and ferritic and martensitic stainless steels. Use all at 20°C. Reagents active for 2–4 h. Discard when yellow. Cd or Zn coatings inhibit staining. Use solution a for cast iron, carbon and alloy steels, Mn steels; 45 s to 4 min for cast iron, 15 s to 4 min for the others. Solution b is similar to solution a but faster acting. Use solution c for carbon, alloy, and Mn steels; 5–30 s. To detect retained austenite (brown or blue), use 45–90 s. Use solution d for stainless steels, Mn steel, and some tool steels; 30 s to 3 min. Use plastic container and forceps with solution d.

102. Solution a
  100 mL water
  15 g ammonium molybdate
  100 mL HNO$_3$
Solution b
  2 mL of solution a
  100 mL alcohol
	Malette's reagent. Colors ferrite. Dissolve ammonium molybdate in water, add HNO$_3$, age solution 4 days, filter. Mix solution b and use as etchant, 30–45 min.

	Inclusion etchants
103. 15 g CrO$_3$ 1000 mL water	Attacks sulfides. Immerse sample about 60 s. Stronger solutions also used, up to 10%. Sulfides reddish under bright-field illumination.
104. 5 mL H$_2$SO$_4$ 95 mL water	Dissolves sulfides.

Etchants for iron and steel *(continued)*

Etchant composition	Comments

Inclusion etchants (continued)

Etchant composition	Comments
105. 240 g sodium thiosulfate 24 g lead acetate 30 g citric acid 1000 mL water	Beraha's lead sulfide tint etch. Sulfides stained bright white, colors matrix also. Mix in order given. Store 24 h at 20°C in dark bottle. Add 200 mg sodium nitrate (optional) to 100 mL solution, good for 30 min. Immerse sample 60–90 s.
106. 100 mL water 0.5 g palladous chloride 3 mL HCl	Beraha's tint etch for sulfides in stainless steels. Preetch with Marbles reagent. Add a few drops of a nonionic wetting agent (Triton X100). Immerse sample until the surface is black. Sulfides silvery bright. Store stock solution in dark bottle.
107. 5 g gelatin 20 mL water 20 mL glycerol 2 mL H_2SO_4 0.8 g silver nitrate	Sulfide etch of Kunkele. Produces halos around sulfides.
108. 0.2 g oxalic acid 100 mL water	Attacks sulfides. Immerse sample 20–30 s.
109. 5 g silver nitrate 100 mL water	Whiteley's method for coloring sulfides. Unused Selvyt cloth soaked several minutes in solution. Wash cloth thoroughly under running water. Place cloth on glass plate, rub polished sample on cloth gently for about 15 s. Sulfides coated white.

110. Solution a
  1 g KCN
  100 mL water
Solution b
  0.25 g dithizone
  10 mL chloroform
	Preetch with 4% picral. Mix solutions a and b, swab sample for up to 3 min. Lead particles appear red in polarized light (Melton).

111. 50 mL alcohol 3 mL acetic acid 20 mL water 2 g potassium iodide	Immerse sample 1–2 min. Colors Pb yellow.
112. 10% aq. ammonium acetate.	Electrolytic, 5 V dc, 30 s. Reveals Pb.
113. 1–2 mL HNO_3 98–99 mL alcohol	Saturate nital with potassium iodide, filter off excess KI. Immerse sample in solution for 10–30 s. Colors lead greenish yellow under bright-field illumination and bright yellow under dark-field illumination (Vegesack).
114. 10 g CrO_3 100 mL water	Immerse sample 10 min. Colors Pb yellow-red (also attacks sulfides).
115. Mercury	Immerse sample in Hg at 100°C. Attacks lead.
116. Heat, 482–536°F (250–280°C)	Heat tint. At 250°C, steel brownish, lead particles distinct. At 280°C, steel dark brown, lead bluish.

Etchants for iron and steel *(continued)*

Etchant composition	Comments
	Inclusion etchants *(continued)*
117. 10 g tartaric acid 100 mL water	Used to enhance detectability of inclusions. Immerse sample for 5 min, rinse and dry. Lightly repolish with final abrasive to remove surface film, rinse and dry.
	Selective carbide etchants
118. 2 g picric acid 25 g NaOH 100 mL water	Alkaline sodium picrate. Immerse sample in boiling solution for 1–15 min or use electrolytically at 6 V dc, 20°C, 0.5–2 A/in^2, 30–120 s, stainless steel cathode. Colors cementite (Fe$_3$C) dark brown to black. Does not attack cementite containing substantial Cr. Attacks Fe$_4$W$_2$C and sulfides.
119. 1 g pyrogallol (or gallic acid) 20 g 30% aq. NaOH	Darkens Fe$_3$C in 8–15 min at 20°C (van Klooster and Schaefer).
120. Solution a 　5 g pyrogallol 　15 mL water Solution b 　120 g KOH 　80 mL water	Mix solutions a and b. Immerse sample 7–10 min at 20°C. Darkens Fe$_3$C (Liebig).
121. 1–4 g K$_3$Fe(CN)$_6$ 10 g KOH (or 7 g NaOH) 100 mL water	Modified Murakami's reagent. Use fresh. Etch up to 15 min in boiling solution. Cementite darkened, pearlite brown.
122. 10 g K$_3$Fe(CN)$_6$ 10 g KOH (or 7 g NaOH) 100 mL water	Murakami's reagent. Use fresh, cold or hot, up to 10 min. Cold—darkens chromium carbides and tungstides, Fe$_3$C unattacked or barely attacked. Hot—attacks cementite.
123. 1 g CrO$_3$ 100 mL water	Electrolytic etch, 2–3 V dc, 30 s. MC and M$_7$C$_3$ darkened, Mo$_2$C outlined (Blickwede and coworkers).
124. 10 mL H$_2$O$_2$ (30%) 20 mL 10% aq. NaOH	Etch for 10 s at 20°C. Fe$_2$MoC, Mo$_2$C, and M$_6$C outlined; M$_6$C also colored.
125. 4 g KMnO$_4$ 4 g NaOH 100 mL water	Groesbeck's reagent. Fe$_2$MoC and M$_6$C outlined and colored (Fe$_2$MoC blue, M$_6$C brown). Mo$_2$C colored brown. (Fe,Cr)$_{23}$C$_6$ attacked but (Fe,Mo)$_{23}$C$_6$ not attacked.
126. 4 g NaOH 100 mL sat. aq. KMnO$_4$	Mo$_2$C and M$_7$C$_3$ attacked, M$_6$C outlined and colored brown (Kayser and Cohen).
127. 5 g NaOH or KOH 100 mL water	Use boiling, 5–10 min. Darkens Fe$_3$C.
128. 20 g K$_3$Fe(CN)$_6$ 10 g KOH 100 mL water	Use boiling. Chromium carbides and tungstides darkened in about 20 s, cementite colored after about 5 min (Daeves).

Etchants for iron and steel *(continued)*

Etchant composition	Comments

Potentiostatic etchants

129. Solution a
    8 N NaOH
Solution b
    1.25 N NaOH

Etch to distinguish iron phosphide from cementite. Use solution a at -750 mV vs. SCE to color Fe_3C; Fe_3P and Fe_4N not attacked. Etch in solution b at -200 mV vs. SCE to color Fe_3P; Fe_3C and Fe_4N not attacked (Langenscheidt and Nauman).

130. 10 N NaOH

Used to differentiate Fe_3C from Fe_4N. Use at -700 to -600 mV vs. SCE. Fe_3C colored in about 5–10 min, Fe_4N unaffected.

131. Solution a
    2 N sodium sulfate
    0.2 mL 1 N NaOH per liter
Solution b
    2 N sodium sulfate
    2 mL 1 N H_2SO_4 per liter

To differentiate between high- and low-phosphorus regions. Use solution a at -680 mV vs. SCE to stain areas $>0.3\%$ P. Use solution b at -700 mV vs. SCE to stain areas $<0.3\%$ P (Naumann and coworkers).

132. 40% aq. NaOH

For heat-treated alloy steels. Bainite etched at -400 to $+800$ mV vs. SCE, martensite unetched (Lichtenegger and coworkers).

Stainless steel etchants

133. 1 g picric acid
5 mL HCl
100 mL ethanol

Vilella's reagent. Use at 20°C for up to 1 min. Outlines constituents such as carbides, sigma phase, and delta ferrite; etches martensite.

134. 10 mL HNO_3
20 mL HCl
10 mL H_2O_2 (30%)
20 mL glycerin

Vilella's mixed-acid etch. Immerse sample at 20°C. Applicable to most stainless steels. Can vary amount of HCl. Use under a hood, do not store.

135. 1 part HNO_3
1 part HCl
1 part water

General-purpose etch for most stainless steels. Stir solution during etching (20°C) for uniform, stain-free results. Outlines constituents, reveals grain structure. Can be stored.

136. 4 parts HCl
3 parts HNO_3
4 parts water

Follow same procedure for use as for etchant no. 135.

137. 10 g $FeCl_3$
30 mL HCl
120 mL water

Curran's etch for most stainless steels. Swab sample gently for 3–10 s. Can dilute etchant to slow down attack.

138. 5 g $CuCl_2$
100 mL HCl
100 mL ethanol

Kalling's no. 2 etch for duplex stainless steels. Ferrite attacked most readily, carbides unattacked, austenite slightly attacked. Use at 20°C by immersion of sample.

139. 1.5 g $CuCl_2$
33 mL ethanol
33 mL water
33 mL HCl

Kalling's no. 1 etch for martensitic stainless steel. Martensite dark, ferrite colored, austenite not attacked. Use at 20°C by immersion of sample.

Etchants for iron and steel *(continued)*

Etchant composition	Comments
Stainless steel etchants (continued)	

140. 40 mL HCl
    5 g $CuCl_2$
    30 mL water
    25 mL ethanol
	Fry's reagent for martensitic and precipitation-hardenable grades. Use at 20°C by immersion of sample.

141. 3 parts glycerol
    2 parts HCl
    1 part HNO_3
	For martensitic and ferritic stainless steels. Use fresh. After 1 h, etch response is too fast. Warm sample in hot-water bath. Swab sample 15–30 s to etch sigma, 60 s or more outlines carbides. Discard etch when it acquires a strong chlorine color. Do not store.

142. Solution a
    10 mL HCl
    90 mL water
  Solution b
    50 mL HCl
    50 mL water
	Use solution a for martensitic stainless steels, use boiling for 3–10 s. Use solution b for grades containing Mo. Use boiling. Delineates chi and sigma phases (Koh).

143. 4 g $CuSO_4$
    20 mL HCl
    20 mL water
	Marble's reagent used for most stainless steels. Use at 20°C for 3–10 s. Reveals grain structure, attacks sigma.

144. HCl saturated with $FeCl_3$	For ferritic and austenitic stainless steels. Activate with small amount of HNO_3 (optional). Reveals grain structure, sometimes colors delta ferrite.

145. 100 mL HCl
    7 g mercurous nitrate
    100 mL water
	For ferritic stainless steels.

146. 92 mL HCl
    5 mL H_2SO_4
    3 mL HNO_3
	For precipitation-hardenable grades.

147. 2 parts glycerol
    2 parts HCl
    1 part HNO_3
	For austenitic stainless steels. Can accelerate action by increasing HCl content or by adding 1 part 3% H_2O_2.

148. 25 mL HCl 5–50 mL 10% aq. CrO_3	For austenitic stainless steel. Control speed of attack by amount of 10% CrO_3. Good, rapid, even etch.

149. 25 mL HCl
    7.5 g CrO_3
    50 mL water
	"Chrome regia." Use at 20°C for 3–30 s. Attacks austenite vigorously, ferrite nearly as fast. Carbides and sigma in relief.

150. 400 mL water
    5 mL HCl
    10 g $FeCl_3$
    10 mL zephiran chloride
	GE Turbo-chrome etch for martensitic grades. Swab sample about 15 s. Attacks martensite tempered above 1000°F and diffusion-controlled products.

151. 20 g $CuSO_4$
    50 mL H_2SO_4
    100 mL HCl
    100 mL water
	Modified Marble's reagent for austenitic stainless steels. Swab sample.

Etchants for iron and steel *(continued)*

Etchant composition	Comments

Etchant composition	Comments
152. 15 mL HCl 5 mL HNO_3	Aqua regia. For austenitic grades. Use fresh. Use at 20°C for about 5 s. Attacks sigma, outlines carbides. After 20 s, sigma completely dissolved. Reveals grain boundaries. Do not store etchant.
153. 45 mL HCl 15 mL HNO_3 20 mL methanol	Methanolic aqua regia. For austenitic grades. Outlines ferrite and sigma, reveals grain structure.
154. 5 mL acetic acid 5 mL HNO_3 15 mL HCl	Aqua regia plus acetic acid. For ferritic grades. Swab sample 15 s. Deep etch for SEM (scanning electron microscope) after 45 s.
155. 15 mL HCl 5 mL HNO_3 100 mL water	Dilute aqua regia for austenitic grades. Uniform etching of austenite, outlines carbides, sigma, and ferrite (in relief). Ferrite sometimes attacked. Good preetch before heat tinting or use of Murakami's reagent.
156. 100 mL 1.2% picral 10 mL HCl 3 mL acetic acid	For stainless steels and high-speed steels.
157. 3 parts HCl 1 part HNO_3 1 part glycerol	"Glyceregia." For austenitic grades. Reveals grain structure, outlines sigma and carbides.
158. 200 mL water 100 mL HCl 30 g $K_3Fe(CN)_6$	For austenitic stainless steels.
159. 10 mL HNO_3 5 mL HCl 0.1 g $CuCl_2$	For austenitic grades. Swab sample a few seconds. Mix fresh and discard after use. Use under hood. Do not inhale fumes (Ebling).
160. 7–8 mL HNO_3 2–3 mL HCl 0.5 g $CuCl_2$	For austenitic grades. Swab sample 5–20 s. Mix fresh and discard after use. Use under hood. Do not inhale fumes (Huseby).

Etchant composition	Comments

161. Solution a
   25 mL HCl
   75 mL ethanol
Solution b
   10 mL HCl
   90 mL water
	For ferritic grades. Use polarized light and sensitive tint. Sigma colored lemon-yellow to bluish white with stage rotation, ferrite and austenite remain maroon. For austenitic grades, etch up to 30 min.

162. 2 parts 15% aq. ammonium
   persulfate
2 parts 50% alcoholic HCl
1 part sat. alcoholic
   o-nitrophenol
	Ortho-nitrophenol contrast etch. Austenite darkened, ferrite and sigma remain bright (Braumann and Pier).

Etchants for iron and steel *(continued)*

Etchant composition	Comments
	Selective etchants for stainless steels *(continued)*
163. 4 parts 15% aq. ammonium persulfate 4 parts 50% ethanolic HCl 1 part sat. ethanolic *o*-nitrophenol	Modified ortho-nitrophenol contrast etch for steels containing sigma. Darkens austenite and delta ferrite, sigma unaffected (Wagner and coworkers).
164. 100 mL water 2 g $KMnO_4$ 12 g KOH	For austenitic grades. Use at 20°C for 5–15 s. Darkens carbides.
165. 1 part sat. aq. $KMnO_4$ 1 part 8% aq. NaOH	For austenitic grades. Stains sigma pink, carbides light brown. With deeper etch, sigma brown-orange, carbide green (uneven).
166. 4 g $KMnO_4$ 4 g NaOH 100 mL water	Groesbeck's reagent. Use at 140–194°F (60–90°C) for 1–10 min. Carbides dark, sigma gray, ferrite and austenite unaffected. Can also use 1 g NaOH.
167. 10 g $K_3Fe(CN)_6$ 10 g KOH (or 7 g NaOH) 100 mL water	Murakami's reagent. Usually works better on ferritic grades than on austenitic grades. Use at 20°C for 7–60 s: reveals carbides, sigma faintly attacked with etching up to 3 min. Use at 80°C (176°F) to boiling for 2–60 min: carbides dark, sigma blue (not always attacked), ferrite yellow to yellow-brown, austenite unattacked. Do not always get uniform etching.
168. 30 g KOH 30 g $K_3Fe(CN)_6$ 60 mL water	Modified Murakami's reagent (Burgess and Forgeng). Use fresh. Difficult to dissolve at 20°C. Etch at 20°C for 3–5 s. Reveals sigma; carbide and austenite unaffected. Use at 176°F (80°C) to boiling for 10–60 s. Sigma light blue, ferrite yellow, carbides barely attacked.
169. 30 g KOH 30 g $K_3Fe(CN)_6$ 150 mL water	Modified Murakami's reagent. Use at 194–203°F (90–95°C) for about 15 s. Austenite light, ferrite tan, sigma reddish brown. Can also be used at 20°C.
170. 30 g KOH 30 g $K_3Fe(CN)_6$ 100 mL water	Modified Murakami's reagent (Kegley). Use at 203°F (95°C) for 5 s. Sigma reddish brown, ferrite dark gray, austenite white or light gray, carbide black.
171. 20 g KOH 20 g $K_3Fe(CN)_6$ 100 mL water	Modified Murakami's reagent (Le May and White). Use cold to 176°F (80°C). Carbide dark, ferrite yellow, sigma blue.

Etchants for iron and steel *(continued)*

Etchant composition	Comments

Selective etchants for stainless steels *(continued)*

Etchant composition	Comments
172. Solution a 16 g $FeCl_3 \cdot 6H_2O$ 50 mL water Solution b 9 g ammonium persulfate 50 mL water Solution c 60 mL HCl Solution d Cold sat. aq. sodium thiosulfate	WII etch (Wallner) for Cr-Ni steels. Mix solutions a and b, then add solution c. Age 1 h before use. Immerse sample up to 30 s. Remove from etch and place a few drops of solution d on the surface still wet with the etchant. Surface darkens, etchant becomes cloudy. Rinse after a few seconds. Colors delta ferrite, sigma not attacked but is outlined.
173. Heat in air, 932–1292°F (500–700°C) for up to 20 min	Heat tint. Austenite colored first, then sigma, then carbide. After 20 min, austenite mottled blue-green, sigma orange, carbide white. Very effective. Requires a good polish. Light preetch sharpens resolution.

Electrolytic etchants for stainless steels

Etchant composition	Comments
174. 10 g oxalic acid 100 mL water	Use at 6 V dc, 25-mm spacing. Carbides revealed by etching for 15–30 s, grain boundaries after 45–60 s, sigma outlined after 6 s. 1–3 V also used. Dissolves carbides, sigma strongly attacked, austenite moderately attacked, ferrite unattacked. To detect embrittlement [885°F (475°C)], use 5–7 V dc, 0.1–0.2 A/cm^2, 5–10 s. Unembrittled ferrite faint bluish green, embrittled ferrite brownish.
175. Sat. aq. oxalic acid	Use at 2.5–3 V dc for 15 s to distinguish carbide from sigma. Can be difficult to distinguish fine carbide from sigma or fine ferrite from sigma.
176. 2–10 g CrO_3 100 mL water	Use at 6 V dc for 10–30 s. Rapid attack of sigma and carbides (carbides sometimes outlined), austenite attacked, ferrite outlined and sometimes recessed. Difficult to outline sigma.
177. 10 g NaCN 100 mL water	Use at 6 V dc, 5 min, 25-mm spacing, Pt cathode. Sigma darkened, reveals carbides (light), austenite unaffected (revealed after 30 min), outlines ferrite. Slow action makes it easy to control. Very popular for revealing carbide, better than Murakami's reagent.
178. Sat. aq. NaCN	Use at 6 V dc. 1 min reveals austenite grain boundaries, 30 s stains sigma, 6 min reveals ferrite and austenite grain boundaries, 9 min fully reveals austenite grain boundaries and sigma.
179. 10 mL HCl 90 mL methanol	Use at 1.5 V dc at 20°C. Attacks sigma. Use at 6 V dc for 3–5 s reveals structure.

Etchants for iron and steel *(continued)*

Etchant composition	Comments
Electrolytic etchants for stainless steels (continued)	
180. 60 mL HNO$_3$ 40 mL water	Electrolytic etch to attack austenite boundaries but not twin boundaries. See Chap. 3 and Table 3-5. Also used to etch austenitic steel-carbon steel weldments; etch first with nital, then with electrolytic etch (Bell and Sonon).
181. 50 mL HNO$_3$ 50 mL water	Use at 2 V dc. General-purpose etch for austenitic grades.
182. 10 *N* NaOH (50 g NaOH in 100 mL water)	Use at 2–6 V dc for 5–10 s. Reveals sigma in austenitic grades.
183. 10N KOH (56 g KOH in 100 mL water)	Use at 1.5–3 V dc for 3 s. Reveals sigma (red-brown) and ferrite (bluish). Very effective. For austenitic PH grades, use 2 V dc for 5 sec; ferrite and sigma dark brown, α′ brown to pale blue to outlined. Ni$_3$(Al,Ti) and Ni(Al,Ti) outlined. M$_{23}$C$_6$ pale yellow, austenite unattacked.
184. 20 g NaOH 100 mL water	Use at 20 V dc, 20°C, 5 s, stainless steel cathode. Delta ferrite outlined and colored tan. Very effective.
185. 45 mL lactic acid 45 mL methanol 10 mL HCl	Use at 6 V dc, 1.2 A/cm^2, 20°C, few seconds. Heavily attacks austenite, sigma, and carbide; ferrite outlined and in relief.
186. Sat. aq. Ba(OH)$_2$ (about 5%)	Use at 4.5 V dc, Pt cathode, 20 s. With PH grades containing Ti, 12% Cr, and 4% Mo, chi is stained mottled purple, matrix is tan, and laves unstained. For austenitic grades, use 1.5 V dc. Carbides attacked well before sigma; at 3–6 V dc, both attacked at same rate.
187. 10 g lead acetate 100 mL water (Final pH 6)	Use at 6 V dc for 0.6 s. Surface covered with PbO$_2$ film. Forms most readily on austenite, less rapidly on sigma, least on carbide. Austenite light blue, sigma dark blue, carbide tan. For best results, preetch with a general-purpose reagent, e.g., Vilella's reagent.
188. 10 g cadmium acetate 100 mL water	Use at 6 V dc for 0.6 s. For austenitic grades, stains carbide more rapidly than rest of structure. At 1.5 V dc for 15 s, colors M$_{23}$C$_6$ only (dark blue), sigma white, matrix pale yellow.
189. Conc. NH$_4$OH	Use at 1.5–6 V dc for 10–60 s. Colors carbide. Very selective. At 1.5 V, carbide completely etched in 40 s, sigma not colored after 180 s. At 6 V, sigma etched after 40 s.
190. 10 g ammonium persulfate 100 mL water	Use at 6 V dc for 10 s. Stains carbide dark brown.
191. 45 g FeCl$_3$·6H$_2$O 100 mL water	Use at 4.25 V dc, 0.7 A, 5 min, Ni cathode. Attacks austenite.

Etchants for iron and steel *(continued)*

Etchant composition	Comments

Electrolytic etchants for stainless steels (continued)

192. 5 mL HCl 95 mL methanol	Use at 450 mA/cm^2 for 2 min. Reveals grain-boundary precipitates and phases in austenitic grades.
193. 2 parts HNO$_3$ 1 part acetic acid	Electrolytic, 10 s. For PH grades.
194. 10 mL HNO$_3$ 10 mL acetic acid 15 mL HCl 5 mL glycerin	For austenitic grades. Use at 2 V dc, 0.2 A, 1–5 s, Pt cathode. Keep cool (Kisiel).

Tint etchants for stainless steels

195. 3 g potassium metabisulfite 1–2 g sulfamic acid 0.5–1 g ammonium bifluoride 100 mL water	Beraha's tint etch for ferritic and martensitic stainless steels, Mn steels, and tool steels. Immerse sample at 20°C for 30–180 s.

196. Solution a
  1000 mL water
  200 mL HCl
Solution b
  0.5–1.0 g potassium
    metabisulfite per 100 mL
    of solution a
	Beraha's tint etch for austenitic grades, maraging steels, and PH grades. Immerse sample at 20°C for 30–120 s with agitation. Colors austenite, carbides unaffected.

197. 1000 mL water 200 mL HCl 24 g ammonium bifluoride	Beraha's tint etch for stainless steels. Before use, add 600–800 mg potassium metabisulfite to 100 mL of this stock solution (100–200 mg for martensitic grades). After mixing, reagent is active for about 2 h. Use plastic tongs and beaker. Immerse sample for 20–90 s at 20°C, shake gently while etching. Longer times intensify colors. Grain and twin boundaries clearly revealed. Second-phase particles bright and uncolored.
198. 5–10 mL HCl 1–3 mL selenic acid 100 mL ethanol	Beraha's tint etch for stainless steels. Can use 20–30 mL HCl for higher alloy grades. Immerse sample at 20°C for 1–10 min until a yellow or light-brown surface color is formed to detect carbides and nitrides, or until the surface is orange to red to detect delta ferrite. Immersion times decrease with higher HCl.

Potentiostatic etches for stainless steels

199. 10N NaOH (50 g NaOH to 100 mL H$_2$O)	Use at +300 to +350 mV vs. SCE. Ferrite brown, martensite light (PH grades) (Grutzner and Schuller).
200. 10 mL HNO$_3$ 30 mL Vogels Sparbeize 100 mL HCl 100 mL water	Use at −275 to −300 mV vs. SCE, 20°C, 10–45 min.

Etchants for iron and steel (continued)

Etchant composition	Comments

Potentiostatic etches for stainless steels (continued)

Etchant composition	Comments
201. 20 mL H_2SO_4 80 mL water	For austenitic PH grades, use at -0.5 to 0 V vs. SCE. For maximum contrast use -0.35 V for α'; -0.30 V for α, σ, and γ; -0.15 to -0.10 V for γ; 0 V for $Ni_3(Al,Ti)$ or $Ni(Al,Ti)$. Cannot distinguish α from σ by potential (use morphology), same for $Ni_3(Al,Ti)$ and $Ni(Al,Ti)$. For austenitic 18/8 grades use -0.45 V for 1 h for δ, -0.35 V for 1 h for γ, and $+1.05$ V for 3–5 min for δ (Clhal and Prazak).
202. 5 mL H_2SO_4 95 mL water 0.1 g NH_4CNS per liter of solution	For austenitic 18/8 grades use -0.35 V vs. SCE for 60–250 s for δ, -0.40 V for 60–150 s for σ, -0.15 V for 20–120 s for γ, -0.10 V for 1–3 min for austenite grain boundaries, and $+1.57$ V for 20 to 6 min for δ (Clhal and Prazak).
203. 1 N H_2SO_4 0.01% ammonium thiocyanate	For 316 stainless steel, use -0.40 to -0.30 V vs. SCE for δ, -0.30 to -0.21 V for γ', and -0.25 to -0.21 V for γ (Ito and Okamoto).

Oxide scale etchants

Etchant composition	Comments
204. 25 mL HF 25 mL acetic acid 60–70 mL water	Etch for NiO (Wolf). Etch electrolytically at 2–4 mA, 6–12 V dc, 30–45 s, stainless steel cathode.
205. 5 mL 1% HNO_3 5 mL 5% citric acid 5 mL 5% thiglycolic acid 10 mL water	For Fe_2O_3 (Hussey and coworkers). Swab sample 15–60 s. Fe_3O_4 and Fe remain unetched.
206. 5 mL 10% citric acid 5 mL 10% NaSCN	For Fe_2O_3 (Hussey and coworkers) when Fe is not present. Swab sample 45–90 s. Fe_3O_4 unetched.
207. Solution a 5 mL formic acid 15 mL water Solution b 5 mL HBF_4 15 mL water	For Fe_3O_4 (Hussey and coworkers) when Fe is not present. Swab sample 5 s with solution a, rinse, swab 2 s with solution b. To etch both Fe_2O_3 and Fe_3O_4, use etchant no. 206 then etchant no. 207.
208. 10 mL thioglycolic acid (5%) 5 mL potassium acid phthalate (5%) 5 mL ammonium citrate (5%) 50 mL Na_2CrO_4 (0.5%)	For Fe_3O_4 (Hussey and coworkers). Add Na_2CrO_4 before etching. Use at 2–4 mA, 9 V dc, 15 s, stainless steel cathode. Fe and Fe_2O_3 are not etched.
209. 10 mL thioglycolic acid (5%) 5 mL potassium acid phthalate (5%) 2 mL ammonium citrate (5%) 3 mL citric acid (5%)	For FeO (Hussey and coworkers). Swab sample 30–60 s. Fe, Fe_3O_4, and Fe_2O_3 unetched.

Etchants for iron and steel *(continued)*

Etchant composition	Comments
	Oxide scale etchants *(continued)*
210. 100 mL ethanol 0.5–1 mL HCl	Darkens FeO, does not attack Fe_3O_4. Etch by immersion of sample (Edstrom).
211. 100 mL HCl 2 g Sb_2O_3 5 g $SnCl_2$	To differentiate Fe_3O_4 from Fe-Cr spinel (Clarke). Cover specimen with several drops for 1–5 sec. Rapid etching of Fe_3O_4, phase boundary between Fe_3O_4 and spinel defined.
212. 40 mL HCl 0.25 g Armohib 28 60 mL water	To differentiate between Fe_3O_4 and Fe-Cr spinel (Hurdus and Tomlinson). Immerse sample 15–30 s. Similar to etchant no. 211 but slower acting.
213. 0.5 g $Na_2CrO_4 \cdot 4H_2O$ 100 mL water	To differentiate between Fe_3O_4 and Fe-Cr spinel (Hurdus and Tomlinson). If etched cathodically for 15 s at about 25 mA and 5–20 V dc, Fe_3O_4 changes color from gray to light gray, boundary between Fe_3O_4 and spinel defined, and some Fe_3O_4 grain boundaries revealed. If etched anodically at about 110 mA for 45 s at about 45 V dc, Fe-Cr spinel rapidly etched, color changes from gray to dark gray, and Fe_3O_4 not attacked.
214. 50 g oxalic acid 5 drops Teepol 500 mL water	To differentiate between Fe_3O_4 and Fe-Cr spinel (Hurdus and Tomlinson). Etch anodically at 10–20 mA, 2–5 V dc, about 10 s. Behaves like etchant no. 213 used anodically but is slower acting.
215. 7 g CrO_3 70 mL water	To differentiate Fe_3O_4 from Fe-Cr spinel (Hurdus and Tomlinson). Etch anodically at about 140 mA, about 14 V dc, for 10 s. Behaves like etchant no. 213 used anodically.
216. Solution a 1% bromothymol blue dye in 85% ethanol and 14% water Solution b 1.5% bromothymol blue dye in 80% ethanol and 17.5% water	Dye adsorption technique for scale on steel. Immerse sample 2 h in solution a or 1 h in solution b. FeO stained blue, Fe_3O_4 beige, Fe_2O_3 white (Chicco).
217. 1% bromophenol red dye in 90% ethanol and 9% water	Dye adsorption technique for scale on steel. Immerse sample 2 h. FeO stained dull green-gray, Fe_3O_4 beige, Fe_2O_3 white. Dye deposition on the steel substrate masks the structure. Poor contrast between FeO and epoxy resin (Chicco).

Lead and alloys

Etchant composition	Comments
1. 84 mL glycerol 8 mL acetic acid 8 mL HNO$_3$	For Pb and alloys. Use fresh, few seconds, 68–176°F (20–80°C).
2. 60 mL glycerol 15 mL acetic acid 15 mL HNO$_3$	For Pb and alloys. Use fresh solution, 176°F (80°C). Concentration of acetic and nitric acids can be reduced by one-half or doubled (Vilella and Beregekoff).
3. 100 mL alcohol 1–5 mL HNO$_3$	For Pb and alloys. Immerse sample. Wash well. Remove stain, if present, in 10% alcoholic HCl.
4. 90 mL water 10 mL HNO$_3$	For Pb and alloys. Grain contrast etch. Can add CrO$_3$ (Beckinsdale and Waterhouse).
5. 90 mL water or ethanol 20–30 mL HCl 0–10 g FeCl$_3$	For Pb alloys and solders. Immerse sample 1–10 min.
6. 50 mL water 50 mL HCl	For Pb solders and Pb-type alloys. Immerse sample 1–10 min.
7. 95 mL alcohol 5 mL HCl.	For Pb and Pb-Sn alloys. Immerse sample 1–5 min.
8. 80 mL water 15 mL acetic acid 20 mL HNO$_3$	For Pb, Pb-Sn alloys (up to 3% Sn), and Pb solders. Use fresh, 104°F (40°C), 5–30 min (Bassett and Synder).
9. 50 mL water 25 mL acetic acid 25 mL HNO$_3$	For Pb, Pb-Sn alloys (up to 25% Sn). Use fresh, 104°F (40°C), 5–30 min.
10. 75 mL acetic acid 25 mL H$_2$O$_2$ (30%)	Popular etch for pure Pb, Pb-Sb and Pb-Ca alloys. Immerse sample 5 to 15 min depending on alloy. After etching, dip in conc. HNO$_3$, then cold water, dry. (60-30 and 100-10 ratios also used) (Worner).
11. 60 mL acetic acid 14 mL water 6 mL H$_2$O$_2$ (30%)	Popular etch for Pb and alloys. Immerse sample 3–30 s, dip in conc. HNO$_3$, then cold water, dry.
12. 90–100 mL water 5–10 g silver nitrate	For Pb alloys. Swab sample.
13. 100 mL water 50 g NaOH	For Pb-Sn alloys, can also use 100 g NaOH (Guertler).
14. Conc. HCl	For Pb-Sn alloys. Grain-boundary etch.
15. 95 mL ethanol 5 mL acetic acid	For Pb, some alloys. Reveals grain structure, 1–10 min.
16. 85 mL methanol 10 mL HCl 5 mL HNO$_3$	For Pb-Sn eutectics, solders (Hargreaves).
17. 90 mL methanol 10 mL HNO$_3$ 2 ml sat. aq. CrO$_3$	For Pb-rich alloys. Use fresh, do not store.

Lead and alloys *(continued)*

Etchant composition	Comments
18. 50 mL lactic acid 30 mL HNO$_3$ 20 mL H$_2$O$_2$ (30%)	For Pb-Bi alloys. Swab sample 30–60 s. Alpha bright, epsilon stained (Rhodes and Spurling).
19. 10 g ammonium molybdate 10 g citric acid 100 mL water	For Pb and alloys. Immerse sample 15–30 s (Pollack). Other compositions used are 9g:15g:80mL and 10g:25g:100 mL (Voce).

20. Solution a
  140 mL NH$_4$OH
  100 mL molybdic acid
  240 mL water
Solution b
  50 mL HNO$_3$
	For Pb and alloys. Mix solution a and filter. Add filtrate to solution b. Immerse sample up to 5 min.

21. 49 mL acetic acid 7 mL H$_2$O$_2$ (30%) 7 mL ethanol 14 mL water	For Pb. Polish chemically, then etch 4–5 s, dry, reetch 3–4 times in this manner. Examine with polarized light (Gifkins and Nicholls).
	Electrolytic etchants
22. 30 mL perchloric acid 70 mL acetic acid	Use at 1–2 V dc, Pb or Cu cathode, 1 min. Mix carefully, keep cool. Produces grain contrast.
23. 135 mL water 15 mL perchloric acid	For Pb and Pb-Sb alloys (up to 2% Sb). Use at 2 V, 10 s, specimen as cathode (Adcock).

Magnesium and alloys

Etchant composition	Comments
1. 1 mL HNO_3 75 mL ethylene glycol 25 mL water	Glycol etch, general-purpose etch for pure Mg and alloys. Swab sample 3–5 s for F and T6 temper alloys, 1–2 min for T4 and O temper alloys (Hess and George).
2. 1 mL HNO_3 20 mL acetic acid 60 mL ethylene glycol 19 mL water	Acetic-glycol etch, for pure Mg and alloys. Swab sample 1–3 s for F and T6 temper alloys, 10 s for T4 and O temper alloys. Reveals grain boundaries in solution-treated castings and most wrought alloys (Hess and George).
3. 1–10 mL HNO_3 100 mL alcohol	Nital, for pure Mg and alloys. Immerse sample for up to about 60 s.
4. 10 mL HF 90 mL water	For pure Mg and some alloys. Immerse sample for 3–30 s, agitate gently. Darkens $Mg_{17}Al_{12}$, leaves $Mg_2Al_2Zn_3$ unetched (George).

5. Solution a
  5 g picric acid
  100 mL ethanol
Solution b
  90 mL water
	Use after etch no. 4 to darken matrix for increased contrast. Use fresh. Use 10 mL of solution a plus solution b, immerse sample 15–30 s (George).

6. 5 g picric acid 100 mL ethanol 10 mL water	For Mg and alloys. Use fresh. Immerse sample for 15–30 s. Produces grain contrast (George).
7. 5 g picric acid 100 mL ethanol 100 mL water	For Mg-Si alloys. Good contrast between Mg_2Si and Mn. Mg_2Si blue, Mn dull gray. Immerse sample for up to 30 s (George).
8. 0.7 mL H_3PO_4 5 g picric acid 100 mL alcohol	Phospho-picral etch, for pure Mg and some alloys. Composition is critical. Use fresh, immerse sample 1–30 s, agitate gently. Used to estimate amount of massive $Mg_{17}Al_{12}$ compound in heat-treated castings or wrought alloys. Stains solid solution, leaves compound white (Hess and George).
9. 0.2–2 g oxalic acid 100 mL water	For pure Mg and most alloys. Swab sample 6–10 s.
10. 10 mL acetic acid 5 g picric acid 95 mL alcohol	For Mg-Al and Mg-Al-Zn alloys. Immerse sample 15–60 s, agitate gently. Use fresh. Sometimes reveals grain boundaries (Dow Chemical).
11. 100 mL ethanol 5 g picric acid 5 mL acetic acid 10 mL water	For Mg and alloys. Reveals grain boundaries.
12. 30 mL acetic acid 15 mL water 6 g picric acid 100 mL alcohol	For Mg-Al, Mg-Al-Zn, and Mg-Zn-Zr alloys. Immerse sample 1–30 s, agitate gently. Use fresh.

Magnesium and alloys *(continued)*

Etchant composition	Comments
13. 3 g picric acid 50 mL ethanol 20 mL water 16–20 mL acetic acid	For Mg and alloys. Reveals trace of basal plane. Sensitive to aging temperature. Use fresh, immerse sample 15 s. Forms amorphous film. When dry, film cracks parallel to the basal plane. Reveals compositional variations within grains (George).
14. 95 mL water 5 mL acetic acid	For Mg-Al alloys up to 6% Al. Swab sample 3–5 s. Also used for pure Mg.
15. 2–10 g tartaric acid 90 mL water	For Mg-Al (to 6% Al), Mg-Mn, and Mg-Mn-Al-Zn alloys. Sometimes reveals grain structure in castings. Immerse sample 5–15 s. For higher Al content, use 20 g tartaric acid (Ogilvie).
16. 2–11 g citric acid 100 mL ethanol	For Mg, Mg-Cu, and Mg die-casting alloys. Immerse sample about 30 s.
17. 5–10 g citric acid 100 mL water	For Mg-Mn wrought alloys and solution-treated castings. Reveals grain boundaries. Swab sample 5–30 s.
18. 12 g CrO_3 15 mL HNO_3 85 mL water	For Mg-Al alloys. Sometimes produces grain contrast in heat-treated castings. Immerse sample 10–30 s. Increase water content for high-Al alloys.
19. 15 mL HNO_3 85 mL ethylene glycol	For alloys of Mg, 1% Zn, and 0.6% Zr. Immerse sample 2 s (Pepper).
20. 1 part water saturated with sodium fluosilicate and potassium tartrate 1 part HNO_3	For Mg-U alloys (Chiotti and coworkers).
21. 1.5 mL HCl 2.5 mL HNO_3 0.5 mL HF 95.5 mL water	For Mg-Zn alloys. Mix 1 mL etch with 100 mL water. After 10-s etch, Mg_7Zn_3 attacked, MgZn relatively unattacked (Clarke and Rhines).
22. 50 g CrO_3 4 g Na_2SO_4 1000 mL water	For Mg-Zn alloys. After 2-s etch, MgZn severely attacked, Mg_7Zn_3 slightly attacked (Clarke and Rhines).
23. 10 parts 6% picral 2 parts water 1 part H_3PO_4	Polarized-light etchant for Mg. Sharp extinctions when basal plane is parallel or perpendicular to plane of polish (Hartt and Reed-Hill).
24. 100 mL water 5 g malic acid 2 mL HNO_3	For Mg and wrought alloys. Immerse sample 10–30 s.
25. 10 g ammonium persulfate 100 mL water	For wrought Mg alloys. Produces grain contrast. Swab sample until surface is brown.
26. 100 mL ethanol 2 mL HCl	For Mg and alloys, immerse sample 10 s.
27. 3000 mL ethanol 25 mL HNO_3 15 mL HCl	For Mg and alloys, immerse sample 1–5 s (Oberländer and Lillerud).

Magnesium and alloys *(continued)*

Etchant composition	Comments
	Electrolytic etchants
28. 10 g NaOH 100 mL water	For Mg alloys. Use at 4 V dc, Cu cathode, 2–4 min. Etch immediately after polishing.
29. 20 mL water 20 mL ethanol 40 mL H_3PO_4	For Mg and many alloys. Use at 10–35 V dc, Mg cathode, 1–10 min.
30. 10 mL HF 100 mL water	Color etch for Mg and alloys. Use stainless steel cathode, 20°C, 0.6–0.9 V dc, 10–15 mA/dm^2, 20–30 min, moderate stirring. Remove sample with current on (Lelong and Dosdat).

Manganese and alloys

Etchant composition	Comments
1. 90–95 mL water 5–10 mL HF	For ferromanganese, manganese silicate, and Mn-Si-Cr alloys. Etch up to a few minutes.
2. 98 mL ethanol 2 mL HNO_3	Nital. For Mn-Fe, Mn-Ni, Mn-Cu, and Mn-Co alloys. Etch up to a few minutes.
3. 40 mL glycerol 30 mL HF 25 mL HCl 10 mL HNO_3	For Mn-Ge, Mn-Si, Mn-Sn-Ge, and Mn-Sn-Si alloys. Etch 1–3 s for Mn-Ge and Mn-Si alloys. Etch 5–10 s for Mn-Sn-Ge and Mn-Sn-Si alloys.
4. 200 mL acetyl acetone 1 drop–2 mL HNO_3	For pure Mn and lean alloys. Etch in ultrasonic cleaner up to 18 min. Wash in acetone (Anderson).
5. 60 mL glycerol 20 mL HNO_3 20 mL HF	For Mn-Ti alloys (0–30 atomic % Ti) (Waterstrat).
	Electrolytic etchants
6. 1 part H_3PO_4 1 part glycerol 2 parts ethanol 4 parts water	For Mn-Cu alloys. use stainless steel cathode, 16 V dc, 1 s at < 20°C (Kennon and coworkers).

Molybdenum and alloys

Etchant composition	Comments

1. Solution a
   100 mL water
   10 g KOH
  Solution b
   100 mL water
   10 g $K_3Fe(CN)_6$
	Murakami's reagent. For Mo and alloys. Mix solutions a and b, immerse sample for up to 1 min. Use fresh. If film forms, remove with 10% aq. HCl.

2. 100 mL water
  30 g $K_3Fe(CN)_6$
  10 g KOH
	Strong etch for Mo. Immerse sample at 20°C. If film forms, remove with 10% aq. HCl.

3. 1 g NaOH
  35 g $K_3Fe(CN)_6$
  150 mL water
	For Mo and alloys. Immerse sample 15–120 s (Coons).

4. 100 mL water
  15 g $K_3Fe(CN)_6$
  5 g NaOH
	For Mo and some alloys. Excellent etch. Immerse sample at 20°C. If film forms, remove with 10% aq. HCl.

5. 100 mL water
  5 g $K_3Fe(Cn)_6$
  2 g KOH
	For Mo-Re alloys. Use at 20°C by immersion of sample.

6. 200 mL water
  6 g $K_3Fe(CN)_6$
  1 g NaOH
	For Mo and alloys. Excellent etch. Immerse sample at 20°C for up to 5 min. If film forms, remove with 5% aq. HCl.

7. 50 mL water
  50 mL H_2O_2 (3%)
  50 mL ammonia
	For Mo and Mo-Ni alloys. Use boiling up to 10 min.

8. 10–20 mL glycerol
  10 mL HF
  10 mL HNO_3
	For Mo and Mo-Ti alloys. Immerse sample for up to 5 min.

9. 10 mL HF
  30 mL HNO_3
  60 mL lactic acid
	For Mo alloys. Swab sample 10–20 s. Vary HF content to control etch speed. For cast-Mo alloys, reduce HNO_3 to 20 mL, swab sample 5–10 s, rinse, dry, and etch with Murakami's reagent.

10. Solution a
  10 g $CuSO_4 \cdot 5H_2O$
  40 mL water
  Solution b
  20 mL NH_4OH
	For Mo and some alloys. Mix solution a, filter solution, add solution b. Immerse sample 30–50 s. Reveals grain structure (Millner and Sass).

11. 40–60 mL $FeCL_3$ solution
  (1300 g per liter H_2O)
  25 mL HCl
  75 mL ethanol
	Color tint etch for Mo. Colors vary with crystal orientation. Immerse sample without agitation for 40–50 s at 20°C. Do not exceed 70 s. $FeCl_3$ can be dissolved in ethanol but etching is slower, 2–3 min (Hasson).

12. 70 mL water
  20 mL H_2O_2 (30%)
  10 mL H_2SO_4
	For Mo alloys. Immerse sample 2 min. Wash with water and dry; immersion produces colors, swabbing produces grain-boundary etch (Oak Ridge Natl. Lab.).

Molybdenum and alloys *(continued)*

Etchant composition	Comments
	Electrolytic etchants
13. 10 g oxalic acid 100 mL water	Produces grain contrast in Mo. Use stainless steel cathode, 1.5–6 V dc, 2–10 s.
14. 95 mL water or ethanol 5 mL HCl	For Mo and alloys. Use stainless steel cathode, 5–10 V dc, up to a few min.
15. 100 mL water 10 g NaOH	For Mo and some alloys. Use at 1.5–3 V, 1–5 s.
16. 5 mL H_2SO_4 1 mL HF 100 mL methanol	For Mo alloys. Use at 50–60 V dc, 10–20 s.
17. 65 mL water 17 mL HNO_3 17 mL HF	For Mo. Use Pt cathode, 12–30 V dc, up to a few minutes.
18. 25 mL HCl 10 mL H_2SO_4 75 mL methanol	For Mo alloys. Use at 30 V dc, 30 s, < 75°F (24°C).

Nickel and alloys

Etchant composition	Comments
General-purpose etchants	

1. 50 mL HNO_3
   50 mL acetic acid
   (50 mL water—optional)

   General-purpose etch for Ni, Ni-Cu, and Ni-Ti alloys and superalloys. Use fresh, under a hood, do not store. Immerse or swab sample 5–30 s. Sulfidized grain boundaries, if present, are etched before normal grain boundaries (Thompson).

2. 80 mL HNO_3
   3 mL HF

   For Ni. Use under a hood. Warm sample in boiling water before immersing for 10–120 s.

3. 10 g $CuSO_4$
   50 mL HCl
   50 mL water

   Marble's reagent, for Ni, Ni-Cu, and Ni-Fe alloys and superalloys. Immerse or swab sample 5–60 s. Can increase activity with a few drops H_2SO_4. Reveals grain structure of superalloys.

4. 7.5 mL HF
   2.5 mL HNO_3
   200 mL methanol

   For Ni and alloys. Immerse sample 2–4 min (Coons).

5. 8 g $FeCl_3$
   25 mL HCl
   100 mL water

   For Ni-Ag alloys. Swab sample 5–30 s.

6. 5 g $FeCl_3$
   2 mL HCl
   100 mL ethanol

   For Ni-Ag alloys and superalloys. Swab sample 10–60 s.

7. 5 g NH_4Cl
   3 g CrO_3
   10 mL HNO_3
   90 mL water

   For Monel, Ni-Al, and Ni-Fe alloys. Do not store. Swab sample 5–30 s. Use polarized light with Monel, reveals deformation (Woodard).

8. 0.1–1 g CrO_3
   100 mL HCl

   For Ni-Al alloys. Age solution a few minutes before using. Immerse or swab sample up to a few minutes.

9. 10 g $K_3Fe(CN)_6$
   10 g KOH
   100 mL water

   Murakami's etch for Ni-Cu alloys and superalloys. Darkens α' and σ, use at 167°F (75°C).

10. 10 mL HF
    100 mL HNO_3

    For Ni-Cr alloys. Immerse sample 30–180 s.

11. 20 mL HNO_3
    80 mL HCl

    For Ni-Cr alloys. Immerse sample 5–30 s.

12. 2 g $CuCl_2$
    40 mL HCl
    40–80 mL ethanol

    Kallings no. 2 etch ("waterless" Kallings) for Ni-Cu alloys and superalloys. Very popular. Immerse or swab sample up to a few minutes.

13. 5 mL HNO_3
    100 mL water

    For Ni-Fe alloys. Immerse sample 10–30 s.

14. 5 g $FeCl_3$
    50 mL HCl
    100 mL water

    For Ni-Cu alloys. Immerse or swab sample up to a few minutes.

Nickel and alloys *(continued)*

Etchant composition	Comments
General-purpose etchants (continued)	
15. 5 g $FeCl_3$ 15 mL HCl 60 mL alcohol	For Ni-Fe alloys. Immerse or swab sample up to a few minutes.
16. 50 mL HCl 2 mL H_2O_2 (30%) 50 mL water	For Ni-Fe alloys. Immerse sample 10–30 s. Do not store.
17. 1–5 mL HNO_3 100 mL alcohol	For Ni-Fe, Ni-Mn, and Ni-Mo alloys. Swab sample 5–60 s.
18. 60 mL HCl 20 mL HNO_3 40 mL glycerin	Orientation sensitive etch for Ni-Fe alloys. Use under a hood, do not store. Swab sample up to a minute. Discard solution when it turns dark yellow.
19. 10 mL HF 25 mL HNO_3 150 mL water	For Ni-Ti alloys. Swab sample 5–30 s.
20. 85 mL NH_4OH 15 mL H_2O_2 (30%)	For Ni-Zn alloys. Immerse sample 5–15 s. Do not store, reagent decomposes.
21. 5 mL H_2SO_4 3 mL HNO_3 92 mL HCl	For superalloys. Use under a hood. Add sulfuric acid slowly to HCl, stir, allow to cool, then add nitric acid. Discard when solution turns dark orange. Swab sample 10–30 s (Beattie and Hagel).
22. 97 mL HCl 2 mL H_2SO_4 1 mL HNO_3	For Inconel X550, Inco 700, Waspaloy, and M252 in solution-treated condition. Reveals grain boundaries, may heavily attack carbide interfaces. Immerse sample 30–120 s (Wilde and Grant).
23. 10 mL HNO_3 50 mL HCl 60 mL glycerin	For superalloys. Reveals precipitates. Use under hood, do not store. Add HNO_3 last. Discard when dark yellow. Immerse sample 10–60 s (Mihalisin and Decker).
24. 20 mL HNO_3 60 mL HCl	Aqua regia. For superalloys, Ni-Cr alloys. Use under hood, do not store. Immerse or swab sample for 5–60 s.
25. 50 mL HCl 50 mL ethanol	For revealing fine precipitates in superalloys. Immerse sample 10–100 s.
26. 100 mL HCl 0.5 mL H_2O_2 (30%)	For passive superalloys. Use under a hood, do not store. Immerse or swab sample up to 3 min. Add peroxide dropwise to sustain etching.
27. 50 mL HCl 1–2 mL H_2O_2 (30%)	Etch for superalloys, attacks γ'. Immerse sample 10–15 s.
28. 25 g CrO_3 150 mL HCl 50 mL water	For Hastelloy W. Immerse sample 5–20 s.

Nickel and alloys *(continued)*

Etchant composition	Comments
General-purpose etchants (continued)	

29. Solution a
    10 g ammonium persulfate
    100 mL water
  Soution b
    10 g KCN
    100 mL water
	For pure Ni, reveals grain boundaries. Use under hood. Mix equal volumes of solutions a and b. Swab sample 30–60 s (Sinizer).

30. 150 mL water
  30 mL H_2SO_4
  360 mL HCl
  100 mL HNO_3
  150 mL acetic acid
  90 g $FeCl_3$
	For Udimet 700 and René 41 (Wlodek). Reveals depth of preferential surface oxidation of Al and Ti (γ' free zone).

31. 30 mL lactic acid
  20 mL HCl
  10 mL HNO_3
	For Ni-Al alloys, 3–25% Al (Pettit).

32. 15 mL HCl
  5 mL HNO_3
  15 mL glycerin
	"Glyceregia," for superalloys and Ni-Cr alloys. Immerse or swab sample for 5–60 s. Do not store, use under a hood.

33. 70 mL HCl 30 mL H_2O_2 (30%)	For TD-Ni, DS-NiCr, Inconel MA-754, TD-NiCrAl, and DST-NiCrAl (Whittenberger).

34. 50 g $CuCl_2$
  360 mL acetic acid
  230 mL HCl
  50 mL H_2SO_4
  1 g CrO_3
	For SM-200, swab sample (Univ. of Michigan).

35. 50 mL HCl 0.2–0.6 g Na_2O_2 (granulated)	For superalloys. Reveals grain boundaries, γ', carbides. Immersion time varies with Na_2O_2 content, 15–75 s (Meisel and coworkers).

36. 50 mL HCl
  10 mL HNO_3
  10 mL H_3PO_4
  5 mL H_2SO_4
  5 mL HF
  10 mL acetic acid
  50 mL water
  5 g $FeCl_3$
	For René 95, reveals γ'. Prolonged etching (> 2 min) reveals grain boundaries (Walker).

37. 50 mL lactic acid
  30 mL HNO_3
  2 mL HF
	For Ni alloys (Buchheit).

38. Sat. aq. ammonium persulfate	For Ni-Fe alloys.

39. 5 g $FeCl_3$
  2 mL HCl
  99 mL methanol
	Carapella's etch for Ni and Ni-Cu (Monel) alloys.

Nickel and alloys *(continued)*

Etchant composition	Comments
General-purpose etchants *(continued)*	
40. Solution a 12 mL HNO$_3$ 8 mL acetic acid Solution b 0.5 g cupric ammonium chloride 4 mL water 0.5 mL NH$_4$OH	Precision no. 1. Add solution b to solution a. For Ni alloys. Grain-boundary etch for Monel. Swab annealed samples 20 s, less time for cold-worked samples (Flachbarth and Pondo).
41. Solution a 3 mL HF 6 mL acetic acid 9 mL HNO$_3$ Solution b 1 g Cupric ammonium chloride 8 mL water 1 ml NH$_4$OH Solution c 0.6 g sodium dichromate	Precision no. 2. High-contrast etch for high-nickel alloys. Mix solution a in order given. Add 9 mL of solution b to solution a, then add solution c. Swab annealed samples about 20 s, cold-worked samples about 10 s (Flachbarth and Pondo).
Tint etchants	
42. 5 mL sat. aq. sodium thiosulfate 45 mL water 20 g potassium metabisulfite	Klemm's III reagent. Immerse sample 6–8 min for Monel.
43. 1–3 mL selenic acid 20–30 mL HCl 100 mL ethanol	Beraha's tint etch for superalloys. Immerse sample 1–4 min at 20°C. Colors carbides and γ′, matrix unaffected.
44. Solution a 1 part HCl 2 parts water Solution b 1 part HCl 1 part water	Beraha's tint etch for Ni-based alloys. Add 0.6–1 g potassium metabisulfite to 100 mL stock solution a. Immerse sample for 60–150 s, keep sample moving. If colors are not well developed, add 1–1.5 g FeCl$_3$ or 2–10 g ammonium bifluoride to 100 mL stock solution b. Immerse sample for 60–150 s, agitate gently. Both solutions color matrix, leaving carbides unaffected. Polarized light sometimes enhances results.
Heat tint	
45. Heat in air to 1112°F (600°C) for 5–10 min.	Heat tint for TD-NiCr (Kane and coworkers).

Nickel and alloys *(continued)*

Etchant composition	Comments
	Electrolytic etchants
46. 70 mL H_3PO_4 30 mL water.	For Ni, Ni-Cr, and Ni-Fe alloys. Use 5–10 V dc for 5–60 s.
47. 20 mL H_3PO_4 80 mL water	For Ni. Use 10 V dc for 10–15 s (53 mL H_3PO_4 and 100 mL water also used).
48. 3–10 mL H_2SO_4 100 mL water	For Ni and Ni-Cu alloys. Use at 6 V dc for 5–10 s.
49. 10 g ammonium persulfate 100 mL water	For Ni. Use at 6 V dc for up to 60 s.
50. 10 g $NaNO_3$ 100 mL water	To reveal grain-boundary sulfidation in Ni. Use at 0.2 A/cm^2 for 60 s (Hancock).
51. 5 mL acetic acid 10 mL HNO_3 85 mL water	For Ni-Ag, Ni-Al, Ni-Cr, Ni-Cu, Ni-Fe, and Ni-Ti alloys. Use under hood, do not store. Use at 1.5 V dc, 20–60 s, Pt cathode and lead wires. Reveals subboundaries in Ni (Hardwick and coworkers).
52. 5 mL HF 10 mL glycerin 85 mL water	For Ni-Al, Ni-Cr-Al, and Ni-Cr-Ti alloys. Use at 2–3 V dc for 5–10 s (Nordheim and Grant).

53. Solution a
   10 g sodium thiosulfate
   100 mL water
Solution b
   10 mL HCl
   90 mL water
	For Ni-Cr alloys. Etch in solution a first at 10 V dc, 5–10 s, sample as the cathode. Then etch in solution b, sample as anode, 10 V dc, 5–10 s.

54. 2 mL H_2SO_4 100 mL water	For Ni-Cr alloys. Use 3–10 V dc, 5–15 s, Pt lead wires. Can increase the H_2SO_4 content up to 20 mL to deepen the etch.
55. 10 g oxalic acid 100 mL water	For Ni-Cr alloys. Use at 6 V dc for 10–15 s. Reveals inhomogeneities in superalloys.
56. 5 mL H_2SO_4 8 g CrO_3 85 mL H_3PO_4	To reveal inhomogeneities in superalloys. Reveals Ti- and Nb-rich areas before grain boundaries. Use at 10 V dc, 0.2 A/cm^2, 5–30 s.
57. 1 g thiourea 1–2 mL H_3PO_4 1000 mL water	For superalloys. Use at 0.005–0.01 A/cm^2 for 1–2 min. Produces colors.
58. 10–12 mL H_3PO_4 45–50 mL H_2SO_4 40–43 mL HNO_3	To reveal substructure in superalloys. Stains matrix when γ' is present. Use under a hood. Mix H_3PO_4 and HNO_3 thoroughly, then add H_2SO_4 slowly while stirring. Allow to cool. Use fresh at 6 V dc for a few seconds. Attacks Bakelite. Can add up to 100 mL water to retard action (Bigelow and Amy).

Nickel and alloys *(continued)*

Etchant composition	Comments

Electrolytic etchants *(continued)*

Etchant composition	Comments

59. Solution a
    20 mL water
    20 mL HCl
    10 mL HNO_3
    0.5 g $FeCl_3$
  Solution b
    5 g CrO_3
    100 mL water
	Double etch for twins and grain boundaries in alloy of Ni, 20% Cr, and 2% ThO_2. Swab sample with solution a to reveal twins, etch electrolytically with solution b at 5 V dc to reveal grain boundaries.

60. 7 mL HCl 93 mL ethanol	For TD-nickel. Use at 5 A/cm^2.
61. 10 g NaCN 100 mL water	For superalloys. Use 1.5 V dc, 0.003–0.005 A, 20–30 s. Outlines carbides and sigma. Then, etch with Murakami's reagent at 20°C for 2–4 s. Colors sigma gray to blue-gray, carbides light straw to brownish yellow or buff.

62. 100 mL water
  40 mL acetic acid
  40 mL HCl
  15 mL H_2SO_4
  40 mL HNO_3
  25 g $FeCl_3$
	For Hastelloy X. Use at 3 V dc with Pt cathode.

63. 5 mL HF
  10 mL glycerol
  10–50 mL ethanol
  Water to bring total volume to
    100 mL
	For Ni-Al-Ti alloys, Attacks γ′ preferentially. Electrolytic (Bigelow and coworkers).

Niobium and alloys

Etchant composition	Comments
1. 10 mL HF 30 mL HNO_3 60 mL lactic acid	For Nb and alloys. Swab sample 10–20 s. Can vary HF content to control etch speed. Reveals grain structure. Do not store.
2. 30 mL HF 15 mL HNO_3 30 mL HCl	For Nb and alloys. Swab sample 3–10 s or immerse up to 2 min.
3. 10 mL HF 10 mL HNO_3 20 mL glycerol	For Nb and alloys. Swab sample 5–15 s. Equal parts of each also used (Pochon and coworkers).
4. 5 mL HF 20 mL HNO_3 50 mL acetic acid	For Nb and alloys. Swab sample 10–30 s.
5. 20 mL HF 15 mL H_2SO_4 5–10 mL HNO_3 50 mL water	For Nb and alloys. Immerse sample for up to 5 min. Reveals grains structure (Anderson).
6. 25 mL HNO_3 5 mL HF 50 mL water	For Nb and alloys. Immerse sample for up to 2 min. Equal parts of each also used.
7. 50 mL HNO_3 30 g ammonium bifluoride 20 mL water	Grain-boundary etch for Nb and alloys. Use under hood, handle with care. Swab sample 3–10 s.

8. Solution a
  50 mL lactic acid
  30 mL HNO_3
  2 mL HF
Solution b
  30 mL lactic acid
  10 mL HNO_3
  10 mL HF
	For Nb and alloys. Swab sample 1–3 min with solution a, acts as a chemical polishing agent and etchant. Then, swab 5 s with solution b. Repeat if necessary. HF content in solution b controls etch speed.

9. 30 mL H_2SO_4 30 mL HF 3–5 drops H_2O_2 (30%) 30 mL water	For Nb and alloys. Immerse sample 5–60 s.
10. 20 mL HNO_3 60 mL HF	"Fluor regia." For Nb and alloys. Immerse sample about 10 s.
11. 50 mL water 5 mL HNO_3 14 mL H_2SO_4	DuPont Nb reagent. For Nb-Hf and Nb alloys.
12. 1 part H_2SO_4 1 part H_2F_2 or HF 2 parts HNO_3 1 part water	For Nb-V and Nb alloys. Immerse sample. (Wilhelm and coworkers, Hansen and coworkers).

Niobium and alloys *(continued)*

Etchant composition	Comments
13. 2 mL HF 18 mL HNO$_3$ 5 mL glycerin	For Nb-O alloys (Seybolt).
14. 1–2 mL HF 98–99 mL HNO$_3$	For Nb-Re alloys. Immerse sample 2–3 s. Stains chi first, then sigma, finally alpha Nb. Short etch reveals grain boundaries (Glessen and coworkers).
15. 3 parts HF 3 parts H$_2$SO$_4$ 3 parts water 1 part H$_2$O$_2$	Grain-boundary etch for Nb$_3$Sn$_2$ matrix, attacks Nb$_2$Sn$_5$ and NbSn$_2$ (produces holes) (Kapoor and Wright).
16. 9 parts lactic acid 1 part HNO$_3$ 1 part HF	Grain-boundary etch for Nb (Sandelin and Birks).
17. 1 part HF 1 part water	For Nb-Rh alloys (<25 atomic % Rh). Stains only alpha Nb, does not attack alpha Nb$_3$Rh or sigma (Ritter and coworkers).
18. 100 mL sat. aq. CrO$_3$ 10 g NaF	For Nb-Sn alloys (Levinstein and Buehler).
19. 60 mL lactic acid 40 mL HNO$_3$ 10 mL HF	For Nb$_2$O$_5$ (Gupta and Jena).
20. 40 mL HNO$_3$ 40 mL water 10 mL HF	For Nb$_3$Sn, immerse sample 30 s (Cullen).
21. 50 mL water 50 mL HNO$_3$ 1 mL HF	For Nb-Zr and Nb-Zr-Re alloys (Rapp and Goldberg).
22. 250 mL water 60 g NaOH 20 g tartaric acid 50 mL lactic acid 30 mL H$_2$O$_2$ (30%)	For alloy of Nb and 1% Zr (McCoy).
23. 50 mL H$_2$O$_2$ (30%) 25 mL HNO$_3$ 25 mL ethanol 1 mL HF	For Nb-Zr alloys (Richter and coworkers).
24. 20 mL HNO$_3$ 20 mL HF 60 mL glycerin	For Nb-N alloys (Evans; Rostoker and Yamamoto).
25. 170 mL HNO$_3$ 100 mL HF 30 g NH$_4$F 500 mL methanol	For Nb oxides. Polarized light enhances details (Krudtaa and Stokland).

Niobium and alloys (*continued*)

Etchant composition	Comments
26. 1 part 10% NH_4F 1 pt H_2O_2 (3%)	For Nb. Use at 100°C for 5 min (Eary and Johnston).

27. Solution a
   10 g $FeCl_3 \cdot 6H_2O$
   30 mL HCl
   120 mL water
Solution b
   5 mL HF per 100 mL solution a
	For Nb. A 2-min etch reveals grain boundaries (Eary and Johnston).

28. 3 mL HNO_3 1 mL HF 96 mL water	For Nb-Ti alloys. Immerse sample (Hansen and coworkers).
29. 95 mL HNO_3 3–5 mL HF	For Nb-Th and Nb noble-metal alloys (Greenfield and Beck, Carlson and coworkers, Geach and Summers-Smith).
30. 50 mL acetic acid 50 mL HNO_3 10 mL HF	For Nb. Useful when coring interfers with etching results.

Electrolytic and anodizing etchants	
31. 65 mL water 17 mL HNO_3 17 mL HF	For pure Nb. Use 12–30 V dc, Pt cathode, up to a few minutes.
32. 60 mL ethanol 35 mL water 10 mL lactic acid 20 mL glycerin 5 mL H_3PO_4 2 g citric acid	Picklesimer's anodizing solution for Nb and alloys. Samples must be carefully polished. Best etch voltage and time found by trial. Voltages from 20–140 V dc and times from 10–60 s or longer are used. (18–28 and 55–65 V commonly employed. Hold voltage until current density reaches zero). Colors can be observed under bright-field illumination and enhanced with polarized light.
33. 50 mL H_2O_2 (30%) 50 mL NH_4OH 4 g NaF	Anodizing solution for Nb-Sn alloys. Use 2 V dc, 100 mA, Sn cathode (Levinstein and Buehler).
34. 0.1 N H_3PO_4	Anodizing solution for Nb. Reveals nonhomogeneities. Use 60–80 V dc, 20°C, 5–30 s, stainless steel cathode (Wolff).
35. 90 mL H_2SO_4 10 mL HF	For Nb-Zr alloys. Use 50 V dc, up to 30 s, 20°C (Love and Picklesimer).
36. 50 mL ethanol 10 mL water 1 mL H_3PO_4	Anodizing solution for Nb_3Si. Use 80 V dc for 1 min. Colors Nb_3Si matrix red, Nb solid solution green, Nb_5Si_3 yellow. Also used on Nb-Ga alloys (Olden and Siemens). Anodize until Nb is light green, Nb_3Ga blue-green, Nb_3Ga_2 violet, NbGa orange, Nb_2Ga_3 yellow-orange, $NbGa_3$ light yellow.

Niobium and alloys *(continued)*

Etchant composition	Comments
	Electrolytic and anodizing etchants *(continued)*
37. 5 g oxalic acid 5 g citric acid 5 mL H_3PO_4 10 mL lactic acid 35 mL water 60 mL ethanol	Anodizing solution for Ti developedby Ence and Margolin, used by Crouse to identify phases in Nb. Use stainless steel cathode, 19 V dc, 5 s. Produces vivid blue macroscopic surface color. Nb pale aqua-blue, Nb_2N cherry-rose, NbN butter yellow, Nb_2C peach, NbC light maize, NbO light turquoise-green, NbO_2 light beige, and Nb_2O_5 light tan (mottled).

Osmium and alloys

Etchant composition	Comments
1. 150 mL water 3.5 g $K_3Fe(CN)_6$ 1 g NaOH	For Os and Os-W alloys. Immerse sample for a few minutes. Epitaxial film reveals grain structure.
	Electrolytic etchants
2. 10 mL HCl 90 mL ethanol	For Os alloys. Use at 10 V dc, 30 s, graphite cathode, Pt lead wires. Excellent etch (Buchheit and coworkers).
3. 6 N H_2SO_4	For Os-Ir alloys. Use 1–4 V ac, stainless steel cathode (Raub and coworkers).

Palladium and alloys

Etchant composition	Comments
1. 60 mL HCl 40 mL HNO$_3$	For Pd and alloys. Use under hood. Immerse sample up to 60 s.
2. 1–5 g CrO$_3$ 100 mL HCl	For Pd and alloys. Swab or immerse sample up to 60 s.

3. Solution a
   20 g ammonium persulfate
   90 mL water
Solution b
   20 g KCN
   90 mL water
	For Pd and alloys. Use under a hood, avoid fumes, dangerous! Mix equal parts of solutions a and b before use. Immerse or swab sample up to several minutes. To discard, neutralize with ammonia and flush with copious water. 10 g of each compound also used.

4. 30 mL water 25 mL HCl 5 mL HNO$_3$	For pure Pd. Use hot for 1–5 min.
5. Conc. HNO$_3$	For Pd. Use hot.
Electrolytic etchant	
6. 10 mL HCl 90 mL ethanol	For Pd and alloys. Use at 10 V dc, 30 s, graphite cathode, Pt lead wires.

Platinum and alloys

Etchant composition	Comments
1. 5 mL HNO_3 25 mL HCl 30 mL water	For pure Pt. Use hot, immerse sample up to 5 min.
2. 10 mL HNO_3 100 mL HCl 50 mL water	For pure Pt. Use hot, immerse sample 1–5 min.
3. 30 mL HCl 10 mL HNO_3	Aqua regia. For Pt and alloys. Use boiling, 10–20 min (2:1 ratio also used).

4. Solution a
  10–20 g KCN
  100 mL water
Solution b
  10–20 g ammonium
    persulfate
  100 mL water
	For Pt and alloys. Mix equal parts of solutions a and b before use. Immerse sample up to 2 min.

	Electrolytic etchants
5. 20 mL HCl 25 g NaCl 65 mL water	For Pt and alloys. Use 6 V ac, 1 min, graphite electrode, Pt lead wires.
6. 5 g NaCN 100 mL water	For Pt and alloys. Use under hood, avoid fumes, dangerous! Use at 1–5 V ac, 1–2 min, Pt cathode, 0.5–1.5 A/cm^2. To discard, neutralize with ammonia and flush with copious water.
7. Conc. HCl	Grain contrast etch for Pt. Use 5 V ac, Pt or graphite cathode, 1–5 min, 0.5 A/cm^2.
8. 90 mL water 10 mL H_2SO_4	For Pt alloys. Use at 1–5 V ac, 0.05–0.2 A/cm^2, graphite cathode, up to 60 min. (80:20 ratio also used at 6 V ac, 2–5 min.)

9. Solution a
  40 g NaCl
  100 mL water
Solution b
  Conc. HCl
	For Pt. Use 4 parts solution a to 1 part solution b at 6 V ac, 1 min, 0.02–0.2 A/cm^2, graphite cathode, Pt lead wires. Excellent results, reveals grain boundaries (Buchheit and coworkers).

10. 90 mL alcohol 10 mL HCl	For Pt. Use 10 V ac, 30 s. Excellent results.

Radioactive metals and alloys

Etchant composition	Comments
1. 1 mL HF 30 mL HNO_3 30 mL lactic acid	For U beryllides and U-Zr and U-Nb alloys. Swab sample 5–30 s, rinse with water then alcohol, dry.
2. 30 mL lactic acid 30 mL HNO_3 3 drops HF	For U silicides. For U-Zr alloys, use 10 drops HF. For U-Ti alloys, use 50 mL lactic acid, 50 mL HNO_3, 6 drops HF (Saller and coworkers). For U-Zr-Mo alloys, use 5–10 drops HF (Farkas and coworkers).
3. 30 mL HNO_3 30 mL acetic acid 30 mL glycerol	For U and alloys. Swab or immerse sample 5–30 s.
4. 30 mL HNO_3 30 mL acetic acid 30 mL water	For U carbide. Swab sample 5–30 s (Accary).
5. 10 mL HF 10 mL HNO_3	For Th and alloys. Swab sample a few seconds.
6. 100 mL water 38 mL HNO_3 1 ml HF	For U-Al alloys. Etch up to a few min. UAl_2 light blue, UAl_3 yellow, UAl_4 gray.
7. 70 mL H_3PO_4 25 mL H_2SO_4 5 mL HNO_3	For U alloys. Immerse sample up to a few minutes.
8. 40 mL glycerol 40 mL HNO_3 10 mL HF	For U-Mo and U-Zr alloys. Immerse or swab sample 5–10 s.
9. 100 mL water 10 g $K_3Fe(CN)_6$ 10 g KOH	Murakami's reagent, for U-Zr alloys. Use boiling.
10. 100 mL water 5 g CrO_3	For alloys of U and 10% Nb. Add 10 drops HF before use.
11. 10 mL water 20 mL HNO_3	For U. U attacked slowly, UO_2 rapidly. Immerse sample 15–45 s. Sometimes produces coloration.
12. 90 mL H_2O_2 (30%) 10 mL H_2SO_4	For UO_2 and UO_2CeO_2 (Hunlich). Reveals grain boundaries.
13. 196 g oxalic acid 3 g $Fe(NO_3)_3$ 4 mL HF 1000 mL water	For U-Ti alloys (Douglass and Marsh).
14. 10 mL H_2O_2 (30%) 5 mL HNO_3 100 mL water 0.5 g EDTA	For alloys of U and 5% fission products (Cheney).

Radioactive metals and alloys (continued)

Etchant composition	Comments
15. 130 mL H_2SO_4 50 ml H_2O_2 (30%) 0.2 g Na_2SiF_6 60 mL water	For U. Reveals grain boundaries (Posey). Add H_2SO_4 last, immerse sample immediately after adding H_2SO_4 for about 30 s.
16. H_2O_2 (30%)	Stain etch for UO_2. Immerse sample until surface is blue, about 6 min. Film can be removed with dilute H_2SO_4 (Ambler and Slattery).
17. 1 part HNO_3 1 part HF	For PuO_2. Use at 158–212°F (70–100°C) for 30–60 s (Sari and coworkers).
18. 40 mL HF 10 mL HNO_3	For PuO_2. Immerse sample 60–90 min, rinse, neutralize thoroughly with dilute NaOH, rinse, dry (Smith and coworkers).
19. 80 mL water 20 mL HNO_3 3 drops HF 0.1 g cerium nitrate	For UN-PuN, UO_2-PuO_2, and irradiated UO_2-PuO_2 alloys. For UN-PuN alloy, swab sample 60–90 s, rinse well. Photograph within 1 h. For UO_2-PuO_2 alloy, immerse sample 60–90 min, rinse, dry. For irradiated samples, cyclic etching for brief periods sometimes required (Smith and coworkers).
20. 50 mL HNO_3 50 mL water	For ThC_2 and $(Th,U)C_2$. After polishing, wash immediately with ethanol and, without drying, etch immediately for 1–5 min depending on composition. Produces color contrast (Kegley and Leslie).
21. 70 mL acetic acid 30 mL HNO_3	Color etch for U_3Si, depends on orientation. Differentiates between U, U_3Si, and U_3Si_2 (Kimmel and coworkers).

Electrolytic etchants	
22. 10 mL perchloric acid 10 mL 2-butoxyethanol 70 mL ethanol 10 mL water	For U and alloys. Keep cool during mixing and use. Use at 30–65 V dc for 10–60 s.
23. 5 mL perchloric acid 80 mL acetic acid	For Th, U, and alloys. Keep cool during mixing and use. Use at 20–60 V dc for 1–5 min. (10:90 ratio also used at 18–20 V dc for 5–15 min.)
24. 30 mL H_3PO_4 30 mL ethylene glycol 50 mL ethanol	For U and alloys. Use at 18–20 V dc, 0.03 A/cm^2, 5–15 min.
25. 50 mL H_3PO_4 50 mL ethylene glycol 80 mL ethanol	For U alloys. For U-rich and U-Pu-C alloys, use 5–10 V dc, 15–20 mA/cm^2, 30–60 s (Rosen and coworkers).
26. 18 g CrO_3 75 mL acetic acid 20 mL water	For U and alloys. Dissolve CrO_3 in hot water, cool before adding acetic acid. Keep temperature below 35°F (2°C). Use at 80 V dc for 5–30 min. Do not store.

Radioactive metals and alloys *(continued)*

Etchant composition	Comments
	Electrolytic etchants *(continued)*
27. 3 mL perchloric acid 35 mL 2-butoxyethanol 60 mL methanol	For U-Zr alloys. Use at 60–150 V dc for 5–30 s.
28. 5 mL HNO$_3$ 50 mL ethylene glycol 20 mL alcohol	For Pu alloys. Use at 0.05 A/cm^2, 2 min, stainless steel cathode.
29. 50 mL acetic acid 5 g CrO$_3$	For U. Use at 120°F (49°C), 0.8–1.2 A/cm^2, 1–3 min. Reveals grain boundaries. For U-Ti alloys, use 40 mL acetic acid (Douglass and Marsh).
30. 70 mL ethylene glycol 5 mL H$_3$PO$_4$ 15 mL HNO$_3$ 10 mL H$_2$SO$_4$	For Th. Do not store. Use at 104–113°F (40–45°C), 75 mA/cm^2, 60 s; reverse polarity for 15–30 s after etching (Baumbrucker).
31. 150 mL water 10 mL perchloric acid	For Th. Use at 35 V dc.
32. 2 g citric acid 0.5 mL HNO$_3$ 97.5 mL water	For high-purity U. Use at 15 mA/cm^2 (Blumenthal).
33. 10 mL of 110 g CrO$_3$ in 100 mL water 180 mL acetic acid	Bright-field etch for U. Use at 20 V dc, 0.25–1.0 A/in^2, 1–2 min (Dickerson, Saller). Polarized light produces better detail.
34. 10 g citric acid 10 mL HNO$_3$ 90 mL water	For alloy of U and 2% Zr. Use at 3 V dc, 0.2 A/cm^2, 5–15 s (Hills and coworkers).
35. 50 g CrO$_3$ 60 mL water 600 mL acetic acid	For U-C alloys. Use at 10 V dc for 15 min (Accary).
36. 65 mL lactic acid 45 mL H$_3$PO$_4$ 30 mL water 10 mL dioxane	For alloys of U and 5% fission products. Use at 3 V dc for 10 s (Cheney).
37. 80 mL H$_3$PO$_4$ 50 mL ethanol 50 mL ethylene glycol	For Pu-Ce-Co alloys. Use 5–6 V dc for 15–20 s (Ellinger and coworkers).
38. 3 parts 10% aq. ammonium persulfate 2 parts glycerol	Grain-boundary etchant for U. Use stainless steel cathode, 8–10 V dc, 3–5 min, with agitation. Short electropolish used to remove any stains present (Ambler and Slattery).
39. 10 mL water 14 mL glycerol 75 mL H$_2$SO$_4$	For U-Si alloys. Use at 10 V dc, stainless steel cathode, 1–5 s. Use fresh to reveal U$_3$Si$_2$, U$_3$Si, α-U, and UC. Use stale to reveal structure of U$_3$Si (Moore and Walker).

Radioactive metals and alloys *(continued)*

Etchant composition	Comments
	Electrolytic etchants (continued)
40. 10 mL HNO$_3$ 20 mL ethylene glycol 70 mL methanol	For α-Pu. Use at 30 mA/cm^2 for 1.5–3 min. Reveals grain boundaries (Rencken).
41. 200 mL ethanol 116 g citric acid 10 mL of 25 g KNO$_3$ or NaNO$_3$ in 100 mL H$_2$O	For Pu-Al or Pu-Ga alloys. Use at 5–10 V dc for 2–3 min. Reveals grain boundaries (Hays).
42. 3 parts H$_3$PO$_4$ 4 parts glycerol 4 parts alcohol	For α-Pu and alloys. Use 10 V dc, 30 s, 113°F (45°C) by swabbing for compound identification; 20 V dc, 120 s, 113°F (45°C) for grain structure (Greeson and coworkers).
43. 8 parts H$_3$PO$_4$ 4 parts glycerol 4 parts alcohol	For δ-Pu and alloys. Use 8–10 V dc, 140°F (60°C) by swabbing. Etch 15–20 s for impurities, 30–60 s for phase identification, 60–120 s for coring, and 120–240 s for grain structure (Greeson and coworkers).
44. 1–10 g Na$_2$S$_2$O$_3$ 100 mL water	For γ phases in U-Mo alloys. Use at 2–4 V dc for 10–120 s (Azan and Bouleau). If etching is difficult, increase to 10–12 V dc.
45. 90 mL methanol 10 mL HNO$_3$	For α-Np. use 12 V ac, 0.5 A/cm^2, 75 s. Produces coloration (Rechtien and coworkers).
	Anodizing solution
46. 80 mL ethanol 20 mL NH$_4$OH	Picklesimer's color and anodizing solution for U alloys. Voltage and time determined by trial, 20–140 V dc used.
	Potentiostatic etchant
47. 5 *M* citric acid	For U-Nb alloys. Doubly distilled water used, pH 7. Optimum etching at 6 mA/cm^2, 3–6 min (Mihajlovic and Mance).

Rare earth metals and alloys

Etchant Composition	Comments
1. 75 mL acetic acid 25 mL H_2O_2 (30%)	For most rare earth (RE) metals and alloys. Immerse or swab sample 5–15 s.
2. 49 mL ethanol 1 mL HNO_3	1–5% nital has been used widely. Rinse with acetone or alcohol, dry. For pure Gd and RE-Co alloys, immerse sample 2–3 min. Reveals grain boundaries. Preetch with 30 mL HNO_3—70% glycerin may be required, especially for Sm-Co alloys (Herget and Altenhoff). 0.75% nital used for Y-Mn alloys (Myklebust and Daane) and for Y-Ni alloys (Beaudry and Daane). 2–5% nital used for Sm-Zn alloys (Chiotti and Mason). Nital used for Yb-Zn alloys, examined with polarized light (Mason and Chiotti). 1% nital used for Y alloys (Gibson and Carlson, Domagala and coworkers). Nital also used for RE-Mg alloys (Fishman and Crowe) and Ce-Zn alloys (Chiotti and Mason).
3. 10 g ammonium persulfate 100 mL water	For RE-Co alloys. Use boiling, short immersion of sample (Hergert and Altenhoff).
4. 10 mL HNO_3 100 mL methanol	For Ce. Do not store (Etter and Selle).
5. 30 mL HNO_3 25 mL glycerin	For Ce and alloys, swab sample. Remove stain by swabbing with 42 mL H_3PO_4, 11 mL 2-ethoxyethanol and 47 mL glycerin (Klodt and McManis).
6. 12.5 mL HNO_3 2.5 mL HF 85 mL water	For RE metals.
7. 25 mL HNO_3 75 mL glycerin	For most RE metals and alloys. Swab sample until the first dark film has been removed, revealing the structure and producing a gold-to-green surface color (Lundin).
8. 40 mL HNO_3 60 mL acetic acid	For RE metals (Iowa State Univ.).
9. 42 mL H_3PO_4 48 mL glycerin 11 mL ethylene glycol mono-ethyl ether (Cellosolve)	For RE alloys. Apply a few drops to sample surface. After 10–12 s, wash surface with alcohol, dry.
10. 42 mL H_3PO_4 47 mL glycerin 11 mL ethoxyethanol	M-etch for Y-Ti, Y-Zr, and Y-Hf alloys (Lundin and Klodt).
11. 10 mL H_3PO_4 10 mL lactic acid 30 mL HNO_3 20 mL acetic acid	For RE metals, used for Gd, Er, Ho, and Dy. Etches with slight chemical polishing action (Roman).
12. 95 mL HNO_3 5 mL HF	Grain-boundary etchant for scandium (Geiselman).

Rare earth metals and alloys *(continued)*

Etchant composition	Comments
13. 100 mL water 5 g CrO_3	Grain-boundary etchant for scandium. Use polarized light (Geiselman).
14. Conc. HNO_3	For Sc-Ti alloys (Beaudry and Daane).
15. 30 mL acetic acid 30 mL H_3PO_4 30 mL HNO_3	For Y. Immerse sample (Oak Ridge Natl. Lab.).
16. 30 mL HNO_3 30 mL acetic acid 30 mL water	For cerium dicarbide. Examine with polarized light (Oak Ridge Natl. Lab.)
17. 30 mL lactic acid 10 mL HNO_3 2 mL HF	For Y-Al-C alloys. Swab sample. Carbide phase reacts with water (Rosen and Sprang).
Heat tint	
18. Heat in air to 390°F (200°C)	Heat tint for most RE metals. Heat in air minutes to hours.
Anodizing solution	
19. 2 g KOH 100 mL water	Anodizing solution for La and Ce. Use at 20–24 V dc. Produces color contrast between FCC (blue) and double HCP (yellow) in La. Use polarized light and sensitive tint. FCC phase does not change color on rotation, while double HCP phase changes from red to blue (Koch and Picklesimer).

Rhenium and alloys

Etchant composition	Comments
1. 10 g K$_3$Fe(CN)$_6$ 10 g KOH 100 mL water	Murakami's reagent, for Re. Swab or immerse sample. Slow action. (5 g K$_3$Fe(CN)$_6$, 2 g KOH, and 100 mL water used for Re-Mo alloys).
2. 30 mL lactic acid 10 mL HNO$_3$ 5 mL HF	For Re. Swab sample (Buchheit and coworkers).
3. 30 mL lactic acid 30 mL HNO$_3$ 1 mL HF	For Re. Swab sample (Buchheit and coworkers).
4. 70 mL lactic acid 5 mL HNO$_3$ 1 drop HF	For Re-Hf (<10% Hf) alloys. Swab sample.
5. 50 mL water 50 mL HNO$_3$ 50 mL HF	For Re silicides.
Electrolytic etchants	
6. 10 g oxalic acid 100 mL water	For Re. Use at 6–10 V dc, stainless steel cathode, nichrome or Pt lead wires (Buchheit and coworkers).
7. 37 mL H$_3$PO$_4$ 36 mL glycerol 7 mL water	For Re. Use at 6 V dc, 0.12 A/cm^2. Reveals grain structure (Kanne and Smith).
8. 5 mL acetic acid 10 mL HNO$_3$ 85 mL water	For Re. Use fresh, 1.5 V dc, Pt cathode (Churchman).

Rhodium and alloys

Etchant composition	Comments
1. 30 mL HCl 10 mL HNO$_3$	Aqua regia, for some Rh alloys.
Electrolytic etchants	
2. Conc. HCl	For Rh and alloys. Use at 5 V ac, 1–2 min, graphite cathode, Pt lead wires (Buchheit and coworkers).

3. Solution a
    40 g NaCl
    100 mL water
    Solution b
    Conc. HCl
	For Rh-W alloys. Use 4 parts solution a to 1 part solution b at 10 V ac for 25 s. After etching, remove film by reversing the polarity.

4. 65 mL water
    20 mL HCl
    25 g NaCl
	For Rh alloys. Use 10 V ac, 25 s, graphite cathode.

5. 80 mL water 20 mL H$_2$SO$_4$	For Rh. Use at 1–5 V ac, 0.05–0.2 A/cm^2, graphite cathode, up to 60 min.

Ruthenium and alloys

Etchant composition	Comments
1. 200 mL 20% aq. HCl 1–2 mL H$_2$O$_2$	For Ru-Mo alloys. Electrolytic. Sigma unattacked (Anderson and Hume-Rothery).

2. 20 mL HCl
    25 g NaCl
    65 mL water
	For Ru alloys. Use 5–20 V ac, 1–2 min, graphite cathode, Pt lead wires.

3. Solution a
    40 g NaCl
    100 mL water
    Solution b
    Conc. HCl
	For Ru. Mix 4 parts solution a to 1 part solution b, use 5–20 V ac, 1–2 min, graphite cathode, Pt lead wires. Excellent results (Buchheit and coworkers).

Selenium, tellurium, and alloys

Etchant composition	Comments
1. 40 mL water 10 mL HF 10 mL H_2O_2 (30%)	For Se and ZnTe. Immerse or swab sample for up to 3 min.
2. Conc. HNO_3	For Se, Te, selenides, and tellurides. Can dilute with water or add HCl. Immerse sample for up to a few minutes. Use cold or heated.
3. 50–100 g NaOH 100 mL water	For Se and Te. Etch rate increases with NaOH content, 2–20 min. For Te, sometimes requires heating.
4. 30 mL HCl 10 mL HNO_3	Aqua regia, for Se. Immerse sample up to 5 min. Do not store.
5. 50 mL water 50 mL HNO_3	For pure Te. 55% HNO_3 used for Te-Ag-Sb alloys (Johnson).
6. 60 mL water 40 mL H_2SO_4	For pure Te. Equal parts also used.
7. 30 mL water 10 ml HCl 10 mL HNO_3	For bismuth telluride.
8. 50 mL water 5 mL HCl 5 mL HNO_3	For lead telluride.
9. 10 mL HNO_3 10 mL HCl	For bismuth selenide. Rinse with acetic acid, then water (Faust).
10. 10 mL HNO_3 2 g CrO_3 38 mL water	For Se-bismuth selenide. Immerse sample about 6 min. Se dark gray, selenide brightened (Chang).
11. 10 g KOH 10 g $K_3Fe(CN)_6$ 100 mL water	Murakami's reagent, for antimony telluride (Haven and Stegherr).
12. 20 mL HCl 14.5 mL water 5.5 mL H_2O_2	For Te-bismuth telluride. Immerse sample about 2 min. Te brightended, telluride brown (Chang).

Electrolytic etchant	
13. 56 g NaOH 48 g tartaric acid 570 mL water	For bismuth selenide and bismuth telluride. Use at 500 mA/cm^2, 20°C (Faust).

Silicon and alloys

Etchant composition	Comments
1. 90 mL water 5 mL HNO$_3$ 5 mL HF	For Si and alloys. Immerse sample up to 20 s.
2. 1 part HF 1 part HNO$_3$	For Si and alloys. Immerse sample up to a few minutes.
3. 100 mL water 50–100 g NaOH	For Si. Immerse sample up to a few minutes.
4. 90 mL water 15 mL HCl 10 mL HF	For Si, to reveal SiO$_2$.
5. 3 parts HF 1 part HNO$_3$	"Fluor regia," for Si.
6. 10 mL water 50 mL HF 50 mL HNO$_3$	For Si. Immerse sample about 1 min. Protect bath from contamination by other metals.
7. 40 mL HF 20 mL HNO$_3$ 40 mL 3% aq. mercuric nitrate	For Si. Immerse sample 3–5 s, dip in HNO$_3$, rinse in water, then alcohol, dry.

Silver and alloys

Etchant composition	Comments
1. 50 mL NH_4OH 20 mL H_2O_2 (3%)	For pure Ag, Ag solders, and Ag-Pd alloys. Immerse sample up to 60 s. Discard after etching.
2. 1–5 g CrO_3 100 mL HCl	For pure Ag and Ag alloys. Swab or immerse sample up to 60 s.
3. 60 mL HCl 40 mL HNO_3	For Ag alloys. Use under hood. Immerse sample for up to 60 s.

4. Solution a
  25 mL HNO_3
  1 g $K_2Cr_2O_7$
  1000 mL water
Solution b
  40 g CrO_3
  3 g Na_2SO_4
  200 mL water
	For Ag alloys. Mix equal parts of solutions a and b, apply with an artist's brush. A nonadherent silver chromate film should form. If film is adherent, add more of solution a. If no film forms, add more of solution b. Solution b used alone for Ag-Cd alloys (Speich and Mack). Combination etch used for Ag-Mg-Sn alloys (Raynor and Frost) and for Ag-Mg-Zn alloys (Raynor and Smith).

5. 1–2 g CrO_3 1–2 mL H_2SO_4 1000 mL water	For Ag alloys (Ag-Cu alloys). Immerse sample for up to 60 s. Reveals grain boundaries in Ag-Cu alloys.
6. 2–10 mL H_2SO_4 2 g CrO_3 100 mL water	For Ag alloys (Ag-Ni and Ag-Mg-Ni alloys). Immerse sample up to 60 s.
7. 25 mL NH_4OH 25 mL water 50 mL H_2O_2 (3%)	For Ag-Cu alloys. Add peroxide last. Use fresh. Swab sample for up to 45 s.
8. 2 g $FeCl_3$ 100 mL water	For Ag solders. Immerse sample 5–30 s (Tarasov).
9. 10 mL H_2SO_4 100 mL sat. aq. $K_2Cr_2O_7$ 2 mL sat. aq. NaCl	For pure Ag, Ag alloys, Ag solders. Before use, dilute 1 part etch with 9 parts water. Can delete sulfuric acid.
10. 90 mL water 2 g CrO_3 10 mL H_2SO_4	For Ag-Sn and Ag-Pb-Sn alloys.

11. Solution a
  5–10 g ammonium persulfate
  100 mL water
Solution b
  5–10 g KCN
  100 mL water
	For pure Ag and some alloys. Mix equal parts of solutions a and b. Use fresh, under a hood with care. Avoid fumes. Immerse sample up to 2 min. To discard, neutralize with ammonia and flush with copious water.

12. 100 mL water 4 mL H_2SO_4 7.5 g CrO_3	For Ag and Ag-Cu alloys (Silver chromate etch). Dilute 1 part etch with 9 parts water.
13. 2 g $K_2Cr_2O_7$ 8 mL H_2SO_4 100 mL water	For Ag-Th alloys (Hensel).

Silver and alloys *(continued)*

Etchant composition	Comments
14. 2 g $K_2Cr_2O_7$ 1 g NaF 3 mL H_2SO_4 100 mL water	Crowell's etch for Ag-Sn-Zn-Cu dental amalgam alloys. Rate of attack depends on Ag content. Attacks beta phase Ag-Sn matrix. Small amount of NaCl can be added.

15. Solution a
  10 mL H_3PO_4
  10 mL water
Solution b
  100 mL sat. aq. CrO_3
  45 mL 10% aq. HCl
  800 mL water
	For Ag. Add 2 drops of solution b to solution a. Immerse or swab sample 1–2 min. Rinse with water, alcohol, and ethyl ether, then dry (Kilner and Plumtree). Solution b is a chemical polish for Ag (Gilpin and Worzala).

16. 1 part 10% aq. NaCN 1 part 10% aq. ammonium persulfate	Etch for Ag alloys. Use by immersion of sample (Buchheit).

Electrolytic etchants

17. 10 g citric acid 100 mL water	For Ag alloys. Use at 6 V dc, Ag cathode, 15–180 s. A few drops of HNO_3 can be added.
18. 35 g AgCN 30 g KCN 38 g K_2CO_3 1000 mL water	For Ag. Use fresh, under hood, avoid fumes. Use Ag cathode, Ag lead wires, 4-cm spacing, 0.5 V dc, 5 mA/cm^2, 90 s (Shuttleworth).

Thermal etch

19. 1652°F (900°C) in N_2	For Ag. Hold 19 h, gas must be pure (free of oxygen). Reveals grain boundaries.

Tantalum and alloys

Etchant composition	Comments
1. 10 g NaOH 100 mL water	For pure Ta. Swab or immerse sample.
2. 5 mL HF 20 mL HNO$_3$ 50 mL acetic acid	For Ta alloys. Swab sample 10–30 s (Anderson).
3. 30 mL HF 15 mL HNO$_3$ 30 mL HCl	For Ta alloys. Swab sample 3–10 s or immerse sample for up to 2 min. Can stain sample (Anderson).
4. 20 mL HF 20 mL HNO$_3$ 60 mL lactic acid	For Ta. Swab sample 2 min or more. Polishes surface, produces light etch.
5. 30 mL H$_2$SO$_4$ 30 mL HF 3–5 drops H$_2$O$_2$ (30%) 30 mL water	For Ta alloys. Immerse sample 5–60 s.
6. 25 mL HNO$_3$ 5 mL HF 50 mL water	For Ta alloys. Immerse sample 5–120 s. Equal parts of each also used (Pochon and coworkers).
7. 50 mL HNO$_3$ 30 g ammonium bifluoride 20 mL water	Grain-boundary and inclusion etch for Ta alloys. Use under hood with caution. Swab sample 3–10 s.
8. 100 mL 20% aq. ammonium bifluoride 50 mL HNO$_3$	For Ta. Immerse or swab sample. Use under hood with care (Buchheit).
9. 10 mL HF 10 mL HNO$_3$ 10–30 mL glycerin	Grain-boundary etch for Ta alloys. Swab sample. Equal parts used for Ta and high-Ta alloys (Forgeng).
10. 50 mL water 50 mL HF	For Ta and Ta-Ir and Ta-Rh alloys. Immerse sample about 10 s.
11. 1 part HNO$_3$ 1 part HF 2 parts H$_2$SO$_4$ 5 parts water	For Ta-Re alloys. Swab sample (Brophy and coworkers). For Ta-Pd alloys (Waterstrat and coworkers).
12. 75 mL HNO$_3$ 25 mL HF	For Ta (Schussler and Brunhouse).
13. 4 parts HF 4 parts HNO$_3$ 1 part water	For Ta-W-Re alloys. Swab sample (Brophy and coworkers).
14. 10 mL HNO$_3$ 5 drops hydrofluosilicic acid	For Ta-Zr alloys. Use with care! Swab sample 3–10 s (Pease and Brophy).
15. 10 mL HF 10 mL H$_2$SO$_4$ 80 mL water Few drops H$_2$O$_2$ (30%)	For Ta (Koo).

Tantalum and alloys *(continued)*

Etchant composition	Comments
16. 3 mL HNO_3 1 mL HF 96 mL water	For Ta-Ti alloys. Immerse sample (Hansen and coworkers).
17. 95 mL HNO_3 3–5 mL HF	For Ta-Mo and Ta-noble-metal alloys. Immerse sample (Greenfield and Beck; Carlson and coworkers; Geach and Summers-Smith).
18. 10 g $K_3Fe(CN)_6$ 10 g KOH 80 mL water	Murakami's reagent, for Ta-Mo alloys, reveals coring. Immerse sample (Geach and Summers-Smith).
19. 5 parts H_3PO_4 1 part HNO_3 4 parts HF	For Ta and some high-Ta alloys. Use cold, swab sample (Anderson).
20. 50 mL water 10 g ammonium fluoride 25 mL H_2O_2 (3%)	For Ta. Colors sulfides but does not attack matrix. Use boiling.
21. 25 mL water 5 g ammonium fluoride 25 mL HNO_3	For Ta. Rapid attack of sulfides, slow matrix attack. Use at 140°F (60°C) for several minutes.
22. 25 mL water 5 g ammonium fluoride 50 mL H_2SO_4	For Ta. Develops matrix structure, does not attack sulfides. Use at 140°F (60°C) for 1–2 min.

Electrolytic etchants	
23. 90 mL H_2SO_4 10 mL HF	For Ta. Mix slowly. Use fresh, good for about 1 h. Use 1–2 V dc, 10-cm² area, 1–2 min, graphite cathode, Pt lead wires (Buchheit and coworkers).
24. 1–10 g NaOH 100 mL water	For Ta and alloys. Use 1.5–6 V dc, graphite or stainless steel cathode.
25. 75 mL methanol 10 mL H_2SO_4 25 mL HCl	For Ta and alloys. Use 30 V dc, stainless steel cathode, 30 s.
26. 45 mL water 45 mL H_2SO_4 10 mL HF 4.5 g CrO_3	For Ta and alloys. Use 6 V dc for 1–10 s (Lott).

Anodizing solutions	
27. 60 mL ethanol 35 mL water 20 mL glycerin 10 mL lactic acid 5 mL H_3PO_4 2 g citric acid	Picklesimer's anodizing solution for Ta and alloys. Samples must be well polished. Best voltage and time requires experimentation. Voltages from 20–140 V dc and times from 10–60 s, or longer, are used (18–22 and 55–65 V are commonly used). Maintain voltage until current reaches zero. Observe with bright-field illumination or polarized light.

Tantalum and alloys *(continued)*

Etchant composition	Comments
	Anodizing solutions *(continued)*
28. 1–10 g Na$_2$SO$_4$ 1000 mL water	Vermilyea's anodizing solution for Ta. Use 0.1% solution at 2 mA/cm^2, 118°F (48°C), up to 390 V dc; or use 1% solution at 8 mA/cm^2, 60°F (19°C), up to 240 V dc. Produces Ta$_2$O$_5$ oxide film.

29. Step a
  Vermilyea's anodizing
    solution
Step b
  Thermal etch, 1472°F
    (800°C) in vacuum
Step c
  Conc. HF
	Dunn's method for revealing crystal orientation in Ta. In step a use Vermilyea's anodizing solution (etchant no. 28) to produce a 160-nm thick Ta$_2$O$_5$ film [1% solution, 8 mA/cm^2, 60°F (19°C) 110 V dc, 150 s]. In step b, heat sample 5 min at indicated temperatures. In step c dip in conc. HF for a few seconds to produce multicolored oxide; or reanodize the sample in 1% Na$_2$SO$_4$. As voltage is raised above zero, straw and light-brown colors appear followed by color variations resulting from crystal orientation.

Thallium

Etchant composition	Comments
1. 98 mL ethanol 2 mL HNO$_3$	Nital, for Tl. Immerse sample up to a few minutes.
2. 100 mL water 10 g CrO$_3$	For Tl. Immerse sample up to 10 min.
3. 40 mL water 10 mL HF 10 mL H$_2$O$_2$ (30%)	For Tl. Immerse sample 5–10 s.
4. 95 mL water 5 mL H$_3$PO$_4$	For Tl.
5. 100 mL water 2 mL H$_2$SO$_4$	For Tl.
6. 90 mL alcohol 10 mL HF	For Tl.

Tin and alloys

Etchant composition	Comments
1. 100 mL alcohol 1–5 mL HNO$_3$	For pure Sn and alloys. Swab or immerse sample several minutes (nital).
2. 90 mL water 10 mL HNO$_3$	For Sn alloys.
3. 60 mL alcohol 30 mL water 5 mL HCl 2 g FeCl$_3$	For pure Sn and Sn-Bi alloys. Taffs' reagent. Add 1 drop H$_2$O$_2$ (30%) per 100 mL.
4. 50 mL glycerin 30 mL acetic acid 10 mL HNO$_3$	For pure Sn and alloys of Sn and 1% Pb. Use at 100–108°F (38–42°C) for up to 10 min (Vilella and Beregekoff).
5. 100 mL alcohol 2–10 mL HCl	For pure Sn and alloys. Reveals grain structure. Swab or immerse sample 1–5 min.
6. 80 mL glycerin 10 mL acetic acid 10 mL HNO$_3$	For Sn-Pb, Sn-Sb, and Sn-Cd alloys. Use following same procedure as with etchant no. 4.
7. 50 mL glycerin 2 drops HNO$_3$ 4 drops HF	For Sn-Pb alloys and Sn coatings on steel. Immerse sample up to 60 s.
8. 100 mL water 5–10 g ammonium persulfate	For Sn coatings on steel and for Sn-bearing alloys. Immerse sample up to a few minutes.
9. 100 mL water 10 g K$_3$Fe(CN)$_6$ 10 g KOH (or 7 g NaOH)	Murakami's reagent, for Sn-Cd-Sb alloys. CdSb etched, SbSn unaffected.
10. 95 mL water 2 mL HCl 5 mL HNO$_3$	For Sn-based babbitt metal. Immerse sample up to 5 min.
11. 100 mL water 2 mL HCl 10 g FeCl$_3$	For Sn-based babbitt metal. Immerse sample up to 5 min.
12. 100 mL water 10 g K$_2$Cr$_2$O$_7$ 1 mL HCl	For Sn-Cd alloys.
13. 100 mL water 10 g stannous chloride 5 mL HCl	For Sn-rich alloys.
14. 100 mL water 10 mL HNO$_3$ 5 g CrO$_3$	For Sn alloys.
15. 100 mL water 1 g CrO$_3$	For Sn-Cd alloys. HCl can be added.

Tin and alloys *(continued)*

Etchant composition	Comments
16. 100 mL water 20 g sodium sulfide 1 mL HCl	For Sn-Sb-Cu alloys. SbSn unaffected, Cu_6Sn_5 brown.
17. 100 mL alcohol 1 drop HF	For Sn-plated steel (Romig and Rowland).
18. 50 mL acetic acid 50 mL water 1 drop H_2O_2 (30%)	For Sn.
Tint etch	
19. 50 mL sat. aq. sodium thiosulfate 5 g potassium metabisulfite	Klemm's II reagent. For Sn. Immerse sample 60–90 s. Colors grains.
Electrolytic etchants	
20. 80 mL water 20 mL H_2SO_4	For pure Sn. Use Al cathode, 30 V dc, up to a few minutes. Remove with current applied.
21. 300 mL acetic acid 25 mL water 50 mL perchloric acid	For Sn and alloys. Use Sn cathode, 20–30 V dc, 10 min. Mix carefully, keep cool.
22. 70 mL acetic acid 30 mL perchloric acid	For Sn. Use Sn cathode, 15 V dc, 1.5–3 min, no stirring.

Titanium and alloys

Etchant composition	Comments
	General-purpose etchants
1. 10 mL HF 5 mL HNO$_3$ 85 mL water	For Ti and alloys. Swab sample up to 60 s.
2. 1–3 mL HF 2–6 mL HNO$_3$ 100 mL water	Kroll's reagent for Ti alloys, very good etch. Swab sample 3–10 s or immerse sample 10–30 s.
3. 10 mL HF 30 mL HNO$_3$ 50 mL water	For Ti and alloys. Swab sample 2–20 s.
4. 10 mL HF 45 mL HNO$_3$ 45 mL water	Chemical polish and etch for Ti and alloys. Swab sample up to 20 s.
5. 1 mL HF 200 mL water	For Ti and alloys. Immerse sample up to 5 s. Stains the alpha phase. Higher concentrations can be used but are prone to staining problems.
6. 1 mL HF 3 mL HCl 5 mL HNO$_3$ 190 mL water	Keller's reagent, for Ti alloys. Immerse sample 10–20 s.
7. 5 mL HF 10 mL HNO$_3$ 30 mL lactic acid	For Ti alloys. Swab sample up to 30 s. Decomposes, do not store. Good for alpha-beta alloys.
8. 10 mL HF 10 mL HNO$_3$ 30 mL glycerin	Remington A etch, for Ti alloys. Swab sample up to about 15 s (Finlay). Also used with 30 mL glycerin, immerse sample up to 30 s.
9. 25 mL HF 18.5 g benzalkonium chloride 35 mL methanol 40 mL glycerin	R-etch, for Ti-Al and Ti-Al-Zr alloys. Swab sample up to 20 s, or immerse sample up to 90 s with agitation (Margolin and coworkers).
10. 10 mL 40% aq. KOH 5 mL H$_2$O$_2$ (30%) 20 mL water	For alloys of Ti, 5% Al, and 2.5% Sn and Ti, 6% Al, and 2% Sn and other Ti alloys. Swab sample up to 20 s, or immerse sample 30–60 s at 158–176°F (70–80°C). Stains alpha and transformed beta, retained beta remains bright (Mallory-Sharon Titanium Corp.). Alternate immersing and drying alloy of Ti, 5% Al, and 2.5% Sn for 1–3 min produces coloration (Cooney and Echer).
11. 2 drops HF 1 drop HNO$_3$ 3 mL HCl 25 mL glycerin	For Ti-Si alloys. Swab sample up to 20 s.

Titanium and alloys *(continued)*

Etchant composition	Comments
	General-purpose etchants *(continued)*
12. 1 mL HF 30 mL HNO_3 30 mL lactic acid	For outlining and darkening hydride in some Ti alloys. Swab sample up to 30 s. Decomposes readily, do not store. 2 mL HF used for alloy of Ti and 10% Sn (Lenning and coworkers).
13. 10 mL HF 25 mL HNO_3 45 mL glycerin 20 mL water	For revealing hydrides in alloy of Ti, 5% Al, and 2.5% Sn. Swab sample up to 20 s.
14. 1–10 mL HF 1–10 mL H_2SO_4 100 mL water or glycerin	For Ti alloys. Attacks alpha Ti. Rate of attack slower with glycerin.
15. 2 mL HF 5 mL H_2O_2 (30%) 100 mL water	For Ti and alloys. Reveals grain boundaries. Immerse sample up to 60 s. Nonstaining.
16. 98 mL 20% aq. oxalic acid 2 mL HF 1 g ferric nitrate	For Ti-Sn alloys (up to 25% Sn).
17. 10 mL glycerin 10 mL HF	Remington B etch, for Ti. Swab sample. Darkens alpha Ti, outlines beta phase.
18. 196 mL sat. aq. oxalic acid 4 mL HF 3–4 grains of ferric nitrate	For Ti and alloys (Battelle). Ferric nitrate optional. Immerse sample. 1% HF used for Ti-Pd alloys (Rosenberg and Hunter).
19. 30% aq. $K_3Fe(CN)_6$ 10% aq. NaOH	Modified Murakami's etch, for Ti-V-Mo alloys (Taylor).
20. 12 mL HNO_3 1–2 mL HF 86–87 mL water	For Ti alloys and Ti-Pd alloys (up to 42% Pd) (Rosenberg and Hunter). Swab sample.
21. 60 mL propionic acid 20 mL HNO_3 10 mL HF	For beta-Ti alloys heat-treated below beta transus. Swab sample. Reveals grain boundaries (Smith). Good results also with 30:60:10 mixture.
22. 60 mL lactic acid 20 mL HNO_3 10 mL HF 10 mL water	For Ti-Cu alloys (Gallaugher and coworkers).
23. 10 mL HF 10 mL HNO_3 10 mL H_2SO_4 1 g succinic acid	For Ti alloys. Heat to 104–122°F (40–50°C), immerse sample 20–180 s. Reveals beta phase (Gurevich and coworkers).
24. 80 mL ethanol 2 mL HF 20 mL HNO_3	For Ti. Results enhanced with polarized light.

Titanium and alloys *(continued)*

Etchant composition	Comments

General-purpose etchants (continued)

Etchant composition	Comments
25. 1–4 mL HCl 1 mL H_2SO_4 95–98 mL water	For Ti alloys. Use boiling, 3–10 min. Differentiates phases in alpha-beta alloys (Ogden and Holden).
26. 100 mL water⁻ 5 mL HCl 1 mL HF	For barium titanate (Kulcsar).
27. 10 mL HF 10 mL HNO_3 30 mL lactic acid	For TiB_2 (Kaufman).
28. 4 parts HF 1 part HNO_3 3 parts water	For TiB_2 (Lynch and coworkers).
29. 6 parts methanol 1 part H_2SO_4	For TiB_2 (Lynch and coworkers).

Tint etchants

Etchant composition	Comments
30. 5 g ammonium bifluoride 100 mL water	Weck's tint etch for Ti and alloys. For pure Ti, immerse sample at 20°C for a few seconds. Longer times required for alloys. Alpha grains and twins colored according to orientation.
31. 3 g ammonium bifluoride 4 mL HCl 100 mL water	Weck's tint etch for Ti alloys. Immerse sample at 20°C for a few seconds. High-quality polish required. Colors alpha grains; secondary alpha, alpha prime, and intermetallic phases are colored or unaffected.
32. 2–3 g sodium molybdate 5 mL HCl 1–2 g ammonium bifluoride 100 mL water	Beraha's tint etch for as-cast Ti alloys. Immerse sample at 20°C until surface is colored. Colors alpha matrix blue or green, TiC yellow or dark brown.

Heat tint

Etchant composition	Comments
33. Heat in air, 752–1300F (400–704°C)	Heat tint air at 752–1300°F (400–704°C) until surface colored red-violet. Colors phases preferentially. Very effective. Ence and Margolin used 1112°F (600°C) for 60 s. Retained beta deep violet to bright blue, alpha dull to golden yellow, martensite yellow with violet coloring due to fine retained beta, carbides brilliant bright blue or yellowish. Temperatures below 932°F (500°C) produced orientation effects, colors not constant. Eylon heat-tinted an alloy containing Ti, 6% Al, 2% Sn, 4% Zr, and 2% Mo for 2 h at 900°F (480°C) to differentiate between primary and secondary alpha. Testa and Litzinger heat-tinted an alloy containing Ti, 6% Al and 4% V at 1300°F (704°C) after a preetch with Keller's reagent.

Titanium and alloys *(continued)*

Etchant composition	Comments
	Electrolytic etchants
34. 10 mL perchloric acid 10 mL 2-butoxyethanol 70 mL ethanol 10 mL water	For pure Ti and alloys. Keep cool during mixing and use. Use at 30–65 V dc, 10–60 s.
35. 3 mL perchloric acid 35 mL 2-butoxyethanol 60 mL methanol	For pure Ti and alloys. Use at 60–150 V dc, 5–30 s.
36. 5 mL perchloric acid 80 mL acetic acid	For pure Ti and alloys. Use at 20–60 V dc, 1–5 min, stainless steel cathode. Jacquet used perchloric acid diluted 20 times with acetic acid to anodically etch Ti at 104–122°F (40–50°C), 5–30 s, 1 A/dm², stainless steel cathode, producing an oxide film whose colors varied with crystal orientation.
37. 25 mL water 390 mL methanol 350 mL ethylene glycol 35 mL perchloric acid	For pure Ti. Use at 30–50 V dc, stainless steel cathode, 41–50°F (5–10°C), 10–40 s.
38. 10 g NaCN 100 mL water	Electrolytic swab etch for Ti alloys. Tip of stainless-steel cathode rod is covered with cotton, saturated with the solution, and touched against the surface of a sample preetched with a general reagent. Distance between rod and sample <3 mm. Sample etched 60 s at 8–10 V dc, 0.14 A. Surface appears violet or blue. Carbides are yellow or orange-yellow, alpha and transformed or retained beta appear violet or blue. Can distinguish between boride phases: TiB_2 white, Ti_2B light gray, and TiB dark gray. Higher voltage required for Ti-Mn and Ti-Mn-Fe alloys (Ence and Margolin).
39. 10 g NaOH 490 mL water	For titanium borides. Use at 20°C, stainless steel cathode. Ti light blue, TiB light brown, and TiB_2 unaffected (Rudy and St. Windisch).
	Anodizing solutions
40. 60 mL ethanol 35 mL water 10 mL lactic acid 5 mL H_3PO_4 5 g citric acid 5 g oxalic acid	Ence and Margolin's cumulative etch anodizing solution (H-etch) for Ti alloys. Composition is critical. Can add 110 mL glycerin (HG-etch). A 2–6 mm mask of Bakelite is placed between stainless steel cathode and the sample, which is centered over a hole (25–75 mm²) in the mask. Voltages from 20–130 V dc are used (100–130 V most common). Circuit is opened and closed quickly 5–10 times. Best contrast when surface is colored blue for the second time. Preetch with general reagent is helpful. Colors phases.

Titanium and alloys *(continued)*

Etchant composition	Comments
	Anodizing solutions *(continued)*
41. 5 g oxalic acid 5 g citric acid 5 g tartaric acid 3 mL H_3PO_4 50 mL water 20 mL Carbitol 27 mL ethanol	Anodizing solution for iodide Ti. Use at 40 V dc, 5–120 s (in 5-s intervals). 20 s produced good results (first blue). Grains with basal-plane orientation are yellow. Grains $\frac{1}{2}$–2° from basal plane are orange, grains 2–5° are pink (Hiltz).
42. 60 mL ethanol 35 mL water 20 mL glycerin 10 mL lactic acid 5 mL H_3PO_4 2 g citric acid	Picklesimer's modification of Ence and Margolin's anodizing solution used by Grosso and Nagel for a Ti-Nb diffusion couple. Use at 90 V dc, peak current of 25 mA/cm². Time from closing circuit until current dropped to near zero was about 3 s. Produced vivid colors.
43. 1 g CrO_3 100 mL water	Anodizing solution for Ti and alloys. Use at 18–30 V dc, 3 s to produce a dark-blue anodic film. Enhances anisotropy of as-electropolished Ti under polarized light, reveals precipitates under bright-field illumination (Coons and Iosty).

Tungsten and alloys

Etchant composition	Comments

1. Solution a
    100 mL water
    10 g KOH
  Solution b
    100 mL water
    10 g $K_3Fe(CN)_6$
	Murakami's reagent, for W and alloys. Use fresh, immerse sample up to a minute.

2. 50 mL water
  50 mL HNO_3
  50 mL HF
	For W-Th alloys. Immerse sample up to a few minutes.

3. 80 mL water
  15 mL HNO_3
  3 mL HF
	For W-Th alloys. Immerse sample up to a few minutes.

4. 150 mL water
  3.5 g $K_3Fe(CN)_6$
  1 g NaOH
	Modified Murakami's reagent, for W and lean alloys.

5. 50 mL water
  50 mL H_2O_2 (3%)
  50 mL ammonia water
	For W and alloys. Use boiling, up to 10 min.

6. 100 mL water 1 mL H_2O_2 (30%)	For W and alloys. Use boiling, up to 90 s.
7. 20 mL water 10 mL H_2O_2 (30%)	For W. Use boiling. Reveals grain boundaries.
8. 1 part HCl 1 part H_2O_2 (3%)	For W-Co alloys.

9. 100 mL water
  2 g picric acid
  25 g NaOH
	Alkaline sodium picrate, for W-Co eutectic alloys. W blackened. Use boiling, 15 s.

10. H_2O_2 (3%)	For W. Use boiling for 30–90 s. Reveals grain boundaries.
11. 60 mL NH_4OH 15 mL H_2O_2 (30%)	For W. Use fresh, immerse sample up to 10 min.

12. Solution a
    10 g $CuSO_4 \cdot 5H_2O$
    40 mL water
  Solution b
    20 mL NH_4OH
	For W. Mix solution a, then filter and add solution b. Immerse sample 30 s. Reveals grain boundaries (Millner and Sass).

13. 70 mL lactic acid
  20 mL HNO_3
  10 mL HF
	For W and alloys. Swab (Lott).

14. 30 mL lactic acid
  10 mL HNO_3
  10 mL HF
	For alloy of W and 3% Re. Immerse sample 1 min (Taylor).

15. 98 mL HNO_3 2 mL HF	For W-Hf alloys. Immerse sample 2–40 s (Giessen and coworkers).

Tungsten and alloys *(continued)*

Etchant composition	Comments
Tint etch	
16. 94 mL 10% aq. HCl 20 g CrO$_3$	Orientation-sensitive tint etch for W. Immerse sample at 131°F (55°C). Use 2 or 3 stages (view between etches) of 15, 10, and 10 min. Preetch with a grain-boundary etchant for best results. Solution good for 1–2 days, until it turns black (Lehwald and coworkers).
Electrolytic etchants	
17. 100 mL water 10 g NaOH	For W and alloys. Use stainless steel cathode, 1.5–6 V dc, up to a few minutes.
18. 100 mL methanol 5 mL H$_2$SO$_4$ 1 mL HF	For W and alloys. Use 50–60 V dc for 10–20 s.
Anodizing solutions	
19. 0.1 N H$_3$PO$_4$.	For W and alloys. Use 60–80 V dc, stainless steel cathode, 5–30 s. Reveals inhomogeneities (Wolff).

Vanadium and alloys

Etchant composition	Comments
1. 1 mL HF 30 mL HNO_3 30 mL lactic acid	For pure V. Swab sample in 10-s intervals. Higher HF content increases grain-boundary attack.
2. 30 mL HF 30 mL HNO_3 30 mL glycerin	Grain-boundary etch for pure V. Swab sample 60 s. Reveals structure of V alloys.
3. 2 mL HF 5 g $AgNO_3$ 100 mL water	For V alloys. Swab sample 5 s.
4. 10 mL HNO_3 10 mL HF 10–30 mL glycerin	For V and alloys. 30 mL glycerin used for V-Mn alloys (Waterstrat) and for binary V alloys (Rostoker and Yamamoto).
5. 10 g KOH 10 g $K_3Fe(CN)_6$ 100 mL water	Murakami's reagent, for V (Loria) and V-O alloys (Henry and coworkers). Swab samples.
6. 20 mL HF 20 mL HNO_3 40 mL water	For V alloys (Lott). Swab sample. 40 mL HNO_3 used for $(Fe,Co,Ni)_3V$ alloys (Liu and Inouye) for 30–60 s. Equal parts of each used for V-U alloys. Swab sample. Reveals grain boundaries (Saller and Rough).
Electrolytic etchants	
7. 5–10 mL HCl 90–95 mL ethanol	For pure V. Use 6 V dc, 10 s, stainless steel cathode, Pt or nichrome lead wires. Excellent etch (Buchheit and coworkers).
8. 5–10 g oxalic acid 100 mL water	Grain-boundary etch for pure V. Use 6 V dc, 2–20 s, stainless steel cathode.
9. 75 mL methanol 10 mL H_2SO_4 25 mL HCl	For V and alloys. Use 30 V dc, 30 s, stainless steel cathode.
10. 1–10 mL HCl 90–100 mL water	For V. Use 3–6 V dc, several seconds.
Anodizing solution	
11. 90 mL ethanol 20 mL glycerin 1.5 mL H_3PO_4 20 mL water	Anodizing solution for V-Ga, V-Si, V-Al, and V-In alloys. Use 35 V dc, 60–100 s, etch until matrix is colored dark blue. V-Ga solid solution is light azure, V_3Ga light rose, V_6Ga_5 lilac, V_2Ga_5 yellow-brown (Vorob'eva and Kunakov).

Zinc and alloys

Etchant composition	Comments

1. 40 g CrO_3
    3 g Na_2SO_4
    200 mL water
	Palmerton reagent, for pure Zn and alloys. Immerse sample up to 3 min. Rinse in 20% aq. CrO_3. Very popular (Mathewson and coworkers).

2. 40 g CrO_3
    1.5 g Na_2SO_4
    200 mL water
	Modified Palmerton reagent, for Zn-Cu alloys. Immerse sample a few seconds, rinse in 20% aq. CrO_3.

3. 10 g CrO_3
    1 g Na_2SO_4
    200 mL water
	Modified Palmerton reagent, for Zn die-casting alloys. Immerse sample for several seconds, rinse in 20% aq. CrO_3.

4. 100 mL water 10 g NaOH	For pure Zn and Zn-Co and Zn-Cu alloys. Swab or immerse sample 5–15 s.
5. 100 mL alcohol 0.5–5 mL HNO_3	For Zn-Fe, Zn-Al, and Zn-Cr alloys and Zn-coated steels. Immerse sample for up to 60 s. Use low concentration for Zn-coated steels.
6. 100 mL water or ethanol 1–5 mL HCl	For Zn and lean alloys. Immerse sample up to a few minutes.

7. 100 mL water
    50 g KOH
    10 g cupric nitrate
    25 g KCN
    2 g citric acid
	For commercial Zn alloys. Immerse sample 10–20 s. Zn-rich phases brown, Fe-rich phases white (rods), Pb phase white (spots).

8. 84 mL water
    15 mL H_2SO_4
    1 mL HF
	For Zn alloys. Immerse sample 10 s at 100°F (38°C). Reveals grain boundaries (Gennone and Kersey).

9. 98 mL lactic acid 2 mL HNO_3	For Zn. Immerse sample 15 min (Gelles).

10. 10 parts water
     1 part iodine
     3 parts KI
	For Zn and alloys (Gulliver).

	Tint etch

11. 50 mL sat. aq. sodium
     thiosulfate
     1 g potassium metabisulfite
	Klemm's I reagent, for Zn and lean alloys. Immerse sample 30 s.

	Electrolytic etchants
12. 100 mL water 10–20 g CrO_3	For Zn-Cu alloys. Use at 12 V dc, 0.2 A/cm², 5 s, Pt cathode. Differentiate between γ and ϵ in Zn-Cu alloys.
13. 100 mL water 25 g NaOH	For pure Zn and lean alloys. Use Cu cathode, 6 V dc, 15 min.

Zirconium and hafnium

Etchant composition	Comments
1. 30 mL HF 15 mL HNO$_3$ 30 mL HCl	For Zr, Hf, and alloys. Swab sample 3–10 s, or immerse sample up to 120 s.
2. 5 mL HF 2 mL 5% aq. AgNO$_3$ 200 mL water	For Hf, swab sample 5–60 s. For Zr, use 100 mL water, swab sample 10–60 s.
3. 8–10 mL HF 45 mL HNO$_3$ 45 mL H$_2$O (H$_2$O$_2$ or glycerin)	Cain's chemical polish and etch for Hf, Zr, and alloys. Can dilute aqueous solution with 3–5 parts water to stain the structure (swab sample) after chemical polishing. Chemically polish and etch sample by swabbing 5–20 s. Use polarized light. Used for Hf-Ir alloys (Copeland and Goodrich). 8 mL HF used for Zr-Nb alloys (Dalgaard). 7 mL HF used for Zr-Cr-Fe alloys (DeLeon).
4. 50 mL HNO$_3$ 45 mL water 5 mL HF	For β-phase Zircaloy (Garde and coworkers).
5. 65 mL water 35 mL HNO$_3$ 5 mL HF	For Zircaloy-2 and Hf (Westinghouse).
6. 100 mL water 1–10 mL HF	For Zr and alloys. Swab sample with 1% HF for Zr-Be and Zr-H alloys (McGurty and coworkers); 10% HF for Zr and Zr-Nb alloys (Rogers and Chiotti).
7. 90 mL HNO$_3$ 10 mL HF	For most Zr alloys.
8. 50 mL HNO$_3$ 50 mL HF	For Zr alloys containing Al, Be, Fe, Ni, and Si.
9. 40 mL HCl 10–15 mL HNO$_3$ 3 drops HF	For Zr-Nb alloys (Hodge). Used to identify inclusions (Saller and Dickerson).
10. 75 mL HCl 3 mL HF 25 ml HNO$_3$	For Zr-Nb alloys.
11. 99 mL HNO$_3$ 1 mL HF	For Zr-Th, Zr-Sn, and Zr-Nb alloys (Wilhelm and Carlson).
12. 98 mL HNO$_3$ 2 mL HF	For Hf-W alloys. Swab sample 2–40 s (Giessen and coworkers).
13. 98 mL water 1 mL HF 1 mL HNO$_3$	For Zr-Cu alloys (Rogers and Chiotti).
14. 95 mL water 2 mL HF 3 mL HNO$_3$	For Zr-Si alloys (McPherson and Hansen).

Zirconium and hafnium *(continued)*

Etchant composition	Comments
15. 94 mL water 4 mL HF 2 mL HNO$_3$	For Zr-Ni eutectics and Zr-Si alloys (Steinberg and coworkers).
16. 92 mL water 5 mL HF 3 mL HNO$_3$	For Zr alloys containing Al, Be, Fe, Ni, Si, and up to 10% Pt. Good for examination with polarized light (Treco and coworkers).
17. 80 mL water 20 mL HF 1 mL HNO$_3$	For Zr. Swab sample 1–2 s. Attacks carbides (Roberson).
18. 50 mL water 50 mL HNO$_3$ 6 drops HF	For Zr and Zr-Al and Zr-U alloys (Saller and co-workers). Use 1 drop HF for Hf-Re alloys.
19. 65 mL water 10 mL HNO$_3$ 20 mL HF 3 mL sat. aq. NaCl 1 g K$_2$Cr$_2$O$_7$ 5 mL H$_2$SO$_4$	For Zr. Attacks carbides.
20. 80 mL water 20 mL HNO$_3$ 2 mL HF 2 g NaCl 2 g sodium chlorate	For Zr-Hf-Ti alloys.
21. 50 mL water 50 mL HNO$_3$ 4 drops hydrofluosilicic acid	For Zr and Zr-Th alloys.
22. 85 mL glycerin 5 mL HF 10 mL HNO$_3$	For Zr-Mg, Zr-Sn, and Zr-U alloys (Treco and coworkers).
23. 30 mL glycerin 10 mL HF 5 mL HNO$_3$	For Zr, Zr-Si, Zr-B, Zr-Nb, and Zr-Fe alloys. Swab sample 3–5 s. Versatile etch. Carbides not attacked (Roberson).
24. 30 mL glycerin 10 mL HF 10 mL HNO$_3$	For Zr-Sn, Zr-Mo, Zr-Cu, Zr-Si, Zr-N, Zr-O, and Zr-Al alloys (McPhearson and Hansen, Domagala and co-workers, Lundin and coworkers).
25. 15 mL glycerin 10 mL HF 5 mL HNO$_3$	For Zr-Mg and Zr-Ni alloys (Hayes and coworkers).
26. 45 mL glycerin 45 mL HNO$_3$ 10 mL HF	Cain's chemical polishing and etching reagent, used for Hf-W eutectoid alloys. Swab sample 10 s (Giessen and coworkers).
27. 80 mL glycerin 20–40 mL water 10 mL HF 5 mL HNO$_3$	For Zr and alloys of Zr and 5% Ta. Swab sample 1–2 s (Roberson).

Zirconium and hafnium (*continued*)

Etchant composition	Comments
28. 30 mL glycerin 10 mL water 10 mL HF 5 mL HNO$_3$	For Zr, Zr-Ni, Zr-Cr, Zr-Si, Zr-Ag, and Zr-Al alloys. Swab sample a few seconds (Shelton).
29. 50 mL ethylene glycol 40 mL water 5 mL HF 5 drops Tween (wetting agent) 3 mL HNO$_3$	For Zr, excellent etch (Baumrucker). Used without wetting agent on alloys of Zr containing 15 to 36% Pt (Kendall and coworkers).
30. 30 mL lactic acid 30 mL HNO$_3$ 2 mL HF	For Zr and Zr-U alloys. Decomposes, do not store (Saller and coworkers). 6–10 drops HF used for Zr-U alloys (Bauer and coworkers).
31. 10 mL glycerin 10 mL HNO$_3$ 10 mL HCl 0.1 mL HF	For HfB$_2$ and ZrB$_2$ (Kaufman and coworkers).
32. 250 mL water 22 mL HNO$_3$ 3 mL HF	For Hf. Follow by heat tinting at 1000°F (538°C) (Danielson).
33. 10 mL HF 30 mL HNO$_3$ 50 mL water	For Hf-C alloys (Sara).
34. 45 mL H$_2$O$_2$ (30%) 45 mL HNO$_3$ 1 mL HF	For Zr$_3$Al-based alloys. Swab sample 15 s. Zr$_3$Al in relief, alpha Zr(Al) etched out (Ambler and coworkers).
35. 45 mL water 45 mL H$_2$O$_2$ (30%) 2 drops HF	For Zr$_3$Al-based alloys. Reveals only the alpha-Zr(Al) particles. Swab sample 30 s (Ambler and coworkers).
36. 10–20 mL HNO$_3$ 0.5–1 g NH$_4$FHF 80–90 mL water	For alloy of Zr, 4% Sn, and 1.6% Mo (Chubb).
37. 1 mL HF 3 mL HNO$_3$ 3 g Pb(NO$_3$)$_2$ 95 mL water (Plus excess metallic Pb)	For difficult-to-etch Zr alloys. Gentle, slow etch, good grain-boundary etch but stains carbides (Roberson).
38. 50 mL H$_2$O$_2$ (30%) 25 mL HNO$_3$ 25 mL ethanol 2 drops HF	For Zr and alloys. Fast (Bölsing and Dressler).
39. 70 mL water 30 mL HNO$_3$ 2–5 mL HF	Chemical polishing and etching reagent for Zircaloy-2 and Hf (Cain). Swab or immerse sample for up to 60 s. Use polarized light.

Zirconium and hafnium *(continued)*

Etchant composition	Comments
40. 50 mL water 47 mL HNO_3 3 mL HF	Chemical polishing and etching reagent for Zircaloy-4 (Perez and Saggese). Examine with polarized light. 5 mL HF used for Zr-Al alloys, 10 min (Schulson).
41. Solution a 50 mL water 45 mL HNO_3 5 mL HF Solution b 70 mL water 27 mL HNO_3 3 mL HF Solution c 70 mL water 25 mL HNO_3 5 mL HF	Chemical polishing and etching reagents for zirconium hydride phases. Use solution a for alpha phase (60 s), solution b for delta phase (30–90 s), and solution c for epsilon phase (90–120 s). Times are reduced if sample is attack-polished (Paetz and Muller).

	Heat tint
42. Heat in air, 750°F (399°C)	Heat tint for Zr, 5 min (Cain).

	Electrolytic etchants
43. 10 mL perchloric acid 10 mL 2-butoxyethanol 70 mL ethanol 10 mL water	For Hf, Zr, and alloys. Keep cool during mixing and use. Use at 30–65 V dc for 10–60 s.
44. 3 mL perchloric acid 35 mL 2-butoxyethanol 60 mL methanol	For Hf, Zr, and alloys. Use at 60–150 V dc for 5–30 s.
45. 5 mL perchloric acid 80 mL acetic acid	For Hf, Zr, and alloys. Use at 20–60 V dc for 1–5 min.
46. 10 mL perchloric acid 10 mL glycerin 70 mL ethanol 10 mL water	For Zr alloys. Use at 15–50 V dc for 15–60 s. Keep cool during mixing and use.
47. 5 mL HF 10 mL HNO_3 100 mL glycerin	For Zr and alloys. Use at 9–12 V dc, Pt cathode, 1–10 min. Do not store.
48. 80 mL alcohol 20 mL HCl	For Zr. Use at 0.001 A/cm^2 for 10–20 s.
49. Solution a 0.5 g oxalic acid 100 mL water Solution b 6 parts HNO_3 2 parts HCl 2 parts HF	Solution a is an electrolytic etch for Hf-Cr and Hf-V alloys. Use 25% aqueous acid solution of solution b to remove stain (Rudy and St. Windisch).

Zirconium and hafnium *(continued)*

Etchant composition	Comments
	Electrolytic etchants *(continued)*
50. 40 mL HF 40 mL ethanol 20 mL water	For zirconium boride. Use at 4.5 A/in^2 for 2–5 s (Wachtell).
	Anodizing solutions
51. 60 mL ethanol 35 mL water 20 mL glycerin 10 mL lactic acid 5 mL H$_3$PO$_4$ 2 g citric acid	Picklesimer's anodizing solution for Zr and alloys. Use 20–140 V dc, 20°C, 5–10 s, specimen about 12.5 mm from stainless steel cathode. Only hydrides are colored at 20 V dc. Higher voltages color structure. Anodized oxide film is stable and preserves very well. Ambler used method on Zr$_3$Al-based alloys at 95 V dc for 10 min.
52. 100 mL water 5 g KOH	Anodizing solution for Zr alloys. Layer thickness is voltage-dependent and is formed by applying voltage until the current drops to zero (Oak Ridge Natl. Lab.).

Carbides

Etchant composition	Comments
1. Sodium or potassium bicarbonate	Molten-salt etch for SiC. Immerse sample about 10 min.
2. Sodium tetraborate	Molten-salt etch for SiC. Immerse sample a few minutes.
3. 2200°F (1200°C) in vacuum	Thermal etch for SiC.
4. 10 mL water 10 mL HNO$_3$ 10 mL HF	For CrC or HfC.
5. 10 mL glycerol 10 mL HNO$_3$ 10 mL HF	For VC.
6. 10 mL HF 10 mL HNO$_3$ 20 mL lactic acid	For oxides, nitrides, or carbides of Ta.
7. 10 mL HF 50 mL lactic acid 30 mL HNO$_3$	For Ta-C alloys (Brizes).
8. 10 mL HF 30 mL HNO$_3$	For TaC. Immerse sample for 2 min (Roeder and Hornstra).
9. 10 g KOH 10 g K$_3$Fe(CN)$_6$ 100 mL water	Murakami's reagent. Use hot, 30–40 min for alloys of SiC containing 1% B$_4$C (Bind and Biggers), or boiling for B-doped SiC (Prochazka and Charles).
10. 10 mL HNO$_3$ 10 mL HCl 10 mL H$_2$SO$_4$	For TaC. Can substitute HF for HCl.
11. 2822°F (1550°C) in argon	Thermal etch for B-doped SiC, 30 min (Prochazka and Charles).

Electrolytic etchants	
12. 190 mL 8% aq. NaOH 190 mL H$_3$PO$_4$ 50 mL of aqueous solution containing 100 g CuSO$_4$ and 23 mL H$_2$SO$_4$ per liter	For TiC-C alloys. Use 3.5 V dc, 5.6 A/in^2, Cu cathode, 80°F (25°C), 20–30 s. Remove Cu oxide from Cu cathode by dip in HNO$_3$ (Hays and Kendall).
13. 50 mL lactic acid 30 mL HNO$_3$ 8 mL HF	For NbC and NbC$_2$. Use at 17–20 V dc, stainless steel cathode 68–77°F (20–25°C).
14. 100 mL water 20 g KOH	For TiC and TaC. Use 2 V dc, 30–60 mA/cm^2, Pt cathode, 2–30 s with agitation. For SiC, use 6 V dc, 1A/cm^2, 20 s (Robinson and Gardner). For alloys of SiC containing 1% B$_4$C, use 6–10 V dc for a few seconds (Bind and Biggers).

Carbides *(continued)*

Etchant composition	Comments
	Electrolytic etchants *(continued)*
15. 100 mL water 1 g KOH	For B$_4$C. Use 40 V dc, 3 A/cm^2, stainless steel cathode. Champagne and coworkers used 0.04 A/cm^2, 20°C, 30–60 s.
16. 400 mL acetic acid 120 g CrO$_3$ 380 mL water 30 mL H$_2$SO$_4$ 2 mL ethanol	For SiC. Use at 6 V dc, 0.4 A, 6 s. Produces colors with respect to grain orientations (Robinson and Gardner).
17. 10 g oxalic acid 100 mL water	For self-bonded SiC. Use at 5–10 V dc, 1 A, up to 30 s. (Walker).
18. 10 g CrO$_3$ 100 mL water 0.2 mL HF	For pyrolytic SiC. Use at 10–15 V dc, 4–5 A, 2–3 min. Use fresh solution. For electromechanical polishing and etching, use 25 V dc, 1.8–2 A, 2–10 min. Remove any spots or scale by swabbing sample with 10% aq. HF (Gyarmati and Hoven).

Nitrides

Etchant composition	Comments
1. 2912°F (1600°C) in dry N$_2$	Thermal etch for Si$_3$N$_4$. Use high-purity N$_2$, about 5 h.
2. 95.4 g potassium carbonate 12 g sodium fluoride	Molten-salt etch for Si$_3$N$_4$. Immerse sample 1–4 min.
3. Conc. H$_3$PO$_4$	For Si$_3$N$_4$. Use boiling, up to 15 min.
4. Conc. HF	For Si$_3$N$_4$. Immerse sample up to 15 min.
5. 10 mL water 10 mL acetic acid 10 mL HNO$_3$	For aluminum or titanium nitride.
6. 4 parts KOH 4 parts NaOH 1 part LiOH (By weight)	For β-Si$_3$N$_4$. Use at 392°F (200°C) for 20 min (Greskovich).

Oxides

Etchant composition	Comments
1. 2012–2732°F (1100–1500°C) in air	Thermal etch for Al_2O_3, mixtures of Al_2O_3 and MgO, or SnO_2. Reveals grain boundaries. About 2 h for Al_2O_3, 4 min for others. Heuer and Roberts used 2912–3272°F (1600–1800°C) for 5–10 min for Al_2O_3. Metcalfe and Sant used 2912°F (1600°C) for 10–30 min, for mullite ($3Al_2O_3 \cdot 2SiO_2$).
2. Conc. HCl	For CaO or MgO. Immerse sample 3 s to 6 min.
3. 10 mL water 10 mL HCl	For Y_2O_3-ThO_2. Use boiling (Greskovich and Woods).
4. Conc. HF	For BeO, BaO, MgO, ZrO_2, and Zr_2O_3. Immerse sample 2 s to 6 min.
5. Conc. H_3PO_4	For MgO, ThO_2, Al_2NiO_4, and Y_2O_3-ZrO_2. Use boiling for up to 30 min. For stabilized zirconia, use 1–60 min (Slepian); for $CoAl_2O_4$, use 9 min (Petrak); for sodium-beta-alumina, use 30 min (May and Henderson). Caution—do not immerse Bakelite mounts in boiling phosphoric acid!
6. 15 mL water 85 mL H_3PO_4	For Al_2O_3. Use boiling for up to 2 h.
7. 50 mL water 50 mL H_2SO_4	For ZrO_2. Use boiling for 1–5 min.
8. 100 mL water 5 mL acetic acid	For ZnO.
9. 20 mL water 20 mL HNO_3 10 mL HF	For CeO_2, $SrTiO_3$, Al_2O_3, and ZrO-ZrC. Immerse sample up to 15 min.
10. 10 mL HCl 3 mL HF	For $BaTiO_3$ and $BaTi_3O_7$. Immerse sample up to 2 h (see also Ti etch no. 26).
11. Sat. aq. sodium sulfide.	For CaO. Immerse sample up to 60 s.
12. 90 mL lactic acid 15 mL HNO_3 5 mL HF	For BeO. Use at 149°F (65°C) for up to 60 min. Soden and Monforte used 104–140°F (40–60°C) 5 min for MnZn ferrite and MgMn ferrite and 10 min for BeO.
13. 30 mL lactic acid 15 mL HNO_3 5 mL HF	For $Y_3Fe_5O_{12}$ and $Y_3Fe_4AlO_{12}$. Use at 149°F (65°C) for 10 min (Soden and Monforte).
14. 15 mL lactic acid 15 mL HNO_3 5 mL HF	For NiZn ferrite and Ni ferrite. Use at 149–176°F (65–80°C) for 20 min (Soden and Monforte)
15. 5 mL HF 95 mL water	For MgO (Riegger and coworkers).
16. 2 mL HF 98 mL water	For porcelain. Immerse sample 10–15 min (Neuberger and coworkers). Chaudhuri used 40% HF, 20°C, 90 s.

Oxides *(continued)*

Etchant composition	Comments
17. 2912°F (1600°C) in purified argon	Thermal etch for UO_2. Hold 5 min, surface is scratch-free (Gibbs and Rawson).
18. 50 mL HNO_3 50 mL water	For MgO and UO_2. Use at 20°C, 1–5 min (Houle and Coble).
19. $KHSO_4$ (potassium bisulfate)	Molten-salt etch for Cr_2O_3 and Al_2O_3. Immerse sample 3–15 s, sometimes have thermal shock problems (Houle and Coble).
20. 3092°F (1700°C) in dry H_2	Thermal etch for Al_2O_3. Hold 1–2 min. Reveals grain-boundaries, better than fused $KHSO_4$ (Houle and Coble).
21. Conc. H_2SO_4	For Al_2O_3. Use at 392–518°F (200–270°C) for 5–20 min (McVickers and coworkers).
22. 1922°F (1050°C) in air	Thermal etch for PLZT [(Pb,La)(Zr,Ti)O_3]. Hold 1 h. Reveals grain boundaries (Hardtl).
23. Conc. HCl	For PLZT. Use at 176–212°F (80–100°C) (Okazahi and Nagata).
24. 2912–3092°F (1600–1700°C) in air	Thermal etch for HfO_2 (Buckley and Wilder).
25. 50–100% HF (aq.)	For HfO_2. Use at 122°F (50°C) (Buckley and Wilder).
26. 20 mL HCl 10 mL HNO_3 70 mL glycerin	For CoO. Immerse sample 30 s (Petrak and coworkers).
27. Solution a 50 mL HF 50 mL water Solution b 50 mL HCl 50 mL water	For CeO_2. Immerse sample in solution a at 20°C for 15 min. Then, swab with solution b for 1–2 s to remove etching residue (Williams and coworkers).
28. 45 mL HNO_3 50 mL water 5 mL HF	For CeO_2. Use at 20°C, 15 min, agitate. No film formation (Yust and Haltom).
29. Mixture a 2 g dehydrated disodium tetraborate 0.02 g chromium electrolyte powder Reagent b 1 part water 1 part HF 1 part HNO_3	Two-step etch for Al_2O_3-TiC sintered cermets. Melt mixture a in small Pt crucible. Preheat sample over melt for 10 s, then etch in stirred melt for 10 s. Quench in water, rinse in boiling water. Etch TiC in reagent b for 2–9 min at 20°C (Puppel and coworkers).

Polymers

Etchant composition	Comments
1. Osmium tetroxide	Blocks of rubber-reinforced plastics, e.g., high-impact polystyrene (HIPS) or acrylonitrile-butadiene-styrene polymers (ABS), can be soaked overnight at 20°C in 1% aqueous OsO_4 or for several hours at 122°F (50°C). Thin sections can be stained by the vapor. The rubber particles are degraded and hardened by oxidation and selectively stained. Good for bright-field transmitted optical illumination or transmission electron microscopy (TEM) (Kato).
2. 6 M CrO_3 (600 g CrO_3/liter)	For bulk polypropylene. Immerse sample 96 h at 158°F (70°C). Produces weight loss of 8×10^{-6} g per hour and thickness change of 0.1 µm per hour. Attacks amorphous regions preferentially but slowly (Armond and Atkinson).
3. 400 mL H_2SO_4 130 mL H_3PO_4 125 mL water 20 g CrO_3	For ABS, HIPS, and PPO (2,6-dimethyl-1,4-phenylene oxide). Microtomed blocks immersed for periods of 15–180 s. Conditions critical for ABS (Bucknall and coworkers).
4. 30% aq. HCl	For polyoxymethylene (POM). Use at 20°C for 20 s (Linke and Kopp).
5. Xylene	For polyamid (PA) and polyethylene (PE). Use at 158°F (70°C) for 60 s (Linke and Kopp). Used for Nylon 6 (Bartosiewicz) at 149–158°F (65–70°C) for 2–3 min and for Nylon 6, 6 at 167°F (75°C) for 3–4 min.

6. Solution a
    100 mL HNO_3
Solution b
    100 mL glass cleaning solution (add 800 mL H_2SO_4 to 92 g $Na_2Cr_2O_7 \cdot 2H_2O$ dissolved in 458 mL water)
	For polypropylene (PP). Use at 158°F (70°C) for 120 s (Linke and Kopp).

7. 1 part benzene 1 part chloroform 1 part xylene	For polypropylene (PP). Use at 176–185°F (80–85°C), immerse sample 20–30 s increments to prevent overheating (Bartosiewicz).

8. Reagent a
    Heptane
Reagent b
    Benzene
Reagent c
    Xylene
Reagent d
    Gasoline
Reagent e
    Chloroform
Reagent f
    Carbon tetrachloride
	Etchants for low-density polyethylene. Use reagent a 1–3 min at 149°F (65°C); use reagent b 3–6 min at 149°F (65°C); use reagent c 15–60 s at 158°F (70°C); use reagent d 5 min at 104–122°F (40–50°C); use reagent e 1–2 min at 131°F (55°C); and, use reagent f 2 min at 70°C. Note that some of these liquids are dangerous and their use is restricted (Kowatschewa and Semerdjiev).

Sintered carbides

Etchant Composition	Comments
1. 10 g K$_3$Fe(CN)$_6$ 10 g KOH (or 7 g NaOH) 100 mL water	Murakami's reagent, for WC-Co and complex sintered carbides. Immerse sample seconds to minutes. Use 2–10 s to identify eta phase (colored). Longer times attack eta. Reveals phase and grain boundaries. Normally used at 20°C.
2. 100 mL water 5 g KOH 3 g K$_3$Fe(CN)$_6$	For sintered carbides. Use boiling.
3. HCl saturated with FeCl$_3$	To blacken the Co binder phase. Immerse sample 1–5 min at 20°C (Chaporova).
4. 97 mL water 3 mL H$_2$O$_2$ (30%)	For WC, Mo$_2$C, TiC, or Ni in sintered carbides. Use boiling for up to 60 s (Kopp and Linke). For coarse carbides or high Co content, use short etch. Veld and Bogers used 4 min for an alloy of WC and 6% Co, 3 min for an alloy of WC and 15% Co, 30 s when TaC was present.
5. 15 mL water 30 mL HCl 15 mL HNO$_3$ 15 mL acetic acid	For WC, TiC, TaC, and Co in sintered carbides. Use at 20°C for 5–30 s (Kopp and Linke).
6. 100 mL HCl 5 mL H$_2$O$_2$ (30%)	For Co sintered carbides. Use at 20°C for up to 60 s. Attacks Co.
7. 97–98 mL ethanol 2–3 mL HNO$_3$	For Fe-TiC sintered carbides (nital). 4% picral does a better job of outlining the TiC (add about 1% HCl). To etch martensite in hardened samples, use 10% aqueous sodium metabisulfite.

Heat tint	
8. Heat to 600–1100°F (316–593°C) in air	Heat tint for WC-Co and similar sintered carbides. Hold 5 min at 600°F (316°C) to color Co brown. Co preferentially colored up to about 750°F (399°C) for 5 min. WC starts to color at about 1000°F (538°C) after 5 min. Time affects color.

Electrolytic etchants	
9. 3 g KOH 2 g Na$_2$CO$_3$ 100 mL water	For mixed sintered carbides. Use at 3 V dc, 0.1 A/cm^2, 10 s. Increased KOH attacks mixed carbides more strongly. Increased Na$_2$CO$_3$ attacks WC more strongly (Peter and coworkers).
10. 2 g Na$_2$CO$_3$ 25 mL ethanol 75 mL water	For alloys of WC and Co. Use at 2.5 V dc, 1 A, short-circuited (Mader and Müller).

DISLOCATION ETCHING TECHNIQUES

Material	Etchant composition	Plane	Comments
Ag	Solution a 50 mL aq. sat. CrO_3 50 mL water 5 mL 10% aq. HCl Solution b 9% aq. KCN Solution c 25 mL NH_4 OH 5 mL H_2O_2	(111)	Chemically polish with solution a or electrolytically polish with solution b at 4–5 V dc, 0.15 A/cm^2 with current on 1 s and off 1 s. Etch in solution c for 30 s (Levinstein and Robinson).
Ag	1 part oxygen 9 parts argon		Electropolish samples, deform and anneal samples at 800°C for 10 h. Then, thermally etch in gases at 600°C for 10 min (Hendrickson and Machlin).
AgBr AgCl	5 mL ethylenedia- mine 30 mL water		Etch 40 s at 20°C (Mitchell).
Al (99.99%)	50 mL HCl 47 mL HNO_3 3 mL HF		Immerse sample (Amelinckx).

Material	Etchant composition	Plane	Comments
Al (CP or dilute alloys)	2 parts acetic anhydride 1 part perchloric acid		Electropolishing solution of Jacquet, must be used on Al at least 100 h before it is useful. Electropolish in mature solution at 25 V dc, then reduce to 1.5 V for 30–60 s (Biloni and Bolling).
Al (CP,SP)	35 mL HNO$_3$ 61 mL HCl 4 mL HF		Use plastic container. Cool to 0–8°C, etch 5–15 s (Tucker and Murphy).
Al (CP,UP)	Solution a 65 mL HCl 35 mL HNO$_3$ Solution b 49 mL HF 51 mL water	All	Electropolish samples first. Add 2 parts solution a to 5 parts solution b. Use plastic beaker. Cool to 0–15°C, etch about 3 min (Barber).
Al (CP,SP)	Solution a 71 mL HCl 4 mL HF 25 mL alcohol Solution b 42 mL HCl, 41 mL glycerol 15 mL HNO$_3$ 2 mL HF (mix in this order)		Electropolish and wash thoroughly in cold water before etching. Use solution a or b. Cool to 0–8°C, etch 7–10 s (Tucker and Murphy).
Al (99.945%)	50 mL methanol 50 mL HNO$_3$ 32 mL HCl 2 mL HF 50 mL water		Electropolish sample and etch in Keller's reagent to reveal grain boundaries. Then etch in solution at left for 1 min (Wrazej).
Al (HP)	70 mL HNO$_3$ 50 mL HCl 3 mL HF		Modification of Lacombe and Beaujard's etch (Servi and Grant).
Al (UP)	9 parts HCl 3 parts HNO$_3$ 2 parts HF 5 parts water		Use large volume of etchant, avoid heating. Immerse sample for 2 min (Schatt and Garz).
Al	80 mL HCl 25 mL water 5 mL HF		Beck's solution. Cool etch in an ice bath (Lauriente and Pond).
Al$_2$O$_3$	Conc. H$_3$PO$_4$	(0001) {20$\bar{2}$1}	Etch in boiling solution, few minutes. Etch time varies with the plane (Scheuplein and Gibbs).

Material	Etchant composition	Plane	Comments
Al_2O_3	Fused potassium bisulfate	(0001) $\lvert 11\bar{2}0\rvert$	First used by Seebach in 1926. Use at 675°C for 15–25 s for (0001) or for 135 s for $\lvert 11\bar{2}0\rvert$ (Alford and Stephens).

Al_2O_3 (ruby and sapphire)	Solution a
	  Fused potassium
	    bisulfate
	Solution b
	  Conc. H_3PO_4
	Solution c
	  10 N KOH
	Solution d
	  3½ parts $KHSO_4$
	  1 part cryolite
	Solution e
	  Fused potassium
	    bisulfate
		$\lvert 0001\rvert$
		
		$\lvert 10\bar{1}1\rvert$
		$\lvert 10\bar{1}2\rvert$
		
		$\lvert 1\bar{1}00\rvert$
		$\lvert 11\bar{2}0\rvert$
			Methods used by Champion and Clemence. Use solution a at 700°C for 20–25 s. Solution b used by gradually increasing the temperature to 290°C over a 75-min period. For solution c, preheat sample and immerse 10 min at 325°C, gives sharpest pits. Rhombohedral planes etched in solution d after 120 s at 750°C. Etch prism planes in solution e at 750°C for 120 s.

AlSb	Solution a
	  Equal parts H_2O_2
	  (30%),
	  HF, and water
	Solution b
	  Equal parts HCl
	  and HNO_3
		(111)	Etch in solution a for 1 min at 25°C, then in solution b for 2 s at 25°C (Gatos and Lavine).

$BaTiO_3$	4% HNO_3 2% HF (in water)		Etch 10–40 s (Rothwell).
Be	20% CrO_3 14% H_3PO_4 1% H_2SO_4	(0001) (10$\bar{1}$0) (11$\bar{2}$0)	Electropolish single crystals, then etch in solution for 10 s (Hepfer and coworkers).
BeO	1 part hydrofluosilicic acid 6 parts water		Etch basal planes up to 10 min, etch first-order and second-order prism planes and pyramidal planes for 30–60 min (Digiallonardo and Vandervoort).

Material	Etchant composition	Plane	Comments

BeO	Solution a
	  Conc. H_3PO_4
	Solution b
	  Conc. HF
	Solution c
	  Li_2MoO_4
	  2–10% MoO_3
	  V_2O_5, $LiBO_2$,
	  or $Na_2B_4O_7$
	Solution d
	  Li_2MoO_4
	  5–50% MoO_3,
	  V_2O_5, $LiBO_2$,
	  or $Na_2B_4O_7$
	Solution e
	  Water saturated
	  with NaOH
	Solution f
	  Fused NaOH
	Solution g
	  Fused KOH
	Solution h
	  1 part Li_2MoO_4
	  1 part $NaPO_3$
			Methods used by Austerman and co-workers. Use solution a at 20°C for 100 h or 10–60 min at 175°C. Use solution b at 100°C for 10 min. Use solution c at 800°C for 10 min. Use solution d at 800°C for 30 min. Use solution e at 50–100°C for 24 h. Use solution f at 500°C for 1 min or 800°C for 10 min. Use solution g at 600°C for 60 min. Use solution h at 800°C for 10–60 min.

BeO	Conc. HCl	$\{000\bar{1}\}$ $\{10\bar{1}1\}$	Etch at 120°C for 20–60 min (Ehman and Austerman).
Bi	1% I_2 in methanol	(111)	Immerse cleaved surface 15 s, rinse in HCl, then water (Lovell and Wernick).

Bi	Solution a
	  32% aq. HNO_3
	Solution b
	  50% aq. solution
	  of HCl and
	  HNO_3 (1:2)
		
		(111)
			Use solution a for 1–2 min or solution b for several minutes (Yamamoto and Watanabé).

Bi	Solution a
	  50% aq. HNO_3
	Solution b
	  Aqua regia
		(111)
		
		(111)
			Use solution a for 15 s or solution b for 15 min.
			Etchant b also pits the $(44\bar{1})$, $(55\bar{1})$, $(66\bar{1})$, (449), and (337) planes (Yamamoto and Watanabé).

BiSe	2 parts HNO_3 1 part HCl 1 part ethanol Add I_2 and Br_2 until saturated	(0001)	(Kolakowski.)
BiTe	2 parts HNO_3 1 part HCl 6 parts water	(0001)	Etch 1–2 min at 20°C, rinse in water (Teramato and Takayonagi).

Material	Etchant composition	Plane	Comments
C (synthetic diamond)	Molten potassium nitrate in Ni or silica crucible		Etch cleaved surfaces for 4 h at 600°C (Patel and Goswami).
C (diamond)	Fused KNO_3	(111) (110) (100)	Use at 500–700°C for 1 h (Pandya and Tolansky).
C (diamond)	Fused kimberlite	(111)	Use at 1450°C. Rapid heating and cooling required (Frank and Puttick).
$CaCO_3$	1% nital	(010)	Etch 5 s to 5 min, rinse in water, then alcohol (Watts).
$CaCO_3$	Formic acid	(010)	Etch at 25°C for 15 s, rinse in water, ethanol, then ether (Keith and Gilman).
$CaCO_3$	Conc. acetic acid		Etch at 25°C for 6 min, rinse in water, ethanol, then ether (Keith and Gilman).
CaF_2	Conc. H_2SO_4	(111)	Etch cleaved surface at 20°C for 10–30 min, or at 55°C for 1 min (Bontinck).
CaF_2	10% aq $NaHSO_4$	(111)	Etch at 70°C for 10 min (Cockayne and coworkers).
CaF_2	Solution a 50% HCl (boiling) Solution b 20% HCl (near boiling)	$\lbrace 111 \rbrace$	Chemically polish specimen for 5 min in solution a, followed by hot water and alcohol rinses. After deformation, etch specimen in solution b for 5–10 s, followed by rinsing in hot water, then alcohol (Burn and Murray).
Cd	10 g CrO_3 1 mL H_2SO_4 25 mL acetic acid 100 mL water	$(10\bar{1}0)$	Etch 1–2 min (Wernick and Thomas).
Cd	2 parts H_3PO_4 2 parts glycerin 1 part water	All	Electropolish in solution at 2.1–2.2 V dc for 9–12 min. To etch, drop voltage to 0.9–1.0 V for 20–40 s (Predvohitiv and Tiapunia).
Cd	1 part H_3PO_4 1 part water 2 parts glycerin	(0001)	Electrolytically etch at 0.4–0.8 V dc (Predvoditelev and coworkers).
CdS	1 g Cr_2O_3 12.5 mL H_2SO_4 1250 mL water	(0001) $(000\bar{1})$ $\lbrace 10\bar{1}0 \rbrace$	Heat to 80°C, immerse 10 min, rinse in water and then methanol (Woods).

Material	Etchant composition	Plane	Comments
CdS	Equal parts H_3PO_4, 30% HCl, and water	(0001)	Immerse in vigorously boiling solution for 30–60 s. Rinse immediately in boiling water, then with alcohol (Wösten).
CdSe	Equal parts H_3PO_4, 65% HCl, and water	(0001)	Immerse in vigorously boiling solution for 30–60 s. Rinse immediately in boiling water, then with alcohol (Wösten).
CdSe	Equal parts H_3PO_4 and 65% HCl	$(10\bar{1}0)$	Use as with previous etch (Wösten).
Cu (pure)	20 mL sat. $FeCl_3$ solution 20 mL HCl 5 mL acetic acid 5–10 drops Br_2	(111)	Etch 15–30 s, rinse in NH_4OH, then with water (Lovell and Wernick).
Cu (impure)	60 mL H_3PO_4 40 mL H_2O	(112)	Decorate by annealing at 500°C for several hours before etching electrolytically (Young and Canberra).
Cu-35%Zn alloy	0.2% aq. $Na_2S_2O_4$	All	Etch at 0.6 A/in² for 60 s at 18–20°C. Rinse 1 s in HCl (Jacquet).
Cu (OFHC) Cu-30%Zn alloy	50% aq HCl saturated with $FeCl_3$	{100} {100}{111}	Etch 10 min for OFHC Cu. For alpha brass, dilute etch with an equal amount of water, immerse 20 min (agitate every 2 min).
Cu-30%Zn alloy	4% aq. $Na_2S_2O_3$	{100} {111}	Electropolish sample in 66% aq. H_3PO_4 at 1.75 V dc, 0.18 A/cm², 30 min. Then etch in solution at left at 1.3 V dc for 40 s (Vidal and coworkers).
Cu	70 g ammonium persulfate 0.5 g ammonium chloride (in 100 mL NH_4OH)	{110}	Etch for a few seconds, rinse immediately in water (Livingston).
Cu	0.5–2 parts bromine 7.5–45 parts acetic acid 12.5–75 parts HCl 90 parts water	{111}	Etch about 5 s, rinse in water, then in alcohol (Livingston).
Cu-30%Zn alloy	Solution a 2 parts H_3PO_4 4 parts methanol 3 parts H_2O Solution b 70% aq. HNO_3	{100}	Mechanically polish surface parallel to {100} plane, then electropolish in solution a at 2.4 V dc. Immerse in solution b for 2–3 s to etch pit. Use solution b immediately after mixing, or if cooled after mixing, reheat to 35°C (Orava). Examine with replicas.

Material	Etchant composition	Plane	Comments
Cu-48.9%Zn alloy (atomic %)	20 g ammonium persulfate 0.8 mL HCl 100 mL water	{001}	Chemically polish or electropolish samples before etching (Ito and coworkers).
Cu-Al alloys (to 50%)	20–50% HNO$_3$ 10–80% acetic acid 10–80% H$_3$PO$_4$	All	(Erdman.)
Fe	Fry's reagent		Chemically polish sample, etch 10 s.
Fe	Solution a 1% nital Solution b 0.5% picral		Pits result only in samples slow-cooled from 843–746°C. Etch in solution a for 1 min, rinse in alcohol, etch in solution b for 5 min, agitate gently (Boswell).
Fe	98 mL 2% nital 2 mL sat. picral		Etch 15 min (Van Wijk and Van Dijck).
Fe	Saturated picral		Anneal at 954°C to decorate dislocations (Samuel and Quarrell).
Fe, mild steel	15 g CuCl$_2$ 40 mL HCl 30 mL H$_2$O 25 mL ethanol		Modified Fry's reagent. Electropolish samples before etching. After deformation, age samples 3–6 days at 20°C for 15 min to 4 h at 150–200°C. Etch annealed samples 10–15 s, cold-worked samples 2–5 s (Hahn).
Fe-Si alloys	Solution a 5 mL HF 80 mL H$_2$O$_2$ (30%) 15 mL water Solution b 20 mL HF 80 mL H$_2$O$_2$ (30%) 15 mL water	(001)	Chemically polish in solution a, avoid overheating. Pour small amount of solution b on surface, get strong effervescence. After 1 s, rinse in water, then dip a few seconds into HF. Use thin sample or warm large sample before etching (Beguinot and Lesbato).
Fe	10 mL HCl 3 mL HNO$_3$ 100 mL methanol 4 g CuCl$_2$	{110}	Decorate dislocations by slow cooling from 800°C (Gorsuch).
Fe	10 mL HCl 3 mL HNO$_3$ 100 mL ethanol 4 g CuCl$_2$ 2.5 g picric acid	{110}	Not necessary to decorate dislocations (Gorsuch).

Material	Etchant composition	Plane	Comments
Armco Fe	5 g $CuCl_2$ 40 mL HCl 30 mL H_2O 25 mL ethanol		Deform then age samples 20 min at 100–200°C to decorate dislocations. Electropolish sample, then etch with solution at left (Fry's reagent) for 10 s (Hahn and Sapey).
Fe	2% nital	(100)	Chemically polish samples in 5 mL HF, 80 mL H_2O_2 (30%), and 15 mL water. Etch in nital. Reveals both fresh and aged dislocations (Sestak and Kadechova).
Fe-3%Si alloy	7 mL H_2O 133 mL acetic acid 25 g CrO_3		Morris's electropolishing solution. Polish at 12–18°C and 22.5 V, etch at 5 V (Hahn and Sapey).
Fe	Solution a 1% nital Solution b 0.5% picral	(100)	Electropolish sample with Morris's electrolyte (above solution). Then, etch 1 min in solution a and 5 min in solution b. Reveals fresh dislocations (Coleman).
Fe-3%Si alloy	10% aq. ammonium persulfate (3–30% can be used)		Chemically polish surface in a 1:1 solution of H_3PO_4 and H_2O_2. Etch with fresh solution for up to 30 min. Rinse thoroughly in distilled water, alcohol, and ether to prevent oxidation (Wiesinger; Yamamoto and Watanabé).
AISI 304	10% aq. oxalic acid		Electropolish sample, then electrolytically etch in solution at left for 60–90 s at 0.35–0.40 A/cm^2 (Armijo).
Fe_3C in cast iron	4% nital		Electropolish samples or, if mechanically polished, etch-polish using solution at left to remove any deformation. Thermally etch by heating under vacuum to 200–600°C for 30 min to reveal dislocations (Skoblo and Sandler).
GaP (doped with S)	Thermal etch a 800–1100°C for 15 min in vacuum (5×10^{-4} torr) Thermal etch b 1050°C for 15 min in vacuum	(100) (110)	Surfaces lightly etched with 1 part HCl and 1 part HNO_3, rinsed in deionized water before thermal etch (Kitada).
GaP	3 parts H_2SO_4 2 parts H_2O_2 2 parts HF	(100) (111)	Freshly prepared solution heats spontaneously to about 90°C and produces etch pits within a few minutes. Also good for (111) in GaAs (Kuhnenfeld).

Material	Etchant composition	Plane	Comments
GaS	10 mL H_2SO_4 10 g $K_2Cr_2O_7$ 70 mL water	(0001)	Immerse sample (Harsy and Lendvay).

GaSe	Solution a
	  Bromine in
	    methanol
	Solution b
	  1 g iodine in 50
	    mL methanol
		(0001)	Etch up to 45 min. Wash in alcohol (avoid water) (Williams).

GaAs	Fused KOH	{001}	Use at 300–350°C (Ishii and coworkers).
Ge	8 g $K_3Fe(CN)_6$ 12 g KOH 100 mL water	(100)	Grind to 600-grit finish, etch in solution for 2–5 min, boiling (Billig).
Ge	40 mL HF 20 mL HNO_3 40 mL water containing 2 g $AgNO_3$	(111) (110)	Westinghouse silver etch. Etch for 1 min. Works better on (111) (Wynne and Goldberg).

Ge	Solution a
	  6 mL HF
	  10 mL HNO_3
	  6 mL acetic acid
	  3 drops Br_2
	Soltuion b
	  5 mL HF
	  5 mL superoxol
	  20 mL water
		(100)	Etch in solution a for 4 min, then in solution b (Oberly).

Ge	1 part HF 1 part H_2O_2 4 parts water	(111) (100)	Superoxol etch. Etch 1 min. Works better on (111) (Ellis).
Ge	1 part HNO_3 2 parts HF 1 part 10% aq. $CuNO_3$	(111) (100)	Etch 2 min or more (Holmes).
Ge	4 parts HNO_3 2 parts HF 15 parts acetic acid	(111)	Decorate dislocations with lithium. Mechanically polish samples then etch in 10 parts HF and 1 part HNO_3 for 20 min. Then etch with solution at left (Tyler and Dash).

Material	Etchant composition	Plane	Comments
Ge	Solution a 50% aq. HNO_3	(100)(111) (110)	Methods used by Yamamoto and Watanabé. Etch 4 min at 70°C, or 40 min at 20°C (70°C best).
	Solution b 30% aq. HNO_3	(100)(111) (110)	Etch 3–6 min at 70°C.
	Solution c 45 mL HNO_3 45 mL water 10 mL HF 50 mg $AgNO_3$	(100)(111) (110)	Etch 30–90 s at 20°C.
	Solution d 20 mL HNO_3 40 mL water 40 mL HF 2 g $AgNO_3$	(111)(110)	Etch 2 min at 20°C.
	Solution e 1 part HF 1 part H_2O_2 4 parts water	(100)(110) (111)	Etch 3 min at 20°C.
	Solution f Conc. H_2O_2 (30%)	(100)(110) (111)	Etch 1–1.5 min at 100°C.
HgSe	Solution a 50 mL HNO_3 10 mL acetic acid 1 mL HCl 20 mL 18 N H_2SO_4 Solution b 6 parts HCl 2 parts HNO_3 3 parts water	(111)	Chemically polish in solution a at 40°C for 10–15 min. Etch in solution b at 25°C for 2–5 min (Warekois and coworkers).
HgTe	Solution a 6 parts HNO_3 1 part HCl 1 part water Solution b HCl and HNO_3, equal parts	(111)	Chemically polish in solution a at 25°C for 10–15 min. Etch in solution b using three 1-min immersions (Warekois and coworkers).
In	0.5 g $KClO_3$ per liter HCl		Immerse electropolished sample in solution (Van Der Biest and Van Der Planken).
InSb	2 parts HNO_3 1 part HF 1 part acetic acid	(111)	Etch 4 s at 25°C (Gatos and Lavine).
InSb	HF and HNO_3, equal parts	(110)	Etch for 2–5 s (Venables and Broudy).

Material	Etchant composition	Plane	Comments
InP	3 parts 1 M $K_2Cr_2O_7$ 1 part H_2SO_4 2–3 parts HCl	(001)	Etch at 60°C.
KBr	Conc. acetic acid	(100)	Etch 3 s (Moran).
KBr KCl	1.75 wt % Ba (as $BaCO_3$) dissolved under reflux in propionic acid	(100)	Etch for 30 s, rinse in ether (Cooks).
KCl	10 mg $FeCl_3$ in 25 mL isopropanol (add 1 or 2 drops water if the bottle is new)	{100}	Add just enough $FeCl_3$ to produce a slightly yellowish color. Rinse with isopropanol. Etch about 1 min for cleaved surfaces, about 2 min for polished surfaces (Subramanian).
KCl	95 mL ethanol saturated with $BaBr_2$ 5 mL of 100 g $BaBr_2$ per liter of methanol	(100)	Etch 30–90 sec (Moran).
KI	Isopropyl alcohol	(100)	(Moran.)
LiF	Solution a 100 mL HF 160 mL HNO_3 100 mL acetic acid 1 mL Br_2 At least 15 mg Fe Solution b 1 part HF 1 part acetic acid saturated with FeF_2		Etch 20 s to several minutes (Gilman).
LiF	100 mL HF 100 mL acetic acid 160 mL HNO_3 2 mL Br_2	(001)	CP-4 reagent. Fresh CP-4 must be modified by dissolving some iron before etching. 25 mL of reagent is good for about 10 min of etching. Typical etch time is about 30 s. Wash in alcohol, then in ether. Attacks both screw and edge dislocations (Gilman and Johnston).
LiF	2×10^{-6} M FeF_3 in water	(100)	Immerse crystal in solution and stir vigorously. After 1 min, remove and rinse in alcohol, then in ether (Gilman and coworkers).

Material	Etchant composition	Plane	Comments
LiF	0.27 g anhydrous ferric fluoride dissolved in 50 mL HF		"F" etch. Stir frequently. Produces good etch pits 30 min after preparation (Ives).
LiF	Solution a ("A" etch) 1 part HF 1 part acetic acid 1 part HF sat. with FeF$_3$ Solution b ("W" etch) Dilute aq. solution of FeF$_3$ or FeCl$_3$ (1.5×10^{-4} M)	(100)	Etch in solution a for 30–60 s, rinse in alcohol, then in ether. Etches both fresh and aged dislocations. Etch in solution b 2 min, rinse in alcohol, then in ether (Gilman and Johnston).
LiNbO$_3$	1 part HF 2 parts HNO$_3$	(0001) (10$\bar{1}$0) (11$\bar{2}$0)	Use boiling (110°C). 10-min etch reveals negative domains on (0001), 1-h etch reveals pits in positive domains on (0001) and other planes (Nassau and coworkers).
MgF$_2$	Conc. H$_2$SO$_4$	(100) (110)	Etch at 200°C for 10 s (Berber).
MgO	Solution a Equal parts aq. sat. ammonium chloride and H$_2$SO$_4$ Solution b Conc. H$_3$PO$_4$		Solution a produces etch pits at 20–95°C. Etchant b is primarily a chemical polish but will produce etch pits and pyramids (Stokes and coworkers).
MgO	5 parts sat. ammonium chloride 1 part H$_2$SO$_4$ 1 part water		(Stokes and Li.)
MgO	0.5 M aq. AlCl$_3$	(100)	Etch a few minutes at 50°C (Stiefbold and coworkers).
MgO	Solution a 2 parts H$_3$PO$_4$ 1 part H$_2$SO$_4$ Solution b Conc. H$_3$PO$_4$	(110)	Etchant a also produces pits on |001| surfaces. Etchant a requires 3–5 min, etchant b requires only a few seconds at 105°C (Cass and Washburn).
MgO	6 parts NH$_4$Cl 1 part H$_2$SO$_4$ 1 part water	(100)	Etch 30 s at 20°C (Clauer and Wilcox).
MgO	Conc. H$_2$SO$_4$	(100)	Etch at 55°C. Distinguishes between fresh and aged dislocations.

Material	Etchant composition	Plane	Comments
Mo	Solution a 2 parts H_2SO_4 2 parts ethanol 1 part $HClO_3$ Solution b 1 part H_2SO_4 1 part ethanol 1 part $HClO_3$	{100}	Add sulfuric acid slowly to ethanol in flask surrounded by ice, stir. Add $HClO_3$ drop by drop, keep cool. Electropolish sample. Etch in solution a at 48–50°C, 2 V dc, 0.12 A/cm^2, or in solution b at 22–26°C, 2 V dc, 0.3 A/cm^2. Use Pt cathode and 5-s etch with either (Das).
Mo	100 mL methanol 20 mL H_2SO_4		Etch at less than 5 V dc and up to 100 mA/cm^2 (Pink).
Mo	Solution a 20 parts H_2SO_4 1 part methanol Solution b 5% H_2SO_4 in methanol	(100)	Electropolish in solution a at 110°C, then etch in solution b at 1.7 mA/mm^2 at 260°C (Demkin).
NaCl	Thermal etch at 593°C for 15 min in vacuum (10^{-5} to 10^{-6} torr)		Etches cleaved faces (Budke).
NaCl	4 g $FeCl_3$ in 1 liter acetic acid	(100)	Etch at 25°C for 30 s, moderate agitation (Mendelsohn).
NaCl	3 g $HgCl_3$ in 1 liter ethanol	(100)	Etch at 25°C for 30 min (Moran).
NaCl	3 g $Fe(NO_3)_2$ in 1 liter ethanol	(100)	Etch 20 s.
NaCl NaF	1.75 wt % Ba (as $BaCO_3$) dissolved under reflux in propionic acid	(100)	Etch for 30 s, rinse in ether (Cooks).
Nb	18 mL HF 34 mL H_2SO_4 48 mL lactic acid	{111}	Pelleg's electropolishing solution. Used at 1.7 V dc, 70 mA/cm^2. No need to decorate dislocations (Pelleg).
Nb	Solution a 90 mL H_2SO_4 10 mL HF Solution b 10 mL H_2SO_4 10 mL HF 10 mL H_2O Few drops H_2O_2	All	Electropolish in solution a at 25°C and 0.1 A/cm^2, then etch in solution b by immersion. Reveals aged dislocation (Michael and Huegel).
Nb	10–15% HF in H_2SO_4	{111}	Electropolish with a cylindrical graphite cathode at 10 V dc, then etch at 0.25–0.50 V (Vardiman and Achter).

Material	Etchant composition	Plane	Comments
Nb	Solution a 1 part HF 1 part HNO$_3$ Solution b 3% KBr Solution c 1 part HF 1 part HNO$_3$ 1 part water	(100) (110)	Chemically polish with solution a for 1 min, then anodize in solution b at 35–50 V dc for 3–4 s to form a thin blue oxide on surface. Immerse in solution c at 35–50°C. Oxide dissolves in 5–10 min, and pits formed in 20–40 s (Baranova and Fionova).
Nb	90 mL H$_2$SO$_4$ 10 mL HF	All	Dislocations must be decorated by aging 16 h at 300°C. Electropolish and electroetch in solution (Koppenal and Evans).
Nb	5 parts H$_2$SO$_4$ 2 parts HNO$_3$ 2 parts HF	All	Etches aged dislocations (Bakish).
Ni (CP,HP)	Solution a 60% H$_2$SO$_4$ Solution b 35% H$_3$PO$_4$	All	Electropolish with solution a and etch in solution b at 0.2–0.4 V dc for 30 s to 3 min. Dislocations must be decorated by heating to 500–900°C (Guard).
Ni-Mn alloys	1 part H$_3$PO$_4$ 1 part ethanol	(100)	Etch at 2 A/cm^2 at 40°C for 2 min. Rinse in water, then in ethanol (Taoka and Aoyagi).
NiO	Conc. HNO$_3$	(100)	Use hot (Takeda and Kondoh).
Pb (99.9%)	3 parts H$_2$O$_2$ 2 parts acetic acid 2 parts water	{100}	Etch 10 min.
PbS PbSe	Solution a 30 mL HCl 10 mL HNO$_3$ 1 mL acetic acid Solution b 10% acetic acid Solution c 1 part HCl 1 part 100 g thiourea per liter water	(100)	Chemically polish in solution a at 50°C for a few minutes. Use fresh. Rinse in solution b. Etch in solution c at 60°C for 1–10 min. Use fresh (Brebrick and Scanlon).
PbSe	10 g KOH in 100 mL water 1 mL glycerol 0.5 mL H$_2$O$_2$(30%)	(100)	Cool to 20°C before adding H$_2$O$_2$. Etch freshly cleaved surfaces at 25°C for 2 min. Rinse in water (Norr).
PbTe	5 g NaOH 0.2 g I$_2$ 10 mL water	(100)	Add I$_2$ after NaOH. Etch freshly cleaved surfaces at 94–98°C for 5 min (Houston and Norr).

Material	Etchant composition	Plane	Comments
PbTe	10 mL of 0.5% aq. NaIO$_3$ 5 g NaOH	(100)	Etch freshly cleaved surfaces at 94–98°C for 5 min (Houston and Norr).
PtSb$_2$	1 part HNO$_3$ 3 parts HCl 3 parts water	(100) (110) (111)	Etch at 70°C for 15 min (Sagar and Faust).
RbFeF$_3$	Solution a 1–3 g KOH in 100 mL water Solution b 1 part H$_2$O$_2$(30%) 1 part acetic acid	(100)	Polish sample, etch in solution a to remove deformation. Immerse in solution b to etch-pit. Film forms during etching in solution a, which turns red and flakes off in solution b. Etch time in solution b is 15 s or more (Levinstein and Guggenheim).
Sb	3 parts HF 5 parts HNO$_3$ 3 parts acetic acid 1 part Br$_2$	(111)	CP-4 reagent, 2–3 s on cleaved surfaces (Wernick and coworkers).
Sb	1 part HF 1 part H$_2$O$_2$ 4 parts water	(111)	Superoxol etch, 10 s (Theuerer, U.S. Patent 2,542,727).
Sb	10 g FeCl$_3$ 30 mL HCl 120 mL water	(111)	Etch up to several minutes at 25–45°C (Shigeta and Hiramatsu).
Sb	28 mL acetic acid 5 mL HNO$_3$ 4 mL HF 3 mL Br$_2$	(111)	Etch 30–90 s (Kosevich).
Si	70 mL acetic acid 21 mL HNO$_3$ 7 mL HF in which 100 mg As is dissolved	(111) (100) (110)	Etch chemically polished surface 15 min to several hours (Dash).
Si	4 parts HF 2 parts HNO$_3$ 4 parts 3% aq. Hg(NO$_3$)$_2$	(100) (111)	Grind samples to 600-grit SiC, then etch (Faust).
Si	3 parts HF 5 parts HNO$_3$ 3 parts acetic acid 1.5–2 parts 3% aq. Hg(NO$_3$)$_2$	(100)(111)	Grind samples to 600-grit SiC, then etch 2 min. Use deionized water. Utensils and specimen must be dry. Etch improved by aging solution up to 6 weeks in closed polyethylene bottle (Vogel and Lovell).
Si	160 mL HF 80 mL HNO$_3$ 160 mL water containing 8 g AgNO$_3$	(100)(111)	Grind samples to 600-grit SiC, then etch (Wynne and Goldberg).

Material	Etchant composition	Plane	Comments

Si	Solution a
	  2 parts HF
	  3 parts HNO_3
	  3 parts acetic acid
	Solution b
	  15 parts acetic acid
	  3 parts HNO_3
	  1 part HF
		(111)(100)	Chemically polish in solution a and etch in solution b (Johnston and coworkers).

Si	Sat. aq. KOH	(100)(111) (522)	Etch with boiling solution for 40–60 s, or 1.5 min at 100°C, or 5–10 min at 70°C (Yamamoto and Watanabé).
Si	Sat. aq. NaOH	(100)(111) (411)	Etch with boiling solution for 60–90 s, or 2–3 min at 100°C, or 10 min at 70°C (Yamamoto and Watanabé).
SiC	Fused $NaCO_3$	All	Etch at 1000°C for 20 min (Horn).
SiC	$NaNO_2$ 10% Na_2O_2	(111)	Etch at 500°C for 10 min (Liebmann).
SiO_2	Water sat. with NH_4HF_2	All	Produces some etch figures (Augustine and Hale).

Sn	Solution a
	  95% HCl
	  5% CrO_3
	Solution b
	  Aqua regia or diluted 50% with water
		(001)(100)
		(101)(301)
		(211)
		(001)(100)
		(101)
			Methods used by Yamamoto and Watanabé.
			Etch with solution a 4 min at 20°C.
			Etch with solution b for 30 s or 3 min, respectively, at 20°C.

	Solution c Sat. aq. ammonium persulfate	(001)(100) (101)	Etch with solution c for 15 min at 20°C.
	Solution d 100 or 50% sat. aq. $FeCl_3$	(001)(100) (101)	Etch with solution d for 30 s or 2 min, respectively, at 20°C.
	Solution e Sat. aq. $Fe_2(SO_4)_3$	(001)(100) (101)	Etch with solution e 1–2 min at 20°C.
	Solution f 5% sat. aq. $CuCl_2 \cdot 2H_2O$	(001)(100) (101)	Etch with solution f 3 min at 20°C.
Ta	5 parts H_2SO_4 2 parts HNO_3 2 parts HF	(112)	Decorate by oxidizing 30 min in air at 1400°F (760°C). Degas in vacuum 30–40 min at 3450°F (1899°C) (Bakish).
Te	3 parts HF 5 parts HNO_3 6 parts acetic acid	$(10\bar{1}0)$	Etch cleaved surfaces for 30–60 s (Lovell and coworkers).

Material	Etchant composition	Plane	Comments
Ti Ti-Al alloys	21 mL HF 64 mL HCl 106 mL HNO_3 160 mL water	(0001)	Keller's reagent. Etch a few seconds (Cass).
Ti	5 mL HNO_3 3 mL HF 92 mL H_2O		Electropolish sample, then immerse a few seconds in etch (Tanabe and coworkers).
Ti-V alloys (>20% V)	Thermal etch in vacuum at 900°C		Mechanically polish through alumina, then electropolish. Encapsulate in Vycor at 4×10^{-6} torr and anneal 2 h at 900°C. Break capsule in ice water (Ling and Starke).
TiO_2	Conc. H_2SO_4	(110)	Cleave samples on (110) plane, grind through 600-grit SiC, chemically polish with KOH at 650°C for 8 min. Clean in HCl for 10 min. Etch in hot sulfuric acid for 13 min (Hirthe and Brittain).
UC	Conc. H_3PO_4	(100)	Etch at 20°C for 10–15 min or at 50–60°C for 30–60 s. Wash in alcohol (avoid water) (Briggs).
UO_2	Solution a 6 parts H_2O_2 3 parts H_2O 1 part H_2SO_4	{111}{100}	Methods used by Shabbir and Robins. Etch in solution a 3 min at 20°C.
	Solution b Conc. H_2SO_4	{111}	Etch in solution b 5 min above 100°C.
	Solution c 9 parts H_2SO_4 1 part H_2O_2	{111}	Etch with solution c 5 min above 20°C.
	Solution d Conc. HNO_3	{111}{100}	Etch with solution d 10 s at 120°C.
	Solution e Conc. H_3PO_4	{111}{100}	Etch with solution e 5 min above 50°C.
	Solution f KCl sat. with Cl_2 gas	{111}{100}	Etch with solution f 4 min at 840°C.
W	100 parts sat. $K_3Fe(CN)_6$ 5 parts sat. KOH 95 parts H_2O	{110}	Etch 15 min, agitate every 2 min. Composition is critical.

Material	Etchant composition	Plane	Comments
W	Solution a 4% NaOH	(001)	Methods used by Tamura and coworkers. Etch with solution a at 0.5 V dc, 0.07 A/cm^2, 10–60 s.
	Solution b 4% NaOH 20 g/L picric acid	(001)	Etch with solution b at 0.7 V dc, 0.3 A/cm^2, 10–120 s.
	Solution c 4% KOH	(111)	Etch with solution c at 0.3 V dc, 0.33 A/cm^2, 120–180 s.
	Solution d 16% NaOH 40 g/L picric acid	(111)	Etch with solution d at 0.2 V dc, 0.06 A/cm^2, 90 s.
	Solution e 1 part 30% K$_3$Fe(CN)$_6$ 1 part 3% NaOH	(001)	Etch with solution e for 2–40 s.
Y$_3$Fe$_5$O$_{12}$	Conc. HCl	(110)	Etch boiling, 1 h (Brower and Farabaugh).
Y$_2$O$_5$	Solution a H$_3$PO$_4$	{111}	Cleave on {111} plane or cut on {100} plane. Cut surfaces mechanically and chemically polished in solution a at 290–300°C. Etch cleaved or chemically polished surfaces in solution b for 3–5 min (Ramsey).
	Solution b Boiling HCl in water	{100}	
Zn	Solution a 160 g CrO$_3$ 20 g hydrated Na$_2$SO$_4$ 500 mL water		Add 0.1 atomic % Cd to Zn. Heat samples to 300–400°C, air-cool, deform, age at 20°C for 1 week. Before etching, clean with 50% HCl, dip in solution a for 20 s, wash in water, redip. Agitate strongly. Dip in solution b for 60 s, agitate mildly. Dip in solution c to remove film (Gilman).
	Solution b 160 g CrO$_3$ 50 g hydrated Na$_2$SO$_4$ 500 mL water		
	Solution c 160 g CrO$_3$ 500 mL water		
Zn (99.99%)	7 parts sat. CuCl$_2$·2H$_2$O 3 parts HCl 90 parts water	{10$\bar{1}\ell$}	Etch for 3 min. Wipe off Cu deposit every 30 s. ℓ has many values.

Material	Etchant composition	Plane	Comments
Zn	Solution a Conc. HCl, 50% HCl, or 5% HCl (aq.)	(0001) $(11\bar{2}0)$	Methods used by Yamamoto and Watanabé. Etch with solution a for 5 s, 2–3 min, or 15–25 min, respectively, at 20°C.
	Solution b 5–10% aq. H_2SO_4	(0001) $(11\bar{2}0)$	Etch with solution b 10–15 min at 20°C.
	Solution c Conc. HF or 50% HF	(0001)	Etch with solution c 5–10 min or 3–5 min, respectively, at 20°C.
	Solution d Sat. aq. NaOH	$(0001)(11\bar{2}0)$ $(10\bar{1}0)$	Etch with solution d boiling for 40 min.
	Solution e Sat. aq. KOH	$(0001)(11\bar{2}0)$ $(10\bar{1}0)$	Etch with solution e boiling for 20 min.
	Solution f Sat. aq. $CuCl_2$	(0001)	Etch with solution f 5–20 min at 20°C.
	Mixtures of sat. aq. solutions of Na_2SO_4 and CrO_3:	(0001)	Etch at 20°C for following times:
	95:5		5–10 min.
	92:8		More than 1 min.
	90:10		More than 3 min.
	87:13		More than 2 min.
	85:15		More than 1 min.
	80:20		More than 2 min.
	Solution g 50% or 5% sat. aq. ammonium persulfate	(0001)	Etch with solution g 10–20 min at 20°C.
Zn (dilute alloys)	Solution a 32 g CrO_3 4 g Na_2SO_4 2 g $Cu(NO_3)_2$ 100 mL water Solution b 50 mL ethanol 20 mL $H_2O_2(30\%)$ 5 mL HNO_3 Solution c 2 g $NH_4(NO_3)_2$ 10 mL NH_4OH 50 mL water	$(10\bar{1}0)$	Chemically polish in solution a for 1 min at 25°C, rinse in water. Polish in solution b for 5 s, rinse in water. Etch in solution c for 10 s, rinse in water, then in alcohol (Sinha and Beck).
ZnS (synthetic)	0.5 M $K_2Cr_2O_7$ in 16 N H_2SO_4	(0001)	Polish and etch specimen at 95°C for 10 min (Warekois and coworkers).
Zr	250 mL water 35 mL HNO_3 21 mL HCl 1 mL HF		Etch for 5–20 s (Dickson and coworkers).

Material	Etchant composition	Plane	Comments

Zr	90 mL ethanol
	10 mL *n*-butyl
	  alcohol
	28 g anhydrous zinc
	  chloride
	6 g anhydrous alu-
	  minum chloride
			Electropolish in solution at left using
			austenitic stainless steel cathode,
			20–35 V dc, 2 A, for at least 30 s.
			Then etch at 0.4 A for 30 s
			(Tanabe and coworkers).

Note: Use distilled water in all reagents where water is specified.

NAME INDEX

Aaron, H. B., 469
Abrams, H., 432, 450
Accinno, D. J., 138, 247–248
Ahmed, W. U., 69
Aldous, C. W., 344
Alexander, B. H., 26
Allmand, T. R., 473
Anderson, R. L., 137, 148, 151, 155, 156, 206
Asundi, M. K., 482, 485
Atkins, A. G., 367
Atkinson, J. T. N., 129
Avient, B. W. E., 401

Baczewski, A., 84
Baldwin, D. H., 302
Bardgett, W. E., 53–56
Bareiss, R. A., 396
Barker, L. J., 197
Bartz, G., 186
Bastin, D., 363–364
Batchelder, G. M., 383, 385, 387
Baxter, A., 402–403
Beauchamp, R. H., 145–146
Beaujard, L., 221
Bechet, S., 221
Beck, P. A., 32
Belaiew, N. T., 481–483, 485
Beland, R. A., 242
Belk, J. A., 404
Bell, F. C., 235
Bellot, J., 479
Bender, J. H., 140
Benscoter, A. O., 63, 172–174, 214, 217, 222, 298, 323, 456

Benson, D. K., 36
Beraha, E., 174–177, 197, 206, 208–209, 223, 226, 239, 243–244
Bergh, S., 474
Berglund, T., 3, 48
Bianchi, G., 195
Birkbeck, G., 482
Bish, R. L., 8–9, 36
Blann, G. A., 135
Blau, P. J., 403
Bleecker, W. H., 185
Blickwede, D. J., 211
Blin, J., 403
Booth, F. F., 170
Bowden, F. P., 113
Bramfitt, B. L., 23, 326
Brassard, T. V., 142
Brenner, P., 404
Brooks, W. J. D., 197
Brose, R. A., 115
Brown, A. R. G., 375, 378, 382
Brown, D., 482–483
Brunet, J. C., 479
Bubar, S. F., 154
Buchheit, R. D., 14, 35, 111–112, 196, 204, 206, 211, 242, 246–247, 249, 388
Bückle, H., 373–375, 403
Budd, M. K., 170
Bühler, H. E., 189
Buhr, R. K., 6–7, 25
Byron, E. S., 92

Cahn, J. W., 432
Cahoon, J. R., 392–393

SUBJECT INDEX

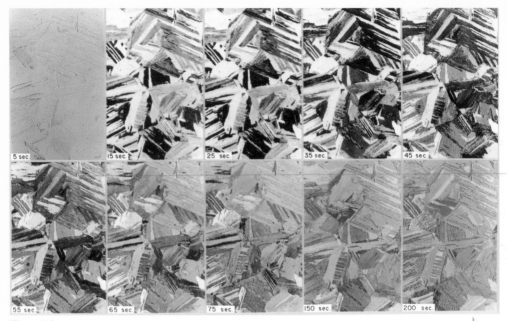

Figure 3-5

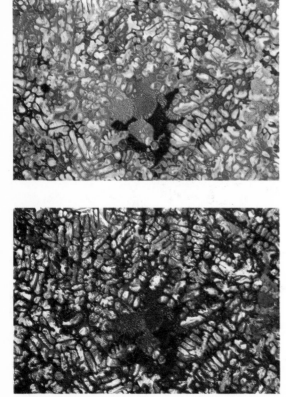

Figure 3-24

Figure 3-17